BEHAVIOR AND EVOLUTION

BEHAVIOR
and
EVOLUTION

Edited by Anne Roe

and George Gaylord Simpson

New Haven

YALE UNIVERSITY PRESS

Preface

IN 1953 the idea of holding one or more conferences on behavior and evolution was presented simultaneously to the American Psychological Association and the Society for the Study of Evolution. Officers of these organizations approved joint sponsorship and each appointed a committee:

For the American Psychological Association: Frank Beach, Harry Harlow, Henry Nissen, and Anne Roe, Chairman.

For the Society for the Study of Evolution: Marston Bates, Donald Griffin, Alfred S. Romer, and George Gaylord Simpson, Chairman.

The two committees met together as a Joint Steering Committee under the chairmanship of Dr. Roe and proceeded to formulate a concrete plan and to issue invitations. These preliminaries were supported by a grant from the Rockefeller Foundation of New York. A first conference, financed by a grant from the National Science Foundation, was held at Arden House, Harriman, New York, on April 4 to 8, 1955. The aim was primarily exploratory: to see whether there was enough community of interest and enough pertinent, communicable information to make further joint study profitable. Specific subjects, which they were asked to present at length, but informally, were assigned to a number of conferees. Others were invited as discussants. The consensus at the close of the conference was that the interdisciplinary reaction had been substantial and profitable. It was voted to hold a second conference for the explicit purpose of producing a publishable symposium.

The second conference, also supported by a grant from the National Science Foundation, was held at the Nassau Tavern, Princeton, New Jersey, April 30 to May 5, 1956. Most of the participants had also attended the first conference, but there was some change in personnel consonant with the change in purpose. For the second conference participants were asked to present advance drafts of formal papers on assigned topics. Copies were sent to all members before the conference. At the conference, each author presented the gist of his paper in a few minutes and most of the time was devoted to general discussion of each contribution, with emphasis on possible revision, so that the conference was essentially editorial. After the conference, each author revised his paper in the light of discussion at the conference, and the final drafts were assembled into the present book by Roe and Simpson, selected as editors by vote of the group.

PARTICIPANTS IN THE TWO CONFERENCES ARE LISTED
BELOW:

Marston Bates	Harry Harlow	Karl Pribram
Frank Beach	Robert Hinde	Bernhard Rensch
Theodore Bullock	Julian Huxley	Anne Roe
C. Ray Carpenter	Ernst Mayr	Alfred S. Romer
Ernst Caspari	Margaret Mead	George Gaylord Simpson
Edwin Colbert	C. D. Michener	Herman Spieth
F. F. Darling	James Miller	Roger W. Sperry
Alfred Emerson	Raoul Naroll	W. R. Thompson
William Etkin	Henry Nissen	Niko Tinbergen
L. Z. Freedman	Bryan Patterson	Sherry Washburn
Donald Griffin	Colin Pittendrigh	

Some of the listed participants are not represented as authors in the present book. It should, nevertheless, be emphasized that all contributed essentially to the discussions at the conferences and in that way also to this publication. All the members of the conferences are in a sense co-authors of the whole symposium in their contribution of ideas and helpful criticisms, even though not all have written actual words published.

At the first conference, Rensch presented a paper that has since been published elsewhere [1] and is not here reprinted. Although unable to attend either conference, Huxley sent a paper that was discussed at the second conference and is included in this symposium (Chapter 20). The subject presented by Washburn (Chapter 19) was revised with the help of Miss Avis, who has become its co-author although she was not present at either conference. One topic was presented at the conferences by an authority who was unable to provide the written version. That chapter (Chapter 1) was therefore written later by another author and did not, in this form, have the benefit of conference criticism. The final chapter was also necessarily, from its nature, written after the conferences.

1. B. Rensch. 1956. Increase of learning capability with increase of brain size. Mar.–Apr. American Naturalist, *90*, No. 851, 81–95.

Contents

Introduction

IN RECENT YEARS great progress has been made in the study of behavior and in the study of evolution. Much less, however, has been done in fields simultaneously involving both subjects. The evolutionary study of behavior and the behavioral study of evolution, although not wholly neglected, have comparatively little literature and few triumphs. It is true that the label "evolutionary" has been attached to a number of studies in comparative psychology, but all too often a student of biological (other than psychological) evolution found this to be a misnomer. Use of evolutionary theory and concepts in such work was frequently naïve or badly outdated, when it was not downright wrong. On the other hand many students of evolution were no less ignorant or inept in handling the behavioral, psychological elements that even they realized must enter into the history of life and the mechanisms of evolution. The generally accepted modern theory of evolution is called "synthetic," but comparative psychology has been an element not yet fully incorporated in the synthesis. Realization of these shortcomings and a hope to do something about them led to organization of the conferences mentioned in the preface and so eventually to the book now before you.

When plans for this symposium were first being made, a prominent place was given to the topic "Review of theories of behavior." The students of behavior quickly objected. There are, they said, no theories of behavior. There are theories, or, at least, formal generalizations, about particular categories of behavior, such as the theory of imprinting. (Numerous other examples are given in Part III.) But as to theories in a broader sense, which might apply to and unify the whole field of behavioral studies, they were said simply not to exist. One or two possible candidates, such as general systems theory, were proposed and were recognized as valuable and stimulating but were not accepted as being literally theories of behavior. No one could be found who was willing to review the topic of theories of behavior, and few would admit that the topic has real substance in the present state of the science.

Exactly the same reaction might have occurred if there had been proposed a "Review of theories of morphology." In fact it is so universally accepted as not to need explicit statement that the

1

theory of morphology is simply evolution, with its various concomitants such as homology, analogy, adaptive radiation and progression, and so on. It should by now be equally obvious that there
is, indeed, a general theory of behavior and that the theory is, again,
evolution, to just the same extent and in almost exactly the same
ways in which evolution is the general theory of morphology. To
make the relationship more obvious and to demonstrate that morphology, physiology, and behavior are aspects of organisms all
inseparably involved in and explained by the universal fact of
evolution became a principal object of this symposium.

A symposium on so vast a subject is necessarily a sampling and
not an over-all review. Explicit and in some cases even quite narrow
topics must be selected, and economy demands that each be treated
but once. The symposial attack permits assignment of each topic
to an expert, but it follows that the point of view shifts with each
chapter. It is useful that there should be a sampling of attitudes
and approaches, as well as a sampling of subject matter. A symposium is a mosaic, but a mosaic is (or can be) a picture and not a
casual assortment of tiles. While admitting that not all the wanted
tiles were available for this particular picture, and that its frame
would not admit all that might have been used, we do maintain
that there is a picture, and that its composition is modern and original to an extent that the reader will judge.

Achievement of a thorough synthesis of behavior and evolution
or a clear statement of the evolution of behavior is not accomplished here and is not possible now. The aims have had to be more
modest: to show that the synthesis is desirable and is eventually
possible; to expound the elements in each pertinent discipline
that may be applicable in other fields; to review present status in
such a way as to provide basis and stimulus for future construction.

Part I is provided by students of the history of life. The most
widely current general theory of evolution is summarized, and
historical examples with behavioral aspects and implications are
given. The evolution of behavior must depend on the rise and history of mechanisms that initiate and mediate behavior. In Part II
students of such structural and physiological mechanisms review
present knowledge of some of the most important of them. Behavior, itself, what it is descriptively and how its different aspects
may be explained and interrelated through evolution, is the very
heart of the book's theme. The subject is enormously too intricate

for this or any other one volume, but in Part III it is rather thoroughly exemplified by seven highly diverse contributions from specialists in comparative behavior, ranging from psychologists to systematists. If the zoologists have things to say about evolution to psychologists, they are also increasingly aware that comparative psychology is equally pertinent to zoology. They have questions to ask and applications to make, as three zoologists demonstrate in Part IV. Without depreciating comparative studies for their own sake, most of us must feel that the highest aim of evolutionary psychology is to provide a historical basis for and explanation of human psychology. Such applicability is shown in Part V, with some emphasis on the fact that in our unique species biological evolution has led into a whole new array of mechanisms, those of human cultures, which evolve in their own way and extend the processes of biological adaptation. Finally, a summary and, it is hoped, unifying commentary on the whole subject is provided in the last chapter.

The Study of Evolution and Its Record

THERE IS the theory of evolution and there are theories of evolution. The theory of evolution is the fact—it may surely be called "fact" in the vernacular —that all the organisms that now live or ever lived, all they are and all they do, are the outcome of genetic descent and modification from a remote, simple, unified beginning. Theories of evolution, taking the reality of evolution as given, seek to explain how this almost incredible diversification and complication have come about. Many such theories have been proposed, and a generation ago there seemed so little reason to choose among some of them, so much to say against any one of them, that the nonpartisan student could feel only confusion or despair. Now one theory has emerged that is judged superior and, as far as it yet goes, virtually irrefutable according to a large consensus.

That theory is outlined, about as briefly as possible, in Chapter 1. Another point there made is that many studies of evolution can be categorized as involving either events or processes, and some reference is made to methods of reconstructing historical sequences of events. Direct evidence is overwhelmingly morphological, and the student is compelled to use inference and extrapolation if he is to correlate the morphological data with their behavioral concomitants. Chapter 2 demonstrates by means of several striking, concrete examples that such correlation can be accomplished.

In Chapter 3 both comparative and directly his-

torical data are used to reconstruct, in broad outline, the long phylogenetic sequence from an early
invertebrate metazoan to man. This is done simultaneously in terms of behavior and of correlated
morphology. Behavioral factors of the sort called
"elemental" or "first order" in Chapter 1, especially
in locomotion but also in feeding and in reproduction, are shown to be crucial in the whole historical
sequence. The history here outlined must, in turn,
be basic in any evolutionary understanding of the
behavior of recent animals, including man.

1

The Study of Evolution: Methods and Present Status of Theory

George Gaylord Simpson

THE AMERICAN MUSEUM OF NATURAL HISTORY
AND COLUMBIA UNIVERSITY, NEW YORK

INTRODUCTION

SAMUEL BUTLER said that a hen is an egg's way of producing another egg. Thus in the Darwinian epoch he foreshadowed a reorientation of evolutionary studies that did later occur. Without expressing it in that way, the evolutionary scientists of Butler's and earlier times held the common-sense view that an egg is a hen's way of producing another hen. They were trying to explain the evolution of the hen, not of the egg. It was the geneticists, after 1900, who came around to Butler's view that the essence of the matter is in the egg, not in the hen.[1]

Those contrasting points of view reflect different ideas as to the involvement of behavior in evolution. The 19th-century evolutionary theories of the naturalists were largely, if not primarily, behavioral. The behavioral element tended at first to be minimized in the 20th-century evolutionary theories of the geneticists, who might in some cases be accused of leaving the hen out of the picture altogether except as a means of learning what the egg "knows."

The first great issue in naturalistic evolutionary theory was between the neo-Lamarckians and the Darwinians. (There were and are nonnaturalistic alternative schools, such as those of vitalism or

1. Without, indeed, any real debt to Butler. That an egg somehow "knows" how to produce a hen and thus produces another egg that "knows" just a little more seems brilliantly apt in retrospect. But, like other flashes of Butler's peculiar genius, this bit of insight was so embedded in nonsense that it was not really helpful at the time and had no useful outcome.

7

of finalism, but their metaphysics can legitimately be omitted from this brief account.) Lamarck, himself, stressed behavior almost to the point of considering it the sole effective cause of evolution. It is, he taught, the habitual actions of organisms—in other words, their behavior—that modify their morphology, and these modifications accumulated through the generations *are* evolution. It is true that Lamarck also believed in a perfecting principle that somehow has driven organisms up the *scala naturae,* but the neo-Lamarckians discarded that essentially nonnaturalistic element in his theory. The neo-Lamarckians also incorporated into their views the accumulation of direct results of the action of the environment on organisms, a hypothesis that is non-Lamarckian and nonbehavioral.

Darwin's theory of evolution was hardly less behavioral than Lamarck's. Darwin saw no reason to question the Lamarckian belief in the direct influence of behavior on evolution, through the induction of heritable modifications. Darwin's own main contribution, the theory of natural selection, also involved essential relationships between behavior and evolution. He saw and illustrated with many examples that the behavior of animals is often determined and always circumscribed by their heredity, although he knew even less than we do about the mechanisms involved. The behavior of animals is also obviously and crucially involved in their survival and success in reproduction. Thus natural selection provides another way, less direct but truer than the supposed Lamarckian way, in which behavior is bound in with the changes in heredity that constitute evolution.

Few now doubt that the Lamarckian and neo-Lamarckian views are essentially false, and we need pay no further attention to them here. The point is that Lamarck, Darwin, and their many colleagues and followers were all primarily interested in the behaving animal, the hen, rather than in the egg, which has no behavior in usual senses of the word, and that one of the things they sought and stressed was a relationship between behavior and evolution. It is a pity, in a way, that we cannot accept a direct and simple relationship, but Darwin pointed out a relationship that is surely present, in some degree, and that is all the more effective for being indirect and subtle.

Then came the shift of emphasis to the egg by the geneticists from about 1900 onward. In extreme form, their views practically eliminated behavior as an essential element in evolution. What a hen is and does depends on the egg, that is, on the mechanism of heredity complete within the fertilized egg. Evolutionary changes in the hen, so some of the early geneticists submitted and a dwindling few still hold, arise without any prior relationship to the hen and its behavior. Evolution is reduced to processes in the precursor cells of the gametes and in the confluence of gametes in the fertilized egg (zygote). The hen (the man, the tree) is largely irrelevant except, as Butler said, as a device for producing another egg.

The most widely held modern theory of evolution may be presented as a reconciliation between the naturalists' hen-evolution and the geneticists' egg-evolution. It reinstates behavior not merely as something to which evolution has happened but as something that is itself one of the essential determinants of evolution. Accepting the geneticists' knowledge of egg-processes, it shows that these are not autonomous but are strongly influenced by hen-processes. The means of that influence is, as Darwin thought, natural selection. In the course of this theoretical synthesis natural selection has turned out to be something broader than and in some respects different from Darwin's concept.[2]

METHODS OF EVOLUTIONARY STUDY

The topic assigned for this chapter requires some notice of methods before proceeding to summarize the present status of evolutionary theory. Methods are, indeed, so numerous and diverse that a catalogue of them would be redundant to those who are using them, confusing to those who are not, and of little interest or usefulness in either case. It will be best to avoid detail and to present only a few broad considerations as to aims, the ways of achieving them, and implications or criteria involved in those ways.

In the first place, most of the aims of evolutionary study involve either events or processes. The study of events is historical; it seeks to reconstruct the whole history of organisms on this planet. That (unattainable) goal is of course approached by accumulation of restricted studies of the histories of particular groups of organisms, of particular anatomical or physiological features, and the like. The procedure is by levels: comparative descriptive studies, then infer-

2. In justice, however, it should be emphasized that practically nothing that Darwin wrote about natural selection is invalidated by the modern concept. Darwinian selection still stands, but its complexities and bearings are better understood and it becomes part of a more inclusive principle.

ential placing of the units of description in phylogenetic sequences, and finally, generalizations as to the kinds of sequences that have most frequently occurred and the conditions that accompany and therefore may determine a particular kind of sequence.

The objective data for historical study, the things described at the first level of research, are characteristics of (1) organisms or parts thereof, (2) their activities, (3) the conditions surrounding and influencing them, and (4) the temporal sequence of the items observed.[3] It is especially pertinent to the subject of this book that all four kinds of data are only very exceptionally available in any one study. There are in this respect two quite different cases, each with its distinct methodological problems. A temporal sequence long enough to involve marked evolutionary change usually extends into geological time, and the organisms involved are, or include, fossils. Then the documents are directly historical in nature, but their data are primarily of classes (1), mainly morphological, and (4), sequential. Observations of class (3), environmental, are limited and more often involve inferences than direct observation. Direct observations of class (2), including behavior, are almost entirely lacking.[4] Morphological evolution of, for instance, a bone in the lower jaw of a group of reptiles can sometimes be observed without the slightest ambiguity in a directly historical record. Behavioral evolution cannot be so observed. Inferences as to behavior can be based on the morphology of fossils and analogy with living animals. That can, for instance, usually be done for food habits and locomotion, but such possible inferences include little beyond what might be called elemental or first-order behavior. For example, practically all of the habitual or possible movements of a bird may be inferred from its fossilized skeleton, and those movements are the elements from which the bird's total behavior was necessarily compounded. But it would be impossible to infer just what series of movements occurred in courtship, an example of compound or second-order behavior. The evolution of first-order

3. The temporal order of a really long sequence is rarely directly observed but it is commonly on so factual a basis that it may be considered an objective datum.

4. There are, to be sure, surprisingly numerous examples of what may be called "fossilized behavior": tracks, burrows, wounds and tooth marks, even animals fossilized in the act of parturition or copulation. Nevertheless I know of only one or two rather unimportant examples in which change, actual evolution, of behavior can be observed in such materials.

behavior is important and interesting, and we have some good examples documented by the fossil record, such as the evolution of locomotion in the horse family. Nevertheless, the evolution of second-order behavior is even more important and more interesting, and this is quite properly the principal preoccupation of the evolutionary psychologist. In that field the fossil record is of almost no direct (although it is of some indirect) help.

In the second main sort of historical study the documents are essentially contemporaneous. If the organisms under study are dead (fossils; the usual taxonomic collections of recent organisms; specimens for post-mortem dissection) the limitations are even greater than for fossil sequences, and data for the study of behavioral evolution are few, indeed. If, however, the subjects of study are living, data of classes (1), (2), and (3) are freely available. This is the source of practically all of our observational information on behavior. That is almost too obvious to require statement, but the point to be emphasized is that *such information is in itself completely nonhistorical;* it includes no data of class (4). Almost all students agree with that statement when it is made, but many of them do not really keep it in mind in their own work. In comparative anatomy some such sequence as dogfish-frog-cat-man is still frequently taught as "evolutionary," i.e. historical. In fact the anatomical differences among those organisms are in large part ecologically and behaviorally determined, are divergent and not sequential, and do not in any useful sense form a historical series. The same objection applies with perhaps even greater force to studies of behavior which state or assume an evolutionary (historical) sequence in, for instance, comparison of an insect [5] ("invertebrate level"), a rat [5] ("primitive mammalian level"), and a man.

The three main bases for inference from contemporaneous data to historical sequence are well known. (1) Related lineages often evolve more or less in parallel but some faster than others; at any one time, then, the contemporaneous representatives of the various lineages may form a series that approximates the historical se-

5. Apart from the point that there are hundreds of thousands of different kinds of insects, with almost incredibly diverse behavior patterns, and hundreds of kinds of rats, with much less but still important behavioral differences. In the conferences on which this symposium is based, the naturalists present repeatedly had occasion to call attention to the absurdity of speaking of "the insect," "the rat," or "the monkey" in studies of behavior, as if there were only one insect, rat, or monkey, or as if all insects, rats, or monkeys behaved alike.

quence leading to the more advanced members of the group. (2) Certain historical trends (e.g. from smaller to larger size, from simpler to more complex behavior) are so frequent or logical that they may be assumed to have occurred in a given case. (3) Characteristics shared by contemporaneous organisms are likely to have been present in their common ancestry. There is no reason to doubt that methods based on these principles, long used in comparative anatomy, are equally pertinent for the historical study of behavior. There are, however, many pitfalls in these methods, and these are probably (at least in the present state of the subject) even more serious for behavioral studies than they have proved to be for morphological studies. Problems and precautions cannot be further discussed here than to indicate the general nature of a few of the more serious in each category. (1) Divergence is more common than parallelism, and a contemporaneous series may not at all resemble an ancestral sequence; different characteristics commonly evolve at different rates so that the animal most primitive in one respect may be most advanced in another; truly ancestral stages are liable to complete replacement and are frequently totally unrepresented at the present time. (2) No trends have been universal and comparatively few are established as usual; trends may go in either direction, or both ways from the middle, and data without an objective time factor provide no directional signpost; any array of data can be arranged in a logical sequence, but if the data are contemporaneous the logical sequence may have no relationship to a true historical sequence. (3) Parallelism and convergence in evolution have been extremely common and they produce resemblances not present in a common ancestor; homoplasy is, therefore, widespread and is difficult to distinguish from homology, especially when, as in most studies of behavior, direct historical evidence is lacking.

The second main class of evolutionary studies involves processes rather than (historical) events. Study of a process necessarily includes study of the mechanism that performs it; joint study of genetic mechanisms and processes is an example more or less familiar to everyone with any interest in biology or evolution. The methods are for the most part experimental, and it is really not necessary to discuss them here: they are most familiar to the students least familiar with the matter of the present chapter, and they are richly exemplified in other chapters of this book. It is perhaps well just to point out that there is no natural, deep cleavage between the study of events and that of processes, or between the observational methods characteristic of the former and the experimental methods usual in the latter. Both sorts of methods are used to some extent in both fields, and the two can sometimes hardly be distinguished. Processes can to some extent be inferred from the historical record, and prior events lie implicitly behind existing processes. The importance and long-range effects of processes established by experimentation are best judged in the light of the historical record. Alternative possible interpretations of historical sequences must be judged by compatibility with known processes.

ELEMENTS OF THE SYNTHETIC THEORY OF EVOLUTION

Among students of evolution the world around there are still neo-Lamarckians, old-line Darwinians, vitalists, finalists, orthogeneticists, hologeneticists, mutationists, even spiritualists, not to mention theories so particular to certain individuals that they hardly fall into an -ism. All those now heterodox views are interesting, and many of them have points of emphasis, at least, that still should be kept in mind. Nevertheless, in a brief review of the present status of evolutionary theory it is now possible and proper to concentrate on a single school of theory. No one would maintain either that this theory is complete or that it is correct in all details. An overwhelming majority of students really familiar with the evidence do maintain that the theory has a sound basis and is proving most fertile in increasing understanding of the tremendously intricate course and process of evolution. This strong consensus, if not near unanimity, is a comparatively recent development. The name here preferred is the *synthetic theory*,[6] so-called because it is a new synthesis from all fields of biology and not the offspring exclusively of any one of the numerous preceding theories. Works

6. Numerous other tags have been applied, especially "neo-Darwinian," because of the large role assigned to natural selection in the theory. But "neo-Darwinian" in this application is misleading on two important counts. First, natural selection (itself no longer purely Darwinian) is here synthesized with equally important factors unknown to Darwin and even in strong contradiction with his views, especially on heredity. Second, the label "neo-Darwinian" historically belongs to a school that was literally neo-Darwinian, quite distinct from the present synthetic theory and only one of the several forerunners incorporated in the synthesis.

cited at the end of this chapter consider various aspects of the synthetic theory in more detail, and several of them discuss and give
references to various alternative theories not considered here.

Genetic Mechanisms. The medium of evolution, the thing in
which the processes of evolution occur and hence the thing that is
actually evolving, is a population. A population, in this sense, is a
group of organisms, similar among themselves and dissimilar from
other organisms with which they live, descended from a not remote
common ancestry, living in the same general region and environment, and with a continuity of many generations through time. The
inclusiveness of the term is vague and necessarily variable. At its
least inclusive it is synonymous with the deme or local population
of the biogeographers and systematists or (in a biparental population) the so-called Mendelian population of the geneticists. At its
most inclusive it is practically synonymous with the species of most
modern students. In the usual case of biparental organisms, the
population is also characterized and unified by interbreeding
among its actively sexual members. In the less common case of
uniparental (asexual, apomictic, etc.) organisms, the unity of the
population is still real but is looser and the evolutionary mechanisms are simpler but less flexible and potent.

The characteristics of any individual organism within a population are determined by interaction of its heredity with its environment, in the broadest sense, as the organism develops and, to less
extent, thereafter as long as it lives. Heredity may be determined
in part by the nature and organization of directly inherited cytoplasm (in metazoans mostly or entirely maternal, in the egg) and
sometimes by extranuclear bodies (plastids in plants, etc.), but to
far greater degree it is determined by the chromosomes in the
nucleus. Chromosomes are differentiated longitudinally, and the
irreducible (or at least experimentally unreduced) units of that
differentiation are called genes. Different genes have different effects (necessarily, in practice, because the genes are distinguishable
or recognizable in no other way), but the whole chromosomal complement acts and interacts, and it is that complement as a complex
unit that is the main determinant of heredity. It may be considered
as setting a reaction range, sometimes rigidly narrow and sometimes
very broad, within which the characteristics of the developing organism must lie. The characteristics actually arising at one point or
another of the reaction range, for instance the exact size of an

organism when the range permits much variation in size, depend for the most part on environmental influences during development.

The population as a whole has characteristics likewise determined by the interaction of the genetic mechanism and of the environment. Its total genetic structure at any one time usually depends almost entirely on the kinds and combinations of chromosomes and genes present and their relative frequencies. Continuity of the population depends on the processes of reproduction in which sets of chromosomes are passed on from parent to offspring. In asexual reproduction the parental set (generally double) is simply passed on, usually unchanged. In sexual, biparental reproduction two homologous sets (each usually single) are received, one from each parent. Then there is reduction of a parental double set to a single set in the gamete, and this involves the mechanism of meiosis, with two concomitants of special importance for evolution: (1) the single chromosome set of the gamete is a random assortment from each of the two sets of the parent, and (2) occasional crossing over from one homologous parental chromosome to the other produces different combinations of genes in the chromosomes received by the offspring. Fusion of gametes into a zygote brings together sets of homologous chromosomes from different sources. That factor means that the combinations actually realized will be influenced by breeding structure and habits in the population. The extent to which breeding is random or promiscuous, monogamous, polygamous, etc., becomes important, and above all any influence which makes individuals with certain genetic characteristics more likely than others to have offspring. Also important is the likelihood of hybridization between different populations or, much less commonly, different species.

Changes in characteristics induced by changing environmental influences on identical genetic reaction ranges are not heritable. Such changes may affect evolution quite indirectly, but they cannot in themselves constitute secular evolutionary change. True evolutionary change involves changes in the genetics of the population, which are almost always changes in the relative frequencies of the various kinds of genes and of chromosomes and of their combinations. In sexual, biparental populations constant changes in individual combinations are guaranteed by the mechanisms already mentioned: random assortment of chromosomes and crossing over in meiosis, and biparental origin of chromosomes. These may but, as will be seen, usually do not in themselves bring about changes in relative frequencies in the population as a whole.

The mechanisms hitherto mentioned make for constant and radical individual rearrangements of genetic factors already present in any biparental population. The appearance of new factors in both biparental and uniparental populations is due to mutations which, broadly speaking, include changes in the numbers of chromosomes, in the internal structure of chromosomes (other than by simple crossing over), and in genes. It is the past occurrence of mutations that guarantees that homologous chromosomes rarely have exactly the same forms (alleles) of homologous genes and often are structurally different (have, for instance, the genes arranged in different sequence). Occurrence of new mutations, unless counteracted in various ways, further tends slowly but steadily to change the genetics of a population.

Random Processes and Evolution. It is an extraordinary fact that most of the processes inherent in the genetic mechanism of evolution occur at random. It must be understood that the word "random" in this connection (and, indeed, etymologically) does *not* mean that all of a number of possible outcomes are equally probable. It means that the results of the processes are not oriented toward some end external to the processes themselves. In evolution the relevant end is the adaptedness of the population as a whole, its capacity to continue through future generations within an available environment. The random genetic processes are those that are not inherently adaptive for the population. Assortment of chromosomes in meiosis does seem normally to be random not only in this sense but also in the fullest possible sense that all combinations are about equally probable. Crossing over, as it affects association of any two genes, has probabilities almost directly proportional to the distance (along the chromosome) between the genes, but still is random as regards adaptation. For reasons yet unknown, different genes mutate at quite different rates and mutations of a given gene to (or from) different alleles also have decidedly different rates, so that possible gene mutations—and the same is true also of chromosome mutations—have very diverse probabilities, but these processes are still random by the pertinent definition of that word. Mating or more broadly reproduction is usually not entirely random, a fact to be stressed in the next section, but it may be at least approximately so. Here randomness involves likelihood that parents of given genetic types occurring with given frequencies in the population tend to produce offspring in about the same frequencies, or, what comes to the same thing, that relatively higher production of offspring is not significantly correlated with genetic factors in the parents.[7]

If reproduction is random, in combination with the inherently random processes in meiosis, there is no statistical tendency for change in frequencies of genetic factors within a population; in other words there is no tendency for directional evolutionary change to occur. That is the so-called Hardy-Weinberg law, the mathematical expression and derivation of which are given in most textbooks of genetics. Even if mutation is taken into account, there is a point of equilibrium where a given mutation is balanced by back-mutation and random loss (see below), and there is no (or no further) tendency toward evolutionary change in the population. Thus the random genetic processes, all together, do *not* tend statistically to produce evolution. That statement applies equally to sexual populations with mutation, meiosis, and fertilization and to asexual populations with mutation and mitosis, only.

Although the random processes noted do not tend systematically to change the mean frequencies of genetic factors in a population, those frequencies through the generations do tend to fluctuate around the mean. Populations of organisms are of course always finite, and each generation is in effect a sample drawn from the long-range total population of all generations or from the purely theoretical infinite population of statistical estimation. The genetical constitution of each generation is thus subject to statistical sampling error, which is its departure from the mean of the long-range or infinite population. Such departures or statistical sampling errors also occur, and may be quite radical, when a new area is populated by a few individuals spreading from a larger population elsewhere, or when for any reason a segment of a large population becomes reproductively isolated from the rest of that population. Sampling errors are larger the smaller the population. In very large populations they are so small as to be negligible, at least in

7. Because of doubts or equivocation as to the precise meanings of "random" in application to these various processes, they are sometimes called "stochastic." Appropriate definition may, nevertheless, be as readily made for "random" as for "stochastic."

comparison with effects of selection (below), but they are never reduced to zero in populations of finite size.

Under the influence of random sampling error, commonly called "genetic drift" in this connection, the frequency of a given chromosome number or arrangement or of a given gene allele may increase, even to 100 per cent, or decrease, even to zero. Evolution has then obviously occurred, and as far as now known this is the *only* process by which random (unoriented with respect to adaptation) evolution can occur. That it does occur, for instance in the colonization of an oceanic island from a mainland, is beyond any question. How commonly it occurs and how important it is in the overall picture of evolution are still strongly disputed questions. The present consensus seems to be that it is rather common but that its importance in long evolutionary sequences or radical evolutionary transformations is largely, or almost completely, overshadowed by the nonrandom effects of selection. One special case of completely demonstrated reality has evidently played an important role in the diversification of plants, at least, on lower taxonomic levels. Polyploid mutants or hybrids, with increased (usually doubled) numbers of chromosomes, may be unable to breed back with a parental stock. If they do survive and increase to become populations, they are thus genetically distinct samples isolated forthwith from their ancestral populations.[8]

Oriented Processes and Adaptation. Thus the usual random processes of the genetic mechanism tend to produce either no evolutionary changes at all or changes that are sampling errors and that are nonadaptive or, so to speak, only accidentally adaptive. Yet it is perfectly clear that evolution does occur and that it is, to say the least, often adaptive and not entirely random. It was often urged against Darwin and, with more basis, against De Vries and other early geneticists who assigned too exclusive a role to mutation that evolution cannot have occurred "by accident." The fairly obvious answer, which was in fact already emphasized and soundly established by Darwin, is that the adaptive orientation of evolution must involve the one genetic process that is not necessarily or, as a matter of conclusive observation, usually random: reproduction. If reproduction is differential, if there is a correlation between dis-

8. It is not usual to consider the origin of a polyploid species as an example of sampling error, but it does seem logically to fall into that category as an example of random evolutionary change.

tinctive genetic factors in the parents and their relatively greater success in reproduction, then there will be an increase in the frequencies of those genetic factors (and combinations of them) within the population from one generation to another. Evolution will occur, and it will be oriented, not random. That, in brief and shorn of numerous complications, is the modern concept of natural selection. Natural selection, as defined, is known really to exist and to be effective, both by observation in nature and by experimentation. No other nonrandom genetic factor has been objectively demonstrated, even though several have been postulated (e.g. Lamarckian influence of use or disuse, nonrandom mutation, inherent tendency—whatever that may mean—to progress toward a goal). Most students now believe that this only demonstrably real nonrandom process is also sufficient to account for all the observed nonrandom events in the course of evolution. *Proving* sufficiency amounts to proving a negative, which is generally deemed impossible; but sufficiency is the stand of the synthetic theory, and the burden of proof would seem to lie with its (now few) opponents.

Reproductive success may be comparatively simple in asexual organisms. It often amounts only to this: a genetic difference arises by mutation, there is direct competition between mutant and non-mutant forms, members of one group or the other survive more often to reproduce, and the less successful group eventually disappears. Even there complications are ignored, and in biparental populations the matter becomes highly intricate. (1) Male and female must occur in proximity or must find each other. (2) In many, especially the more complex, animals they must be sexually acceptable to each other and must mate. (3) Fertilization must occur. (4) The gametes must be genetically compatible. (5) Normal embryological development must occur. (6) Offspring must survive to breeding age and become successful reproducers in their turn. Relatively greater or less success may occur at any one of these stages, and at substages within them, and selection depends on the total outcome.

Darwin was aware of the selective possibilities of all the listed stages, but he stressed (6) above all others, and some of his followers did so almost to the exclusion of any others. Thus Darwinian natural selection was based mainly on differential mortality, and the Darwinians and neo-Darwinians hardly grasped the whole process as one of differential reproduction. Darwin also devoted much attention to stage (2) as involving sexual selection, which he distinguished from natural selection.

Until quite recently it was generally implied or assumed that selection always favors individual survival or, more in the spirit of the modern theory, individual success in reproduction. Now it is evident that selection favors successful reproduction of the population and not necessarily of any or of all particular individuals within it. A striking, although rather exceptional, example of that fact is provided by the social insects, among which only a very small fraction actually reproduce although their success in reproduction is completely dependent on the nonreproducing individuals. Of more general import is the recently accumulating evidence that the most successful populations usually have considerable genetic heterogeneity and much heterozygosity in individuals. But that favored characteristic of a population can be maintained only at the expense of constantly producing a certain proportion of definitely inferior, less heterozygous individuals.

A central problem of evolutionary theory has always been the explanation of adaptation, and the synthetic theory maintains (as did Darwin, but with a different understanding of the mechanism) that adaptation is a result of natural selection. But it also demonstrates that natural selection always favors reproductive success of a population, and nothing else. It might be suitable to redefine adaptation as such reproductive success, but some confusion might arise from the fact that most of the characteristics generally considered adaptive seem to be so in the old Darwinian sense of promoting survival of the individual and seem to have little or nothing to do with population reproduction *per se*. The anomaly is only apparent, however, for clearly reproductive success of the population involves all phases of individual life cycles and will incomparably more often than not be favored by individual adaptation to the environment. Such adaptation will therefore almost always be favored by natural selection. Nevertheless the possibility remains that selection, as here defined, could favor population reproduction at the expense of individual adaptation. We have already noted that it does so, indeed, in the cases of homozygous individuals in heterotic populations. It has also been variously claimed that a species may become so specialized for reproductive ends, for example in development of sexual weapons and competition, as to put the whole population at a disadvantage in competition with other species. The reality or importance of such possible phenomena are not, however, clearly established.

An aspect of the synthetic theory especially pertinent here is that it again brings in behavior as a central element. It not only points the way to evolutionary, historical explanations of existing behavior patterns but also involves behavior as one of the factors that produce or guide evolution. Some phases of selection, as in zygote and embryo, are not directly behavioral, but aspects of breeding, care of young, and subsequent survival are pre-eminently so and are obviously crucial elements in selection.

SOME HISTORICAL GENERALIZATIONS AND PRINCIPLES

Those, in brief, are the most essential features of the mechanisms and processes now believed to underlie the phenomena of evolution. An understanding of comparative behavior, or other biological aspects of our contemporary world, further involves consideration of what those phenomena have, in fact, been, of how the processes have worked out in the prodigious history of life. A review of the vast body of information and theory on this subject is of course beyond the present scope. There are, however, certain generalizations and principles that stand out from that record and that can be particularly useful in any reconstruction of behavioral (or other) evolution. Just a few of the most important of these will be mentioned.

Irrevocability, Opportunism, and Transformation. From a certain point of view all study and knowledge of nature can be divided into processes, immanent and changeless characteristics of the universe, and configurations that result from those processes, transient and historically cumulative states of the universe. The difference is that between gravity, a timeless structural feature of our world, and a falling stone, acted on by gravity but determined as to time, place, and condition by the whole previous history of the matter in the stone. The configuration of the living, as of any other, world depends from instant to instant on its last previous configuration and on how the immanent processes, the "laws" of nature, tend to act on any given configuration. Involved is historical causation, which includes everything that has ever happened and which is thus an inherently nonrepeatable accumulation.

In application to evolution, those rather abstract considerations mean that the actual course of evolution is determined not only by its processes but also by the cumulative total of *all* previous events. It follows that evolution is irrevocable. That law (it seems to be about as near to a true law as anything in the realm of biology) has two major corollaries. One is the famous doctrine of the irreversibility of evolution. No organism, no population, no community returns precisely to any antecedent structure or state. A gross but impressive example: whales are descended from fishes; they have returned to the water and resumed the ecological status of fishes; but they have not again become fishes, and every system, organ, tissue, or cell of a whale is radically distinct from that of any fish that is or ever was. The other corollary of irrevocability is that the effects of previous conditions are never wholly lost. A whale, again, carries not only in general but also in detail down to the last cell unmistakable effects of its ancestors' sojourn on the land.[9]

As each configuration is derived from the last, and from all previous ones, each can only be a modification of or an addition to what was already there. This gives evolution an opportunistic aspect. Changes take place on the basis of the previous condition and not as a wholly new construction most efficiently adapted to new conditions. Early fishes had lungs. In many later fishes the pre-existing lungs evolved into hydrostatic organs, which, in spite of their radically different function, did not arise *de novo*. In land animals the lungs retained and considerably perfected their respiratory structure and function. Land snails, requiring an organ for the same function, had no lungs in their ancestry and did not evolve lungs, but a structure that was pre-existent, the mantle cavity, could and did evolve to serve that function.

When a way of life is changing in the course of evolution it is evidently simpler, that is, it is genetically more likely, to remodel the existing than to introduce something completely new. That is the principle of transformation. The evolution of lung to swim bladder, already mentioned, is an example. Another striking and

9. Exceptions to both aspects of irrevocability are conceivable, but none are known or likely. The genetic processes of evolution are all reversible, but that all should reverse to just the same extent in conjunction and within an intricate and changing environmental framework is so improbable that it is not likely to have happened in only a few billion years. An event such as a mutation may seem to be quite canceled out if the mutant allele is subsequently eliminated from the population, but again the probability that even the transient presence of the allele left no effects at all is infinitesimal.

widely familiar example is the incorporation of the bones hinging skull and jaw in early reptiles (quadrate and articular) into the middle ear of mammals (where they are renamed incus and malleus).

The principles of irrevocability, opportunism, and transformation are based mainly on anatomical and physiological data, but in the nature of things they must also apply, *mutatis mutandis,* to the evolution of behavior.

Trends and Orthogenesis. It is a common observation, backed by hundreds of concrete examples in the fossil record, that evolutionary change in a given direction once started may tend to continue for a long time. In terms of years, as nearly as highly inaccurate approximations permit conclusion, it is the rule for trending changes to continue for more than 10^6 years and common for them to last on the order of 10^7 years. Much longer trends, however, as of the order of 10^8 years without stop or pronounced change of direction, have apparently not been substantiated. For instance the recorded history of the horse family shows several well-marked trends, as has become common knowledge, but it is less widely known by nonspecialists that no single recognized trend in that family was continuous throughout the 6×10^7 years of its known history. The longest of the known trends did not continue with even approximate constancy for more than about 2×10^7 years. Some trends reached an inherent limit, for instance the premolars (all but the first) once fully molarized could not become more so. Other trends stopped without having reached such an apparent limit; for instance increase in size stopped far short of any mechanical limit.

Similar trends often appear simultaneously or successively in multiple related lines, such as a tendency for the shells to become coiled in relatives of the oyster. Others may appear over and over again in widely diverse groups, for example increase in individual size. Yet there has been no universal trend, no trend that did not stop or change before about 10^8 years and usually much less, and even no trend that was not on occasion reversed.[10] The trend toward larger size noted above for some of the horses and

10. There has been some confusion on the subject of trends and the irreversibility of evolution, with the argument that either trends do not become reversed or else evolution is reversible. The difficulty is semantic, only. A lineage that becomes smaller and to that degree more like an ancestral stage has not except in this one artificially segregated characteristic returned to the ancestral condition.

here in a more general sense is probably the most widespread to be detected among animals. It has occurred repeatedly in groups as diverse as protozoans and primates. Yet it has obviously been neither universal nor, in any one group, constant. If it had been, all animals would by now be elephantine or cetacean in bulk. The opposite trend, toward smaller size, has evidently been less frequent but has certainly occurred many times, and absence of trend, maintenance of about the same size, has probably been the rule.

The foregoing and many other facts about trends lead to the essential conclusion that there is no mysterious, inherent tendency for evolution to proceed indefinitely in straight lines. It accords with everything really known about trends, to the limited extent that they do characterize evolution, to conclude that they occur only when and only as long as they are adaptive. This pre-eminently oriented feature of evolutionary history is adequately explained by the known orienting (nonrandom or antichance) process of evolution: natural selection. The opposite view, that trends may or do occur without relationship to natural selection generally is labeled as "orthogenesis," and there has been widespread belief that the fossil record supports or even proves the postulate of orthogenesis. That idea has always been most widespread among those least familiar with the fossil record. Most paleontologists have long since rejected it.

The facts that trends are adaptive, begin and end at fairly definite times, and rarely persist long, geologically speaking, have another bearing, harking back to methods of inference mentioned early in this chapter. In the absence of really historical documents, it is generally impossible to extrapolate far and accurately from brief sequences or by postulating a previous trend on the basis of comparative data on living animals. It is, for instance, unjustified to conclude that a behavioral sequence from simple to complex among recent primates can be correctly superimposed as a continuing historical trend from Paleocene prosimian to Recent man.

Patterns of Evolution. The fabric of evolution is phylogeny, and above the level of interbreeding and hybridization it has only two elements: splitting and succession. The basic process of evolutionary splitting is speciation, the rise of two or more species from a single species. Isolation of a segment of the population is accompanied or followed by genetic divergence, with more or less divergence also in morphology, physiology, and behavior. In uniparental populations no genetic nexus unites the individuals and speciation is a comparatively simple result of mutation and selection. In biparental populations the crucial feature is the breaking of the nexus of interbreeding. Usually (some would say "always") an initial requirement is some degree of geographic separation. Isolating mechanisms that then reduce and finally stop interbreeding, even if the incipient species do come into contact, are almost innumerable. Many of them are behavioral, for instance in decreasing willingness to mate or success in mating. The eventual and complete barrier, which always does arise finally if the now separate species survive but which may be long delayed, is genetic divergence that makes the gametes so incompatible that hybrid zygotes cannot develop.

The significance of phylogenetic splitting in over-all evolutionary history is increase in diversity, with the occupation of new regions and environments and, within each area of occupation, a parceling out into increasingly numerous and narrow ecological niches, each occupied by a distinctive species. If we had no fossil record, it would be irresistible to visualize a single, broadly adapted, primordial marine species the descendants of which expanded to occupy all the waters and lands and specialized for close fit in each available niche. Expansion and diversification complete, evolution would end. Expansion and diversification are, of course, the main motifs in the rich fabric of life's history, but the whole pattern is astonishingly more complex. Most species, even though already well fitted into a niche or adaptive zone, continue to change. The overwhelming majority finally became extinct without issue and are replaced by other, perhaps quite different organisms.

A few organisms have reached a sort of evolutionary stasis, adequate adaptation to a sufficiently constant environment, and have continued without marked change thereafter to become "living fossils": the horseshoe crab, the opossum, and others. Most environments change enough so that the organisms in them must do so, too. The mere fact that some one species in a community changes, for any reason, means that the environment of all the others is different to some degree. The environmental change requiring adaptive adjustment for a species may even reside within the species, itself—that is probably true of many of the trends toward larger size, the smaller animals of a population always being at a slight competitive disadvantage compared with the larger. Such usually slow shifts of environment and adaptation are nearly, but not quite, universal and they account for the commonest trends in evolution.

Rarer but more striking events result from not merely maintaining adaptation in a changing world but also changing or improving the quality of adaptation. Then there is likely to occur on a smaller or larger scale what has been aptly called a breakthrough. Increased competitive efficiency may permit expansion into already occupied adaptive zones, with extinction for their former occupants, as among the fishes the teleosts have ousted all but a tithe of their ancient competitors. Or new ways of life may be achieved, as the reptiles spread over the lands then effectively empty of competitors. In such episodes more or less radical changes in structure, physiology, and behavior are involved. Selection is then particularly intense, and change is correspondingly rapid. The changes do usually take an appreciable time, apparently as a rule on the order of 10^6 years and upward, but the effect in the over-all picture is steplike, not a trend but a steep transition from one level to another. The behavioral change when man became adept with tools—supposing, as one must, that this was accompanied by a biological and not entirely a cultural evolutionary advance—was such an event, probably one of exceptional rapidity and certainly one of exceptional portent.

REFERENCES

THE PURPOSE of this introductory and background chapter has been to review for the nonspecialist a few points that are matters of common knowledge and general agreement among specialists in the study of evolution. It has therefore been inappropriate to cite individual authority for specific statements. The following recommended books cover the subject, or aspects of it, in greater detail and with many citations of original studies.

CARTER, G. S. 1951. Animal evolution. London, Sidgwick and Jackson.

DOBZHANSKY, TH. 1951. Genetics and the origin of species. 3d ed. New York, Columbia Univ. Press.

DOBZHANSKY, TH. 1955. Evolution, genetics, and man. New York, Wiley.

HUXLEY, J. S. 1943. Evolution: the modern synthesis. New York, Harper.

LERNER, I. M. 1954. Genetic homeostasis. New York, Wiley.

MAYR, E. 1942. Systematics and the origin of species. New York, Columbia Univ. Press.

MOODY, P. A. 1953. Introduction to evolution. New York, Harper.

SIMPSON, G. G. 1953. The major features of evolution. New York, Columbia Univ. Press.

SIMPSON, G. G., PITTENDRIGH, C. S., and TIFFANY, L. H. 1957. Life: an introduction to biology. New York, Harcourt, Brace.

STEBBINS, G. L., JR. 1949. Variation and evolution in plants. New York, Columbia Univ. Press.

2

Morphology and Behavior

Edwin H. Colbert

THE AMERICAN MUSEUM OF NATURAL HISTORY

INTRODUCTION

THAT THERE IS a definite relationship between the morphology of an animal and its behavior seems so obvious as to need little elaboration at this place, yet this is a fact that often does not receive the recognition it deserves. Much of the behavior of animals is determined to a considerable degree by their physical adaptations to the environment in which they live. Or, to put it in a different way, morphology and behavior have developed together as adaptations to the environment.

The relationship is quite evident when one looks at the major taxonomic categories among the animals with backbones. For instance, flying vertebrates must of necessity possess patterns of behavior quite different from those of the vertebrates that run on the ground. Swimming vertebrates, especially those so adapted that they spend their entire lives in the water, must behave in ways quite different from the flying vertebrates or the ground-living forms.

Let us elaborate briefly on these and other simple examples of the relationship between morphology and behavior. Among mammals, the forelimbs of a porpoise are flat paddles with which it controls its motion through the water. They are not used in any great degree for propulsion but rather they determine the direction of motion and turning. The forelimbs of a bat, on the other hand, are the prime locomotor organs; they propel the animal with great speed and uncanny skill through the atmosphere. The forelimbs of a horse act in concert with the hind limbs for getting the animal over the ground at a fast clip. The forelimbs of a kangaroo are not much used for locomotion, they are hands to aid in feeding. The forelimbs of a mole are powerful shovels, with which the animal burrows its way through the hard earth. With such differently adapted forelimbs—to consider only these parts of the whole anatomy—the behavior of porpoise, bat, horse, kangaroo and mole is bound to differ enormously.

Such comparisons may be extended, for instance to the senses. The porpoise has keen sight but no external ear. It does hear rather well, receiving its auditory sensations as vibrations that travel through the water. The bat relies very little on its sense of sight, but it has wonderfully developed ears with which it picks up reflected sound waves to guide it during its nocturnal flights. This is nature's sonar system. The horse depends on good vision plus hearing, plus a well-developed sense of smell. The mole is practically blind, but has a highly adapted sense of touch. With such profoundly different modifications of the senses, the behavior patterns of these animals are bound to show marked differences. Indeed, in some respects there are no common bases for certain aspects of their behavior.

Can comparisons such as these be extended on more restricted bases? Can they be made between animals fairly closely related? And can the correlation between morphology and behavior be projected back through time, to give us by means of a study of the fossils some idea how animals long extinct may have behaved? In many instances such comparisons can be made. Let us begin with a journey back through about 100 million years of time, to the days when dinosaurs ruled the earth.

Morphology and the Possible Behavior in Certain Dinosaurs

The first dinosaurs appeared toward the close of the Triassic period, about 175 million years ago. These early dinosaurs were not particularly large; some of them were quite small. They were lightly built. Their hindlimbs were strong and birdlike, and it is quite obvious that the primitive dinosaurs ran about in much the same fashion as do long-legged ground birds of the present day. The feet had three functional toes and also were quite birdlike. The forelimbs were small, and probably were used mainly for grasping. The body was pivoted at the hips, and there was a long tail that served as a counterbalance to the weight of the body. The neck was rather long and flexible, and the head was small, with long jaws and many sharp, bladelike teeth.

Now, what may be inferred as to behavior patterns in these first dinosaurs, from the morphologic facts briefly outlined above? It is to be remembered that these primitive dinosaurs were reptiles, so that their general behavior was basically reptilian. Their temperatures varied in direct relation to the varying temperatures of their environments, and because of this their metabolic rates went up and down. They had periods of sluggish activity when temperatures were down, and other periods of great activity when temperatures were up. Very likely they were capable of unusual bursts of energy for short periods of time.

Certainly they must have been active and swift reptiles, as indicated by their long and slender but powerful hindlimbs and their trim bodies. They could run at a good rate of speed, at least for short distances. Watching the modern collared lizard (*Crotaphytus*) of the southwestern United States, one may get an idea on a reduced scale of how the early dinosaurs ran, for the collared lizard runs on its hind legs, and it can scoot across the ground at a truly astonishing pace. This is its protection.

But speed in these early reptiles was not only for the purpose of escape. They were obviously carnivorous, as is shown by the form of their teeth and the structure of their jaws. It seems logical to think that they could pursue and capture other fast animals— probably other small reptiles for the most part. The long-toothed jaws were useful for catching their prey, and so were their sharply clawed hands. It is probable that jaws and hands were used together for holding struggling victims and for tearing food into digestible pieces. In brief, the early dinosaurs of Triassic times were for the most part hunters of small game, and they were fast enough to run away from the reptiles of those days that were bigger and more powerful than they were.

This mode of life may be looked upon as representing the basic type of behavior for the dinosaurs. This was the central hub of adaptations from which the later dinosaurs diverged during the long span of their geologic history. And from this beginning the dinosaurs evolved through time along remarkably varied lines of development.

One line of dinosaurian evolution, that of the sauropods, led to extreme giantism. These became the largest of all dinosaurs, and the largest animals that have ever lived upon the land. The sauropods of late Jurassic times, like *Brontosaurus,* were reptiles seventy feet or more in length that stood fifteen feet high at the hip. In life they must have weighed forty tons or more. Anatomically an animal of such dimensions is not going to be much like its small forebear, and this is certainly true of *Brontosaurus* as compared with its ultimate dinosaur ancestor.

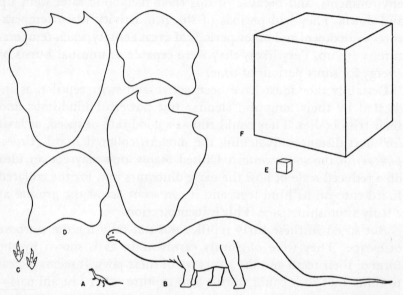

Fig. 2-1. Size comparisons in two saurischian dinosaurs: *Coelophysis,* a small, early theropod dinosaur of Triassic age, and *Brontosaurus,* a giant sauropod dinosaur of late Jurassic age. A and B, body outlines of *Coelophysis* and *Brontosaurus* respectively, drawn to the same scale. C and D, outlines of the footprints of a Triassic theropod similar to *Coelophysis* and an early Cretaceous sauropod similar to *Brontosaurus,* drawn to the same scale. These footprints indicate the relative amount of contact with the ground necessary to support the small, active, carnivorous dinosaur and the gigantic, ponderous, herbivorous dinosaur, they also reflect the differences in the movements of the two. E and F, cubes to represent the relative masses of *Coelophysis* and *Brontosaurus.*

In the first place, the giant sauropod was necessarily quadrupedal, unlike its bipedal ancestor. Its bulk was so great that bone, muscle, and ligament were mechanically unable to hold the body in a bipedal position. All four heavy, postlike legs were needed to support the forty tons against the constant downward pull of gravity. Broad, heavy feet, something like the feet of modern elephants, gave strong, solid support on the ground. Massive shoulder and hip girdles afforded strong connections with the backbone. The backbone itself was tremendously strong and in some ways a marvel of natural engineering. The vertebrae interlocked with each other by expanded and multiplied articular surfaces, yet each vertebra was rather airily built so that it resembled somewhat the steel trusses of a big bridge. Thus the vertebral column was strong but was not burdened by the dead weight of its own structure. A strong backbone was important to the giant sauropods as a support for the weight not only of the body that was suspended from it but also of the neck, a long, derrick-like lever extending far in front of the forelimbs. This greatly elongated neck carried a comparatively small skull, the jaws set with peglike or bladelike teeth. The teeth indicate that the sauropods were plant-eating reptiles. They very probably fed upon succulent water plants that they plucked from the bottoms of lakes and streams or from the lush vegetation that grew in marshes. The tail was also very long.

It is obvious that *Brontosaurus* and his relatives did not run about as did the primitive dinosaurs described above. The huge sauropods must have been comparatively slow, ponderous beasts whose great bulk precluded fast movement.

When set upon by their contemporaries, the giant meat-eating dinosaurs, the giant sauropods probably sought protection by escaping into swamps or lakes or rivers. That they were aquatic reptiles in part and spent a large proportion of their time in the water is indicated not only by the sediments in which they are found but also by the structure of the skull. The nostrils were elevated to the top of the head, an adaptation that almost invariably indicates a water-living animal. *Brontosaurus* was probably quite at home in fairly deep water, with the body submerged and the head thrust up at the end of its long neck so that the nostrils were above the surface of the water. In such a situation this reptile was almost invulnerable to attack.

All of these physical adaptations shown in the structure of the bones indicate a pattern of behavior in the sauropods quite different from that of the ancestral dinosaurs which lived in the tropical forests of Triassic times. It is the difference between small and huge size, between quick and ponderous motion, between safety achieved through flight and safety because of giantism combined with life in a largely inaccessible habitat, between the active and bloody search for game and the peaceful feeding upon surrounding vegetation.

This brief account of dinosaurian adaptations, and the possible behavior patterns that may be inferred from such adaptations, touches on only two structural types among the great variety of dinosaurs that inhabited the world during Mesozoic times. But these comparisons may serve to exemplify the correlation between morphology and behavior in the dinosaurs, without our laboring the argument further here.

Though not all of the dinosaurs were giants, a majority of them were, and the evolutionary history of these two orders of reptiles was certainly marked by a prevalent growth to huge size. They lived during a time in earth history when environmental conditions favored giantism among the reptiles.

Perhaps their great size gave the giant dinosaurs some of the advantages of the warm-blooded mammals in terms of behavior. Modern reptiles are characterized by body temperatures that fluctuate in fairly direct response to the fluctuation of environmental temperatures. When the air is cold a reptile will be cold and sluggish; when it is hot the reptile will be warm and active. In a small lizard these fluctuations are rapid and extreme; the mass of the body is so small that the animal heats up quickly and conversely loses heat rapidly. A fifteen-foot alligator requires a long time to gain or lose a degree of temperature as compared with a two-ounce lizard, because of its large mass of body matter. The fluctuations of body temperature in the lizard might be graphed as a series of sharp up and down zigzags, in the crocodile as an up-and-down undulant line.

What might have been the fluctuations of body temperature in the giant dinosaurs? It seems likely that they were relatively small, both because of the huge size of these reptiles and because they were living in tropical and subtropical environments, where the temperature differences between day and night and between seasons of the year were not great. The giant dinosaurs may have enjoyed fairly uniform optimum body temperatures, day in and day out. Perhaps this made them active animals, at least as compared with most of the reptiles we know; and it may have been a factor contributing largely to the extraordinarily successful manner in which the dinosaurs dominated the continents for almost 100 million years. When thinking of behavior in the dinosaurs, this factor of temperature tolerance should always be kept in mind.

A Passing Glance at Some Mammal-like Reptiles

Long before the first dinosaurs appeared, certain reptiles were rapidly evolving along lines that were to lead to the warm-blooded mammals. These reptiles were the therapsids, the remains of which have been found in considerable abundance in the Permian and lower Triassic sediments of South Africa and northern Russia. They represent an early progressive phase in reptilian evolution quite different from the type of development that resulted in the long dominance of the Mesozoic world by the dinosaurs. The therapsids approached the threshold of the mammalian grade of anatomical development at a time when most reptiles were still rather primitive, and then they evolved themselves out of existence by being the direct ancestors of early mammals. By the end of the Triassic period the therapsids were virtually extinct, and during Jurassic and Cretaceous times their descendants, the ancient mammals, inhabited the continents as the very small and very meek contemporaries of the great dinosaurs. The superior characters of structure and physiology, and presumably the superior traits of behavior, factors that subsequently established the mammals as rulers of the earth, were in middle and late Mesozoic times of little consequence as compared with the highly evolved and varied reptilian characters and traits that made the dinosaurs so supremely successful. Yet the features that make mammals the animals they are were well established early during the time of dinosaurian evolution, ready to be released, as it were, when the dinosaurs came to the end of their long evolutionary development. To get some idea of the base from which mammals arose it may be useful to look at some of the advanced mammal-like reptiles that lived during early Triassic times, just before the beginning of dinosaurian history.

Among the Triassic therapsids or mammal-like reptiles were the cynodonts of South Africa, known from skulls and skeletons that have been studied and described in some detail during the past half-century or so. These reptiles, of which *Cynognathus* is a good example, were small to medium-sized animals, the largest being about the size of a big dog. They were primarily quadrupedal; there were no evolutionary trends among them toward the bipedalism that was so characteristic of many dinosaurs. But whereas many of the four-footed reptiles that we know in life, like the

lizards, have rather sprawling limbs, the cynodonts had limbs
that were carried close to the body so that the feet were placed
well beneath the animal. Locomotion was efficient because the
limbs moved forward and backward without a great deal of lateral

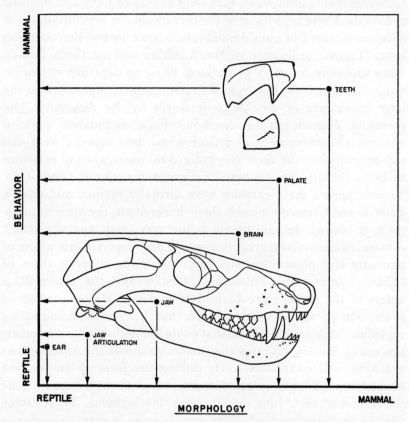

Fig. 2-2. Contrasting mammalian and reptilian characters in certain cynodonts, or
mammal-like reptiles: the skull of *Thrinaxodon,* cheek teeth of *Scalenodon.* Morphological characters are indicated along the horizontal axis, with the distance from the
left- to the right-hand side of the axis representing evolutionary progress from
reptile to mammal. Thus, the ear in this mammal-like reptile is essentially reptilian, the jaw and jaw articulation are advanced but still characteristically reptilian,
the brain is enlarged beyond the usual reptilian brain, the palate is close to the
mammalian type of palate, and the teeth are almost fully mammalian. Along the
vertical axis of the chart are inferred behavior patterns as correlated with these
morphological characters, ranging from reptilian at the bottom to mammalian at
the top. Thus hearing and the action of the jaw were probably typically reptilian.
The somewhat enlarged brain may indicate certain behavior patterns trending
toward the mammalian grade. The advanced secondary palate and the highly specialized teeth indicate a mammalian mode of eating and breathing, which in turn
indicate a probable high rate of metabolism.

swing, and the body was carried well elevated above the ground. Adaptations for this progressive and efficient type of walking and running are seen throughout the skeleton. The shoulder girdle and the pelvis were advanced toward the mammalian condition, with enlarged areas for the attachment of muscles that pulled the legs forward and back. Articulations between the girdles and limb bones and between the lower limbs and the feet were well developed, making for smooth and efficient motion. The feet were compact and strong.

The backbone as well as the limbs reflects the adaptations among cynodonts for an efficient type of four-footed locomotion. The vertebrae were strongly interlocking, and there were differences of structure and function along the vertebral column. There was a distinct neck, a decided thorax with well-developed ribs, a comparatively ribless lumbar region, a long sacrum to give firm attachment between the pelvis and the backbone, and a rather short tail. This description would be commonplace enough as applied to a mammal, but when applied to a reptile it indicates a truly revolutionary advance beyond the primitive reptilian condition of an undifferentiated backbone.

The skull and teeth are especially diagnostic in showing the long evolutionary path the cynodonts had traversed away from a typically reptilian condition and toward a typically mammalian condition. The skull was rather long and had strong, flaring zygomatic arches, for the attachment of jaw muscles. The temporal opening behind the eye was large, and separated from the eye opening by a bar of bone. There was a high sagittal crest above the braincase for the origin of powerful temporalis muscles that worked in concert with the muscles from the zygomatic arch to close the jaws. The lower jaw was very heavy, and was formed to a large degree by a single bone, the tooth-bearing dentary. The other bones of the lower jaw, so prominent in most of the reptiles, were in the cynodonts reduced to small elements behind the dentary. In the mouth there was a secondary bony palate, separating the nasal passage from the oral cavity, a condition that is typical of the mammals.

The teeth were differentiated in shape and in function. In the front of the upper and lower jaws were several small, simple nipping teeth that may be called incisors. Behind these there was a single enlarged canine on either side, above and below, obviously a sharp dagger for stabbing and killing. Behind the canine were cheek teeth, not the simple conical or bladelike teeth found in most reptiles but complex teeth, those further back consisting in each case of a crown that carried several cusps, and below it long roots to hold the tooth in the jaw.

How may we interpret the behavior of a reptile with so many mammal-like characters? It seems obvious that one of these early Triassic cynodonts would have behaved in ways as much like a mammal as like a reptile. The differentiated teeth are a clue. These show that the cynodont was a carnivorous animal, pursuing and killing its prey by using the large canine teeth as stabbing swords. This reptile cut its food into small chunks by using the cusped cheek teeth. In other words the cynodont swallowed its food in pieces of such small size that they could be quickly turned into energy by the digestive system; there was no need for it to lie torpid for hours on end, as do many modern reptiles, in order to digest some unfortunate victim that it had swallowed whole. If there was quick conversion of food into energy, then it follows that the mammal-like reptile must have been very active, as is indicated by the perfected locomotor system of the backbone, the legs, and the feet.

This brings up the question, did the mammal-like reptile have a relatively constant body temperature, like a mammal, or a variable one, like most other reptiles? The differentiated teeth, and the secondary palate to separate the function of breathing from that of eating, suggest that perhaps the cynodonts were, or almost were, endothermic, having an inner source of body warmth. Such a condition would go along with the quick conversion of food into energy. Perhaps they had hair, to insulate the body against the environment and to help maintain a constant body temperature, like the modern platypus of Australia, a primitive mammal which lays eggs and shows other reptilian characters. Lack of ribs in the lumbar region indicates that the cynodonts may have had a diaphragm, a structure lacking in the reptiles we know today; this is another point suggesting that the cynodonts were probably active and efficient reptiles that behaved in many respects in a very unreptilian fashion.

Consequently it is reasonable to suppose that the basis for mammalian behavior was attained by the mammal-like reptiles parallel with the development in these animals of mammal-like anatomical features. Perhaps if the cynodonts had been less mammal-like they might have endured for a longer time during the Mesozoic era, because that was the age of reptiles, when seemingly there was no great advantage in being a mammal. Environments of those days did not particularly favor mammalian behavior, and it was not until the dinosaurs disappeared that the mammals came into their own.

DOGS AND CATS

So far this discussion has been concerned primarily with the correlation of morphology and behavior in animals long extinct. An attempt has been made to show that it is possible to infer behavior among animals of the past through the study of their anatomy. Of course such inferences must be based at least in part upon analogies with the nearest relatives that are living in our modern world.

Perhaps it may be useful to look at the problem in another light. Can the behavior of certain modern animals be explained by a study of their morphological evolution? To the paleontologist this seems quite possible, and for this purpose our knowledge of mammalian evolution is especially useful.

Everybody is familiar with the differences in behavior between dogs and cats. Dogs are friendly and sociable, and very pliant in the hands of their masters. They like to live with men and to work with men. Moreover they like to work for men, and they can be taught to do all sorts of tasks which they perform with gusto. They are cooperative. They adapt themselves to all kinds of strange situations and to new environments, and because they are such remarkably adaptable animals they have been the useful companions of man for many thousands of years.

Cats may be friendly, but they are not very sociable. They like to live with men, but largely because men give them food and protection. They are not in the least pliant. They are very independent, and although they can be trained to some degree they cannot be molded into companions for work and play. They are not particularly adaptable. They like the environment to which they have become accustomed, and they don't like to have it changed. One gets the impression that whereas a dog is a truly domesticated animal a cat is essentially a wild animal that tolerates man as a useful host.

Why should there be such marked differences of behavior between dogs and cats? To answer this question it may be useful to review briefly the evolutionary history of the two groups of carnivores or meat-eating mammals of which dogs and cats are representatives. These are the two families known as the Canidae, or canids, including all of the wild dogs, such as wolves, coyotes, foxes, fennecs, bush dogs, and the like, and Felidae, or felids, including all of the wild cats great and small, such as lions, leopards, cougars, various small wildcats, lynxes, and so on.

All of the modern land-living carnivores had their origin during Eocene times, perhaps fifty million years ago, within a carnivore family known as the Miacidae. The miacids were small, forest-living predators no larger than ordinary house cats. They had long, slender bodies, long tails, and limbs of moderate length. There were claws on the feet. The skull was long and low, and the eyes were large. The teeth were adapted to a diet of fresh meat; there were small nipping incisor teeth in the front of the jaws for biting; large, dagger-like canine teeth with which these animals could stab and kill their prey; and in the sides of the jaws were teeth for cutting meat. The function of cutting was concentrated especially in two teeth on each side of the mouth, the last upper premolar and the first lower molar. These teeth, the carnassials, were specialized as shearing blades, and they worked together like sharp scissors for slicing meat from the carcass. The development of the carnassials in the miacids was an important specialization that was passed on to all of their land-living carnivore descendants, to become a factor of prime importance in the successful evolution of the progressive meat-eating mammals.

In general, these early miacids might be compared so far as size and appearance go with some of the modern Old World civets, the Mediterranean genet for instance. This shy, quick little carnivore is in effect a persistent primitive type that has changed but little from its miacid ancestor.

The canids and the felids, however, showed a marked divergence in their evolutionary histories, from the time of their emergence out of a miacid ancestry. By the beginning of Oligocene times both were well established as predators. And from then until the present they have continued as predators, making their living by hunting other animals, mostly mammals, great and small. In this role they have been most successful and most useful in maintaining an ecological balance among the mammalian faunas of the world.

The specializations for hunting and killing have been quite different in these two groups of carnivores, and, in both, these specializations represent departures from the primitive adaptations of the miacids. In the canids there has been an emphasis upon the pursuit of prey; in general they have been runners, with long legs and compact feet, and long jaws, well adapted to catching their prey on the move and to holding the victims. Moreover, and this is a particularly important point, the canids have been predators that have worked together. A common method of hunting has been for them to run in packs so that they might cooperate with each other in pulling down their victims. Often, as we know from observation of modern wolves, they resort to clever stratagems, chasing their victim in a circle until it is exhausted. Certainly the modern canids are highly intelligent carnivores, and there is reason to think that this was generally true of their predecessors. But physically, beyond the specializations for running and for catching their prey on the run, the canids have been rather generalized carnivores. For example, most modern canids are not above eating carrion, or even vegetable food if they are not successful on the hunt. In the back of the jaws the molars are blunt enough to be used for crushing, which is handy for an animal eating a varied diet.

In the felids there has been from the first an emphasis upon the lone hunt, upon ambush and a sudden dash to overpower the victim before it has time to get away. All of the specializations of the felids have been in accordance with this mode of life. They have been powerful, supple animals and most of them have been good climbers. Generally they have not been adept runners, but they have had the power for a short dash at terrifying speed. They have had powerful, sharp claws that can be extended to form cruel hooks with which they grab and tear their prey. They have had highly specialized skulls and teeth, with the face very short and the canine teeth strong. Behind the canines, the teeth are reduced in number and size except for the carnassials, and these shearing teeth are greatly enlarged, to form long cutting blades. The skull and dentition in the felids have been thus narrowly specialized for stabbing and shearing, and virtually nothing else. Modern felids are interested in meat, and nothing else.

The specializations of the canids, limited though they may be, developed rather slowly through their evolutionary history. Perhaps their behavior patterns also evolved in a gradual fashion. The felids, on the other hand, reached a high degree of specialization almost at the beginning of their evolutionary development. Oligo-

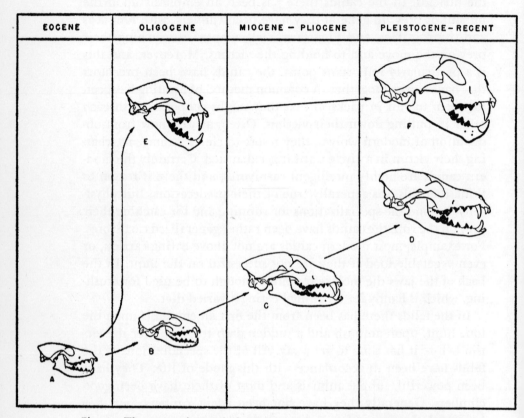

EOCENE	OLIGOCENE	MIOCENE — PLIOCENE	PLEISTOCENE—RECENT

Fig. 2-3. The contrasting evolutionary development in the canids and felids, carnivorous mammals: A. *Miacis*, an Eocene carnivore approximating the ancestor of all modern land-living carnivores. B. *Pseudocynodictis*, C. *Tomarctus*, D. *Canis*, representing evolutionary stages in the canids. E. *Nimravus*, F. *Felis*, representing evolutionary stages in the felids.

Changes in morphology in the canids were gradual and did not reach extreme specialization, and such changes may be correlated with a plasticity of behavior patterns. Notice, for example, the general similarity in number and development of the cheek teeth (black) between the early carnivore *Miacis* (A) and a recent canid (D). Changes in morphology in the felids were rapid during Oligocen times, and resulted in the sudden attainment of high specializations, and these factors may be correlated with a fixity of behavior patterns. In this connection, notice the abrupt change in number and development of the cheek teeth between the early carnivore *Miacis* (A) and the early felid *Nimravus* (E).

cene felids for all practical purposes were as catlike as modern felids, and it is reasonable to think that their behavior was equally catlike.

If these two groups of carnivores are viewed in this way the differences in behavior between modern dogs and cats may be readily understood. Dogs are plastic in their behavior because they are relatively unspecialized physically, while at the same time they are highly intelligent and have a heritage of being very social animals. Cats are fixed in their behavior because they have been highly specialized carnivores, indeed the most highly specialized of land-living predators, for some forty million years. They are intelligent, but they have a long history of nonsocial behavior, of living by themselves and for themselves. Dogs have been growing up in an evolutionary sense to their present state for a long time, but during this long time cats have always been cats. These are facts reflected just as surely in their different behavior patterns as in their very different morphological specializations.

DEER

The behavior patterns of related animals may show marked differences, correlated as in the case of the canids and the felids with differences in morphologic characters that can be traced back through millions of years of past history. What then about differing behavior in one animal; can it be interpreted in the light of that animal's morphology, or of its phylogeny, or both? Suppose we consider briefly the deer, their behavior, their morphology, and something of their past history.

The behavior of the large male deer of the northern hemisphere shows marked differences with the seasons. In North America for instance, the males of the eastern and western deer, of the elk or wapiti, and of the moose are for part of the year shy and retiring animals. They live in the woodlands and they move through the forest with remarkable silence, considering their size. This is particularly true during the summer months, when the antlers are "in velvet," that is when new antlers are growing on the skull and are covered with tender skin.

But with the coming of autumn the behavior of the buck deer and the bull wapiti and moose changes to such a remarkable degree that the animals take on, as it were, new personalities. This is the beginning of the rutting season, and it is also the time when the mantle of tender skin dries up and is shredded from the antlers. Now the antlers are hard, shining weapons of bone, and their possessors become bold and truculent. They are indeed exceedingly dangerous animals. They engage in prolonged and vicious fights between themselves to establish patterns of dominance, to determine which buck or bull will get possession of a harem of females. Moreover, they may show some hostility toward other large animals as well.

So it is that the males among large modern deer of the north temperate and subarctic zones have a cyclic pattern of behavior, an alternation of aggressiveness during the autumnal rutting season and of timidity during the spring and summer when new antlers are forming. This pattern is in decided contrast to the behavior pattern of the males among large deer of more southerly lands. In the Indian sambar, for instance, there is no marked seasonal limitation to rutting, and likewise there is no regular pattern for the dropping of old antlers and the growth of new ones. In fact, the antlers are often retained for more than one year in these deer. Basically the cyclic behavior of the northern deer is to be correlated with the alternation of the seasons.

In the Oriental part of the world are small deer known as muntjacs. These little deer are primitive in many ways, of which their small size is only one manifestation. In the males the antlers are very small and simple, and there are long upper canine tusks. The muntjacs are remarkably aggressive little deer, at least among themselves. In zoological parks the males are constantly engaged in fights, often with serious or fatal results, and during the fights the muntjac bucks rely perhaps more on their long, dagger-like tusks than on the antlers. There seems to be no periodicity in the rutting season, and the growth and dropping of the antlers also goes on all through the year. Consequently the behavior of the male muntjacs is far less cyclic than that of males among the large northern deer. The contrast is striking.

Also in the Oriental part of the world are the chevrotains, which are not deer but traguloids, tiny hoofed mammals that represent in many respects what the ancestors of the deer were like. They are no larger than house cats, and the males lack antlers. Not much is known about the behavior of chevrotains because of their secretive habits; they are very shy and consequently are hard to observe, either in the wild state or in captivity. The general impression among people who have hunted them is that the chevrotains are very timid animals which frequent the undergrowth, where they are almost constantly concealed. There are no good indications of aggressive or cyclic behavior among them, and they seem to breed throughout the year.

Now what do the fossils show about the history of deer and their ancestors? Is it possible by studying the morphology of the fossil forms to get some clues that may explain not only the differences of behavior among modern deer but also the development of behavior in these animals?

As indicated by the fossil record the ancestors of the deer appeared during the Eocene times, perhaps about fifty million years ago. These were small traguloids, related to the modern chevrotains of the Orient. They had slender limbs and tiny hoofs, and the legs were not particularly long. There was a long tail. The skull was devoid of antlers.

Deer as such, the descendants of these early traguloids, did not appear until millions of years later, with the advent of Miocene times. The first true deer showed numerous advances over the traguloids, as might be expected. There had been a growth in size. The legs were relatively longer, an indication of the increased importance of running in the life history of the deer. There were still no antlers, but instead these first deer had long canine tusks.

Antlers appeared during the Miocene epoch, and from then on there was a rapid and varied history of this interesting development in the morphology of the deer. The first antlers were small, and they were carried by small deer. But during the late stages of Cenozoic history, from the beginning of the Pliocene epoch to the present day, the phylogenetic growth of deer and of their antlers continued rapidly. As deer became larger so did the antlers in the males. The culmination of this development is seen in the large deer of late Pleistocene and recent times, the extinct "Irish Elk," and extant stags and moose.

It is reasonable to suppose that the phylogenetic development from Eocene traguloids through primitive Miocene deer to the large antlered deer of the modern world may be matched in an approximate way by a series of modern mammals ranging from

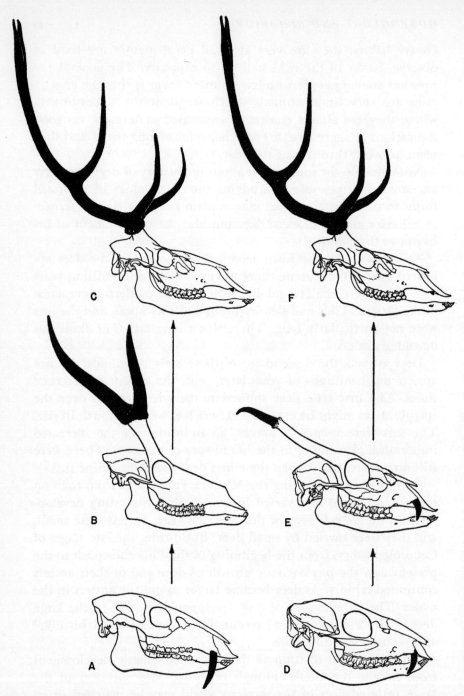

Fig. 2-4. A comparison of a time series in the development of the deer, shown on the left, and a morphological series among modern traguloids and deer, shown on the right: A. *Blastomeryx.* B. *Dicrocerus.* C. *Cervus.* D. *Tragulus.* E. *Muntiacus.* F. *Cervus.* The behavior patterns of D, E, and F are known. Since these morphological types approximate A, B, and C, the behavior patterns of the latter may be inferred. Thus it may be assumed that there was **an** evolution of behavior patterns among the deer from A through C, similar to the sequence **of** behavior patterns that may be observed in the modern forms D through F, these behavior **patterns** being adapted in part to progressive climatic changes through Cenozoic times and **in part** to the increasing importance of the antlers in sexual combat.

chevrotains through the muntjacs to the stags and other large antlered deer. This may give us some clue as to behavior patterns in the deer ancestors and in the primitive deer of past ages.

Following this line of thought, the chevrotains may be regarded as persistent primitive types that indicate fairly accurately what the Eocene traguloid ancestors of the deer were like, in morphology and in behavior. By this token the ultimate ancestors of the deer were probably timid, shy creatures that hid in the undergrowth of the Eocene forests. Behavior patterns that are now so typical of the deer were still to evolve.

It may be that the muntjacs reflect without much change the behavior of Miocene deer adapted to a Miocene climate. Some fifteen million years ago the zonation of climates had not reached the extremes that characterize our modern climates. Temperatures were much more equable over the globe than they now are, and it is probable that the seasonal differences were not great. Consequently, it is possible that the primitive Miocene deer shed their antlers throughout the year as the muntjacs do now, with the result that there was no marked cyclic behavior among the males.

It is possible that the cyclic pattern of behavior in the large modern deer of northern lands represents a fairly recent development in the evolutionary history of these animals. Perhaps the timidity of the males during the spring and summer months is a late pattern of behavior, added to an earlier pattern of male aggressiveness. As the antlers became increasingly important to the life history of the male deer, the need for protecting these antlers during the months when they were forming would also increase. With the development of strongly zoned climates and the consequent round of seasonal changes in regions away from the equator, the period of rutting and antler growth became restricted to a definite part of the year. This led to the cyclic behavior among the males, so characteristic of northern deer.

A conjectural picture has been drawn here, but it may have some validity. Perhaps the patterns of behavior among male deer in the modern world can be explained by the evolutionary development of the antlers and the development of climates since Miocene times. If so, we see in this instance a striking case of a relationship between seasonal changes, a single morphological feature, and a behavior pattern.

CONCLUSION

The purpose of this essay has been to show that there are correlations between morphology and behavior in animals. Examples
have been chosen from among the land-living vertebrates, particularly from among some reptiles and mammals. It has been shown
that there is a distinct relationship between morphology and behavior in modern animals, and moreover that behavior patterns as
we know them in many creatures today can be completely understood only through knowledge of the morphological evolution of
these animals. Animals have evolved morphologically through the
ages, and it seems evident that their behavior patterns have likewise evolved.

Of course we can only infer the behavior patterns of extinct animals, partly through a knowledge of their morphology and partly
by analogy with their living relatives. Such inference is useful, however, and truly necessary if we are to gain a well-rounded knowledge of the correlation between morphology and behavior in modern animals. The past is a key to the present, in the study not only
of the physical evolution of life but of mental development and
behavior as well.

REFERENCES

BROOM, ROBERT. 1932. The mammal-like reptiles of South Africa and the origin of the mammals. London, H. F. and G. Witherby.

COLBERT, E. H. 1939. The origin of the dog. Amer. Mus. Nat. Hist., Guide Leaflet Series, No. 102.

COLBERT, E. H. 1939. The tiger in the parlor. Frontiers, *4* (1), 2–6.

COLBERT, E. H. 1951. The dinosaur book. New York, McGraw-Hill.

COLBERT, E. H. 1951. Environments and adaptations of certain dinosaurs. Biol. Rev., *20* (3), 265–84.

COLBERT, E. H. 1955. Evolution of the vertebrates. New York, Wiley.

COLBERT, E. H., COWLES, R. B., and BOGERT, C. M. 1946. Temperature tolerances in the American alligator and their bearing on the habits, evolution and extinction of the dinosaurs. Bull. Amer. Mus. Nat. Hist., *86*, art. 7, 327–74, pls. 36–41.

FLOWER, W. H., and LYDEKKER, R. 1891. An introduction to the study of mammals living and extinct. London, Adam and Charles Black.

GILMORE, C. W. 1920. Osteology of the carnivorous Dinosauria in the United States National Museum, with special reference to the genera *Antrodemus* (*Allosaurus*) and *Ceratosaurus*. Bull. U. S. Nat. Mus., *110*, 1–154.

GILMORE, C. W. 1936. Osteology of *Apatosaurus* with special reference to specimens in the Carnegie Museum. Mem. Carnegie Mus., *11*, 175–300.

LYDEKKER, R. 1898. The deer of all lands: a history of the family Cervidae, living and extinct. London, Rowland Ward.

MATTHEW, W. D. 1910. The phylogeny of the Felidae. Bull. Amer. Mus. Nat. Hist., *28*, 289–316.

MATTHEW, W. D. 1930. The phylogeny of dogs. J. Mammal., *11*, 117–38.

OLSON, E. C. 1944. Origin of mammals based upon cranial morphology of the therapsid suborders. Geol. Soc. Amer., Special Papers, No. 55, pp. 1–136.

PIVETEAU, JEAN. 1955. Traité de paléontologie, Tome *5*. La sortie des eaux, naissance de la tétrapodie, l'exubérance de la vie végétative, la conquête de l'air. Paris, Masson.

ROMER, A. S. 1945. Vertebrate paleontology. Chicago, Univ. of Chicago Press.

ROMER, A. S. 1949. The vertebrate body.

Philadelphia and London, W. B. Saunders.

ROMER, A. S. 1956. Osteology of the reptiles. Chicago, Univ. of Chicago Press.

SCOTT, W. B., and JEPSEN, G L. 1936. The mammalian fauna of the White River Oligocene. I. Insectivora and Carnivora. Trans. Amer. Philos. Soc. (N.S.), *28*, Pt. 1, 1–153, pls. 1–22.

SWINTON, W. E. 1934. The dinosaurs. London, Thomas Murby.

WATSON, D. M. S. 1942. On Permian and Triassic tetrapods. Geol. Mag., *79* (2), 81–116.

WATSON, D. M. S. 1951. Paleontology and modern biology. New Haven, Yale Univ. Press.

YOUNG, J. Z. 1950. The life of vertebrates. Oxford, Clarendon Press.

3

Phylogeny and Behavior with Special Reference to Vertebrate Evolution

Alfred Sherwood Romer

HARVARD UNIVERSITY

IT IS a commonplace that the anatomical characters of an animal are difficult of interpretation if one attempts to view them as created *de novo* for the functions which they currently serve. Our understanding is far better if we realize that they represent, in general, only a "current" stage in a long series of modifications of structures which in earlier times and under different conditions of existence served very different functions (the auditory ossicles are a familiar example). It is reasonable to believe that an animal's behavior (and the nervous and other structural features which underlie this behavior) can likewise be best understood if we can determine its phylogeny and attempt to reconstruct the successive modes of life of its ancestors and the probable behavior patterns which these ancestors would have exhibited. Comparative study of a given form and its living relatives of seemingly more primitive nature is valuable. But the results of comparable anatomical studies suggest dangerous pitfalls in this method; we know that a survivor of a primitive group may diverge far from the ancestral type in specific structural features, and similar divergencies may well occur in its behavior. Any attempt to trace the phylogenetic development of most animal groups is at best fraught with difficulties and uncertainties; nevertheless, the phylogenetic approach to behavioral problems should always be attempted as a valuable check on conclusions reached from purely comparative studies of living forms.

FEATURES OF INVERTEBRATE BEHAVIORAL EVOLUTION

I shall confine most of the discussion in this chapter to the probable course of evolution of behavior in the vertebrates and their chordate relatives. The vertebrates are a relatively young group, with a known history of but 300 million years or so. Further, most possess hard parts capable of fossilization, so that although our knowledge of their history is very far from perfect we can in most regards sketch out their phylogeny in broad outlines from forms known in the fossil record. Through a consideration of the structure and apparent life environment of these forms one can make reasonable deductions as to their mode of livelihood and behavior.

Quite in contrast is the situation with regard to the invertebrate groups. Most are either so ancient that the major part of their evolutionary progress had been accomplished before the fossil record became adequate or else soft-bodied and hence inadequately known in fossil form. In consequence, our ideas as to invertebrate phylogeny are in an uncertain state, and attempts, in such a situation, to work out a phylogeny of invertebrate behavior can only result, by a piling of hypothesis on hypothesis, in erecting a structure with foundations of a very shaky sort. I shall merely point out here some of the major factors which may have entered into the evolution of behavioral patterns in the metazoan animals. I shall not attempt to discuss the behavior of unicellular forms, in which there is no integration of the behavior of the "animal," each cell reacting as an individual.

In one major respect, presumed increases in complexity in behavior in the evolution of invertebrate groups can be clearly correlated with morphological evolution. For the development of a variety of responses it is necessary that an adequate series of sensory structures be evolved and that an efficient nervous system be present to enable appropriate muscular (or glandular) responses to be brought about. Although the coelenterates (Cnidaria) are in some features specialized forms rather than truly ancestral metazoans, they presumably do represent the ancestral type in that sense organs are little developed and the nervous system is a poorly integrated net; in correlation, their behavior is, on the whole, of a simple type. In more advanced invertebrate groups, we find that special sensory structures make their appearance and the nervous system is more highly developed; in correlation, behavior is more complex. "Ears" and chemoreceptors and eyes of various degrees of complexity are found in various groups; instead of a nerve net, there is a strong trend for the organization of nerve cords and for the development of ganglia and brainlike structures. The varied structure of the sensory organs in the different advanced groups and the varied patterns of their nerve cords indicate that these structural advances were made not by a single stock of common ancestors but in parallel fashion by members of a number of phyletic lines, and that the complex behavior patterns seen in the different invertebrate types were also evolved in parallel fashion from simple origins in structurally simple ancestral metazoans. If the behavior of invertebrates be reviewed broadly, it will be seen that in general the forms with a complex sensory and nervous organization and a concomitant complex behavior are forms which have powers of active locomotion. This tends strongly to acceptance of the belief that the ancestral metazoans were sedentary animals of simple structure, feeders on food particles gathered by ciliary currents, with little in the way of sensory or nervous structures and with behavior of a simple type. This conclusion will not meet with universal acceptance by all students of the invertebrates. It is clear that there have been various cases of secondary simplification of structure and paedomorphosis [1] in invertebrate evolution, and hence simplicity of any specific form tends to be suspect. Further, the fact that the larvae of sessile adults are frequently free-floating or travel by ciliary action is used by those who have retained a stout Haeckelian belief in recapitulation as a proof of the nonsessile nature of ancestral types. But certainly at some time primitive simplicity was present in the metazoan ancestors. An active seeking of macroscopic food materials is surely an advanced feature; the food supply of primitive metazoans presumably consisted of small particles, and their collection by a ciliary apparatus (as in many larvae) is an adequate method. Pursuit of such particles is unnecessary, and a sessile condition satisfactory. The active movement of the larvae of sessile forms can be functionally explained by the necessity for distribution of the young, without recourse to the recapitulation theory. The great variety of locomotor types found in the invertebrates argues strongly for their independent development in the groups concerned. I would

1. Paedomorphosis is the retention of embryonic or larval ancestral structure into the reproductive stage of a descendant.

thus visualize a primitive metazoan as a small sessile creature with somewhat the appearance and simplicity of structure of the simpler hydrozoans but without the specialized tentacles and nematocysts of such an animal, and with an apparatus developed for bringing small food particles to the mouth by ciliary currents. Quite naturally, we do not find today any form which exactly fills the requirements for a diagrammatically ancestral metazoan. But it is of interest that the essential features postulated are present today in a wide variety of groups—both types of Bryozoa (Ectoprocta and Entoprocta), the brachiopods, the Phoronidea, the crinoids and various extinct types of echinoderms, and even the pterobranchs among the vertebrate relatives. Despite various specializations, there are in all these forms many basic common features—a stalk for attachment, a compact body with a mouth on the upper surface, and, surrounding the mouth, "arms" of some sort (usually termed lophophores) which bear food-collecting bands. Sensory and nervous structures are at a minimum, and behavior is of a very simple type, consisting of little but defensive movements of one sort or another, regulation of feeding currents, and release of gametes.

If such a simple sessile animal be tentatively accepted as a metazoan ancestor, it follows that increasing complexity in behavior in any group of descendants is—and must be—correlated in general with the attainment of locomotor powers. Such locomotor development seems, in most cases at least, to be associated with a change in diet to food materials of larger dimensions, which must be sought for or pursued.[2] Locomotion has developed in a variety of fashions in the various animal groups. The echinoderms, some little changed in body form, have evolved the water-vascular system with its tube feet; the mollusks in general have been satisfied with movement on the sea bottom by means of the clumsy "foot," but the cephalopods have developed active swimming in their own peculiar manner. Most common, however, has been the development of a bilaterally symmetrical body form; this is seen in the various worm phyla, the chaetognaths and most chordates, and in the great arthropod groups. In these forms the degree of development of the sensory structures and nervous system is in general correlated with the degree of development of locomotor

2. Exceptionally, coelenterates, even when sessile, have been able to adapt to larger food materials by the development of grasping tentacles and stinging cells.

powers. Although presumably developed primarily in connection
with food seeking, locomotor ability allows the expression of behavior of more advanced type in reproductive activities and in a
variety of other ways.

The behavior of larvae is a topic of considerable interest in various invertebrate groups. Here sexual behavior does not usually
enter the picture; concerns are mainly with larval feeding (usually
of a very different sort from that of the adult) and, frequently,
the attainment of a suitable environment for adult life. In many
marine groups, the larvae (as in the common trochophore type of
annelids and mollusks and the rather comparable larvae of echinoderms) are structurally simple, with little in the way of a nervous
system or sense organs to regulate behavior. Food gathering and
locomotion in common larval types are both accomplished by
ciliary action. As regards feeding, it is reasonable to believe that
this method is a direct inheritance of ancestral adult habits (and
for those who believe the ancestral metazoan to have been nonsessile, ciliary locomotion can be interpreted in the same way).
In arthropods, the larvae are frequently highly organized; even
in crustaceans complex types of larval behavior are seen, and the
behavioral patterns found in larval insects—particularly the groups
with complete metamorphosis—have evolved in a variety of complex fashions.

Related to problems of larval behavior are the complexities seen
in the life cycles of parasitic forms, particularly common among
members of the "lower" worm phyla. In many of these cycles which
involve two or even three hosts in sequence, there have evolved
immature "larval" types exhibiting marked differences from the
"adults" in structure and behavior—differences which appear to
develop in great measure in response to the stimulus of the varied
environmental conditions supplied by the successive hosts.

As noted above, paedomorphosis is believed by many to have
been a major factor in invertebrate evolution. The nature of larval
behavior is hence of as great importance in attempting to work out
the phylogeny of behavior as is the nature of larval morphology in
the solution of problems of structural evolution.

Chordate Phylogeny and Behavior

In the pages which follow I propose to consider a series of
stages leading from early and primitive vertebrates to mammals

and toward man as illustrative of the phylogeny of vertebrates as a whole, giving for each stage such indications as to behavior of the animal as its structure and conditions of livelihood suggest. Particular attention will be paid to the earlier stages, in which major basic patterns were obviously laid down.

But even the most primitive and earliest of known vertebrates were already animals of a considerable degree of complexity in structure and presumed complexity in behavior. To discuss the beginnings of vertebrate behavior we must descend on the scale to the ancestors of vertebrates. And here, to my embarrassment, I find myself (as in the discussion of the invertebrates) stumbling among the pitfalls of a study based only on living lower types. For ancestors of vertebrates are not known as fossils, and we have but isolated remnants, most of them obviously aberrant, of related lower groups, the prechordates.[3] Not only this, but it will be further necessary to diverge to discuss briefly the question of chordate origins, since this subject is one on which there is no unanimity of opinion.

The living lowly relatives of the vertebrates include four distinct types of marine organisms. These are, in descending order, (1) *"Amphioxus,"* the lancelet, which has many distinctively vertebrate features but is obviously more simply built and probably somewhat aberrant; (2) the tunicates, mainly sessile or free-floating forms, normally showing as adults little relationship to vertebrates except a highly developed gill slit system, but in some cases having larval forms clearly of a prevertebrate nature; (3) the acorn worms, such as *Balanoglossus,* burrowers which have a gill slit system as the main proof of vertebrate relationships; (4) the tiny sessile marine pterobranchs, which may lack even gill slits but are tenuously linked to the vertebrates through features showing relationship to the acorn worms. The first two types are universally included with the vertebrates to form a phylum Chordata; the last two, obviously on a lower plane of organization, are frequently placed in a separate but related phylum as Hemichordata.

What is the origin of the vertebrates and this cluster of lowly relatives? Various proposals were made during the last century. But it now seems certain, on grounds ranging from embryology to biochemistry, that closest relationship of the chordates is with the echinoderms; that the two groups, so different in their end forms, spring from common ancestors.

3. These forms have been most recently and adequately described in Grassé (1948).

An elongate, bilaterally symmetrical body associated with a high degree of activity is characteristic of lower vertebrates in general. In consequence the dominant view has been that the line of vertebrate ascent has lain, from exceedingly early days, along a line of active bilaterally symmetrical forms; that sessile forms are degenerate, and that, as sessile organisms, the echinoderms and (up the scale toward vertebrates) the tunicates are aberrant. However, careful consideration of the evidence currently available leads me to adopt exactly the opposite theory, as advocated especially by Garstang (1928) and in great measure by Berrill (1955). This assumes that, like many of the less progressive metazoan groups, the remote ancestors of the chordates (and echinoderms) were sessile marine organisms feeding by ciliary action, and that the development of an active swimming life took place at a relatively late prevertebrate stage of chordate evolution.

In many regards such echinoderms as the Paleozoic cystids or even the modern crinoids exhibit a mode of life and basic structure similar to that which may have characterized the oldest prechordates: a compact body attached to the substrate by a stalk; a mouth on the upper surface surrounded by arms bearing bands of cilia by which food particles are drawn down and in. Such an echinoderm is essentially similar to the simplest prechordates, the pterobranchs. Indeed, the pterobranchs may not be far from the ancestry of the echinoderms as well as of the chordates (and in turn may be not distantly related to the bryozoans and phoronids).

Pterobranchs (Fig. 3-1). Of the pterobranchs, only two genera (*Cephalodiscus* and *Rhabdopleura*) are at all adequately known. Both are tiny deep sea forms, sessile and more or less colonial. The individuals live within chitinous tubes. The antiquity of the group is shown by the discovery of similar tubular structures in early Paleozoic days, and according to Kozlowski and other workers the abundant and varied graptolites of the Lower Paleozoic appear to be offshoots of the pterobranchs. The pterobranch has a stalk for attachment and a compact body in which both mouth and anus lie toward the "upper" surface. From a collar region back of the mouth there extend branching arms— the lophophores—which bear bands of cilia producing a food current toward the mouth. In one genus a single pair of ciliated gill openings is present which aid in bringing the food current into the mouth and pharynx. Above and in front of the mouth there is an adhesive "proboscis." Reproduction is in part by budding, in part sexual, with a release of gametes into the surrounding water.

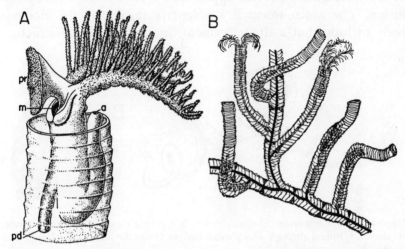

Fig. 3-1. A, an individual of the pterobranch genus *Rhabdopleura* projecting from its enclosing tube; B, a part of a colony of the same (both figures much enlarged). *a*, anus; *l*, lophophore bearing bands of cilia; *m*, mouth; *pd*, stalk (peduncle); *pr*, "proboscis," an anterior projection of the body. Mainly after Delage and Hérouard.

Seldom have pterobranchs been seen alive, but it is obvious that in these simple sessile animals there is little behavioral activity of any sort. The nervous system consists of a simple central ganglion, a few nerve trunks (the components of which are unknown), and diffuse subepithelial fiber plexuses in some areas. There are no known sense organs, and no described endocrines. Presumably there is some control of lophophore position and of the action of the ciliary current. Individuals may retract and extend themselves within their tubes (there are longitudinal muscle fibers) and in *Cephalodiscus,* in which the members of the colony are discrete individuals, the animals may on occasion move about in a fashion comparable to an "inch worm." Presumably there is some control over gamete release, but the stimulus is unknown.

Acorn worms (Fig. 3-2A). Somewhat above the pterobranchs in structural complexity are the Enteropneusta, *Balanoglossus* and other acorn worms. Here there is no colonial organization; the animals are larger; the lophophores are lost from the collar; the proboscis is larger; and there is a notable change in body shape, for there is no stalk and, instead, the trunk is straightened out to give a wormlike form, with a terminal anus. This suggests that we have arrived at the beginnings of the active life characteristic of the vertebrates; but this appearance is for the most part an illusion. The acorn worm is a sedentary burrower; the elongate body includes but a single segment, in contrast to the structure

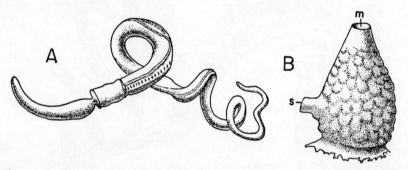

Fig. 3-2. A, an acorn worm (*Balanoglossus*); B, external view of a solitary tunicate. *m*, mouth; *s*, siphon through which water current leaves the body. After Delage and Hérouard.

of the vertebrate trunk and tail.[4] For the most part we are, it seems, dealing merely with pterobranch descendants which have shifted from being colonial tube dwellers to solitary inhabitants of burrows. The one notable advance is in feeding mechanisms. Instead of the food-bearing current being produced by ciliary bands on lophophores, it is produced by cilia within an expanded pharyngeal region; the water drawn into the pharynx is passed outward through gill slits. Instead of the single pair, at the most, seen in pterobranchs, there is a long array of gill slits of complex nature highly comparable to those of *Amphioxus,* for example. There is here developed the typical filter-feeding mode of life characteristic of higher prevertebrates and even, it seems, of the earliest vertebrates themselves.

In the acorn worms, behavior is still at an exceedingly primitive level. Again, there is no brain, and apart from some concentration into nerve trunks and the beginnings of a dorsal tube, the system is a diffuse one—in the skin and to a lesser extent about

4. The elongate balanoglossid body, it must be emphasized, does not include a homologue of the vertebrate tail, which is a purely somatic postaxial structure extending posteriorly beyond the termination of the body cavity and gut.

the gut and other internal organs. There are no positively identified sensory structures of any sort, or identified endocrines. Presumably, as in pterobranchs, there is some control of ciliary activity and gonad release. Smooth muscle fibers are present, but the
animal is essentially inert, doing little more than occasionally
moving back and forth in its burrow.

It is reasonable to believe that the burrowing acorn worms are
somewhat of a side branch, and that the next progressive stage
above a pterobranch was an animal which was persistently small,
stalked, and sessile as in pterobranchs, but in which (as in the
enteropneusts, presumably divergent at this point) lophophores
were reduced, the gill slit system elaborated, and filter feeding
established. From such a form it is but a short step to a tunicate.

Tunicates. The modern tunicates and their allies (Urochordata)
are a highly diversified assemblage, exhibiting a radiation in modern seas somewhat comparable to that of the more lowly graptolites
in earlier times. Many are colonial, many free-floating. Certain
of the solitary tunicates, however, present as adults a picture not
far removed from that of our hypothetical acorn worm ancestor
(Figs. 3-2B, 3). Such forms are sessile, attached directly or by a
stalk, and protected by a cellulose "tunic." The greater part of
the compact body consists of an enormously enlarged slitted
pharyngeal apparatus for filter feeding, appended to which is a
much smaller digestive tract. A water current, due to ciliary action in the pharynx, enters by a siphon at the upper surface, is
filtered through the gill apparatus, and passes out through a
second, lateral, siphon opening.

There is, again, no brain—merely a small central ganglion from
which nerve trunks run out to diffuse nerve nets beneath the
surface of the skin and, as a primitive "sympathetic" system,
about the gut. The skin network, at least, is highly sensitive to
touch and pressure, although there are no specialized sensory
cells. But in the adult tunicate we find, at last, one sensory organ
—the neural gland, not improbably the "ancestor" of the pituitary,
situated at the entrance of the pharynx and beneath the nerve
ganglion. This is said to be sensitive to materials in the in-current
water and to be also an endocrine structure (Carlisle, 1951). In
contrast to the hemichordates, some striated muscle fibers are
present in the body.

Behavior here is still on a very primitive level. The neural gland is said to control the discharge of gametes and presumably in some fashion may affect the water flow. Reflexes due to tactile sensibility in the skin and siphon regions may cause siphon con-

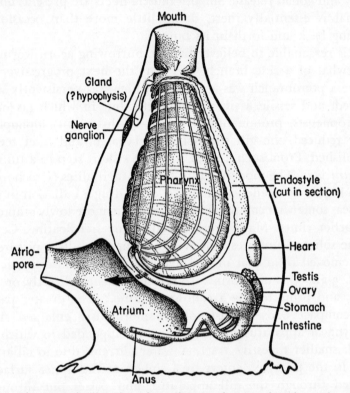

Fig. 3-3. Diagrammatic dissection of a solitary tunicate to show internal anatomy. Most of the interior consists of a pharynx with a complicated set of gill bars as a food-filtering device. The arrow indicates the direction of the water current. After Delage and Hérouard.

traction or a contraction of the whole body, and there has been observed in certain forms a rhythmic, "spontaneous" contraction of the body which aids ciliary action in producing the water current.

ORIGIN OF THE VERTEBRATE BODY PLAN AND BASIC CHORDATE BEHAVIOR

The larval tunicate. In many urochordates reproduction may occur by budding or direct development. In other forms, however, the embryo develops into a larva which swims about freely for some time, then, attaching itself to the substrate, undergoes a radical, degenerative metamorphosis to assume adult form and function. In this larva we see, for the first time, a body organization basically comparable to that of vertebrates. It is universally agreed that this larval type is essentially the form from which vertebrates have developed (although, as will be seen, there are two radically different interpretations of its phylogenetic position).

This tadpole-like larva (Fig. 3-4) is essentially a dual organism. In the expanded "head" develop the structures which form most

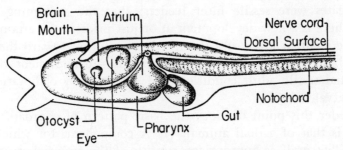

Fig. 3-4. Diagram of the anatomy of the tiny larva of a tunicate (much of the length of the swimming tail omitted). The nerve cord, "brain," sense organs, and notochord are lost in the adult. At this stage the filtering apparatus (pharynx and atrium) is little developed.

of the substance of the adult feeding animal—the expanded pharyngeal apparatus, gut and gonads. But above and behind these organs there is present a whole series of other structures peculiar to the larva. These form, in contrast, a locomotor animal, the function of which is to transport the potential adult to a place suitable for its later vegetative activities. These structures include an elongate swimming tail of vertebrate pattern (i.e. one into which the gut does not extend), containing a typical notochord and striated muscular fibers. As a directive force, there is developed a typical vertebrate dorsal hollow nerve cord terminating anteriorly in a simple brainlike expansion; further, as "navigation aids" there are simple visual and equilibrium organs.

In the larva the adult organs are essentially nonfunctional. It is the locomotor animal which functions, although only for a few minutes or hours, with simple swimming movements under control of the sense organs and nervous system. As far as known, the beginning of this swimming stage is part of a random dispersal movement of larvae, with some positive geotropism; this is followed by a settling to the bottom and attachment to a suitable base (how this is selected is not known). The locomotor animal has now performed its entire function and its materials are resorbed.

In the past it has been assumed by a majority of workers that adult tunicates are degenerate, and that the swimming larva represents an active ancestral type. But a review of our present knowledge strongly suggests the validity of the opposite view, as set forth by Garstang and adopted here: that the ancestors of the chordates were sessile filter feeders; that the swimming larva seen here is a new development at or just prior to the attainment of the ascidian level; and that further evolution toward the true vertebrate stage was by paedomorphosis—abandonment of the original sessile adult condition and evolutionary elaboration of the larval animal.

Under this point of view, the basic pattern of chordate structure is that of a dual animal: (1) A component, for which the term "visceral" is appropriate, consists of the essential structures of the ancestral sessile adult—the elaborate food-collecting ap-

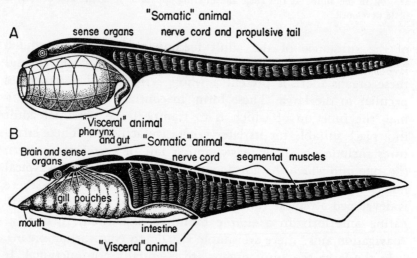

Fig. 3-5. A, diagram of the organization of a chordate comparable to the larval ascidian. Below and anteriorly, the "visceral" animal representing the adult tunicate; above and posteriorly (darker shading) the "somatic" animal, lost in the adult tunicate but retained in higher forms. B, a diagrammatic "dissection" of a cephalaspid, a vertebrate in which the gill region is still very prominent.

paratus, and the gut and gonads, together with such simple nervous and endocrine structures as are associated with these organs. (2) The new addition, first seen in the larval tunicate, is the active locomotor animal, for which the term "somatic" may be used. Here we find for the first time definite sensory structures strongly receptive to external stimuli, and a relatively elaborate nervous system of "brain," spinal cord, and somatic nerves, controlling a locomotor apparatus of striated musculature supported by a notochord (Fig. 3-5). This anatomical duality appears to be represented by a duality in behavior systems: (1) visceral, internal responses, regulated by "sympathetic" nerves and endocrines inherited from the ancestral visceral adult, and (2) external responses, brought about by the development of somatic sensory, nervous, and locomotor structures. I suggest that many features in the neurology and behavior of vertebrates may be explained to some degree by this duality of origin; there has been in higher vertebrates a welding together of somatic and visceral structures and function, but their union is still far from perfect or complete.

AMPHIOXUS

The position of *Amphioxus* (Fig. 3-6) in phylogeny is none too clear. It has been looked upon as (1) almost directly ancestral to vertebrates, as (2) a degenerate vertebrate, or as (3) a somewhat

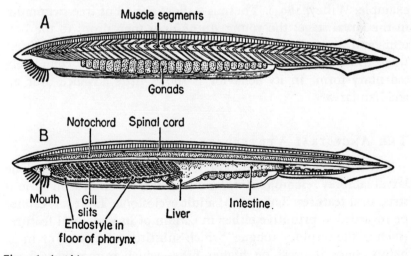

Fig. 3-6. Amphioxus, A, as seen through the transparent skin; B, a sagittal section. After Gregory.

divergent side branch from a stage intermediate between lower chordates and vertebrates. This last compromise view seems most reasonable. If, as here, the Garstang theory be adopted, *Amphioxus* definitely represents a major advance over the tunicate stage. The somatic locomotor apparatus and associated nervous structures are retained throughout life, incorporated with the visceral feeding and reproductive structures to form the functioning adult. A further advance lies in the development of the very simple, unsegmented tail of the tunicate larva into the complex segmented structure of *Amphioxus*. Certain features of *Amphioxus* seem surely aberrant—for example, the continuation of the notochord to the animal's "nose" as a burrowing aid—and since, in the nearly complete absence of a "brain" vesicle and of sense organs, *Amphioxus* is more lowly in development than a larval tunicate, the animal is best regarded as degenerate to at least some degree.

Amphioxus has the appearance of being a "streamlined," active, swimming fishlike form, which one might imagine darting about the ocean floor, with a complex pattern of activities. Actually, this is far from the case. *Amphioxus* has these potentialities; however, they are used but little, and we are still dealing essentially with a sessile filter feeder not too distant in its mode of life from a tunicate. The front half of the body is still a complex branchial apparatus, and *Amphioxus* shows relatively little activity (cf., for example, Willey, 1894). There is a short period of free swimming in the larval stage; the young *Amphioxus* then drops to the bottom, and apart from digging a burrow, and readjusting itself when disturbed, spends the rest of its life as a nearly completely sedentary form. In its behavior it shows little advance over an ascidian larva.

The Ancestral Vertebrate

The cyclostomes are the most lowly of living vertebrates. The larval lamprey resembles *Amphioxus* in habits as well as in various structural features. The typical adult cyclostome, however, cannot be regarded as primitive either in certain of its structural features (such as the rasping "tongue" which substitutes for jaws) or in its habits, since it preys on higher fishes which cannot have been present in early days. We must look rather to the oldest fossil forms for primitive vertebrate structures and primitive vertebrate behavior. In understanding early vertebrate evolution two outstanding points must be kept in mind: (1) the earliest vertebrates were probably fresh-water forms; (2) they were almost of necessity persistent filter feeders.

As soon as there arose some kind of fresh-water vegetation, even if the simplest algal type, it is to be expected that it would be exploited by animal life of some sort. Our knowledge of continental deposits of the older geologic periods is limited, but even so such exploitation appears to have begun at a rather early time in the Paleozoic. Invasion of inland regions is rendered difficult by the fact that water runs downhill. Some groups of sessile or relatively inactive invertebrates (mollusks, for example) have been able to penetrate fresh waters by evolving unusual reproductive methods. But the major victors have been members of groups which had achieved a bilaterally symmetrical body plan and active locomotion, by means of which the constant downward compulsion of stream currents could be countered. Arthropods and vertebrates are both represented before the close of the early Paleozoic in deposits which appear to have been laid down in fresh waters. Work on kidney structure and function affords evidence of a very positive nature that the early evolution of vertebrates took place in fresh waters (Smith, 1953, and earlier technical works on kidney history by the same author), and while the fossil evidence is not (and cannot be) as conclusive, it can be reasonably interpreted in no other fashion (Romer, 1955). *Amphioxus,* we have seen, is relatively sedentary in habits but has the potentialities of greater activity. Ancient prevertebrates at this stage of development would be among the few early Paleozoic animal types capable of exploiting the food potentialities of estuaries and, gradually overcoming the physiological difficulties encountered, of forging upstream as primitive vertebrates.

Such ancestral forms are represented by the variety of primitive fishlike types found not uncommonly in deposits of late Silurian and early Devonian times and frequently termed ostracoderms. Although *Cephalaspis* and its relatives are specialized ostracoderms, they are structurally the best known of the group and may be used here as illustrative (Figs. 3-7, 8).

The typical cephalaspid was generally a small creature, but a few inches in length, with a skeleton well ossified externally and to some extent internally. The general form was fishlike, with a trunk and tail obviously capable of active swimming. Stensiö's studies (1927) prove the existence of a typical (if small) brain, and well-developed sense organs—these including paired eyes, a median eye, nose and internal ear closely resembling those of

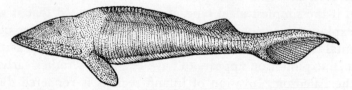

Fig. 3-7. A cephalaspid ostracoderm, seen in side view.

lamprey, and a lateral line system (as well as a further sensory (?) system of unknown nature). One gains, at first, the impression that we are now dealing with a form that would have exhibited an activity comparable with that of a modern fish. But further study indicates that this is not the case. We are in fact dealing with a persistent filter feeder; the expanded anterior part of the cephalaspid body includes an enormous pharyngeal feeding device (Fig. 8). The somatic animal, of sense organs, nervous system, and muscular "tail," is here basically only a set of accessory structures useful in bringing the feeding apparatus to situations where food materials could be found, and maintaining it there.

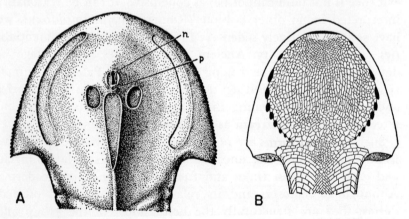

Fig. 3-8. The head region of a cephalaspid ostracoderm. A, dorsal view; B, ventral view. In B, the round openings on either side are gill slits; the mouth is a small anterior slit; *n*, nasal opening; *p*, pineal eye. Nearly the entire head region was occupied by an enormous pharyngeal gill slit apparatus for filter feeding. After Stensiö.

Unless the animal lay in a quiet inland lake, a major need was to counteract, more or less continuously, the tendency of the stream current to carry it down to the sea. It is probable that there was some instinctive behavior favoring a swimming against the current; the lateral line system, useful in other ways when once developed, may have been primarily concerned with registering information on stream current direction. Swimming would further be useful in taking the feeding apparatus to the most favorable areas for food materials, with nose or possibly a primitive "pituitary" sense organ furnishing information as to the suitability of any site reached. A further use of swimming activity would be in attempted escape from enemies; little cephalaspids are, for example, often found associated with predaceous arthropods of considerably larger size (Romer, 1933). Finally, reproduction is a more serious affair in fresh waters. In prevertebrates, gametes are simply shed into the water for fertilization and development. This is impractical in flowing streams; it seems certain that there was an early development of courting and mating behavior of some type to insure successful fertilization and the safety of the eggs and developing embryos.

Despite the presence of a good complement of sense organs and a powerful tail with median fins, it seems probable that ostracoderm swimming was of a relatively inefficient and unregulated type, resembling for example that of a tadpole (Westoll, 1945); for, apart from the presence of pectoral "flippers" in some (but not all) cephalaspids, there is no development in ostracoderms of paired fins, important in typical fish for maintenance of balance and for agile steering.

JAWED FISHES

Early in fish history there took place a revolution in fish feeding habits, and consequently in fish behavior. Filter feeding has persisted in larval lampreys (and is found secondarily in a limited number of other vertebrates). But in general this way of making a living was shortly abandoned by vertebrates in favor of utilizing macroscopic food materials. Even among ostracoderms some forms show mouth parts suggestive of "nibbling" movements or mud scooping, and at some unknown period of time one group of ostracoderm descendants developed the rasping "tongue" apparatus which has enabled the cyclostomes to become predaceous.

The major evolutionary trend, however, was toward the development of jaws and biting powers. At the beginning of the Devonian a varied group of fishes generally termed the placoderms showed early "experiments" in jaw development, and before the end of that period there had appeared a wide variety of fishes with highly developed jaws. With this new feeding mechanism there opened out broad new areas of existence for the once lowly vertebrates. They rapidly spread into a wide variety of environments, marine as well as fresh water, and although jawed fish were primitively predaceous in nature, they diversified to avail themselves of a variety of food materials.

With the development of an active pursuit of food by jawed fishes, it is, of course, to be expected that swimming powers would be greatly increased. The advanced bony fishes of the Devonian had attained a typical fusiform shape and, further, acquired typical paired fins, pectoral and pelvic, highly useful in balancing and steering movements. Presumably, swimming behavior was essentially on as high a plane by then as in modern forms, with resulting possibilities for complexity and variation in methods of food seeking, defense, and reproductive habits.

The line leading toward land vertebrates lay through the crossopterygians. These were in general highly predaceous fishes, abundant for much of the later Paleozoic in fresh waters. They were (except for a group of fresh-water sharks) the dominant fishes of the day, aggressive rather than defensive in behavior, and presumably well adapted to pursuit of prey. In some other fish types, notably those leading to the modern teleosts, the eyes became the dominant sensory structures in the search for food; this is reflected, for example, in the reduction of the cerebral "cortex" in teleosts. The crossopterygians, on the other hand, appear to have been "nose fishes," relying more upon smell than vision in their predatory activities; here the hemispheres are relatively large and normally developed, giving the basal structures upon which more complex neural mechanisms of the cortex were later developed.

PRIMITIVE TETRAPODS

Nearly as radical a change in vertebrate life as that from the jawless to the jawed condition was the shift from water to land.

This, however, was not by any means a sudden jump but a series of steps which presumably occurred over a long period of time during the Devonian and Carboniferous. The structural and behavioral changes associated with this shift seem to be closely correlated with the fact that at that time seasonal droughts appear to have been an important environmental factor.

The development of lungs in certain fish groups in the Devonian was a necessary preliminary to tetrapod evolution. Fishes with functional lungs are rare today, but the high utility of lungs in the Devonian may be illustrated by the fact that in such a late Devonian fresh-water locality as the famous fish deposits of Scaumenac Bay, Canada, at least 95 per cent of the fishes found were probably lung bearers. Use of lungs as accessory breathing organs need cause no change of any importance in fish behavior, however; it is simply a reflex for surfacing when gill oxygen intake is low, due to a stagnant condition of the water.

More radical changes in behavior, however, must take place if adaptation is attempted to survive the more serious stage of drought in which the pool or stream dries up completely. Under such conditions most fishes have no means of survival. Some of the existing (and fossil) dipnoans solve the problem in a unique fashion by burrowing in the mud and estivating until the rainy season returns. The "progressive" solution of the problem, however, was the development, from paired steering fins, of tetrapod limbs.

The crossopterygian paired fins contain well-developed skeletal and muscular elements; only a moderate degree of enlargement and differentiation of the structures already present would be needed to turn crossopterygian fins into tiny tetrapod limbs, such as those present in the most ancient of known amphibians from the late Devonian of East Greenland (Jarvik, 1955). With these present, a form otherwise little changed from a typical crossopterygian might, if its native pool dried up completely, be able to make its way clumsily overland to seek a surviving body of water.

It must be emphasized that the *early* stages in the development of tetrapods involved no major change in the life habits or behavior of the forms concerned. As far as our present knowledge goes, the earliest amphibians, despite their possession of tetrapod limbs, were still water dwellers, and further, it would appear that even the ancestral reptiles were still, like their crossopterygian relatives and cousins, predaceous eaters of smaller fishes and other animal forms in streams and lakes. It was certainly long before any of them ventured on land to any degree. Their food was in the water, their home in the water; legs were merely an accessory adaptation to aid them in staying in the water. The new neural mechanisms necessary for four-footed locomotion were obviously at first merely superposed on those already present for the "normal" swimming pattern (and it is of interest that such an amphibian as a salamander essentially swims on land, forward progression being as much due to body undulation as to positive limb movement).

THE TREND TO LAND LIFE

A primitive tetrapod normally lived as an adult in the water and reproduced, as did his fish ancestors, in the water. In later tetrapods there has been a strong trend toward the land both in adult life and in reproductive behavior. Early tetrapods were eaters of animal food, and it was only relatively late that herbivorous habits developed. In the initial tetrapod stage, terrestrial arthropods would furnish a modest food supply; later, with increase in the variety of terrestrial vertebrates, large predators would develop to prey upon their smaller cousins.

Since our phylogenetic interests here lie toward the reptile side of the picture, little will be said with regard to trends among the amphibians. By Permian times various amphibians were nearly completely terrestrial, and today there is a broad spread from aquatic to terrestrial types. The "normal" reproductive methods of their fish ancestors are maintained by familiar frogs, toads, and salamanders, but many amphibians tend to eliminate the tadpole stage and have direct development with partial or complete emancipation from the water.

In reptile evolution, the fossil evidence suggests that the trend toward terrestrial reproduction was at first stronger than the trend toward terrestrial adult life. The "invention" of the amniote egg (which is definitive of a reptile, as contrasted with an amphibian) occurred at a time in the Paleozoic when a typical adult reptile was, at the most, amphibious in habits. (It is quite possible that the ancestors of certain aquatic reptiles of later days, such as plesiosaurs and ichthyosaurs, never passed through a truly terrestrial phase.) The adaptive value of terrestrial reproduction for Paleozoic reptile ancestors appears to have been protection against drought (in contrast to the situation in modern amphibians, where protection against enemies and tadpole competition are major factors). The amniote egg requires internal fertilization and in consequence modification of mating habits. Parental egg care is seen in a number of fishes and amphibians. Terrestrial egg laying may lead to the development of comparable behavior patterns, as seen in the nesting habits of birds, and, apparently, of at least some of their dinosaurian relatives. A similar development of nesting habits presumably took place in the reptile line leading to mammals.

Although the first reptiles appear to have been mainly aquatic in habits, most members of the class had become terrestrial tetrapods well before the close of the Paleozoic. The primitive body posture (as can be seen in mounted specimens of early Permian reptiles) was a very awkward one, with the limbs sprawled out at the sides of the body. Obviously a primitive reptile, on its way ashore, had to shift its locomotor pattern from body undulation to one in which the limbs themselves furnished the motive power. Within the reptile groups a variety of further changes took place. Prominent was the bipedal gait adopted by the great archosaur group, to which the dinosaurs belonged; from this condition arose the further development of flying, accomplished by pterosaurs and birds.

BIRDS

To diverge briefly, we may note that with the development of flight in birds there appeared a whole new series of complex locomotor behavior patterns, and in association with this (perhaps developed from beginnings in their archosaur ancestors) mating and nesting habits which allow the nestlings to grow physically to a stage where successful flight is possible. Despite the fact that recent work has shown a considerable degree of learning potentialities in birds, it seems clear that in the main we are not dealing, in nestlings, with learning but with the ontogenetic development of inherited instinctive behavior patterns. This is correlated anatomically with the fact that in birds there is negligible pallial development but, on the contrary, an enormous elaboration of the corpus striatum together with the retention of a complex midbrain tectal association center.

Mammal-like Reptiles

In any attempted evolutionary study of mammalian behavior it must be kept strongly in mind that none of the living reptile groups is at all closely related to the reptilian ancestors of mammals. The mammal ancestors diverged from other reptile lines before the end of the Carboniferous, at a time when the stem reptiles were apparently still essentially aquatic. The evolution of mammalian behavior, hence, took place quite independently of that seen in their reptilian cousins.

The mammal ancestors constitute a subclass of reptiles, termed the Synapsida. A primitive subgroup, the Pelycosauria, is characteristic of the late Carboniferous and early Permian; advanced types, the Therapsida, flourished in the later Permian and early Triassic. Throughout most of their history the synapsids included, in addition to side branches, the dominant carnivores of their times. Their general mode of life was obviously that of aggressive predators, large and small.

The locomotor apparatus of the early pelycosaurs was of the crude type described above; the therapsids had become relatively swift, four-footed runners, approaching the typical mammalian condition in limb structure and hence presumably in limb function. In either case these forms appear to have been the most speedy animals of their times. Skull construction suggests a high development of olfactory powers. There is little suggestion of crafty stalking of prey; presumably there was an overt attack, dog fashion rather than cat fashion. The brain was of small, reptilian, size, but one may believe that there was at least a tendency for reduction of the tectum and the initial development of a cortex of mammalian type, with a consequent rebuilding of higher brain mechanisms.

Early Mammalian Evolution

Before the end of the Triassic the archosaurs—the dinosaurs and their kin—rose to prominence and supplanted the mammal-like forms as dominant carnivores for the remainder of the Mesozoic. The therapsids rapidly diminished in numbers and disappeared completely by mid-Mesozoic days, but some of the smaller carnivores of the group survived to evolve into primitive mammals.

The oldest known mammals appear at about the beginning of the Jurassic period. From that time to the disappearance of the dinosaurs at the end of the Cretaceous—roughly about eighty millions of years—our knowledge of mammals is pitifully meager, the material mainly consisting of a relatively few finds of teeth, jaws, and other fragmentary remains. We can, nevertheless, draw something of a picture of the life led by these forms and of the evolutionary progress made during this long period.

The dental characters of most groups of Mesozoic mammals indicate that we are dealing with forms which were still carnivores in a broad sense, as primarily eaters of animal food. But all characteristic forms are of small size—typically the size of a rat or mouse—so that their diet must have consisted in large measure of insects and other small invertebrates. Obviously their modes of seeking food must have differed considerably from those of the dominant carnivores from which they were descended. Their small size relative to their great reptilian contemporaries must have further strongly influenced their behavior. One may readily believe them to have had unobtrusive habits of life not dissimilar to those of modern shrews or the smaller rodents.

But this long period of submergence beneath reptilian dominance was obviously not one of stagnation in structure, function, or behavior. At the beginning of this period members of this evolutionary line were just leaving the therapsid stage; at its end there had evolved not only marsupials but true placentals, ready to give rise to the widely radiating types of the Tertiary.

Brain evolution, and concomitant increase in intelligence, was obviously marked during this period; quite surely brain, rather than brawn, was high in selective value. The placentals of the late Cretaceous and earliest Tertiary were obviously well below the more progressive modern groups in brain development (the brain of the primitive horse *Eohippus* was, as Edinger has shown, no more advanced than that of an opossum). They had, however, advanced notably over their reptile ancestors in brain structure —including the development of a considerable neocortical area —and, quite surely, in brain function.

Strongly influencing mammalian behavior is the fact that they have a high and constant body temperature, which enables them to maintain their activity almost completely independently of external conditions. This is in marked contrast to the situation in any other vertebrate group except the birds. There is some suggestion that thermal regulation had been initiated in synapsids, in correlation with their life as active carnivores, but presumably most of the associated structural adaptations took place in the subsequent history of the Mesozoic mammals.

Of major importance were reproductive changes—the development of the nursing habit, possibly initiated in the synapsid stage, and, subsequently, the shift from egg laying to live birth. As shown by its presence in a variety of lizards and snakes, viviparity in itself need not greatly influence the lives of forms which practice it. The nursing habit, however, had potentialities of the greatest interest. It tended strongly to the establishment of a family group, with notable behavioral consequences. Of major importance is the fact that the continued association of parent and young due to the nursing habit marks the beginning of education. Nursing lengthens the period which elapses before the young individual must make its own way in the world. Very probably an important factor here is that the brain is permitted to develop to a maximum degree before it is put to serious use. In a bird, as noted above, the function of the nesting period seems mainly that of allowing the young bird time to develop physically to a point when inherited patterns can be expressed. In the mammal the nursing period is, in contrast, a time during which cortical behavior patterns can be acquired through parental training. It is perhaps an exaggeration, but not too great a one, to say that our modern educational systems all stem back to the initiation of nursing by the ancestral mammals.

Primate Life

With the extinction of the dinosaurs at the end of the Mesozoic there began the great radiation of mammals which is characteristic of Cenozoic time. It is impossible in any limited space to discuss the varied and striking evolutionary developments in behavior which took place in the differentiation of such diverse groups as whales, horses, cats, bats, or rats (to name a few examples). Our personal concerns are, of course, with the evolution of the order Primates from the insectivore stock. Here we are dealing with a group which, except for such aberrant creatures as man and baboons, is arboreal in nature. As has been emphasized by many workers, the importance in the evolution of human behavior of this ancestral arboreal stage can scarcely be over-emphasized. We may briefly note some of the most significant points related to behavior:

1. A general trend away from carnivorous habits (characteristic of the ancestors from an early fish stage onward) to a mixed diet (and to a dominantly herbivorous one in many primates).

2. The necessity for agile locomotion (and an associated high development of the motor cortex).

3. The development of a grasping hand, ultimately useful as a tool-making and tool-using organ, but equally important in obtaining information.

4. A shift from nose to eyes as the most important source of knowledge of the outer world.

5. A strong trend toward increase in relative brain size, not improbably correlated with development of hand and eyes.

SUMMARY

In metazoans generally, complexities in behavior appear to have gone hand in hand in considerable measure with the development of active locomotion and the essentially concomitant development of complex sensory and nervous structures. A summary of phyletic evolution of vertebrate behavior is attempted. This history shows (1) a gradually increasing complexity in behavior and (2) marked changes in certain behavior patterns at various times.

Under the theory of chordate evolution here adopted, the ancestral types exhibited little behavior except regulation of their feeding apparatus, from which base evolved the "visceral" regulation of internal affairs in vertebrates by the "sympathetic" nervous system and endocrines. The sessile ancestral chordate showed almost no "somatic" behavior in response to external stimuli except protective contracting movements. With the development of an elongate body and tail (and concomitant development of associated sense organs and nervous system) swimming motions were initiated which, to begin with, were simply to bring the feeding mechanism to an appropriate location and, in the case of the ostracoderms, to maintain it there. The need for combatting stream currents, and probably for escaping enemies, necessitated better aquatic locomotion even at the ostracoderm stage, and major advances in aquatic navigation were made concurrently with the acquisition of jaws and predaceous habits. Further locomotor stages in our own direction include (1) a shift to a primitive type of terrestrial locomotion as the reptile stage was attained, (2) a change to the mammalian type of running gait in the therapsids, (3) arboreal locomotion, followed by a bipedal return to the ground.

The greatest change in food-seeking habits lay in the shift from passive filter feeding to positive food seeking which took place with the acquisition of jaws above the ostracoderm level. From this point onward through the stages of higher fish, amphibian, and mammal-like reptiles, the mammal line ran through a series of aggressive carnivores, mainly eaters of other vertebrates—first fishes, later terrestrial reptiles and amphibians (and also, presumably, insects, etc., in the case of smaller forms). In the Mesozoic mammal stage there was a necessary shift to smaller animal materials; in primates a trend toward vegetable food.

In primitive chordates there was apparently no reproductive behavior beyond a release of gametes into the surrounding water. Mating habits may have first arisen with the entry of early fishes into fresh water. The development of the amniote egg required internal fertilization, with presumably more complex breeding behavior, and led to nesting, with major behavioral consequences in birds. Nursing almost inevitably required establishment of family life in mammals and allowed the training of the young made possible by the parallel development of a brain of mammalian type. Arboreal life of typical primates has exerted a major influence on the behavior of members of the group—man included.

REFERENCES

BERRILL, N. J. 1955. The origin of vertebrates. Oxford, Clarendon Press.

CARLISLE, D. B. 1951. On the hormonal and neural control of the release of gametes in ascidians. J. Exp. Biol., 28, 463.

GARSTANG, W. 1928. The morphology of the Tunicata and its bearings on the phylogeny of the Chordata. Quart. J. Micr. Sci., 72, 51.

GRASSÉ, P. P., ed. 1948. Traité de zoologie, Vol. 11. Paris, Masson.

JARVIK, E. 1955. The oldest tetrapods and their forerunners. Sci. Month., *80*, 141–54.

ROMER, A. S. 1933. Eurypterid influence on vertebrate history. Science, *78*, 114–17.

ROMER, A. S. 1955. Fish origins—fresh or salt water? Deep-Sea Research, *3*, Suppl., 261–80.

SMITH, H. 1953. From fish to philosopher. Boston, Little, Brown.

STENSIÖ, E. A. 1927. The Downtonian and Devonian vertebrates of Spitsbergen. I. Family Cephalaspidae. Oslo, Norske Videnskaps-Akademi i Oslo, Skrifter om Svalbard og Nordishavet, No. 12.

WESTOLL, T. S. 1945. The paired fins of placoderms. Trans. Roy. Soc. Edinburgh, *61*, 381–98.

WILLEY, A. 1894. Amphioxus and the ancestry of vertebrates. New York, Macmillan.

PART TWO

The Physical Basis of Behavior

IN ONE SENSE, the physical basis of behavior is
the functional anatomy of the behaving organism,
and especially its sensory receptors and muscular
effectors. A part of the physical basis for the different behaviors of a swallow and a bat, both hunting
insects, is obviously to be sought in their eyes and
ears, just as part of the physical basis for the difference between the hunting of rodents by a snake
and a weasel is in their locomotory apparatus. In
that sense, the physical basis of behavior is simply
the apparatus available, with its potentialities and
limitations. But effective use of the literally millions of behavioral apparatuses demands that each
be constructed, in the first place, and then that its
use be initiated, controlled, and programmed.
These processes constitute, in a more profound
sense, the physical basis of behavior, and it is to
them that we now turn.

A universal physical factor that influences, at
least, the behavior of all animals is chemical. It is
seen most clearly and specifically in the vertebrate
hormones, and in Chapter 4 this sort of control is
explored through the example of evolutionary and
comparative male sexual endocrinology. It is shown
that the variety of such hormones is not great and
that some of them have been highly conservative in
the course of vertebrate evolution. Others have
been more specific, and by the same token have undergone more evolutionary modification. Their
roles are in the development of sexual characteris-

tics and in stimulating or triggering sexual activity. They cannot account for the astonishing diversity of sex behavior in animals, nor for the often elaborate sequential patterns of sexual activity.

In the vast majority of animals, and particularly in all vertebrates, the most essential and also the most complex and mysterious part of the physical basis of behavior is the nervous system. First approach to this problem, as to so many evolutionary problems, is genetical. In Chapter 5 the genetic processes basic for the heredity of behavior, and therefore also for the evolution of behavior, are reviewed. It is further demonstrated that behavior is indeed controlled—that is, its reaction ranges are determined—genetically and that genetics is as pertinent and fundamental for the evolution of behavior as for the evolution of structure.

Between the genetic factors and the behaving organism the processes of development intervene. Those processes, with special reference to the development of the nervous system, are the subject of Chapter 6. One of the most striking conclusions is that the whole pattern of the nervous system in any one species is strongly controlled by inheritance and the developmental processes through which the genetic system produces its effects. Even in the animals of most flexible behavior, conditioning or training seems to have little or nothing to do with the structure of the nervous mechanisms concerned in behavior. Chapter 7 continues with the actual anatomy of the brain and with attempts to correlate its structure with behavior as both have evolved together in the course of vertebrate evolution. Good reason is found for serious doubts as to the now almost traditional correlations of changing brain size and structure with increasing complexity of behavior and capacity for learning. It is proposed, not that no correlation of structure and behavior exists, but that the wrong kind of correlation has been sought.

Finally in Chapter 8 the various known physiological properties of the nervous system are discussed. All the well-established basic properties are shown to be extremely widespread, far beyond the vertebrates and the origin of definite brains. By implication, then, these properties are immensely older than the complex behavior patterns of higher vertebrates, and the question is therefore raised whether the neurophysiological mechanisms now known are adequate as parameters for the most complex behavioral systems.

4

Evolutionary Aspects of Psychoendocrinology

Frank A. Beach

YALE UNIVERSITY

INTRODUCTION

ENDOCRINOLOGY is the study of the ductless glands and their secretions. Psychology is the study of behavior. Psychoendocrinology is concerned with the interrelationships between endocrine products and behavior. The major purpose of this paper is to consider some of these relationships from the evolutionary point of view.

Since we know very little about the glandular systems of extinct animals, the only feasible approach to our objective consists of comparing the psychoendocrinology of various living forms from different phyletic groups. This is a standard procedure in comparative anatomy and physiology, and it frequently yields suggestive evidence concerning evolutional changes in the structures or processes so compared.

Several obstacles to a complete realization of the aim of this paper should be made explicit. Endocrinologists have devoted much more attention to mammals and birds than to poikilothermic vertebrates, and very little indeed to invertebrates. Therefore the evidence concerning hormones is uneven. A comparable bias has characterized the psychologist's approach to behavior with equally limiting results. Finally, it has usually been the case that psychologists and endocrinologists have worked independently. The result is that the hormone system and the behavior of some species are fairly well understood but the interrelations of the two remain a matter of speculation.

Because of these restricting circumstances and because of space limitations it seems advisable in this review to concentrate upon one pattern of behavior which has been investigated from the comparative point of view. This is the pattern of courtship and mating. Studies of the endocrinological correlates of sexual behavior have dealt chiefly with functions of the gonads and the hypophysis, and we will therefore treat these glands exclusively. Since the accessory and secondary sexual characters are often the best indicators of gonadal function they will also receive consideration.

The final qualification is that our survey will be mainly limited to evidence concerning male animals. This is entirely a concession to expediency. To keep the review within the predetermined limits it has been necessary either to exclude one or more phyletic classes or to deal primarily with one sex. The latter alternative seems clearly preferable because it provides a broader scope and because for most vertebrate groups the psychoendocrinology of males and females is similar.

EFFECTS OF TESTIS SECRETIONS UPON SEXUAL CHARACTERS AND BEHAVIOR [1]

The response of the masculine accessory and secondary sex characters to testis hormone is common to so many vertebrates in every class that it must represent a relationship with an exceedingly long evolutionary history. The stimulating effect of the same hormones upon sexual behavior is also observable in widely separated species, but there is reason to suspect several evolutionary changes in this function.

Mammals

There appear to be no exceptions to the rule that the accessory sex structures (penis, seminal vesicles, prostate gland, and associated duct systems) depend upon testis hormone for their normal development and function. These organs fail to mature in the absence of the gonads, and tend to undergo regressive changes when the adult male is castrated. These changes are reversible, and the accessories can be restored to normal by testis implants or by the administration of the appropriate extracts of testicular tissue.

1. Throughout this paper data statements that are not independently documented are taken from a book which summarizes a great deal of the evidence included in this article (Beach, 1948).

The secondary sex characters are affected in approximately the same way. In the human male congenital hypogonadism prevents the normal puberal changes such as lowering of the voice, growth of axillary, pubic, and facial hair, and assumption of the masculine habitus. These changes can be produced by androgen therapy. It is well established that the secondary sex characters of many other mammals are dependent for their full expression upon testis secretions.

It is generally true that the sexual behavior of male mammals depends upon the testis hormone, but the degree of dependence varies with the specis. Castrated male rodents and lagomorphs show only incomplete and infrequent copulatory reactions to the receptive female. They can be stimulated to normal mating activity by androgenic treatment.

In contrast, male cats (Levy and Aronson, 1955) and dogs (Beach, Jaynes, Rogers, et al., 1956) retain a high degree of sexual responsiveness and capacity after castration in adulthood. It is especially true of male monkeys (Kempf, 1917), apes (Sokolowsky, 1923), and humans (Kinsey et al., 1948) that sexual behavior frequently survives for long periods after gonadectomy in adulthood.

It appears that the evolution of carnivores has been different from that of rodents and lagomorphs in that the sexual behavior of the former has become somewhat less dependent upon testis secretion. This trend is even more evident in the primates. It has been suggested (Beach, 1947) that the shift away from hormonal dominance of the sexual pattern is correlated with an evolutionary increase in encephalization and particularly neocorticalization of the control of mating behavior.

Birds

Berthold (1849) was the first to demonstrate that the "external features of maleness" in birds are due to secretions from the testis. He castrated domestic cocks and found that the usual regression of secondary sex characters such as the comb could be prevented if the testis was grafted into a new and abnormal site within the abdomen.

Witschi (1955) has discovered an interesting exception to Berthold's principle. Male African finches of several genera display changes in plumage at the onset of the breeding season. The annual change continues unmodified after castration, and treatment with pituitary extracts reveals that the effective hormones are secreted by the hypophysis.

As far as masculine sexual behavior is concerned it is clear that the bird is heavily influenced by hormonal factors. Carpenter (1933) reported that castration greatly decreases the frequency of copulation in male pigeons, and comparable effects have been described for the ruff (Oordt and Jung, 1936), turkey (Scott and Paynes, 1934), and domestic chicken (Goodale, 1918). According to Marshall (1954) male bower birds do not build bowers or court females if castrated before the breeding season, and when the operation is performed at the height of the season males lose interest in the female and fail to keep the bower in repair.

Reptiles

There have been relatively few studies of hormonal factors affecting the sexual behavior of reptiles, but such evidence as is available clearly implicates the testis.

Castration is reported to eliminate mating responses in the male skink (Reynolds, 1943), and the same effect has been found to occur in the American chameleon (Noble and Greenberg, 1940).

Amphibians

The development and maintenance of secondary sex characters in some male urodeles and anurans appears to depend upon testis hormone, for these structures exhibit regressive changes after castration (Gallian, 1955). Exceptions probably exist, since there is some evidence suggesting a direct action of hypophyseal hormones upon the nuptial pads of male toads of certain species (Gorbman, 1941).

It is reasonably certain that castration before the breeding season prevents the appearance of mating behavior in male frogs (Schrader, 1887; Nussbaum, 1905, Baglioni, 1911; Noble and Aronson, 1942). Less certain are the immediate consequences of gonadectomy during the mating period. Several early workers claimed that no behavioral change occurs under such conditions (Goltz, 1869; Tarchanoff, 1887), but Gallian (1955) states that urodeles show regression of the "psychosexual reflexes" following castration, and can be restored to normal by testicular grafts. Houssay (1954) reports the loss of the "sexual embrace" in male toads after castration and refers this to disappearance of testis secretions.

Fishes

According to Dodd (1955) testis hormone controls the secondary sex characters in the great majority of finshes. Grobstein found that testicular secretions are essential for transformation of the anal fin into a gonopod in the platyfish (1942).

The importance of the testis with respect to sexual behavior in fishes is not clear. Jones and King (Aronson, 1957) reported that the male *Salmo salar* loses interest in the female after castration, but castration does not prevent courtship and spawning in *Bathygobius* (Tavolga, 1955) or in the jewel fish (Noble and Kumpf, 1936).

In at least some fishes pituitary hormones seem to influence mating activities without intervention of the testis. For example, although castration does not eliminate spawning behavior in *Bathygobius*, hypophysectomy does (Tavolga, 1955). It causes regression of the testes in *Fundulus*, but hypophysectomized males exhibit spawning reflexes 30 seconds after an injection of posterior pituitary extract. Androgen will not elicit this reaction, but it can be induced with synthetic oxytocin (Wilhelmi, Pickford, and Sawyer, 1955).

COMPOSITION OF TESTIS SECRETIONS IN DIFFERENT SPECIES

It is well within the bounds of possibility that the chemical composition of the testis hormone has changed in the course of evolution, but comparative evidence suggests a surprising degree of similarity.

Androgenic Character of the Testis Hormone

David (1935) isolated a chemically pure substance from the mammalian testis and named it "testosterone." Purified forms of testis secretions have not been isolated in any other vertebrate, but writing in 1942 Moore could say:

> We do not know that this substance is secreted by the testis of man or any other vertebrate as the testis hormone; nor do we know whether different vertebrates produce the same or a different substance as this hormone; in fact we may say that we do not yet know with any certainty what the testis hormone really is, or whether more than one substance is normally

produced. With testosterone and its compounds, however, we can within limits restore all known changes resulting from castration in any species of mammal, or prevent their development after castration. The same substance is effective in maintaining structural and behavioral characteristics normal to the males of birds, reptiles and amphibians, and it is a good substitute for the testicles of man. We can feel assured, therefore, that whatever the testis hormone is, it must be at least similar in its actions to testosterone or some of its compounds (p. 38).

It might be expected that the genetic changes involved in evolution would have included modification of the hormone system or of systems responding to hormones. It is known that such effects do occur. For instance, genetically different strains of mice vary in their reactivity to cortisone (Ragg and Speirs, 1952). Feral and domestic rats differ in their adrenocortical requirements (Richter, Rogers, and Hall, 1950). Casida, Casida, and Chapman (1952) by selective breeding developed two strains of rats which differed in the ovarian response to standard doses of equine gonadotropin. Regardless of any evolutionary modification of testis function, it is clear that the male gonad of many vertebrates secretes androgenic material. Collias (1950) states that the testis of the domestic cock produces androgen. According to Dodd (1955) in a large majority of fishes the testis hormones are definitely androgenic. Bretschneider and Duyvené de Wit (1947) believe that the sex hormones of fishes are different from those of mammals, but Hoar (1955) feels it is reasonably certain that some fishes secrete androgen. He observes that there is a good deal of evidence suggesting similarity in the testis hormones of teleosts and mammals.

Effects of Mammalian Hormone on Different Species

Arguments favoring the similarity of gonadal hormones in different species are strengthened by the fact that testosterone, which has been identified in mammals only, can serve as a reasonably effective replacement for the testicular hormones of many different species from various classes. In all mammals that have been investigated testosterone propionate stimulates the accessory and secondary sex characters of prepuberal males or castrated adults. Any behavioral change caused by castration can be reversed by administration of testosterone.

The same hormone is remarkably effective in birds. Male chickens only a few days old exhibit the adult cock's mating pattern when treated with testosterone propionate (Noble and Zitrin, 1942). Testosterone acetate induces courtship and copulation in castrated cocks and pheasants (Roussel, 1936). Capons exhibit normal mating reactions after several injections of testosterone propionate (Domm, Davis, and Blivais, 1942). Castrated bower birds display and erect bowers at any time of year if treated with this substance (Marshall, 1954).

Reptiles are also responsive to mammalian gonadal hormone. Treatment of castrated male skinks with testosterone propionate restores the sex accessories to normal condition (Reynolds, 1943). The castrated male American chameleon shows normal mating behavior when given the same hormone (Noble and Greenberg, 1940).

We have found few accounts of the effect of testosterone on breeding behavior in amphibians, but Blair (1946) reports appearance of the adult male warning chirp in juvenile toads injected with testosterone propionate. He also notes that the secondary and accessory sex structures were stimulated by the hormone. According to Greenberg (1942) testosterone propionate causes development of the sex characters in the male cricket frog outside of the breeding season. Houssay (1954) found that testosterone revived the mating clasp in castrated toads only if it was administered in combination with pituitary extract.

Even fishes are affected by the testis hormone of mammals. Testosterone causes growth of a male-like gonopod in female gambusia (Turner and Carr, 1941), and in the platyfish (Grobstein, 1942). Secondary sex characters of the male African mouthbreeder fish regress after castration, and this change can be reversed by injections of testosterone propionate (Levy and Aronson, 1955). To date no investigator has reported the induction of sexual behavior in fishes by exogenous androgen treatment, but this is not surprising since the hormonal factors normally involved have not yet been clarified.

Dodd (1955) states that the secondary sex characters of cyclostomes can be stimulated by mammalian hormones although at present nothing is known concerning the production of comparable secretions by cyclostomes.

Conclusions concerning Functions of the Testis Hormone

The evidence is fragmentary, but a few tentative conclusions can be formulated concerning evolution of certain relationships between testis function and morphological and behavioral characters.

It appears that control of the sex accessories by testis secretions represents a relationship as old as the vertebrate phylum. The capacity of gonadal hormones to stimulate secondary sex characters must have appeared quite early in the history of the vertebrates, but we are confronted with the fact that pituitary secretions also serve this function in some modern amphibians and birds. Since gonadal control is so much more common it might be suggested that shifts to dependence on the pituitary represent cases of later specialization.

The influence of testis hormone upon sexual behavior is quite evident in lower mammals, birds, and reptiles. Most of the evidence indicates that a comparable relationship exists in amphibia. It is fairly certain that mating responses in at least some fishes are dependent upon the pituitary and independent of the gonads. This may represent the ancestral condition from which terrestrial vertebrates have diverged. Or it may be that the few piscian species which have been examined are cases of evolutionary specialization. A choice between these alternatives will remain difficult until more species are studied.

Although the composition of the testis hormone is known only for some mammals it seems probable that the gonadal secretions of mammals, birds, and reptiles are at least closely similar, for testosterone is an effective replacement for the homologous hormone in species from each of these classes. The known effects of testosterone upon amphibians and fishes are limited to its capacity to stimulate the sex accessories and secondary sex characters, but it is generally agreed that the testes of animals in these two classes secrete androgenic hormone. Taken as a whole the data clearly suggest that the capacity of the male gonad to produce androgen is as old as the testis itself.

Gonadotrophic Functions of the Hypophysis

Nature of the Pituitary Gland in Different Vertebrates

The pituitary gland is present in all vertebrates and probably has always been a basic structure throughout vertebrate evolution. This gland is well developed in cyclostomes (Dodd, 1955). It has a complex structure in the lamprey. Highly diversified changes have occurred in Pisces but the gland is fairly standardized in all other vertebrates (Gorbman, 1941).

The mammalian pituitary secretes several hormones, among which are two gonadotrophic hormones, LH (luteinizing hormone) and FSH (follicle-stimulating hormone), and a thyrotrophic hormone. The production of gonadotrophins is associated with activity of a particular type of basophile in the anterior lobe, whereas thyrotrophin is secreted by a different type of cell. Atz (1953) has identified the same two kinds of basophiles in the transitional lobe of the fish pituitary. That they are functionally as well as histologically similar is suggested by Atz's finding that one kind of basophile reacts to thyroid hormone and the other to gonadal hormone.

Functional Relations between Pituitary and Gonads

Gonadotrophic hormones secreted by the mammalian pituitary control the production of testicular androgen and thus indirectly affect behavior. They also regulate the process of spermatogenesis. This combination of effects is typical of all vertebrates thus far investigated. The gonadotrophic potency of the avian pituitary has been demonstrated by several workers (Collias, 1950).

Studies on reptiles are summarized by Kehl and Combescot as follows: "All results are in accord with the general conception of a unified process in the hypophyseal-sexual endocrinology of the vertebrates" (1955, p. 71).

Smith (1955) states that the control of gonadal condition by the amphibian pituitary is firmly established. It is known, for example, that pituitary extracts from the adult frog have a stimulating effect on the testis of newly metamorphosed individuals (Schreiber and Rugh, 1945). Oordt and Oordt (1955) found that spermatogenesis in two species of frogs depends upon gonadotrophins.

In fishes a similar relationship appears to hold. The testes of *Fundulus* regress completely within two weeks after hypophysectomy (Pickford, 1953b). Several investigators have succeeded in stimulating the gonads of fishes by administration of fish pituitary material (Berkowitz, 1941b). The testes of the dogfish, an elasmobranch, regress as a result of pituitary removal and can be restored to normal condition by treatment with dogfish pituitaries. The same is generally true of teleosts according to Dodd (1955).

Interspecific Effectiveness of Gonadotrophins

The gonadotrophic hormones are proteins and have not been chemically analyzed. We can nevertheless arrive at some estimate of their similarity in different species on the basis of experiments on interspecific transfer. Consideration of similarity or difference in the effects of gonadotrophins from different species may suggest tentative conclusions concerning evolutionary changes in pituitary function.

It is known that the fish pituitary performs the functions of FSH and LH, although the hormones involved remain to be identified. They cannot be highly species-specific because pituitary material from a wide variety of fishes will induce precocious sexual development in any family of teleosts (Hoar, 1955). According to Dodd (1955) fish gonadotrophins are almost equally active in all teleost families and orders.

Interclass transfers are sometimes effective. Thus pituitaries taken from bullfrogs at the height of the breeding season stimulate testis growth in immature chicks (Keaty, 1942). Gonadotrophins of mammalian origin have been administered to a variety of vertebrates. The testes of immature cyclostomes are stimulated by mammalian gonadotrophin (Dodd, 1955). Although the pituitaries from other vertebrate groups tend to be less effective in fishes, mammalian gonadotrophins are capable of evoking secretory function in the teleost gonad. This is true for example of the immature male guppy, which shows precocious testis growth and development of secondary sex characters when injected with gonadotrophins derived from mammals (Berkowitz, 1941a).

Other classes appear sensitive to mammalian pituitary secretions. Adult toads respond to mammalian gonadotrophins with immediate sperm release and an increase in interstitial cells of the testis (Oordt and Klomp, 1946). The same substances administered to the domestic chick produce an increase in testis weight and induce the secretion of testis hormone (Shockaert, 1933).

Evidence for Species Specificity

If the pituitary hormones from every vertebrate species were found to be completely interchangeable with those of every other species it might be concluded that no changes in pituitary function had occurred during the evolution of the vertebrates. This is not the case, and as early as 1929 the concept of zoological specificity of some of the pituitary hormones was proposed (Houssay, Guisti, and Lascano-Gonzales, 1929).

It should be noted that direct evidence is lacking because no chemical analyses have been made. If pituitary material from a fish fails to affect the amphibian testis there is a possibility that the difference lies in the testis rather than in the hormone. Nevertheless we would expect the hormones to vary because they are proteins, and corresponding proteins vary even between closely related species (Gorbman, 1941).

For example, the concentration of ribonucleic acid is much higher in liver cells of the rat than in those of the guinea pig (Campbell and Kosterlitz, 1953). It is known also that pure lactogenic hormone from the cow has a different amino acid content than that from the sheep (Gorbman, 1941).

The concept of species differences in gonadotrophic secretions is supported by studies of antihormone formation which in combination with other evidence led Creaser and Gorbman to conclude that "the effectiveness of a gonadotrophic hormone in a foreign species tends to vary directly with the phylogenetic proximity of the donor and the recipient species" (1939, p. 161).

The weaver finch test devised by Witschi (1955) shows that the level of FSH is relatively the same between different vertebrate classes, but LH concentration varies considerably even within the same class. For example, the ratio of FSH to LH ranges from 1:1 in man to 1:1,000 in cattle. In general it seems that the FSH content of the anterior pituitary is higher in homoiothermic than in poikilothermic vertebrate.

There are several indications of qualitative differences in the gonadotrophic secretions of different vertebrates. Das and Nalbandov (1955) have suggested that the avian hypophysis secretes three rather than two gonadotrophins. They point out that implants or injections of mammalian pituitary will maintain testis secretion in the hypophysectomized cock only for a limited period of time (Nalbandov, Mayer, and McShan, 1951). This is due to the fact that mammalian gonadotrophins can cause the existing Leydig cells to secrete androgen but they fail to stimulate the periodic maturation of new generations of Leydig cells. In contrast, treatment of the hypophysectomized cock with chicken pituitary ensures normal testis function for an indefinite period.

Conclusions regarding Evolutionary Changes
in Pituitary Function

There is no doubt that the nature of the hormones secreted by
the pituitary gland has changed during the course of vertebrate
evolution. These changes have quite probably been more pronounced than those occurring in the secretory function of the
testis.

It is clear at the same time that, although pituitary gonadotrophins exhibit demonstrable degrees of species-specificity, they
are far from being completely unrelated. Interchangeability is apparently unrestricted within a class, and many interclass exchanges
are at least partially effective.

As has been pointed out, partial or incomplete interchangeability may well reflect evolutionary changes in target tissues as
well as in pituitary function. The influence of genetic changes
upon tissue response is nicely illustrated by the fact that strains
of rats differing in ovarian reactions to a standard dose of gonadotrophin can be created by selective breeding (Casida, Casida, and
Chapman, 1952).

In certain cases it is apparent that entirely new target organs
have evolved and have come under the control of pre-existing
glandular secretions. For example, a particular hypophyseal hormone is known to control melanophore expansion in fishes. That
hormone also occurs in pigeons and doves, but in this case it affects
the functional development of the crop sac. Finally the same hormone is produced by mammals and governs the process of milk
secretion, for which reason it is known as "prolactin" (Gorbman,
1941).

In somewhat similar fashion the luteinizing hormone of the anterior pituitary appears to have functioned originally in the induction of ovulation. This is a general and ancient function seen
in both lower and higher vertebrates. In some classes, notably reptilia and mammalia, ovulation is followed by the formation of
corpora lutea within the ovary. As this new organ, the corpus luteum, evolved it came under the control of LH, with the result
that this hormone is essential to the growth and functioning of the
corpus luteum in modern reptiles and mammals (Witschi, 1955).

Neural Control of Pituitary Function

We have seen that the stimulating influence of testis hormone upon sex characters including behavior is extremely widespread among the vertebrates and probably reflects a relationship of true evolutionary antiquity. Similarly it has been shown that secretory activity of the gonads is controlled by trophic hormones produced by the hypophysis in all vertebrates that have been examined. It remains to consider some of the factors which in turn govern the functions of the anterior pituitary.

Among the most interesting and widespread of these factors are impulses which originate in the nervous system and are transmitted to the hypophysis via the hypothalamus. Connections between the pituitary and the hypothalamus probably exist in all vertebrates. At any rate in all species that have been studied hypophysectomy results in degenerative changes within the preoptic nucleus (Palay, 1953).

Many other lines of evidence point to the conclusion that hypothalamic function affects the pituitary. Ovulation in the rabbit and cat depends upon LH secretion and release, and this in turn depends upon neural factors. Ordinarily the inciting stimuli are associated with coition, but ovulation can be induced artificially by electrical or chemical stimulation of the hypothalamus. Neither the natural nor the artificial stimulus is effective if connections between the hypothalamus and pituitary have been disrupted by transection of the infundibulum (Harris, 1955).

Most dramatic are recent findings that when the pituitary gland of a male rat is transplanted into the sella tursica of a hypophysectomized female it is capable of maintaining normal estrus cycles (Harris, 1955). This suggests that the characteristic rhythm of FSH and LH secretion may be imposed upon the hypophysis by a central nervous mechanism.

It is well established that several aspects of the pituitary's gonadotrophic activity are regulated at least in part by environmental stimuli, and this of necessity implicates the nervous system. For example female rats normally come into full estrus between the hours of 8:00 and 12:00 P.M. (Ball, 1937) but they can be caused to do so in the middle of the solar day if the light-dark cycle of their environment is artificially reversed (Beach, 1938).

More extended rhythms of pituitary activity are also timed by

external changes. Some annual breeders become fertile and sexually active in early spring and others do so in the fall. The physiological changes which prepare males and females for breeding are
in many instances known to depend upon seasonal changes in
mean temperature, in the amount of rainfall, or in the amount of
daylight per 24 hours (Beach, 1948). For many species the seasonal
timing of mating has adaptive significance for it maximizes the
probability that the young will hatch or be born at a time of year
when the external conditions are optimal for their survival. Thus
environmental control of pituitary activity and indirectly of gonadal function and mating behavior is of considerable evolutionary
importance, and it is significant that such relationships occur in
every vertebrate class.

One other type of external stimulation which influences the
gonads and sexual activity by inducing changes in the pituitary
involves the proximity and behavior of other individuals of the
same species. It was noted above that the ovulation of some mammals is induced by stimuli derived from coitus. It can here be
added that "ripening" or recrudescence of the gonads prior to
fertile mating depends in some species upon exteroceptive stimuli
provided by a potential sex partner or at least a second individual.

Aronson (1945) has shown that the female African mouthbreeder
fish rarely digs a nest or lays eggs unless she can see another mouthbreeder. Matthews (1939) found that isolated pigeons are unlikely
to ovulate but will do so if they can see their own image in a mir-
ror; the presence of a courting male proves an even more effective
stimulus. According to Marshall (1954) the courtship behavior of
the male bower bird is elaborate and prolonged in some species,
and serves to bring the watching female into full reproductive condition, thus promoting fertile mating.

There are indications that comparable relationships may characterize the reproduction of some seasonally breeding mammals.
The spring growth of ovarian follicles in ranch-bred mink is no-
ticeably retarded in females that are geographically separated from
others of their kind (Enders, 1952). It is generally believed that
cattle which are permitted to "run with the bull" tend to come
on season earlier in the spring than females in sex-segregated herds.

Any mechanism that promotes synchronization of pairing behavior contributes to the occurrence of fertile union and is therefore of adaptive value. Since we can find examples of "social" or

"partner" control of reproductive physiology among fishes, birds, and mammals, it may well be that the chain of external stimulus → brain activity → pituitary secretion → gonadal ripening and secretion → mating behavior is of considerable evolutionary antiquity.

BEHAVIORAL DIFFERENCES BETWEEN GROUPS

When the student of reproductive behavior attempts to compare the overt responses which constitute courtship and mating in fishes, amphibians, reptiles, mammals, and birds, he is confronted with a range of differences besides which endocrinological variations seem insignificant. Many such comparisons fail to reveal any common element except for the eventual union of gametes.

Within certain classes intergeneric variations are as radical as are interclass differences. The sexual patterns of different fishes include mass spawning without courtship or pairing, in pelagic forms such as the herring; brief courtship with internal fertilization, in the swordtail and guppy; and extended reproductive unions with oviposition followed by mutual parental care of the eggs and young, as in the jewel fish.

Among amphibia a common mating pattern involves amplexus by the male and simultaneous emission of eggs and sperm. This is characteristic of *Rana* and *Bufo*. In some salamanders, however, the male deposits spermatophores which are later engulfed by the female's cloaca.

Birds also exhibit pronounced species differences in the form or pattern of sexual relations. Marshall (1954) has noted considerable interspecific variation within one genus or bower birds. Collias (1950) pointed out that such variability extends even to single elements in the total picture. For example, male birds of many species vocalize in characteristic ways during courtship. But the sounds produced are quite species-specific. They consist of crowing in the domestc cock and valley quail, booming in the prairie chicken, snap-hiss in the black-crowned night heron, distinctive calls in the laughing gull and herring gull, whistling in the red-headed duck, purring or cooing in the ring dove and pigeon, and singing in the canary, chaffinch, and brambling.

It is of primary importance to recognize that these widely different types of behavior are all produced by androgen, possibly by testosterone, and that the same hormone induces the development of other secondary sex characters and mating behavior in many of the species mentioned (Collias, 1950). This observation suggests the conclusion that evolutionary changes or phyletic differences in sexual activities are due not to genetic modifications of the endocrine system but to alterations in other physiological factors which control behavior.

Evidence provided by the study of mammalian forms is in accord with this working hypothesis. Reed's description (1946) of mating behavior in more than forty species of small mammals reveals pronounced differences in the patterning, timing, and frequency of coital and precoital activities. It is further known that typical sexual performance can be evoked in immature, out-of-season, or castrated males of many mammalian species by administering appropriate amounts of testosterone (Beach, 1948). Once more the indicated conclusion is that interspecific differences in sexual performance cannot be referred to presumed hormonal differences but must reflect evolutionary modifications of some other feature or features of the behavioral machinery.

If we seek to identify the mechanisms which are responsible for the behavioral differences under consideration we are led quite soon to consider the central nervous system and its role in the mediation of behavior, sexual and otherwise. More broadly, perhaps, one should examine all organs upon which hormones appear to exert any effects that eventually can be expressed in behavioral terms. For instance, the variability of courting vocalizations among bird species undoubtedly is due in part to differences in the structure of the sound-producing apparatus. Similarly the copulatory patterns of the Canidae and Felidae are different partly because of differences in genital anatomy.

Of greatest importance, nevertheless, are interspecific differences in those central nervous mechanisms which mediate sexual arousal and its overt expression. Unfortunately knowledge as to the identity of these mechanisms and their functional characteristics is embarrassingly limited. There are reasonably definite indications that they differ in males and females. For example sexual excitement in male rats seems to depend upon the cerebral isocortex (Beach, 1940), whereas this is not true for females of the same species (Beach, 1944). Furthermore, certain areas of the neocortex of male carnivores appear to make essential contributions to organization of the coital pattern in male cats (Beach, Jaynes, and

Zitrin, 1956); but this does not hold true in male rodents such as the rat (Beach, 1940).

[Considering mammals only, it has been suggested (Beach, 1947) that evolutionary changes in the direction of increasing corticalization of sexual functions seem to be associated with increasing complexity and modifiability of the individual's sexual patterns, and also with a decreasing reliance upon gonadal hormones for sexual activation and performance. This does not imply that evolutionary diversification within the class has involved profound changes in the pituitary and gonadal hormones themselves, but rather that the sensitivity and dependence of neural mechanisms upon the endocrine secretions has undergone alteration.]

GENERAL CONCLUSIONS

It is only reasonable to assume that some differences exist in the pituitary and gonadal hormones of the various vertebrate classes. Nonetheless the testis secretions of many if not all species of vertebrates are androgenic and serve the same functions, namely stimulation of the sex accessories and secondary sex characters including behavior. Furthermore a considerable degree of similarity must exist because a single mammalian hormone, testosterone, produces androgenic effects in at least some representatives of every class.

In contrast to the apparent evolutionary consistency of testis function, the behavioral end products of androgenic stimulation vary tremendously between classes and sometimes even within genera. It is obvious that this variability cannot be explained in terms of phyletic differences in endocrine constitution. A much more likely interpretation is that the responsible changes have taken place in other physiological systems upon which hormones tend to exert their effects. A prime candidate for intensive consideration and study is the nervous system.

[In general our review of the evidence pertaining to hormonal factors in masculine sexual behavior tends to support the following statement by Medawar: " 'endocrine evolution' is not an evolution of hormones but an evolution of the uses to which they are put; an evolution not, to put it crudely, of chemical formulae but of reactivities, reaction patterns and tissue competences" (1953, p. 334).]

References

ADAMS, A. E. 1950. Sexual conditions in *Triturus viridescens*. V. The effect of the administration of diethylstilbestrol on adult normal and castrated females. J. Exp. Zool., *113*, 463–98.

ADAMS, A. E., GRANGER, B. and RHODES, R. 1938. Stimulation of the thyroid gland of the guinea pig by anuran anterior pituitary. Anat. Rec., *72*, 491–501.

ADAMS, A. E., and GRANGER, B. 1938a. Induction of ovulation in *Rana pipiens* by pituitaries of *Triturus viridescens*. Proc. Soc. Exp. Biol. Med., *38*, 552–4.

ADAMS, A. E., and GRANGER, B. 1938b. Stimulation of reproductive tract of the infantile female mouse by anuran anterior pituitary substance. Proc. Soc. Exp. Biol. Med., *38*, 585–6.

ADAMS, A. E., and TUKEY, G. 1938. The effect of administering frog anterior pituitary substance to immature female mice. Anat. Rec., *71*, 1–25.

ALLEE, W. C., and FOREMAN, D. 1955. Effects of an androgen on dominance and subordinance in six common breeds of *Gallus gallus*. Physiol. Zool., *28*, 89–115.

ARONSON, L. R. 1945. Influence of stimuli provided by the male cichlid fish, *Tilapia macrocephala*, on the spawning frequency of the female. Physiol. Zool., *18*, 403–15.

ARONSON, L. R. 1957. Ch. 3, Behavior, Pt. 3, Reproductive and Parental Behavior, pp. 271–304 in The physiology of fishes, M. E. Brown, ed., Vol. 2, Behavior. New York, Academic Press.

ASDELL, S. A. 1946. Patterns of mamalian reproduction. Ithaca, Comstock.

ATZ, E. H. 1953. Experimental differentiation of basophil cell types in the transitional lobe of the pituitary of a teleost fish, *Astyanax mexicanus*. Bull. Bingham Ocean. Coll., *14*, 94–116.

BALL, J. 1937. A test for measuring sexual excitability in the female rat. Comp. Psychol. Monogr., *14*, 1–37.

BEACH, F. A. 1938. Techniques useful in studying the sex behavior of the rat. J. Genet. Psychol., *53*, 329–34.

BEACH, F. A. 1940. Effects of cortical lesions upon the copulatory behavior of male rats. J. Comp. Psychol., *29*, 193–244.

BEACH, F. A. 1944. Effects of injury to the cerebral cortex upon sexually-receptive behavior in the female rat. Psychosomat. Med., *6*, 40–55.

BEACH, F. A. 1947. Evolutionary changes in the physiological control of mating behavior in mammals. Psychol. Rev., *54*, 297–315.

BEACH, F. A. 1948. Hormones and behavior. New York, Paul Hoeber.

BEACH, F. A., JAYNES, J., ROGERS, C. et al. 1956. Mss. In preparation. Mating behavior in dogs. Effects of castration and subsequent androgen administration.

BERKOWITZ, P. 1941a. The response of fish (*Lebistes reticulatus*) to mammalian gonadotrophins. J. Exp. Zool., *86*, 247–55.

BERKOWITZ, P. 1941b. The effects of estrogenic substances in the fish (*Lebistes reticulatus*). Ibid., *87*, 233–43.

BLAIR, A. P. 1946. The effects of various hormones on primary and secondary sex characters of juvenile *Bufo fowleri*. Ibid., *103*, 365–400.

BRENEMAN, W. R. 1955. Reproduction in birds: the female. In The comparative physiology of reproduction and the effects of sex hormones in vertebrates. Mem. Soc. Endocrinol., No. 4., pp. 94–113.

BRETSCHNEIDER, L. H., and DUYVENÉ DE WIT, J. J. 1947. Sexual endocrinology of the non-mammalian vertebrates. Monographs on the progress of research in Holland during the war. New York, Elsevier.

BROWN, F. A. JR., and JONES, G. M. 1949.

Ovarian inhibition by a sinus-gland principle in the fiddler crab. Biol. Bull., *96*, 228–32.

BURROWS, H. 1945. Biological actions of sex hormones. Cambridge, Eng., Cambridge Univ. Press.

BURROWS, W. H., and BYERLY, T. C. 1936. Studies on prolactin in fowl pituitary. I. Broody hens compared with laying hens and males. II. Effect of genetic constitution with respect to broodiness on prolactin content. Proc. Soc. Exp. Biol. Med., *34*, 841–4.

BUSH, I. E. 1953. Species differences in adrenocortical secretion. J. Endocrinol., *9*, 95–100.

CAMPBELL, R. M., and COSTERLITZ, H. W. 1953. Species differences in the deoxyribonucleic and ribonucleic acid contents of livers of non-pregnant and pregnant mice, guinea pigs and cats. J. Endocrinol., *9*, 45–51.

CASIDA, L. E., CASIDA, B. H., and CHAPMAN, A. D. 1952. Some differences between two strains of rats developed by selection to differ in their response to equine gonadotrophin. Endocrinol., *51*, 148–51.

CLEGHORN, R. A. 1947. Species difference in the cortical hormone requirement of adrenalectomized dogs and cats. Ibid., *41*, 265–6.

COLLIAS, N. E. 1940. Some effects of sex hormones on broodiness in fowl and pigeon. Anat. Rec., Suppl., *78*, 146–7.

COLLIAS, N. E. 1950. Hormones and behavior with special reference to birds and the mechanisms of hormone action. In E. S. Gordon, ed., Symposium on steroid hormones. Madison, Univ. Wisconsin Press.

CREASER, C. W., and GORBMAN, A. 1939. Species specificity of the gonadotropic factors in vertebrates. Quart. Rev. Biol., *14*, 311–31.

DAS, B. C., and NALBANDOV, A. V. 1955. Responses of ovaries of immature chickens to avian and mammalian gonadotrophins. Endocrinol., *57*, 705–10.

DAVID, K. 1935. Uber krystallinische mannliches Hormon aus Hoden (Testesteron), wirksamer als aus Harn oder aus Cholesterin bereitetes Androsteron. Z. f. physiol. Chem., *233*, 281.

DODD, J. M. 1955. The hormones of sex and reproduction and their effects in fish and lower chordates. In The comparative physiology of reproduction . . . Mem. Soc. Endocrinol., No. 4, pp. 166–87.

ECKSTEIN, P., and ZUCKERMAN, S. 1955. Reproduction in mammals. In ibid., pp. 114–28.

ENDERS, R. K. 1952. Reproduction in the mink (*Mustela vison*). Proc. Amer. Philos. Soc., *96*, 691–774.

FRAPS, R. M. 1955. The varying effects of sex hormones in birds. In The comparative physiology of reproduction . . . Mem. Soc. Endocrinol., No. 4, pp. 205–19.

GALLIAN, L. 1955. The action of sex hormones on the development of sex in amphibia. In ibid., pp. 188–204.

GLICK, D., and OCHS, M. J. 1955. Studies in histochemistry: Quantitative histological distribution of cholesterol in adrenal glands of the cow, rat and monkey and effects of stress conditions, ACTH, cortisone and desoxycorticosterone. Endocrinol., *56*, 285–98.

GORBMAN, A. 1941. Comparative anatomy and physiology of the anterior pituitary. Quart. Rev. Biol., *16*, 294–310.

GORBMAN, A. 1946. Qualitative variation of the hypophyseal thyrotropic hormone in the vertebrates. Univ. Calif. Publ. Zool., *51*, 229–44.

GORBMAN, A., LISSITZKY, S., MICHEL, R., and ROCHE, J. 1952. Thyroidal metabolism of iodine in the shark, *Scyliorhinus (Scyllium) Canicula*. Endocrinol., *51*, 311–21.

GORBMAN, A., and BERG, O. 1955. Thyroidal function in the fishes *Fundulus Heteroclitus*, *F. Majalis* and *F. Diaphanus*. Ibid., *56*, 86–92.

GORDON, M., COHEN, H., and NIGRELLI, R. F. 1943. A hormone-produced taxonomic character in *Platypoecilus Maculatus* diagnostic of wild *P. Xiphidium*. Amer. Nat., *77*, 569–72.

GREENBERG, B. 1942. Some effects of testosterone on the sexual pigmentation and other sex characters of the cricket frog (*Acris gryllus*). J. Exp. Zool., *91*, 435–51.

GROBSTEIN, C. 1942. Endocrine and developmental studies of gonopode differentiation in certain poeciliid fishes. II. Effect of testosterone propionate on the normal and regenerating anal fin of adult *Platypoecilus Maculatus* females. Ibid., *89*, 305–28.

GRUNT, J. A., and YOUNG, W. C. 1953. Consistency of sexual behavior patterns in individual male guinea pigs following castration and androgen therapy. J. Comp. Physiol. Psychol., *46*, 138–44.

HALDANE, J. B. S. 1953. Foreword to Evolution. Sympos. Soc. Exp. Biol., No. 7. Cambridge, Eng., Cambridge Univ. Press, pp. 9–19.

HARRIS, G. W. 1955. Neural control of the pituitary gland. London, Edward Arnold.

HERRICK, E. H. 1944. Some influences of stilbestrol, estrone, and testosterone propionate on the genital tract of young female fowls. Poultry Science, *23*, 65–6.

HOAR, W. S. 1955. Reproduction in the teleost fish. In The comparative physiology of reproduction . . . Mem. Soc. Endocrinol., No. 4, pp. 5–24.

HOUSSAY, B. A. 1954. Hormonal regulation of the sexual function of the male toad. Acta physiol. Latino Americana, *4*, 1–41.

HOUSSAY, B. A., GUISTI, L., and LASCANO-GONZALES, J. M. 1929. Implantación de la hipófisis y estimulación sexual en el gato. Soc. Argent. Biol., *5*, 397–418.

HUMPHREY, R. R. 1944. The functional capacities of heteroplastic gonadal grafts in the Mexican axolotl, and some hybrid offspring of grafted animals. Amer. J. Anat., *75*, 263–87.

KEATY, C. 1942. Bio-assay of the pituitary of *Rana catesbeiana*: a qualitative study. Proc. Louisiana Acad. Sci., *6*, 63–71.

KEHL, R., and COMBESCOT, C. 1955. Reproduction in the reptilia. In The comparative physiology of reproduction . . . Mem. Soc. Endocrinol., No. 4, pp. 47–74.

KEMPF, E. J. 1917. The social and sexual behavior of infrahuman primates with some comparable facts in human behavior. Psychoanal. Rev., *4*, 127–54.

KINSEY, A. C., POMEROY, W. B., and MARTIN, C. 1948. Sexual behavior in the human male. Philadelphia, W. B. Saunders.

LEBLOND, C. P., and NOBLE, G. K. 1937. Prolactin-like reaction produced by hypophyses of various vertebrates. Proc. Soc. Exp. Biol. Med., *36*, 517–18.

LEVER, J., MILTENBURG, J., and VAN OORDT, G. J. 1949. The effect of a short treatment with thiourea upon the fish thyroid gland. Proc. Netherlands Acad., *52*, 3–7.

LEVY, M., and ARONSON, L. R. 1955. Morphological effects of castration and hormone administration in the male cichlid fish, *Tilapia macrocephela*. Anat. Rec., *122*, 450–1.

McCARTNEY, J. L. 1928–29. The male hormone: its standardization. Proc. Soc. Exp. Biol. Med., *26*, 686–7.

McGEE, L. C. 1947. The effect of the injection of a lipoid fraction of bird testicle in capons. Proc. Inst. Med., *6*, 242.

MARSHALL, A. J. 1954. Bower birds: their displays and breeding cycles. Oxford, Clarendon Press.

MARSHALL, A. J. 1955. Reproduction in birds: the male. In The comparative physiology of reproduction . . . Mem. Soc. Endocrinol., No. 4, pp. 75–93.

MATTHEWS, H. L. 1939. Visual stimulation and ovulation in pigeons. Proc. Roy. Soc. London, Series B, *126*, 557–60.

MATTHEWS, L. H. 1955. The evolution of viviparity in vertebrates. In The comparative physiology of reproduction . . . Mem. Soc. Endocrinol., No. 4, pp. 129–48.

MEDAWAR, P. B. 1953. Some immunological and endocrinological problems raised by the evolution of viviparity in vertebrates. In Evolution. Sympos.

Soc. Exp. Biol., No. 7. Cambridge, Eng., Cambridge Univ. Press, pp. 320–38.

MOORE, C. R. 1942. The physiology of the testes and application of male sex hormone. J. UROLOGY, *47*, 31–44.

NALBANDOV, A. V., MAYER, R. K., and McSHAN, W. R. 1951. The role of a third gonadatrophic hormone in the mechanism of androgen secretion in chicken testes. Anat. Rec., *110*, 475–94.

NAYYAR, S. N., and GLICK, A. D. 1955. The quantitative histochemical distribution of beta-glucuronidase in the adrenal of various species and the influence of stress conditions, hormonal treatments and hypophysectomy. Endocrinol., *56*, 67–9.

NOBLE, G. K., and KUMPF, K. F. 1936. The sexual behavior and secondary sexual characters of a gonadectomized fish. Anat. Rec., *67*, 113.

NOBLE, G. K., KUMPF, K. F., and BILLINGS, V. N. 1938. The induction of brooding behavior in the jewel fish. Endocrinol., *23*, 353–9.

NOBLE, G. K., and ZITRIN, A. 1942. Induction of mating behavior in male and female chicks following injection of sex hormones. Ibid., *30*, 327–34.

OORDT, G. J. VAN, and KLOMP, H. 1946. Effects of oestrone and gonadotrophine administration in the male toad (*Bufo bufo*). Koninklijke Nederlandsche Akademie van Wetenschappen. Proc., *49*, 3–8.

OORDT, G. J. VAN, and VAN OORDT, P. G. W. J. 1955. The regulation of spermatogenesis in the frog. In The comparative physiology of reproduction . . . Mem. Soc. Endocrinol., No. 4, pp. 25–38.

PALAY, S. L. 1953. A note on the effects of hypophysectomy on the preopticohypophyseal pathway in *Fundulus*. Bull. Bingham Ocean. Coll., *14*, 42–5.

PICKFORD, G. E. 1953a. The response of hypophysectomized male *Fundulus* in injections of purified beef-growth hormone. Ibid., *14*, 46–68.

PICKFORD, G. E. 1953b. A study of the hypophysectomized male killifish,

Fundulus heteraclitus (Linn.), Ibid., *14*, 5–41.

PICKFORD, G. E. 1954. The response of hypophysectomized male killifish to purified fish-growth hormone, as compared with response to purified beef hormone. Endocrinol., *55*, 274–87.

PICKFORD, G. E. 1954. The response of hypophysectomized male killifish to prolonged treatment of small doses of thyrotropin. Ibid., *55*, 289–92.

PONSE, K. 1941. Zoological specificity in reaction to sex hormones. Arch. Sci. Phys. Nat., *43*, 211.

PUMPHREY, R. J. 1955. Opening remarks. In The comparative physiology of reproduction . . . Mem. Soc. Endocrinol., No. 4, pp. 1–2.

RAGG, L. E., and SPEIRS, R. S. 1952. Strain and sex differences in response of inbred mice to adrenocortical hormones. Proc. Soc. Exp. Biol. Med., *80*, 680–4.

RASQUIN, P. 1951. Effects of carp pituitary and mammalian ACTH on the endocrine and lymphoid systems of the teleost *Astyanax mexicana*. J. Exp. Zool., *117*, 317–57.

REED, C. A. 1946. The copulatory behavior of small mammals. J. Comp. Psychol., *39*, 185–204.

REYNOLDS, A. E. 1943. The normal seasonal reproductive cycle in the male *Eumeces fasciatus* together with some observations on the effects of castration and hormone administration. J. Morphol., *72*, 331–77.

RICHTER, C. P., ROGERS, P. V., and HALL, C. E. 1950. Failure of salt replacement therapy in adrenalectomized recently captured wild Norway rats. Endocrinol., *46*, 233–42.

RIDDLE, O., and BATES, R. W. 1939. Preparation, assay and actions of lactogenic hormones. In E. Allen et al., Sex and internal secretions. 3d ed. Williams and Wilkins, pp. 1088–20.

RIDDLE, O., and LAHR, E. L. 1944. On broodiness in ring doves following implants of certain steroid hormones. Endocrinol., *35*, 255–60.

RIDDLE, O., and SCHOOLEY, J. P. 1944. Tests indicating absence of progesterone in certain avian ovaries. J. Washington Acad. Sci., *34*, 341–6.

RISLEY, P. L. 1941. A comparison of effects of gonadotropic and sex hormones on the urogenital systems of juvenile terrapins. J. Exp. Zool., *87*, 477–515.

ROSENBLATT, J., and ARONSON, L. R. 1956. Personal communication.

ROUSSEL, G. 1936. L'Acetate de testosterone, hormone testiculaire synthétique. Bull. de l'Académie de Médecine, *115*, 458–61.

SCHARRER, B. 1953. Comparative physiology of invertebrate endocrines. Ann. Rev. Physiol., *15*, 457–72.

SCHOCKAERT, J. A. 1933. Differences between anterior pituitary sex-stimulating hormones and pregnancy-urine substances as tested in the male mammal and bird. Amer. J. Physiol., *105*, 497–507.

SCHREIBER, S. S., and RUGH, R. 1945. The effect of anterior pituitary implants and of estradiol benzoate on the gonads and gonaducts of newly metamorphosed frogs, *Rana pipiens*. J. Exp. Zool., *99*, 93–113.

SMITH, C. L. 1955. Reproduction in female amphibia. In The comparative physiology of reproduction . . . Mem. Soc. Endocrinol., No. 4, pp. 39–56.

SMITH, D. C., and EVERETT, G. M. 1943. The effect of thyroid hormone on growth rate, time of sexual differ-entiation and oxygen consumption in the fish, *Lebistes reticulatus*. J. Exp. Zool., *94*, 229–40.

SOKOLOWSKY, A. 1923. The sexual life of anthropoid apes. Urol. Cutan. Rev., *17*, 612–15.

STOLK, A. 1951. Activity of the embryonic thyroid gland in the viviparous cyprinodont *Lebistes reticulatus* (Peters). Koninklijke Nederlandsche Akademie van Wetenschappen. Proc., Series C, *54*, 579–84.

TURNER, C. O., and CARR, H. A. 1941. Gonopodial characteristics produced in the anal fins of females of *Gambusia affinis affinis* by treatment with ethninyl testosterone. Biol. Bull., *80*, 371–83.

WHITMAN, C. O. 1919. The behavior of pigeons. In H. A. Carr, Ed., Posthumous works of Charles Otis Whitman, *3*, 83.

WILHELMI, A. E., PICKFORD, G. E., and SAWYER, W. H. 1955. Initiation of the spawning reflex response in *Fuɪdulus* by the administration of fish and mammalian neurohypophysial preparation and synthetic oxytocin. Endocrinol., *57*, 243–52.

WITSCHI, E. 1955. Vertebrate gonadotrophins. In The comparative physiology of reproduction . . . Mem. Soc. Endocrinol., No. 4, pp. 149–65.

ZUCKERMAN, S. 1955. Closing remarks. In ibid., pp. 249–53.

5

Genetic Basis of Behavior

Ernst Caspari

WESLEYAN UNIVERSITY

THE TERM "genetic" is used in a different sense by biologists and psychologists. For the biologists it means the control of a character by genes, which is demonstrated by breeding experiments. The psychologist employs it for the appearance and development of a character during individual life, a type of study for which "onto-genetic" is frequently used by biologists. In the present chapter the term will be used in its biological meaning. The topic may therefore be stated by posing the question, whether and how genes control behavioral characters, and how the genetic control of behavioral characters will affect their changes in the course of evolution.

The definition of the gene concept has been under some dispute recently. This dispute does not concern us here since it deals with the structure of genes at the molecular level. There is general agreement among geneticists that genes are situated in the chromosomes of the nucleus. Furthermore, the chromosomes are longitudinally differentiated, and gene mutations at a particular locus of the chromosome will lead to characteristic phenotypic changes which will be identical or will at least affect the same characters for different mutational events affecting the same locus. It is concluded from these observations that a particular locus in the nonmutated state has a certain function which is affected by the mutation. The term "gene" is therefore an expression for the established fact that different loci on a chromosome have different physiological functions. The laws of the distribution of genes in crosses (the Mendelian rules), linkage, and crossing over are reflections of the behavior of the chromosomes at meiosis and fertilization. They are of importance for present consideration only insofar as they deter-

mine the transmission of chromosomes from generation to generation and therefore form the basis of evolutionary considerations.

THE ACTION OF GENES

The genes are, then, functionally differentiated portions of the
chromosome, and consequently of the cell nucleus. Every higher
animal contains one pair of each kind of genes in the nucleus of
every one of its cells. The primary activity of genes must therefore
be assumed to be intracellular; in some way every gene affects the
cell in which it is situated in a characteristic way. The function of
most loci seems to be necessary for the life of the cell; Demerec
(1934) has shown that most deficiencies, i.e. small losses of genic
material, are lethal for the cells which carry them in homozygous
condition. The nature of this necessary primary activity of the
genes in the cell is not known. But it is generally assumed that it is
of biochemical nature and may consist in the conferring of specificity on enzymes, proteins, or antigens. From the point of view
of this discussion, the important fact is that a substitution of one
allele for another at one particular locus results in an effect on a
specific character, frequently a specific metabolic step. This is
borne out by many studies of micro-organisms, particularly the
mold *Neurospora*. All mutations observed affecting a particular
metabolic step have been found to be alleles, i.e. to be due to
events at the same locus. Similar specific chemical effects have been
found for specific loci in insects and in plants. It may therefore be
assumed that the function of every locus in a chromosome is highly
specific, possibly controlling one single biochemical reaction step.

In the course of development, the original fertilized egg cell
with all its genes gives rise to a new organism. The genotype in
each cell will carry out its biochemical activities, and in this way
it will express itself during development. This is a very general
statement which leaves unexplained the differentiation of cells
which, though presumably carrying the same genes in their nuclei,
become very different in structure and function. These tissue differences are usually regarded as determined by the cytoplasm. But the
nuclear genes determine at least the substances which a cell can
form and their quantities. It may be assumed that genes may in
this way affect the production of substances with morphogenetic
activity, such as hormones, although little experimental material

bearing on this point is available. There exists furthermore evidence that genes control the ability of cells to react on morphogenetic stimuli—their competence. There may be other mechanisms by which genes can affect developmental processes. At all events it may be stated that the primary intracellular effects of genes express themselves in higher animals in the activity of the cells during development, leading to phenotypic results. These results, as far as different alleles at a particular locus are concerned, are again highly specific, reflecting in this way the specificity of genic action at the cellular level. The actual effects of a locus on the development and structure of particular cells will depend on the role the reaction controlled by the gene plays in the development and function of this particular cell. For instance, if a locus controls the formation of a particular pigment, all cells able to form this pigment may be visibly affected by gene substitution at this locus, while other cells are not. The mechanism that decides which cells are able to form the pigment and which ones are not is unknown, though it is established that it is in turn under the control of genes.

In spite of the specificity of the primary gene action, all genes affect a number of characters. This phenomenon is known as pleiotropism. Grüneberg (1938, 1943), in discussing pleiotropic gene action in the mouse, has postulated that all genes act primarily on one specific process and that the other effects are secondary, being developmentally influenced by the first process. Pleiotropic manifestation of genes is assumed to be due to disturbances in the interaction of different parts in the developing embryo.

Pleiotropism occurs also at the intracellular and biochemical level. If a certain metabolic step is blocked, the precursor is not converted into the normal product and must be either stored or converted by an alternate metabolic pathway. In either case, a new biochemical equilibrium becomes established (Caspari, 1952).

Pleiotropism at the cellular and at the embryological level is due to related principles. Both cells and the developing embryo constitute integrated systems, and it is impossible to interfere with one process in an integrated system without at the same time affecting secondarily a number of other reactions. It is therefore astonishing that in all cases of gene substitution a large number of characters and processes are *not* affected by the changes in the system; in other words, that the whole mechanism is not thrown out of order. Actually it frequently is, and this gives rise to lethal genes causing death of the cell or of the organism. Still, many mutant genes are not lethal, and many organ systems are not affected by the majority of genes.

This fact is explained by stating that the biochemical and embryological processes proceed under a "margin of safety," that they are "buffered." The expression most frequently used for this phenomenon is Cannon's (1932) term, "homeostasis." This originally referred to the regulatory mechanisms present at the level of the physiology of the whole organism. At this level regulatory mechanisms, particularly of the feedback type, have been known for a long time. These mechanisms have been extensively investigated and are known to be frequently of a hormonal or nervous nature. The mechanisms of homeostasis on the developmental and biochemical level are not so well understood, although in the latter case alternate pathways for the metabolism of a single precursor substance may be assumed to play a role. It is, however, well established that on the genotypic level homeostatic mechanisms exist (Lerner, 1954). It should be emphasized that the mechanisms of homeostasis at different levels of integration are different.

It should not be assumed, from these considerations, that genetically determined characters are independent of the environment. The opposite is the case. Developmental processes, though under genetic control, are influenced by the environment, and the resulting phenotype is the product of both genes and environment. The interaction is not simple. Many cases are known in which a particular gene has different phenotypic effects in different environments. In other words, genes control the "reaction norm" of the organism to environmental conditions.

Different phenotypic characters appear to be buffered to a different degree. Those that are well buffered will be influenced by relatively few genes which affect processes more or less closely related to the development of the phenotype. Other characters have apparently a lesser margin of safety and are therefore affected by a large number of gene substitutions. To this group belongs the shape of the spermatheca in *Drosophila*, which Dobzhansky studied in a classical investigation (1927). For a large number of mutant genes, obtained both spontaneously and by X-ray irradiation (Dobzhansky and Holz, 1943), it was found that the spermatheca shape was affected in a characteristic way. Only a small minority of the gene substitutions investigated did not result in a measurable effect on spermatheca shape.

Differences in characters of this kind will behave differently in crosses from those affected by relatively few mutations. They will not show clear-cut Mendelian segregation into well-defined classes. They share, however, the phenomena of segregation and linkage. Segregation is expressed in these characters by an increase of the variability in F_2 over F_1 and the parental strains. There is no reason to assume that there are two different types of genes, major genes and polygenes, as proposed by Mather (1949) (see Robertson and Reeve, 1952a). There is, however, certainly a difference between the probabilities with which any random gene substitution will affect a certain character. Some characters will be affected by a few specific mutations, while others will be affected by practically any change anywhere in the genotype. This does not constitute a difference in the nature of the genes affecting these characters; nevertheless, different methods must be employed for their analysis.

Among the characters showing polygenic inheritance are some which are of great evolutionary significance, such as size, viability, and fertility. Timoféeff-Ressovsky (1934) investigated the effects of different well-defined genes on the viability of *Drosophila funebris*, under different environmental conditions and at different developmental stages. He found that every one of these mutants, on a constant genotypic background, had its characteristic effects on viability. Most genes decreased the viability of their carriers, but to different degrees at different stages of development and in different environments. Some of them, however, were equal to or even superior to the wild type under certain specific environmental conditions. The latter genes would therefore have a selective advantage over their wild-type alleles in a particular environment. Similar results were obtained by Dobzhansky and Spassky (1944) in *Drosophila pseudoobscura*, and by Kühn and Henke (1932) in *Ephestia*.

A good example is the dominant mutant *At* in the moth *Ptychopoda seriata* (Kühn and von Engelhardt, 1937), which arose in a strain of Sicilian origin. This mutation, which increases the amount of pigment, results in lower viability under the climatic conditions of the Mediterranean, i.e. high temperature and low humidity. But at low temperature and high humidity the viability of the mutant is increased as compared to the wild type.

Because of their importance for evolutionary processes, some of the peculiarities of polygenically determined characters should be mentioned. (1) They are frequently influenced by environmental conditions. This is to be expected if the main reason for the polygenic type of determination is a relatively low margin of safety. (2) Since a large number of genes is acting on the same character, the final phenotype will be the result of the whole genotype. A certain phenotypic effect will depend not on the action of one gene but on a complex interaction of several genes, as has been particularly pointed out by Robertson and Reeve (1952a). (3) Since the number of genes affecting characters controlled by polygenes is large, mutations affecting these characters will be relatively frequent. Polygenic characters may therefore be expected not to be very stable in populations.

The interaction between different alleles at different loci is rather complicated. It would be unjustified to assume that there are generally some genes affecting a character in the plus-direction and others acting in the minus-direction. It would be more true to say that certain combinations of alleles at different loci have different effects from other combinations of genes. If all genes except one are held constant, as was done in the classical experiments, the observed effects are ascribed to this particular gene. It has, however, been known for a long time that the phenotypic effects of particular genes depend on their genotypic background. In other words, certain combinations of genes rather than single genes will produce a certain phenotypic effect in the organism. A very striking example of interaction of different loci in the same chromosome is the "synthetic lethals" discovered by Dobzhansky (1946). Two chromosomes, neither of which contained a lethal gene, gave rise to a new lethal chromosome, apparently by crossing over. That means that two genes, neither of which has a lethal effect in itself, may become lethal in combination.

On the other hand, many examples are known in which particular combinations of genes are favorable for the organism or for the species. These gene combinations are called "coadapted." Such a particularly favorable combination of genes will be selected for; but at the same time the combination will always be in danger of being lost as a result of recombination of different genes. There frequently occur mechanisms which tend to transmit a number of such coadapted genes together as a group. Mechanisms of this kind which are usually based on chromosome rearrangements are found in nature, as has been shown particularly by Dobzhansky and his collaborators (Dobzhansky, 1949).

The Behavior of Genes in Populations

It is now generally accepted that evolutionary changes consist primarily in changes of the genotype of a species in time. In order to apply our knowledge of the transmission and action of genes to evolutionary problems, some further considerations are necessary. A population in the present sense is a number of interbreeding organisms. Their genes constitute a "gene pool" in which genes are ideally distributed at random from generation to generation. A very simple law, the Hardy-Weinberg law, which can be easily derived from the Mendelian rules, states that in the absence of mutations, selection, etc., the genetic composition of such a gene pool will remain constant. The picture becomes complicated by the fact that factors such as mutations, selection, breeding structure of the population, size of the population, and migration will affect the composition of the gene pool in predictable ways. The mathematical analysis of these influences on gene pools is more complicated than the derivation of the Hardy-Weinberg law, but has been successfully carried out by Haldane, Sewall Wright, R. A. Fisher, and others. The result is that we can postulate a number of population parameters which will completely describe the genetic characteristics of a population. Which ones of the factors named are most effective in a particular population depends on those parameters, and in this sense every population is unique (Wright, 1931, 1948). The actual determination of the population parameters for a particular species is difficult, but much progress along this line has been made through the work of Dobzhansky and his collaborators.

The breeding structure of a species has no direct influence on the relative numbers of genes in a gene pool, but only on their frequency in homozygous and heterozygous condition in the individuals making up the population. The Hardy-Weinberg law assumes random mating. Any deviation in the direction of inbreeding will lead to the establishment of a relatively higher number of homozygotes over heterozygotes in the population. If the mating pattern favors an amount of outbreeding above random mating, a larger number of heterozygotes will be found in the population. The relative number of genes in the gene pool can be influenced by the mating pattern only indirectly, by means of differences in the selective values of homozygotes and heterozygotes.

The frequency of a gene in a gene pool will be determined primarily by an equilibrium between the frequency with which it arises by mutation and the speed with which it is eliminated by selective pressures. In other words, the frequency of a gene in a population is not arbitrary, but depends on its adaptive value and its mutation rate, and will remain constant as long as these two factors remain unchanged. Any influence tending to change either the adaptive value of a gene (such as changes in environmental conditions) or its mutation rate will therefore result in a change of gene frequencies in the gene pool. This phenomenon enables populations to adapt rapidly to changes in environmental conditions.

The effect of selection on gene pools is of particular importance since it regulates the relation of the organism to its environment. Selective factors act on organisms, i.e. phenotypes, and determine primarily the contribution of each organism to the gene pool of the next generation. In view of what has been said earlier it would be expected that selective forces do not act on individual genes but on coadapted gene systems. They are therefore the main factor in keeping the genotype of a population constant, counteracting mutation pressure and the recombination of genes, which, in the absence of special mechanisms like inversions, tend to break up the coadapted gene system. In other words, the variation inside a population is strongly restricted by the fact that certain coadapted gene systems are favorable in a particular environment and have a selective advantage.

The fact that polygenic effects are subject to selection pressure, and that they are frequently pleiotropic effects of genes with "major" effects, results in an important consequence as far as evolutionary changes are concerned: the adaptive value of a gene may be dependent not on its primary action but on one of its pleiotropic effects. The establishment of a definite gene in a population may be originally a by-product of one of its minor pleiotropic effects. An example may illustrate this principle. The alleles *Rt* and *rt* influence testis color in the moth *Ephestia*. The dominant gene *Rt* causes the testis to be brown, the homozygous recessive *rt rt* has a red testis. From an ecological point of view no selective advantage can be assumed for either allele since their effects are not even visible from the outside. But it could be shown that the alleles have pleiotropic effects on general physiological characters, namely viability and mating of the males. *Rt Rt* males are found more frequently copulating, while *rt rt* organisms show a higher survival in competition. It is frequently found that in genes with pleiotropic effects the different characters show independent dominance relations. In the pair of alleles *Rt-rt* the heterozygote has the brown testis color characteristic of *Rt* and combines the high frequency of copulation of *Rt* with the high viability of *rt*. In other words, the heterozygote is superior to either homozygote (Caspari, 1950). The phenomenon of heterozygote superiority, "heterosis," is frequently found in natural populations, and has been thoroughly investigated. Whether the mechanism of pleiotropism is the only one leading to the superiority of the heterozygote has been doubted, but it is the only mechanism which is clearly understood and which has been definitely demonstrated. From the point of view of evolution, the superiority of the heterozygote results in selection in favor of the heterozygote. This gives rise to polymorphism, the maintenance of two or more alleles at the same locus in the population.

The fact that heterosis enables a gene pool to contain two alleles at a particular locus is of great importance for the evolution of populations. The existence of more than one allele in a gene pool supplies the genetic variability that is necessary for the efficient action of selection. It should be pointed out that because of the existence of heterosis a certain degree of heterozygosity seems to be necessary for the survival of many species (Lerner, 1954). Evidence is accumulating that even closely inbred laboratory strains contain a considerable amount of genetic variability, which is probably due to the necessity of maintaining a certain level of heterozygosity (Gowen, 1952).

Another mechanism which may tend to ensure a certain amount of genetic variability in a population is "genetic drift" (Wright, 1931, 1948). In sexual reproduction each gamete receives only one of the two genes present at every locus in the parent. Furthermore, only a small part of the gametes thus formed will participate in the formation of the next generation. Both the elimination of genes at gamete formation and the preservation of genes in the population through successful fertilization are usually chance events. The transmission of genes from one generation to the next is therefore subject to a certain error of sampling which might preserve or eliminate a gene in a gene pool independently of its selective value. The error of sampling will be relatively small, compared to the number of genes involved, in reasonably large populations, but may become large in small breeding populations. The drift effect will therefore be most noticeable in small populations and in more or less isolated subgroups of a larger population.

A natural population, then, can be said to consist genetically of a pool of genes which is inherently unstable. The occurrence of heterosis guarantees that more than one allele at a particular locus will be present in the population. The forces of selection keep this system stable by favoring coadapted combinations of genes at different loci. On the other hand, the inherent lack of stability of the gene pool gives the population the plasticity necessary to adapt itself to changes in conditions of selection.

EFFECTS OF GENES ON BEHAVIOR IN INSECTS

One other feature in the *Ephestia* experiment is of interest in the present discussion: one of the pleiotropic effects of the genes at the *rt* locus is a behavior character, mating behavior. Influences of well-defined Mendelian genes on mating behavior have been repeatedly described. Reed and Reed (1950) have found that the gene *w* in *Drosophila melanogaster* decreases the frequency of matings by about 25 per cent. In insects, where each mating gives rise to a large number of offspring, differences in the number of effective matings will constitute a powerful selective character. Reed and Reed could show that the selection against the gene *w* in artificial populations can be completely accounted for by lowered mating activity of the males. Similarly Merrell (1953) found that three out of four sex-linked mutations in *Drosophila melanogaster* affect the mating activity of the males and reduce in this way the survival values of these genes.

Pleiotropic effects of morphological mutant genes on mating behavior may be dependent on the environment, just as are other gene-controlled phenotypic characters. Rendel (1951) found that the gene "ebony" in *Drosophila* reduces the mating activity of homozygous males in the light, whereas in the dark they are equal or possibly slightly superior to "vestigial" control males. In this case, it is the "reaction norm" of the organism that is influenced by the gene substitution.

There is good evidence that gene substitutions influence not only mating activity but also the selection of mating partners. Preferential mating has been described, for example by Merrell (1949) and Rendel (1951) for mutants in *Drosophila*. In the moth *Panaxia dominula*, Sheppard (1953) has shown that individuals carrying the gene "medionigra" mate preferentially with partners not carrying this gene. This particular mating behavior tends to keep the gene in the population in spite of the lower fertility, viability, and survival from predation which are associated with it. The evolutionary importance of preferential mating as an isolation mechanism is discussed by Spieth later in this volume.

Most of the behavioral effects of mutant genes described in the literature concern mating behavior, since this factor may be expected to be of extreme evolutionary significance. Cases have been described in which other behavioral characters are affected by genes. Many morphological mutants affect behavior by their effects on sensory organs or on the motor effector structures. An example is the change in the photic reaction of *Drosophila* induced by the mutant *w*, which Scott (1943) interprets as being due to the reduction in eye pigmentation caused by this gene. The existence of effects of genes on behavior by means of their well-established action on sensory or motor organs is obvious. In the following discussion emphasis will be placed on cases in which the nature of the effect of genes on behavioral characters is not apparent. In many cases the more direct effect may be on the activity of the central nervous system. The pleiotropic effects of genes on mating behavior may belong in this class. In addition, Hovanitz (1953) demonstrated differences in the daily activity rhythm of the white and colored phases in the butterfly *Colias eurytheme*. Waddington, Woolf, and Perry (1954) found striking differences in the environment selected by seven strains of *Drosophila*, each of which was marked by one gene with visible effect.

In insects, then, there is abundant evidence for the existence of genes affecting behavior traits. Most of the genic influences on behavior have been found to be pleiotropic effects of genes with morphological manifestation. This is due to practical reasons, since a morphological trait permits the comparison of alleles on a more or less constant genetic background. In view of the theory of polygenic characters presented previously, it would be likely that a behavior trait would turn out to be controlled by several genes. This seems to be indicated in experiments on a behavior trait in *Ephestia* (Caspari, 1951; Cotter, 1951). The larvae of these moths burrow in the food, tunneling all through the food mass, and finally, just before pupation, crawl up to the margin of the food mass, spin their cocoons, and pupate. One strain was observed which in the last larval instar leaves the food and crawls around on the cover of the dish, spinning continuously, so that a dense mat of silk is deposited on the cover of a culture of this strain. This mat-spinning behavior is dependent on environmental factors. (1) It occurs only in cultures containing many organisms; individuals in isolation do not show it. It should be emphasized, however, that the phenomenon does not depend on crowding of the culture. (2) Mat spinning occurs only in the dark. It may be suspected that in the light the negative phototropism of the larvae inhibits them from leaving the food. (3) Mat spinning is dependent on lack of some nutritional factor. It occurs in cultures fed with yellow granulated corn meal but not in cultures fed whole corn gruel. The genetic basis of this character has been studied in F_1, F_2, back-crosses and outcrosses of mat-spinning and normal strains, using the amount of silk deposited on the cover as a measure of the effect. The results are incompatible with the assumption of a single pair of alleles responsible for the character. The trait seems to be determined by several genes, and may be regarded as polygenic.

It is conceivable that a behavior trait like mat spinning will confer an advantage on the organism under certain conditions. This is indicated by the fact that mat spinning, though not as strong as in our laboratory strain, has been found in wild populations. In such a case, genes favoring the character "mat spinning" would be selected for. In addition, selection would favor genes which induce a preference for foods that do not contain too much of the nutritional factor inhibiting mat spinning. Considerations of this kind may give a clue to the evolutionary origin of food specialization, which is so widespread in insects.

All these examples show that behavior traits in insects may be genetically controlled. Many of these genes, particularly those affecting mating behavior, will be strongly subject to selection, and other pleiotropic effects of the same genes may become established in the species as a result of the selective advantage of the behavior trait.

It has been doubted whether the pleiotropic effects of genes may actually play a role in determining the selective value of a gene, since they are sometimes described as "minor." Such doubts have been expressed by Mather (1954) for pleiotropic effects in general and by Scott and Fredericson (1951) for pleiotropic effects on behavior. The above-mentioned experiments of Reed and Reed (1950) in *Drosophila,* of Sheppard (1953) in *Panaxia,* and of Caspari (1950) in *Ephestia* show conclusively that pleiotropic effects on mating behavior may be determining factors in the establishment of genes, both in laboratory and natural populations. Conversely, genes influencing behavior may become established because of the favorable effect of another one of the manifold effects of the same gene. In either case, the remaining genotype will be influenced by selection in such a way that a coadapted system of genes, adapted for the particular conditions under which the species lives, will become established.

The Effects of Genes on Behavior in Mammals

The genetic basis of behavior characters in mammals has been established by three types of observations. (1) It has been shown by Keeler and King (1942) that in the rat spontaneous mutations at well-known loci show pleiotropic effects on behavior. The mutation $A \to a$ causes the animals to become more "tame." Mutation to "stub" causes a greater inclination to fight. The mutation $B \to b$ makes the animals less aggressive, although they will fight well when attacked. Mutations at the c-locus do not seem to influence any behavior traits. (2) Furthermore, different inbred strains of mammals are distinguished not only by morphological characters but also by their behavior. This has been shown by Scott (1942) for several behavior characters in the mouse, of which the fighting behavior of the males has been particularly studied. Further differences in behavioral characters between different inbred mouse strains have been described by Fredericson (1953) and Thompson (1953, 1956). The behavioral differences between different breeds of dogs have been recently studied (Scott and

Charles, 1953; Fuller and Scott, 1954; Scott, 1954; Fuller, 1955).
In this case differences in timidity, aggressiveness, friendliness toward humans, response to food rewards, and performance in certain tests have been demonstrated. Sawin and Crary (1953) observed differences in nest-building activities and care of the young
between different strains of rabbits. (3) Finally, it has been shown
repeatedly that it is possible, in genetically nonuniform material,
to select for certain behavior traits. This has been done by Tryon
(1940, 1942) for "maze-learning ability" in the rat, by Hall (1951)
for "emotionality" in the rat as indicated by his defecation test,
by Rundquist (1933) for the amount of motor activity as recorded
in a revolving cage. In all cases, positive and negative selection
was successful.]

All these lines of evidence indicate that behavior characteristics
in mammals are under the control of genes. Tryon (1942), as
well as David and Snyder (1951), suggested on the basis of the
selection experiments that the genetic basis of the behavioral
characteristics studied is probably polygenic. The findings of
Keeler and King (1942) that individual genes may have pleiotropic
effects affecting behavioral characters would be in agreement with
this assumption. Scott and Fredericson (1951) point out that behavioral effects observed in Keeler and King's experiments may
not be pleiotropic effects of the mutated genes, since the fact that
their strains were only partially inbred leaves open the possibility
of selection for other genes. This difficulty is inherent in all experiments on pleiotropic gene action, and can be overcome only
by studying several independent mutations at the same locus on
the same genetic background (Dobzhansky and Holz, 1943). Scott
and Fredericson (1951), on the basis of older literature, come to
the identical conclusion that most behavioral differences between
strains of mammals are based on multiple factor inheritance. The
same conclusion is drawn by Scott (1954) for the behavior differences between breeds of dogs.

An attempt has been made to determine the number of genes
involved in the behavior differences between different strains by
means of crossing experiments. In all cases where an estimate
was possible, the number responsible for a strain difference in
one particular character was found to be low. Dawson (1932)
studied wildness and tameness in wild and inbred strains of mice,
and found in crosses that the number of genes responsible for

the difference is probably about three. Scott (1954), in analyzing
different behavior traits in two breeds of dogs, found the differences to be based on one or two segregating pairs of genes (these
are minimum estimates).

The selection experiments of Tryon (1940, 1942), Rundquist
(1933), Brody (1942), and Hall (1951) have to be interpreted
in the light of selection experiments on polygenic characters. Careful selection experiments on such characters in animals as bristle
number in *Drosophila* (Mather and Harrison, 1949; Rasmuson,
1955), wing and thorax size in *Drosophila* (Robertson and Reeve,
1952a; Reeve and Robertson, 1953), and body size in the mouse
(MacArthur, 1949; Falconer, 1953) have shown that the results
of selection may be rather complex. The fundamental theory is
based on multifactorial inheritance: numerous genes acting on
the character are gradually selected out and become homozygous.
In this process the variability due to segregation should decrease,
and a final extreme level of homozygosity should be reached which
can be broken only by mutations. Mather (1943) has pointed out
that in the case of characters which are variable under natural
conditions progress will be slow and interrupted by periods of
relative stability, since maximum effect would involve the breaking up of linked coadapted gene complexes.

In the actual experiments, several complicating factors have
been observed. Response to selection in opposite directions is
frequently not equal in strength and speed, but asymmetrical.
Progress in selection is almost always erratic, showing fluctuations
from generation to generation. During the progress of selection,
the variability may decrease or increase, so that the final state
may show a higher variance than the unselected controls (Robertson and Reeve, 1952a). The reasons for this increase in variance
may be different: in some cases, at least, the variability under the
influence of environmental factors may be increased in homozygotes as compared with heterozygotes (Robertson and Reeve,
1952b; Lerner, 1954; Grüneberg, 1954). This has been interpreted
as a special case of heterosis. The superiority of the heterozygote
expresses itself by a better buffering, a higher homeostasis, of the
developmental processes; environmental conditions will therefore
be less effective in the heterozygote in inducing phenotypic
variability. In other cases, genetically unstable states may be produced by selection (Reeve and Robertson, 1953). In these cases

variability increases under the influence of selection and stays high as long as rigorous selection is practiced. Relaxation of selection pressure leads to a decrease in variance. This unstable genetic equilibrium is explained by the presence in the strain of homozygous lethal genes which affect the selected character in the heterozygous state, and by the effect of genes showing heterosis, i.e. a higher effect in the heterozygote than in either homozygote. In either case, a heterozygous state which is genetically unstable would be kept in the line by the process of selection.

In view of such results obtained with morphological characters, it would be expected that in different selection experiments involving behavioral characters different results would be obtained. In all experiments described, selection in both directions has been successful.

Both in Hall's and in Rundquist's experiments the effect of selection was asymmetrical, with respect to the maximum effect as well as to the number of generations in which it was reached. In some selected lines the values obtained were pretty constant from generation to generation, while in others great fluctuations between generations were observed. The variability was reduced in the progress of selection in Hall's experiment, but it remained high or was possibly increased in Rundquist's and Brody's highly active line. That variability for a behavior character may be increased as a result of inbreeding is suggested by the high variability of the tame laboratory strains used in Dawson's (1932) experiment as compared with the lower variance of the presumably genetically much more heterogeneous captured wild mice used in the same experiments.

An unexpected effect has been found in some crosses between selected strains. Tryon (1942) describes F_1 and F_2 from his "maze-bright" and "maze-dull" strains. It was found that the F_1 was intermediate, as expected, but the variability increased tremendously, and did not further increase in F_2. Hall (1951) interpreted Tryon's findings on the basis of the fact that several independent substrains were developed, and all of them pooled in the F_1. But Hall's own F_1 data for "emotionality" published in the same paper show a high value of standard deviation in F_1 as compared with the parental strains. Similarly, Scott (1954) found an increase in variance with respect to aggressiveness in the F_1 from two breeds of dogs. This effect was not found for a number of other behavior traits observed in the same experiments. A crossing experiment, carried out by Brody (1942) using Rundquist's strains selected for high and low spontaneous motor activity, suggests a similar interpretation. The means for the activity character in Brody's data are what would be expected, F_1 and F_2 are intermediate, the backcrosses tend to resemble the strains to which the backcross has been made. The variance in F_2 is not increased over F_1, just as in Tryon's experiment. There is a striking difference between the sexes in Brody's data: in all crosses, F_1 and F_2 and the backcrosses, the average activity of the females is higher than that of the males. In the original inbred strains there is no great difference between the sexes. In other words, in the crosses an increase in variability occurs, this time as a reaction to the sex of the animal. It should be emphasized that it cannot be concluded from the high variability in F_1 that the strains were "impure" (Hall, 1951) and that therefore no genetic conclusions can be drawn from these experiments. A certain amount of genetic heterogeneity may be assumed to be present in all inbred strains.

The material is not sufficient to establish that, contrary to many morphological characters, behavioral traits in mammals may show an increase in variability in the F_1 from inbred strains; more material bearing on this point is urgently needed. But the experiments which have been carried out point to this possibility. This would constitute a difference from many morphological characters in which, as a result of heterosis, the variability of an F_1 between inbred strains is frequently reduced.

Scott (1954), in discussing the increased variance of the F_1 from his two dog strains with respect to aggressiveness, suggests as an explanation that in this case a physiological threshold affecting this character may be situated close to the center of genetic distribution. If a major source of variability depends on the fact that some animals are situated above the threshold, others below it, a population well outside the region of the threshold will have a relatively small variability, while a population whose distribution contains the threshold close to its center will have an increased variability. Other possibilities to account for a higher variance in an F_1 from two inbred strains exist. Lerner (1954, pp. 48 ff) points to a purely genetic mechanism which would explain a higher variance in F_1, as compared to the inbred strains, involving heterozygosity in at least one of the strains, and certain assumptions concerning the frequencies of the two alleles in the two populations, and their dominance relations. Finally, the possibility exists that in the cases under consideration an increase in variability under environmental conditions may be involved.

The frequent occurrence of a decrease in variance in F_1 for morphological characters or fitness is interpreted as being due to a better buffering of developmental processes in heterozygotes. The term "homeostasis" has been applied to the genetic structure of populations (Lerner, 1954; Dobzhansky and Wallace, 1953; Dobzhansky and Levene, 1955) in order to indicate that the co-adapted gene pool of a population shows the criterion of an integrated system and has the property of self-regulation. Lerner, as well as Dobzhansky and Wallace, and Dobzhansky and Levene, came to the conclusion that heterozygote superiority is probably the main mechanism insuring the homeostatic properties of populations. The forces of selection will therefore favor, in outbreeding organisms, genetic systems in which the heterozygous condition at many loci is superior to either homozygote, insofar as it minimizes the sensitivity of the organisms to the environment.

In higher vertebrates, behavior is characterized by high plasticity. The actual behavior pattern developed by an organism is strongly subject to modification by learning. Since the behavior pattern of an organism is a mechanism leading to adaptation to the environment, high modifiability of some behavioral constituents may result in a greater capacity for learning and adaptation, contributing in this way to the homeostasis of the population. It is quite possible that in higher vertebrates selective pressures favor a high modifiability of some behavioral traits. If this is the case, higher variability of the heterozygotes with respect to some behavioral characters may be another expression of heterozygote superiority. It should be added that an evolutionary interpretation of this type is not opposed to a physiological explanation, such as the threshold concept proposed by Scott (1954). In every phenomenon affecting populations it is legitimate to inquire after its meaning in evolutionary terms as well as after the developmental and physiological mechanisms by which it is produced. The threshold concept provides a possible developmental model by which a higher variance in F_1 could arise. In evolutionary terms, the question would concern the selective mechanisms which may have been responsible for the establishment of a threshold at the center of the distribution.

Tryon originally thought that in his experiments he was selecting for problem-solving ability. Searle (1949) investigated Tryon's
selected strains with psychological methods and came to the conclusion that the difference between the two strains could be better
described as "timidity," the lower learning ability of the "dull"
strain being a consequence of the fact that it is more easily upset
by certain experimental conditions. Such an interpretation has
found ample support in the studies of Scott and Fuller on the behavioral differences between breeds of dogs. It has been repeatedly
emphasized (e.g. Scott and Charles, 1953; Scott, 1954) that the
genetically controlled differences in the behavior of dogs affect
emotional traits such as aggressiveness, timidity, etc., motivational
traits, such as the reactivity of animals to rewards, and peripheral
characters, such as sensory and motor abilities and preferences.
It has furthermore been shown that the physiological concomitants
of emotion, such as changes in the rhythm of the heartbeat, differentiate dog breeds more sharply than external behavior (Scott
and Charles, 1953; Fuller, 1953). On the other hand, there appears
to be no evidence for the genetic transmission of a character which
might be called "mental ability" or "general intellectual organizing ability" (Scott and Charles, 1953; Scott, 1954). Differences in
performance tests could be related to one or more of the simpler
components of behavior mentioned above.

The more complex behavior patterns of higher vertebrates
which enable the organism to adapt to its physical and social
environment are the result of learning. The genes of a dog
breed do not seem to affect directly the ability of the breed to
solve a specific problem, but rather the manner in which different
traits are organized in solving a problem (Fuller, 1955). The
total organization of behavior would be expected to be a complex
system, depending genetically on a large number of coadapted
genes. The fact that in all specific breed differences relatively
few genes have been found to be involved does not contradict
this conclusion. It appears that genes primarily influence individual components of behavior, just as they influence components
of adaptive value. Individual learning leads to the organization
of these components into adaptive patterns. In the evolution of the
higher vertebrates, genetic mechanisms which make possible the
establishment of various patterns of behavior in the same species
seem to have been selected for, leading to a higher plasticity and
potential adaptation to different environmental conditions.

SUMMARY

1. The primary action of genes is highly specific. But all gene substitutions have secondary pleiotropic effects. This is due to the fact that cells and organisms are integrated systems in which any changes will produce secondary consequences. The genes control the "reaction norm" of the organism to the environment.

2. Different characters show different degrees of stability against genetic and environmental influences. Some characters have a high margin of safety and will be influenced by relatively few specific genetic changes. Other characters are less well buffered and may be influenced by the majority of gene substitutions and by environmental factors. Effects on characters of the latter type will occur frequently as pleiotropic effects of gene substitutions. They will usually show the multifactorial or "polygenic" type of inheritance. Among characters of this type are viability, fertility, and other traits of great selective importance.

3. Genes at different loci interact in the production of phenotypic characters. Gene combinations of positive adaptive value are called "coadapted gene systems."

4. The genes in populations of interbreeding organisms may be described as gene pools. The frequency of genes in a gene pool is determined by mutation pressure, selection, breeding structure, and other factors. The variability of populations is restricted by the fact that selection for coadapted gene complexes counteracts mutation pressure and the tendency of gene complexes to be broken up by segregation.

5. Heterozygotes frequently have adaptive values superior to either homozygote. This phenomenon of "heterosis" makes it possible for two alleles to remain in a population, and in this way maintains the genetic variability and adaptability of populations. Heterosis is frequently expressed in a lower phenotypic variability of heterozygotes.

6. In insects numerous cases are known in which behavior is influenced by pleiotropic effects of gene substitutions affecting primarily morphological characters. Effects on mating behavior may be assumed to be particularly important in evolution since changes in mating behavior have powerful selective effects.

7. It is possible for a gene with a certain morphological effect to become established in a population as a result of its pleiotropic

effect on a behavior trait with positive adaptive value. Conversely, a gene influencing a behavior trait may become established in a population because of a favorable adaptive value of another character produced by the same gene. In either case, selection pressure will adjust the remaining genotype so that a coadapted gene system is established.

8. In mammals, behavior traits seem to be under the control of numerous genes. Differences in behavior seem to occur as pleiotropic effects of well-known morphological genes. Different breeds of animals frequently differ in behavioral characters. In heterogenic populations, selection for behavior traits has been successful.

9. It is argued that in the evolution of mammals selection may have favored a higher degree of variability for behavioral traits. The frequently observed high variability of hybrids from crosses of strains differing in behavior traits may be regarded as a particular case of heterosis.

Notes added in proof: While this review was in press, an important paper dealing with the mechanism of genic control of mating behavior appeared: M. Bastock's "A Gene Mutation Which Changes a Behavior Pattern," *Evolution, 10,* 421–39, 1956. This deals with the lower mating activity induced by the gene y (yellow body color) in *Drosophila* males. The gene is found to reduce the strength and duration of a particular part of the courtship activity —vibration of the wings, which, mediated through the antennae, has a stimulating effect on the females. y males therefore are less successful in mating activity. The reduced duration of vibratory movements induced by the gene y is interpreted on the basis of a model which assumes that the sexual excitation of the *Drosophila* male proceeds in a fluctuating manner, and that thresholds determine the occurrence of the different parts of the courtship pattern. If the general strength of the sexual excitation of y males is reduced, the threshold for wing vibration would be exceeded for shorter periods, resulting in a reduced duration of periods of wing vibration. Finally, it is pointed out that the change due to the gene y is similar to the differences found in related *Drosophila* species as described by Spieth in this volume. The possibility is considered that if a gene with an effect on courtship pattern, like y, becomes incorporated into a population the change of behavior pattern might act as a mechanism for sexual isolation and at the same time favor the selection for genes leading to a new pattern of courtship. That selective effects of this kind are possible is indicated by the fact that the original yellow stock from which the *y* gene used in the investigation was obtained contained modifying genes which increase the sexual excitability of the female, so that females of this strain mate with equal frequency with wild-type and yellow males.

A recent contribution by Walter C. Rothenbuhler ("Genetics of a Behavior Difference in Honey Bees." Proceedings X. International Congress of Genetics, Montreal, 1958) presents another interesting case for the selective value of behavior characters in insects. Some strains of bees are resistant to foulbrood, a bacterial disease of the larvae, while other strains are susceptible. This difference appears to be controlled by genes. One mechanism of resistance to foulbrood consists in the removal of all diseased larvae by workers of the resistant strain. Worker bees from a susceptible strain remove only a few of the sick larvae. Two more mechanisms of resistance to foulbrood have been described, both of them apparently controlled by genes: the ability to strain bacterial spores out of the food by means of the intestinal tract, and an actual physiological resistance to the bacteria.

REFERENCES

(Star indicates general background reading.)

BRODY, E. G. 1942. Genetic basis of spontaneous activity in the albino rat. Comp. Psychol. Monogr., *17* (5), 1–24.

CANNON, W. B. 1932. The wisdom of the body. New York, Norton.

CASPARI, E. 1950. On the selective value of the alleles *Rt* and *rt* in *Ephestia kühniella*. Amer. Nat., *84*, 367–80.

CASPARI, E. 1951. On the biological basis of adaptedness. Amer. sci., *39*, 441–51.

CASPARI, E. 1952. Pleiotropic gene action. Evolution, *6*, 1–18.

COTTER, W. B. 1951. The genetic and physiological analysis of the silk-spinning behavior of *Ephestia kühniella Zeller*. M.A. thesis, Wesleyan University.

DAVID, P. R., and SNYDER, L. H. 1951. Genetic variability and human behavior. In J. Rohrer, M. Sherif, eds., Social psychology at the crossroads. New York, Harper, pp. 53–82.

DAWSON, W. M. 1932. Inheritance of wildness and tameness in mice. Genetics, *17*, 296–326.

DEMEREC, M. 1934. Biological action of small deficiencies of X-chromosome of *Drosophila melanogaster*. Proc. Nat. Acad. Sci., *20*, 354–9.

DOBZHANSKY, Th. 1927. Studies on the manifold effects of certain genes in *Drosophila melanogaster*. Z. indukt. Abstamm. u. Vererbungsl. *43*, 330–88.

DOBZHANSKY, Th. 1946. Genetics of

natural populations, XIII. Recombination and variability in populations of *Drosophila pseudoobscura*. Genetics, *31*, 269–90.

DOBZHANSKY, TH. 1949. Observations and experiments on natural selection in Drosophila. Proc. 8th Int. Congr. Genetics, Hereditas, Suppl. Vol. *1949*, 210–24.

* DOBZHANSKY, TH. 1951. Genetics and the origin of species. 3d ed. New York, Columbia Univ. Press.

* DOBZHANSKY, TH. 1955. Evolution, genetics and man. New York, Wiley.

DOBZHANSKY, TH., and HOLZ, A. M. 1943. A re-examination of the problem of manifold effects of genes in *Drosophila melanogaster*. Genetics, *28*, 295–303.

DOBZHANSKY, TH., and LEVENE, H. 1955. Genetics of natural populations, XXIV. Developmental homeostasis in natural populations of *Drosophila pseudoobscura*. Ibid., *40*, 797–808.

DOBZHANSKY, TH., and SPASSKY, B. 1944. Genetics of natural populations, XI. Manifestation of genetic variants in *Drosophila pseudoobscura* in different environments. Ibid., *29*, 270–90.

DOBZHANSKY, TH., and WALLACE, B. 1953. The genetics of homeostasis in Drosophila. Proc. Nat. Acad. Sci., *39*, 162–71.

FALCONER, D. S. 1953. Selection for large and small size in mice. J. Genetics, *51*, 470–501.

FREDERICSON, E. 1953. The wall-seeking tendency in three inbred mouse strains (*Mus musculus*). J. Genet. Psychol., *82*, 143–6.

FULLER, J. L. 1953. Cross-sectional and longitudinal studies of adjustive behavior in dogs. Ann. N. Y. Acad. Sci., *56*, 214–24.

FULLER, J. L. 1955. Hereditary differences in trainability of purebred dogs. J. Genet. Psychol., *87*, 229–38.

FULLER, J. L., and SCOTT, J. P. 1954. Heredity and learning ability in infrahuman mammals. In Genetic factors affecting intelligence. Eugenics Quart., *1*, 28–43.

GOWEN, J. W. 1952. Hybrid vigor in Drosophila. In J. W. Gowen, ed., Heterosis. Ames, Iowa, Iowa State College Press, pp. 474–93.

GRÜNEBERG, H. 1938. An analysis of the "pleiotropic" effects of a new lethal mutation in the rat (*Mus norvegicus*). Proc. Roy. Soc. London, Series B, *125*, 123–44.

GRÜNEBERG, H. 1943. Congenital hydrocephalus in the mouse, a case of spurious pleiotropism. J. Genetics, *45*, 1–21.

GRÜNEBERG, H. 1954. Variation within inbred strains of mice. Nature, *173*, 674–6.

HALL, C. S. 1951. The genetics of behavior. In S. S. Stevens, ed., Handbook of experimental psychology. New York, Wiley, pp. 304–29.

HERON, W. T. 1935. The inheritance of maze learning ability in rats. J. Comp. Psychol., *19*, 77–89.

HOVANITZ, W. 1953. Polymorphism and evolution. In Evolution. Sympos. Soc. Exp. Biol., No. 7. New York, Academic Press, pp. 238–53.

KEELER, C. E., and KING, H. D. 1942. Multiple effects of coat color genes in the rat, with special reference to temperament and domestication. J. Comp. Psychol., *34*, 241–50.

KÜHN, A., and HENKE, K. 1932. Genetische Bedingungen der Entwicklungsgeschwindigkeit und der Vitalität. In A. Kühn and K. Henke, Genetische und entwicklungsphysiologische Untersuchungen an der Mehlmotte *Ephestia kühniella Zeller* No. 11. Abh. Ges. Wiss. Göttingen, Math.-Phys. Klasse, N.F., *15*, 197–211.

KÜHN, A., and VON ENGELHARDT, M. 1937. Über eine melanistische Mutation von *Ptychopoda seriata* Schrk. (at+→At) und die Abhängigkeit der at+ und At zugeordneten Merkmale von Aussenbedingungen. Biol. Zentralbl., *57*, 329–47.

*LERNER, I. M. 1950. Population genetics and animal improvement. Cambridge, Eng., Cambridge Univ. Press.

*LERNER, I. M. 1954. Genetic homeostasis. New York, Wiley.

*LI, C. C. 1955. Population genetics. Chicago, Chicago Univ. Press.

MACARTHUR, J. W. 1949. Selection for small and large body size in the house mouse. Genetics, *34*, 194–209.

MATHER, K. 1943. Polygenic inheritance and natural selection. Biol. Rev., *18*, 32–64.

MATHER, K. 1949. Biometrical genetics. London, Methuen.

MATHER, K. 1954. The genetical units of continuous variation. Proc. 9th Int. Congr. Genetics, Caryologia 6, Suppl., Pt. I, pp. 106–23.

MATHER, K., and HARRISON, B. J. 1949. The manifold effect of selection. Heredity, *3*, 1–52, and 131–62.

*MAYR, E. 1942. Systematics and the origin of species. New York, Columbia Univ. Press.

MERRELL, D. J. 1949. Selective mating in *Drosophila melanogaster*. Genetics, *34*, 370–89.

MERRELL, D. J. 1953. Selective mating as a cause of gene frequency changes in laboratory populations of *Drosophila melanogaster*. Evolution, 7, 287–96.

RASMUSON, M. 1955. Selection for bristle numbers in some unrelated strains of *Drosophila melanogaster*. Acta Zoologica, *36*, 1–49.

REED, S.C., and REED, E. W. 1950. Natural selection in laboratory populations of Drosophila. II. Competition between a white-eye gene and its wild type allele. Evolution, *4*, 34–42.

REEVE, E. C. R., and ROBERTSON, F. W. 1953. Studies in quantitative inheritance. II. Analysis of a strain of *Drosophila melanogaster* selected for long wings. J. Genetics, *51*, 276–316.

RENDEL, J. M. 1951. Mating of ebony, vestigial and wild type *Drosophila melanogaster* in light and dark. Evolution, *5*, 226–30.

ROBERTSON, F. W., and REEVE, E. C. R. 1952a. Studies in quantitative inheritance. I. The effects of selection on wing and thorax length in *Drosophila melanogaster*. J. Genetics, *50*, 414–48.

ROBERTSON, F. W., and REEVE, E. C. R. 1952b. Heterozygosity, environmental variation and heterosis. Nature, *170*, 286.

RUNDQUIST, E. A. 1933. Inheritance of spontaneous activity in rats. J. Comp. Psychol., *16*, 415–38.

SAWIN, P. B., and CRARY, D. D. 1953. Genetic and physiological background of reproduction in the rabbit. II. Some racial differences in the pattern of maternal behavior. Behaviour, *6*, 128–46.

SCOTT, J. P. 1942. Genetic differences in the social behavior of inbred strains of mice. J. Hered., *33*, 11–15.

SCOTT, J. P. 1943. Effects of single genes on the behavior of Drosophila. Amer. Nat., *77*, 184–90.

SCOTT, J. P. 1954. The effects of selection and domestication upon the behavior of the dog. In E. S. Russell, ed., Symposium on 25 years of progress in mammalian genetics and cancer. J. Nat. Cancer Inst., *15*, 739–58.

SCOTT, J. P. and CHARLES, M. S. 1953. Some problems of heredity and social behavior. J. Gen. Psychol., *48*, 209–30.

SCOTT, J. P., and FREDERICSON, E. 1951. The causes of fighting in mice and rats. Physiol. Zool., *24*, 273–309.

SEARLE, L. V. 1949. The organization of hereditary maze-brightness and maze-dullness. Genetic Psychol. Monogr., *39*, 279–325.

SHEPPARD, P. M. 1953. Polymorphism and population studies. In Evolution. Sympos. Soc. Exp. Biol., No. 7. New York, Academic Press, pp. 274–89.

*SINNOTT, E. W., DUNN, L. C. and DOBZHANSKY, TH. 1950. Principles of genetics. 4th ed. New York, McGraw-Hill.

*SNYDER, L. H. and DAVID, P. R. 1957. The principles of heredity. 5th ed. Boston, D. C. Heath.

*SRB, A. M. and OWEN, R. D. 1952. General genetics. San Francisco, W. H. Freeman.

*STERN, C. 1949. Principles of human genetics. San Francisco, W. H. Freeman.

THOMPSON, W. R. 1953. The inheritance of behavior; behavioral differences in fifteen mouse strains. Canad. J. Psychol., *7*, 145–53.

THOMPSON, W. R. 1956. The inheritance of behavior. Activity differences in five inbred mouse strains. J. Hered., *47*, 147–8.

TIMOFÉEFF-RESSOVSKY, N. W. 1934. Über die Vitalität einiger Genmutationen und ihrer Kombinationen bei *Drosophila funebris* und ihre Abhängigkeit vom "genotypischen" und vom äusseren Milieu. Z. indukt Abstamm. u. Vererbungsl., *66*, 319–44.

TRYON, R. C. 1940. Genetic differences in maze-learning in rats. In 39th Yearbook, Nat. Soc. for the Study of Educ. Bloomington, Ill.; Public School Publ., Pt. I, pp. 111–19.

TRYON, R. C. 1942. Individual differences. In F. A. Moss, ed., Comparative psychology. New York, Prentice-Hall, pp. 330–65.

WADDINGTON, C. H., WOOLF, B., and PERRY, M. M. 1954. Environment selection by Drosophila mutants. Evolution, *8*, 89–96.

*WHITE, M. J. D. 1954. Animal cytology and evolution. 2d ed. Cambridge, Eng., Cambridge Univ. Press.

WRIGHT, S. 1931. Evolution in Mendelian populations. Genetics, *16*, 97–159.

WRIGHT, S. 1948. On the roles of directed and random changes in gene frequency in the genetics of populations. Evolution, *2*, 279–94.

6

Developmental Basis of Behavior

R. W. Sperry

CALIFORNIA INSTITUTE OF TECHNOLOGY

MOST GENETIC mutations that effect an evolutionary change in adult characters, behavioral or morphologic, do so indirectly by affecting the process of development. Evolutionary change must in a sense be funneled through the developmental mechanisms. In many cases it may be these latter, rather than chromosomal plasticity or selection pressures on the adult character, that constitute the limiting conditions in evolution and determine the direction in which it moves. Given two possible character changes of equal functional survival value, one achieved easily in terms of developmental adjustments, the other involving radical revisions of the growth pattern, it is the former that will be favored. Many evolutionary possibilities that would be entirely feasible so far as survival value and genetic mutability are concerned can never be realized because they could not be achieved within the established framework of embryonic development. Many aspects of evolution are better understood with some consideration for the developmental processes through which, and in terms of which, the genetic mutations must operate.

From the developmental standpoint it is helpful to think of the evolution of behavior in terms of the evolution of the morphological structures that mediate the behavior. The term "structure" may be used here in its broadest sense to include all stable organization patterns of organs and tissues, even at submicroscopic and molecular levels. The inheritance of a behavior pattern then implies the inheritance of certain modifications of the behavioral apparatus responsible for the behavior. The distinction between behavioral and morphological in inherited characters is hardly a basic one from the viewpoint of development. Accordingly, the present discussion will be concerned largely with development of the inherited morphological substrate of behavior, primarily that of the sensorineuromotor apparatus, with special emphasis on the patterning of interneuronal connections in the central nervous system. The subject will be treated not entirely from the perspectives of embryology, but with reference more to the problem of effecting evolutionary change in developmental mechanics.

Generally speaking, gene action during development may and most commonly does occur at many removes from the observed character effect. According to one current theory, gene changes within the nucleus lead to changes in cytoplasmic RNA (ribonucleic acid), which in turn modify protein synthesis, thereby producing alterations in enzyme activity, with consequent effects on cell metabolism and cell differentiation (Horowitz and Fling, 1956). These, in turn, modify organ and tissue development to determine ultimately the observed character change. In view of the numerous levels of organization involved in this chain of events, ranging from that of the gene unit up to the level of the adult nervous, circulatory, and hormonal systems; and in view of the numerous types of potential interaction within and among all these various levels of organization, the possible patterns of causal sequence by which a gene mutation may affect a change in behavior are, for practical purposes, almost infinitely varied. Some inherited characters like pigmentation, enzymatic properties, and inherent immunologic specificity may reflect the genetic mutation rather directly. Behavioral traits on the other hand appear to be at the other extreme where the sequence of developmental events between gene change and behavioral change is a long and devious one and one that, at the present state of our knowledge, can be discussed for the most part only in broad generalities.

It should be recognized at the outset that much remains to be learned with respect to the old problem of the extent to which behavior mechanisms are a product of inheritance on the one hand and of learning and experience on the other. Since the learned and the inherited elements in behavior are frequently present together as inseparable cofunctions, it is difficult or impossible in many cases to evaluate the relative extent and significance of the separate factors. This is particularly true when there is a long period of neural growth and maturation during which learning is also taking place, as in man. However, if we consider the problem with reference strictly to the anatomy, physiology, and growth of the apparatus of behavior, there are some inferences that may be drawn with respect to the vertebrate nervous system in general.

The entire nervous structure, including all the fiber circuit organization demonstrable by the methods of neuroanatomy, is, by and large, a product of growth and inheritance, not of learning. To this anatomically demonstrable structure we must add the mechanisms underlying much organization that is demonstrable only by physiological and behavioral methods. Included here would be all or nearly all the functional organization of the brain stem and spinal cord. Much of the functional organization of the cerebral hemispheres must also be included even in man. For example, all the effects produced by stimulation of the primary sensory and motor areas of the cortex along with other similar effects that are species-constant must be included with the inherited bases of behavior.

Approaching the question from the other direction, one may say that the entire neural apparatus is organized through the forces of growth and inheritance except for the as-yet-undemonstrated memory traces or engrams. Whatever the neural changes of learning and memory may be, they are extremely elusive and inconspicuous and have yet to be demonstrated in any direct manner. Presumably they are infused into or are superimposed upon the more out-of-the-way neural circuits, particularly in the mammalian cerebral cortex. Although the experientially produced mutations in the neural apparatus may make a large and important difference at the behavioral level, they appear to be only a minute fraction of the total neural organization from the anatomical and developmental standpoint. It seems probable that the underlying inherited portion of the neural mechanism involved even in so-called "learned" behavior may be not only more conspicuous but also much more complex in its organization, anatomically and physiologically speaking, than is the superimposed experiential portion of the structure.

The foregoing represents a radical change from earlier views which had pictured the functional patterning of neural circuits as being achieved almost entirely through training and experience (Holt, 1931). Prior to the late 'thirties it was supposed that the outgrowing nerve fibers established their connections in a haphazard, diffuse, and excessive fashion in development tending to form initially an equipotential homogeneous network out of which adaptive pathways were subsequently channeled by means of function. A related view pictured the initial tendency to form excessive central connections as being functionally controlled, the fiber connections that happened to prove adaptive being reinforced and maintained, the nonadaptive ones being eliminated through disuse atrophy, and degeneration. This functional molding of the neural circuits was presumed to begin at the first evidence of neuromotor activity and to continue in the mammal through fetal life into postnatal learning. Common reference was made to the training of the sensory surfaces such as the cutaneous and retinal fields, the macula of the utriculus, the proprioceptors of posture and movement and the like.

Today we think the developing nerve fibers establish their synaptic associations in a highly specific manner from the very beginning. The outgrowing fibers of the developing neuroblasts are believed to form well-organized reflex and integrative patterns that are functionally adaptive from the start but which nevertheless are patterned directly in the growth process. This change in the picture of nervous development is supported by an extended series of observations in which surgical disarrangement of the adult and developing nervous system in many different vertebrates has been found to produce corresponding dysfunctions that persist in machine-like fashion uncorrected by experience (Sperry, 1945; Weiss, 1941). The more recent findings along this line have contradicted earlier reports which had indicated that the vertebrate nervous system was highly plastic in this respect. More direct support for the current concepts derives from investigations dealing with the formation of synaptic connections during nerve regeneration and development. These latter show the normal patterning of synaptic relations to be predetermined in the growth process irrespective of the functional effects for the individual.

The patterning of refined and precisely adapted behavioral patterns has been shown in these studies to be developmentally controlled, and in some cases the experiments yield information about the nature of the growth forces involved. These will be considered later. In general the developmental mechanisms, as we now picture them, appear to be of sufficient specificity and elaboration that one need not hesitate, on the basis of complexity alone, to ascribe to inheritance any behavior pattern found among subhuman vertebrates. One gets the impression that no vertebrate behavior pattern, excepting perhaps language and certain other of the more complicated human activities, is too complex to be built into the nervous system so far as the proficiency of the developmental and genetic mechanisms is concerned. Where the behavior pattern is acquired by learning instead of being handled through inheritance, one may assume this to be a result of other factors rather than a limitation in developmental capacity. These changes in neuroembryological theory have profound implications for the evolution of behavior and for all concepts relating to the role of inheritance in behavior.

Inherited behavioral changes in the nervous system are presumably traceable to changes in the size, number, connectivity, and excitatory properties of the nerve cells. Actually changes in neuron size and number gain their functional effects mostly through secondary influences upon connectivity and excitatory threshold. Our problem centers therefore around the developmental mechanisms responsible for the establishment of excitatory thresholds in nerve cells and for the patterning of their fiber connections. To review here all the known information relating to these matters would be impossible. Extensive descriptions of the gross and microscopic morphogenesis of the nervous system may be found in the textbooks of neurology and embryology. In particular, reference should be made to the expanding literature on experimental analysis of the underlying developmental forces in ontogeny (Willier, Weiss, and Hamburger, 1955).

The resting excitatory threshold and also the interconnections of neurons appear both to depend largely upon specific cell properties attained through gradual differentiation of the nerve cells in development. The process of embryonic cell differentiation, after it has succeeded in setting off future nerve cells from those of muscle, bone, and other tissues, continues to effect differentiation within the nerve cell population itself. As a result the different classes and types of neurons become intrinsically different from one another in constitution. In some parts of the nervous system the process of differentiation continues almost to the point where the individual neurons differ from one another in quality. The resting excitatory threshold characteristic of the different neuron types would seem to be an important factor in neural integration. That it is determined through the differentiation process would seem a safe assumption. However, for lack of evidence there is little more that one can say about the threshold factor at present.

Much more information is available with respect to the role of connectivity in neural function and the developmental forces responsible for the patterning of neuronal interconnection. According to classical neurophysiology the differential fiber connections among nerve cells are of paramount importance and the basis of functional organization. Various other concepts of central nervous integration have been proposed, such as those based on mass electric fields, specific nerve energies, frequency effects, and resonance phenomena. None of these has received sufficient support to warrant its replacing the conventional connectivity doctrine as a basis for our present discussion. Furthermore numerous illustrations of the dysfunction produced by surgical disarrangement of the normal nerve connections have given convincing demonstration of the direct dependence of neural integration upon selective specificity in neuronal connections.

The establishment in development of the proper synaptic connections for any given nerve cell must typically depend upon a host of factors, direct and indirect, including proper timing of the developmental sequence. It would be impossible to consider the whole picture here, and the reader is referred again to the textbooks on descriptive and experimental embryology. The present discussion is limited to brief mention of some of the factors that appear to be most directly responsible for regulating the formation of proper synaptic relations.

These are best illustrated by reference to a concrete example such as the genesis of cutaneous local sign. For the accurate localization of points on the body surface it is necessary that the central reflex relations of the cutaneous fibers match accurately their peripheral connections. When this is not the case, as after the misdirection of regenerating cutaneous fibers into foreign skin, the result is a corresponding false reference of sensation. In a sense, accurate localization requires that the central connections of the cutaneous fibers reflect in an orderly way the entire map of the body surface. Anatomically it is well established that the topography of the body surface is mapped on the various sensory relay stations of the CNS, i.e. the gracilis and cuneate nuclei, the ventral nucleus of the thalamus, the postcentral gyrus of the cerebral cortex, and also on the cerebellar cortex.

The way in which the orderly anatomical arrangement of this cutaneous system is achieved in development has been investigated to a small extent (Miner, 1951; Sperry, 1954) and would seem to be something as follows: An initial outgrowth of cutaneous fibers into the skin leads to terminal connections that are largely random within each dermatome. The integument meantime undergoes an early field-type differentiation that sets off dorsal from ventral skin and head from tail skin. This is believed to be achieved through the establishment of two embryonic gradients of differentiation, an anteroposterior and a dorsoventral gradient, laid down at right angles to each other. As a result of these two axes of differentiation, each cutaneous spot on the body surface becomes marked by a combination of two gradients giving it a latitude and longitude, so to speak, that is unique for each individual spot on each side of the body.

Experiments have shown that the local topographic specificity of the integument becomes impressed in some form upon the cutaneous fibers through their terminal contacts. The specificity stamped on the terminals of the cutaneous fibers then spreads throughout the extent of the nerve cell. In the case of the sensory neurons of the hind limb, for example, this means a spread centrally into the lumbar dorsal root ganglia and along the dorsal roots into the cord. Within the cord the qualitative specificity spreads along the posterior columns for long distances, particularly rostrally where many fibers extend all the way to the nucleus glacilis at the base of the medulla. Within the latter nucleus and at all segmental levels along the cord, the specificity factor must spread also into the fine collateral fibers that arborize within the gray matter to form synaptic connections with the second order sensory neurons.

The local sign specificity that is stamped upon the cutaneous fibers at the periphery and is spread thus centrally into all the growing tips of the finest central collaterals is presumed to determine the type of second order neurons which the growing tips will find acceptable for synapsis. This inference implies the existence of a similarly refined qualitative specificity among the central neurons. Presumably the cutaneous centers of the medulla, thalamus, and cortex undergo self-differentiation, in such a way that the qualitative properties of the neurons become distributed in an orderly pattern with reference to the dermatomes of the body.

Fibers from one nucleus growing into the next higher center presumably have selective tendencies to establish synaptic linkages in the proper part of the nucleus or cortical area into which they grow. Mechanical and other developmental forces are also involved all along the way, particularly in guiding the fibers from one central station to the next.

The foregoing example includes several principles that appear to have rather general applicability, namely: the initial self-differentiation of the end organ, the induction of local specificity in the peripheral nerves through terminal contact with the end organ, the self-differentiation of central neurons, and the regulation of synaptic formation on the basis of specific chemical affinities between the various types of differentiated neurons. Perhaps the central concept here from the standpoint of evolution is that the inherent neuronal connectivity is determined through specific chemical affinities between the different classes of neurons and that these affinities arise out of processes of cell differentiation which are controlled ultimately through gene action. The fact that the particular patterns of chemical affinity that happen to arise in development are just the ones needed to produce circuit connections that are functionally adaptive is attributable to evolutionary selection and related factors in the same manner as is the adaptability of all developmental processes.

The interneuronal affinities are not simple one-to-one relations. Muscle proprioceptive fibers, for example, establish excitatory synaptic relations with the motorneurons of their own muscles and with a variety of internuncials leading to synergic muscles and apparently also inhibitory synapses leading to antagonistic muscles (Lloyd, 1955). In addition the proprioceptors establish connections leading into the ascending cerebellar tracts and into the dorsal columns. It would seem to be the rule rather than the exception that neurons have affinities for a variety of other neuron types. It is not inconceivable that the synaptic predispositions shown by a given fiber may be conditioned by its surroundings and may thus differ as the elongating fiber enters different regions of the central nervous system. These predispositions might differ also with time as the neuron goes through successive phases of maturation. In any case there would appear to be little or no limit to the complexity of neuronal interconnections possible in principle with this kind of scheme.

Many, but not all, behavioral changes in evolution are accompanied by correlated changes in the nonneural sensory and motor apparatus. Often the modifications in the peripheral apparatus are just as critical or more so than those in the central nervous system. Actually one could take almost any phase of development and show it to be important for behavior. The embryonic determination of such things as length of limb bones, size and strength of flight muscles, size and efficiency of endocrine glands, curvature of cornea and lens, even oxygen capacity of hemoglobin, and so on, can all be shown to have more or less direct influence on behavior and its survival value.

In regard to the question of which evolves first, the central nervous behavior pattern or the peripheral apparatus with which to carry it out, it must be a hen-egg type of relationship for the most part with concomitant development of both being necessary. However, from the standpoint of development, the central nervous patterns would seem to be the more difficult to evolve and therefore to constitute more of a limiting factor in evolutionary change. This is not necessarily true of the simpler neural changes that involve only the primary sensory and motor pathways or isolated central nuclei and affect merely numbers of neurons and/or their thresholds. It applies mainly to higher level integrative mechanisms involving complex and widespread interneuronal connections.

The course of cell differentiation in ontogeny may be visualized in a dendritic pattern like the evolution of species in phylogeny. It is then apparent that a developmental change that affects only one or a few closely related terminal twigs in the ontogenetic tree should be easier to initiate and to establish than one which requires coordinated changes in many widely separated branches. Apparently "simple" morphologic changes frequently depend upon numerous integrated alterations of the development process. In the case of a complex pattern of central nervous integration the complications are multiplied manyfold. The evolution of a complex instinctive behavior pattern such as that of nest building, for example, must involve a scattered array of adjustments in many areas of the brain. These could not all spring full blown from a single gene mutation. Changes in one nucleus must be made with reference to those in other nuclei. The whole central nervous pattern must therefore be put together step by step in the course of evolution, each genetic change being made in terms of and with reference to all the others.

With regard to the interrelation of genetic mutations in effecting a coordinated pattern of morphologic change, it should be remembered that genes tend to control development through processes that already are intrinsically adaptive by nature. For example, the fact that eye size is right for orbit size in any species is not achieved by separate genetic control of the absolute size of each. It can be shown that the orbit will adjust itself through a considerable range to fit the sizes of eyes transplanted from other species (Twitty, 1932). This kind of thing occurs all through development. An enlargement of the eye and optic nerve will tend to produce a corresponding enlargement of the optic lobe in the midbrain through the stimulating effect of optic fiber ingrowth upon optic lobe development (Kollros, 1953). The sensory and motor nuclei in general tend to adjust in size to changes in the size of the peripheral load they come to innervate.

Many new developmental problems are associated with the evolution of learning capacity. Since the neural basis of learning is still unknown, there is little that can be said about the developmental processes by which it is installed in the brain. Perhaps it is a matter of increasing the number of association neurons; perhaps of increasing the number of fiber connections per neuron; or perhaps primarily of increasing some type of cytoplasmic plasticity in the nerve cells—or perhaps it is none of these, or that a combination of several such factors with others is required.

Where a given behavior pattern could be organized in development either by learning or by inheritance, one would expect, other things equal, that learning would be favored because it is more plastic and adaptable and therefore should have greater survival value. This would not apply to that background of neural organization that exists as a common denominator invariant in the behavior of all members of a species. The centering reactions of the optic system and the oculogyric reflexes might be examples. There would be no survival value in relegating the development of such to the sphere of learning since there normally is no call for adaptive alterations in these circuits. On the other hand, it is conceivable that, once the learning capacity of a species were sufficiently evolved, it might be easier and more economical from the standpoint of developmental mechanics to drop the genetic support in time and gradually turn the organization task over to learning.

One might infer further that with a sufficiently increased learning capacity all inherent organization could be dropped and all behavioral organization be assigned to the learning process. If it is true, and it seems highly probable, that a rather elaborate and precisely designed neural mechanism is a prerequisite for learning, then the foregoing would be logically impossible. An organized background of neural organization has to be installed in advance by genetically controlled forces before new adaptive behavior patterns can be selected and nonadaptive ones eliminated by process of learning.

Generally speaking, however, it is to be expected that, once the learning capacity has evolved to a certain degree as in the higher primates, further evolution will tend to take the form of increased development of learning capacity rather than of further elaboration of instinctive behavior patterns. This would hold until learning and its effects became so powerful (as in human society) that physiological survival value no longer figures as an important limiting factor. At this point entirely new man-made principles of evolution appear and anything can happen.

For something like imprinting to occur, an elaborate preparation must be made through purely innate developmental mechanisms. Some brains are inherently so organized in growth that imprinting can occur; others are not. The capacity for imprinting must evolve through developmental mechanics just as do fully structured instincts.

The developmental basis of behavior becomes particularly complicated where the normal development or maturation process overlaps early learning. Under these conditions the effects of learning and maturation may be combined in many forms. Furthermore function may also be important as a general nonspecific factor that prevents atrophy from lack of use.

In the evolution of social behavior additional orders of complexity enter the picture in that the evolution of behavior patterns in each sex, caste, or other subgroup have to wait on the concurrently evolving behavior of other members of the group. Although this may not add new problems from a strictly developmental viewpoint, it does multiply those mentioned.

REFERENCES

(Star indicates general background reference.)

HOLT, E. B. 1931. Animal drive and the learning process. New York, Holt.

HOROWITZ, N. H., and FLING, MAR- GUERITE 1956. The role of the genes in the synthesis of enzymes. In O. H. GAEBLER, ed., Enzymes: units of bi- ological structure and function. New York, Academic Press, pp. 139–46.

KOLLROS, J. J. 1953. The development of the optic lobes in the frog. I. The effects of unilateral enucleation in embryonic stages. J. Exp. Zool., *123*, 153–88.

LLOYD, D. P. C. 1955. Principles of spinal reflex activity. In J. F. Fulton, Textbook of physiology. Philadelphia, W. B. Saunders, pp. 91–121.

MINER, N. M. 1951. Integumental specifi- cation of sensory neurons in the genesis of cutaneous local sign. Ph.D. thesis, Univ. of Chicago.

SPERRY, R. W. 1945. The problem of central nervous reorganization after nerve regeneration and muscle trans- position. Quart. Rev. Biol., *20*, 311– 69.

SPERRY, R. W. 1951a. Mechanisms of neural maturation. In S. S. Stevens, ed., Handbook of experimental psy- chology. New York, Wiley, pp. 236– 80.

SPERRY, R. W. 1951b. Regulative factors in the orderly growth of neural cir- cuits. Growth Sympos., *10*, 63–87.

SPERRY, R. W. 1954. Problems in the biochemical specification of neurons. In H. Waelsch, ed., Biochemistry of the developing nervous system. New York, Academic Press, pp. 74–84.

SPERRY, R. W., and MINER, N. M. 1949. Formation within sensory nucleus V of synaptic associations mediating cuta- neous localization. J. Comp. Neurol., *90*, 403–24.

TWITTY, V. C. 1932. Influence of eye growth on its associated structures, studied by means of heteroplastic transplantation. J. Exp. Zool., *61*, 333– 74.

WEISS, P. A. 1941. Self-differentiation of the basic patterns of coordination. Comp. Psychol. Monogr., *17*, 1–96.

*WILLIER, B. H., WEISS, P. A., and HAM- BURGER, V. 1955. Analysis of develop- ment. Philadelphia, W. B. Saunders.

7

Comparative Neurology and the Evolution of Behavior *

Karl Pribram

INSTITUTE OF LIVING

The rules established for localization of function in the brain can best be demonstrated by example. The first structure, which naturally belongs amongst the most important, is the structure dealing with sexual activity, i.e. reproductive functions. The following evidence attests to the proposition that these functions are served by one particular part of the brain: It is larger in those species possessed with greater sexual vigour; it is larger in males than in females (a corollary of the fact that activity is cyclic in the female); after castration or in old age, the structure becomes smaller as the skull increases in thickness. Additional evidence comes from clinical cases where priapism and satyriasis are frequently observed in patients with cervical pathology. The author knew a man in Vienna whose sexual activities were remarkable. This man was so uninhibited and insatiable that he must have six women, one after the other, to satisfy him. Postmortem, this man's cerebellum was found tremendously enlarged. (Gall, 1807, translated and paraphrased.)

So far as the functions of the gyrus cinguli are concerned, experimental evidence is scant, owing to the inaccessibility of this region. I have noted ("The Brain of Helen H. Gardener, Alice Chenoweth Day," *Amer. Jour. Phys. Anthropol.*, 11; 29–79, 1927) that in the two sexes the precuneous shows a greater difference in size than any other portion of the cortex, being more highly developed in the male, and it was suggested that representation of the sex organs may be localized there. This difference between the sexes has been confirmed by Mettler in the brain of the monkey. Sensations related to sex matters possess a high degree of emotional coloring—there seems to be ample justification for the ancient view of La Peyronie, professor of surgery at Montpellier, who, on the basis of such clinical experiences expressed the belief that the region of the corpus callosum is the "seat of the soul." (Papez, 1937.)

* The author is deeply indebted to Professor Jerzy Rose for his guidance of the anatomical studies reported. This in no way indicates, however, that Professor Rose is (or for that matter is *not*) committed to the *ideas* expressed. Discussions with Dr. Lawrence Kruger, who kindly furnished some of the illustrations used, have also been helpful—again, I take full responsibility for the views expressed.

IT IS NOT too surprising that recently an eminent student of the nervous system stated his disappointment with the contribution made by the comparative method to an understanding of cerebral function (Bailey, 1949). On the other hand, formulations such as those which propose the neural correlates of emotion on the basis of comparative anatomical material continue to excite the interest necessary to spawn experiments (Herrick, 1948; Papez, 1937; Mac-Lean, 1949). Which of these rather diverse approaches most appropriately indicates what we might expect comparative neurology to contribute to the understanding of the evolution of behavior? My answer, to be developed by example, lies somewhere between these extremes: I believe that precise comparative data, carefully analyzed, can lead to testable hypotheses concerning the *taxonomy* of behavior; that by observation and experiment such hypotheses can then be tested and the resulting data systematized. These systematic taxonomic schemes then serve as a base for further hypotheses—both at the neural and at the behavioral level—and the observation-experiment-systematization cycle repeated. This approach provides the flexibility which is lacking in *systems of hypotheses* (implicit or explicit) and avoids the nihilism of disappointment resulting from the collapse of such systems when they become sufficiently awkward under the impact of new data.

This approach is not without difficulties, however. As an example of the pitfalls posed, I can tell a story on myself. A specific behavior pattern can be mediated by different neural mechanisms in different species. In studying the functions of the so-called silent areas of the primate cerebral cortex, two behavioral tests have proved especially valuable: the choice reaction, in which an animal chooses one of two *disparate* objects in order to receive a reward, and the delayed reaction, in which the rewarded choice is between *like* objects which are differentiated by some prior signal. Failure to perform these tasks had provided a reliable index of damage to two circumscribed portions of the primate cerebral mantle (the anterofrontal and inferotemporal cortex). Since one of these portions (the frontal) has been referred to by the lofty title "the organ of civilization" (Halstead, 1947), it is not too surprising that, in spite of repeated warnings to myself, I had inadvertently come to view such tasks as measures of some especially high and noble functions. Of this delusion I was quickly divested one afternoon when, to my surprise, I watched *pigeons* (Ferster and Skinner, 1957) perform these and many other more complex tasks as well as, and in some respects better than, my primate relatives. And when I saw and heard that even the octopus (Young, 1953) could perform tasks which had been invented to demonstrate that children and animals had ideas, I had to face the fact that, though monkeys deprived of cortical tissue might experience grave difficulties with such tasks, nonmammalian species manage their affairs remarkably well without a cerebral mantle. The descriptive term "encephalization," used to cover these facts, does not help much in elucidating the problems of cerebral function or those of classification of the behavior exemplified by these "choice" tasks. Nor does it temper an overly enthusiastic evaluation of the importance of the particular neural mechanism and of the behavior patterns it serves.

The task of relating the evolution of any given behavior pattern to the development of neural structure is little different from that of relating behavior patterns to other anatomical entities: two organisms may use phylogenetically unrelated structures to accomplish apparently similar behaviors (analogy); of more interest to us, structures which can be shown related by comparative morphology *may* serve patterns of behavior which superficially appear to have no common element (homology). More often than not, the neural structures involved have undergone some changes (e.g. enlargement, rotation, altered configuration); in addition, the behavior patterns to be compared are frequently ill defined or may even be completely unstudied in one of the species under consideration. Thus, the congruity or disparity of the behavior remains in question until techniques are devised which test *comparable* behavior in both species—this in turn is dependent on a fairly thorough understanding of the behavior patterns under investigation. Why, then, this effort? The assumption underlying such endeavor is that the several behavior patterns served by homologous neural structures *share some common element*. Thus, uncovering a behavioral process which, in spite of superficial modifications, is shown to depend on homologous neural structures provides a valid criterion useful in a taxonomy of behavior —and valid criteria for classification are not abundant in the behavioral sciences. The demonstration of such constancies can then be utilized as the backdrop against which the evolutionary changes (designated above as "superficial") can be understood.

My presentation has the following central thesis: Until now, comparative neurological data have been used in very specific ways to support the notion that certain behavior patterns are innately determined while other patterns are predominantly the result of experience. The argument has been made that innately determined "instinctive" behavior patterns are served by neural mechanisms which are uniform throughout phylogeny; that the neural mechanisms serving "learned" behavior vary considerably among phyla, reaching their maximum development in primates. Furthermore, the difference in forebrain structures which has been invoked to support this characterization of the dichotomy between "instinct" and "learning" has been the difference between paleo- and archipallial formations on the one hand and neopallial formations on the other. I plan to show that this particular formulation is in error (see also Beach, 1952). In its place I propose that a more useful distinction is described between an internal core and an external portion of the prosencephalon; that the internal core is primarily related to changes in central nervous system excitability; that the external portion serves propagation of patterns of signals; that the internal core is primarily concerned in mechanisms necessary to the performance of behavior sequences while the external portion is related to informational processes necessary in discriminative behavior. *Each* of these major divisions of the forebrain has "old" *and* "new" subdivisions; each of the classes of behavior (sequential and discriminative) is *both* innate and experientially modifiable.

The Vertebrate Forebrain

Although an undifferentiated forebrain (prosencephalon) is recognizable in *prevertebrate chordates* (Cephalochordata, e.g. *Amphioxus*), the characteristic division of the vertebrate brain into telencephalon, diencephalon, mesencephalon, metencephalon, and myelencephalon is found in primitive vertebrates (cyclostomes, e.g., lampreys) and is considered prototypical of that of all other vertebrates. In *cyclostomes* the telencephalon has two "cerebral hemispheres"; the diencephalon is divisible into hypothalamus, thalamus proper, and epithalamus—however the thalamus proper is not well developed, especially in its dorsal portion. Still greater differentiation of the forebrain can be observed in the *cartilaginous fishes* (elasmobranchs, e.g. dogfish, skate, shark).

The telencephalon is enlarged both in its basal (striatal and septal) portions and in its roof (pallium). In addition to the diencephalic divisions noted in cyclostomes, the thalamus proper is subdivided into a ventral and a dorsal portion. The primitive pallium of the cartilaginous fish differentiates further in two directions: (1) In certain of the *bony fish* (ganoids and teleosts) paleopallial and archipallial rudiments, though discernible, are not as prominent as a hypopallial (also called neostriatal) formation which results from an exversion of the cerebral mantle increased through ventral growth. (2) In amphibia a primordial archipallium is overshadowed by the development of the paleopallium through medial growth of the cerebral mantle over a thickened septum, amygdala, and paleostriatum; rudiments of a general cortex are recognizable. Concurrently, the amphibian dorsal thalamus enlarges considerably. Thus, the major divisions of the vertebrate prosencephalon are clearly discerned in all tetrapods.

The differentiation of the prosencephalon is even more apparent in the reptiles (and birds) and culminates in mammals. The reptilian (and avian) telencephalon emphasizes the archipallium over the paleopallium and general cortex; in mammals the general cortex assumes ascendancy. In the reptilian (and avian) diencephalon, the dorsal thalamus differentiates recognizable internal and external portions. The internal portion is composed of central, medial (n. rotundus) and anterior nuclear masses; the external portion, of a ventral nuclear mass (n. dorsolateralis anterior), a posterior nuclear mass (n. ovalis) and a geniculate complex (n. geniculatus ventralis)—and in birds a n. geniculatus medialis. A similar grouping can be made of the nuclei of the mammalian thalamus and will be discussed in detail below. (This résumé is based on Kappers, Huber, and Crosby, 1936).

Comparative Behavior of Vertebrates

The broad outlines of the comparative neurology of the inframammalian prosencephalon are thus fairly well delineated: an increasing differentiation of the rostral end of the neuraxis is described as one proceeds from prevertebrate chordates through cephalochordates, cyclostomes, fishes, amphibia, reptiles, to birds and mammals. Can a parallel increase in the differentiation (complexity) of behavior patterns, or of certain classes of behavior patterns, be traced in these organisms? Precise behavioral data regarding prevertebrate chordates, cephalochordates, and cyclostomes are practically nonexistent. Precise comparative behavioral studies of fishes, amphibia, reptiles, and birds do *not* support any notions that these forms differ significantly from each other or from mammals with regard to the complexity of the total behavioral repertoire displayed. Discriminations as in mazes (Tinklepaugh, 1932; Franz, 1927; Yerkes, 1903), speed of learning (Churchill, 1916), and the duration of retention of learned responses (Goldsmith, 1914), when they have been measured, show remarkable similarity among these various vertebrates. Differences, when they do occur, are attributable to differences in peripheral receptive and manipulative structures and do not correlate with differences between the forebrains of these animals (Warden et al., 1936). Nonetheless, fundamental differences in the structure of behavior, though not as yet subjected to rigorous experimental comparisons, are noted by the comparative psychologist.

Yerkes (1904, 1905), in a series of studies, presented different auditory stimuli to a frog. Some of these stimuli (e.g. splashing water) altered the rate of respiration without any change in the overt response of the animal. If, however, the sound was shortly followed by a visual stimulus, the frogs jumped sooner than if no auditory stimulation had preceded. Other results show that amphibia may be "tensed" by one or another stimulus so that response to a subsequent stimulus of a different type may be influenced. This ability to delay a response (hesitate) represents a different type of sensory control of action from the rather inflexible immediate response to stimulation which is found in fishes. This trend toward the multiple "sensory" determination of an action is paralleled by a trend toward a multiple "motivational" determination of response—e.g. fish under the influence of factors leading to reproductive behavior are insensitive for long periods to factors which at other times lead to feeding, flight, or rest (Warden et al., 1936).

The trend toward "multiple" determination of action in these vertebrates is, at the present writing, the one generalization derived from the study of comparative behavior which correlates with the comparative neurological generalization that describes the progressive differentiation of the forebrain. This trend in behavior has, as a rule, been ascribed to the emergence of a general or neocortex in the tetrapods—I prefer to consider the differentiation of all of the diencephalic and prosencephalic structures in making a correlation. The more restricted correlation was derived from the premise that paleopallial and archipallial formations function exclusively as olfactory structures, a premise which has been shown erroneous (Pribram and Kruger, 1954). In nonmammalian tetrapods, the archi- and paleopallial forebrain structures and their diencephalic correspondents *are* the predominant new formations—new behavioral manifestations may as well be attributed to the appearance of these formations as to the appearance of a rudimentary general cortex. My plea: let us not ignore the archi- and paleopallial formations and their diencephalic correspondents by relegating to them only olfactory functions; let us keep open the possibility that the trend toward multiple "sensory" and "motivational" determination of behavior in submammalian vertebrates is correlated with the progressive differentiation of the *entire* forebrain, and not with the appearance of one or another specific structure such as the general cortex.

THE MAMMALIAN FOREBRAIN

With this introduction to the comparative evolution of the vertebrate forebrain and the possibilities of the correlation of observed structural differences to differences in behavior, let us turn to a more minute examination of the mammalian forebrain and correlations between the evolution of its structure and the evolution of behavior. The neurological truism that the key to the understanding of the forebrain is to be found in an understanding of its input is given new impetus by recent advances in neurophysiology. A most significant series of contributions has delineated differences between those systems in the neuraxis which lie close to the central canal and those more laterally placed. The systems near the central canal are characterized by many synapses, by fine, short fibers, by a diffuseness of interconnections. Those systems which are remote from the central canal are characterized by large, long fiber tracts so constituted that considerable topological correspondence is maintained between periphery and central terminus. Receptor excitation is mediated through both systems (Starzl et al., 1951). Destruction of the internally placed

systems grossly alters central nervous system excitability fluctuations as measured by the electroencephalogram. Such destruction also interferes with normal activity cycles such as sleep-
wakefulness, though leaving intact the organism's specific reactions
to specific stimulation (e.g. turning head and eyes toward a light)
(Lindsley, et al., 1950). Destruction of the more laterally placed
input systems interferes with these specific reactions (mode specificity, e.g. visual, auditory, somesthetic; topographic specificity,
e.g. anesthesia or paralysis of a hand, a visual field defect). The
initial terminus of these various input systems in the forebrain is
the diencephalon. As we have already noted, the vertebrate diencephalon early differentiates into a hypothalamus, a thalamus
proper, and an epithalamus. Hypothalamic nuclei situated in
proximity to the third ventricle partake of the characteristics of
the diffuse "activating" input systems (Magoun, 1950); little is
known concerning the input relationships of the epithalamus.
The thalamus proper is our main concern. It may be divided into
a ventral and a dorsal portion. The development and functions of
the ventral portion (reticular and dorsolateral geniculate nuclei)
are not well understood. Some experiments suggest that there is
a diffuse input to the reticular nucleus and that diffuse activation
or facilitation of the telencephalon results from stimulation of the
reticular and dorsolateral geniculate nuclei (Jasper, 1949). Other
evidence (Chow, 1952; Rose, 1950), however, suggests that the
connections of the reticular nucleus with the endbrain are more
specific and that no diffuse activation results (Starzl and Magoun,
1951) from stimulation of this structure. It is clear, however, that
the proportion of ventral thalamic structure to dorsal thalamus is
larger in submammalian vertebrates than in mammals. As the
thalamus proper becomes more and more differentiated in various
mammals, the increased differentiation (and increased mass) takes
place exclusively within the dorsal thalamus. It is to this structure,
therefore, that we turn for an understanding of the functions of
the mammalian forebrain.

THE DORSAL THALAMUS AND ITS TELENCEPHALIC PROJECTIONS

The mammalian dorsal thalamus is composed of several nuclear
groups which are identifiable in practically all mammalian species
(Fig. 7-1). On the basis that some of these nuclei bear a fairly

consistent relation to one another, an external portion and an internal core of the thalamus can be distinguished. The external portion is composed of the ventral, the posterior (lateral and pulvinar), and the geniculate nuclei. In carnivores and primates this external portion is, for a considerable extent, demarcated from the internal core of the dorsal thalamus by an aggregation of fibers, the internal medullary lamina and its rostral extensions surrounding the anterior nuclear group (Figs. 7-1 and 2). The internal core of the dorsal thalamus may also be subdivided into three large groups: the anterior, the medial, and the central (midline and intralaminar) (Fig. 7-1).

Each of the major subdivisions (external and internal) may be further characterized according to the type of its nontelencephalic major input (Fig. 7-3). Thus, the ventral and geniculate nuclei of the *external division* are the terminations of the large, topologically discrete "specific" afferent tracts (e.g. spinothalamic, trigeminal, lemniscal, and the brachium conjunctivum, as well as the optic and otic radiations) of the somatic, gustatory, auditory, and visual systems (Walker, 1938). Within the *internal core,* the anterior nuclei receive an input from the posterior hypothalamus through the mammillothalamic tract; the central nuclei receive those nonspecific diffuse afferents by way of the reticular formation of the mesencephalon, and in addition a probable input from the anteromedial hypothalamus (Morin, 1950; Morin et al., 1951). (The hypothalamus, as we have already seen, partakes of the characteristics of the diffuse systems.) Thus the constancies of morphology in the mammalian thalamus reflect certain gross distinctions which can be made in the types of input to the forebrain.

The other two nuclear groups, the *posterior* in the external portion and the *medial* in the internal core, do not receive any such major extrathalamic input and have been classified therefore as the "intrinsic" nuclei of the thalamus (Rose and Woolsey, 1949). Important to our argument, which is detailed below, is the fact that there is an *intrinsic* nucleus in *each* of the major thalamic divisions (see Fig. 7-3).

The projections to the telencephalon of the dorsal thalamus have been delineated in several mammals. The external portion of the dorsal thalamus projects to the dorsolateral and posterior cortex (Fig. 7-4). The nuclei of the internal core project to the

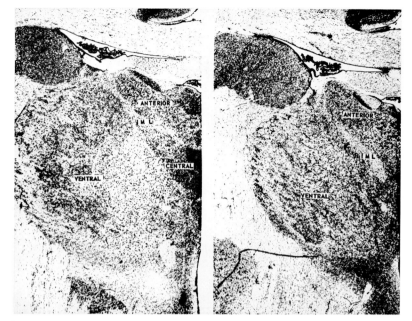

Fig. 7–1A. Frontal section through rostral dorsal thalamus of monkey. Note clear separation of anterior and ventral groups by fibers of the internal medullary lamina (IML).

Fig. 7–1B. Section somewhat caudal to that in Fig. 1A. Note how the central group lies within the fibers of the IML.

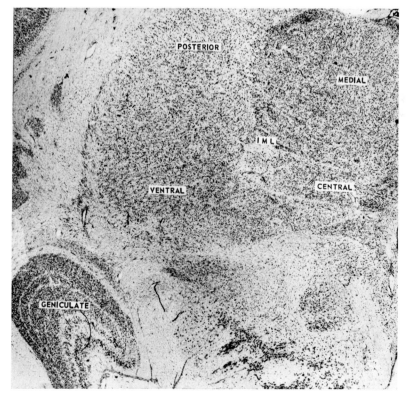

Fig. 7–2. Section about halfway through thalamus. Note the visible distinction between the internal core (medial and central nuclei) and the external portion of the thalamus (ventral and posterior groups).

frontal and mediobasal portions of the forebrain, including the basal ganglia. Specifically, the ventral group of the *external* portion of the dorsal thalamus projects to the dorsolateral cortex of the frontal and parietal lobes (Walker, 1938; Chow and Pribram, 1956); the geniculate group to the lateral portion of the temporal and the posterior portion of the occipital lobe (Walker, 1938);

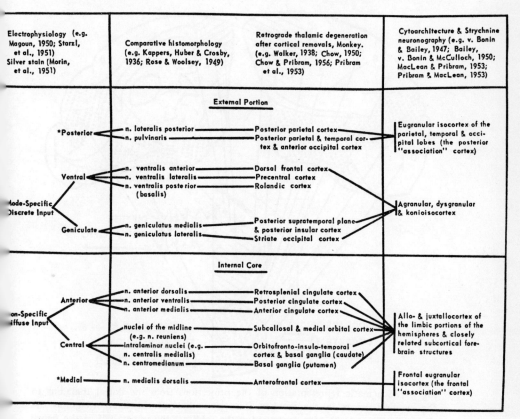

Fig. 7-3. Diagram of the distinctions between an internal core and an external portion of the forebrain. Examples of the techniques and particular studies used in making the classification are given across the top. As in any such classification, its heuristic value should not obscure its deficiencies: there is, of course, a multiplicity of forebrain systems, each of which partakes to a greater or less extent of the characteristics defining the internal core and those defining the external portion. In general, however, the nearer a system is to the central canal (or ventricular system) of the central nervous system, the greater the number of its "internal core" characteristics; the further from the central canal, the greater the number of its "external portion" characteristics. Also, the interaction of these various systems must not be ignored: this scheme is a restricted *analysis* and does not deal with such interactions.

the posterior nuclear group to the remaining cortex of the parieto-temporo-occipital (PTO) convexity (Chow, 1950; Chow and Pribram, 1956).

Within the internal core (Fig. 7-4) the medial nuclei project to the anterofrontal cortex (or orbitofrontal, as it has been called in subprimate mammals) (Rose and Woolsey, 1948b; Walker,

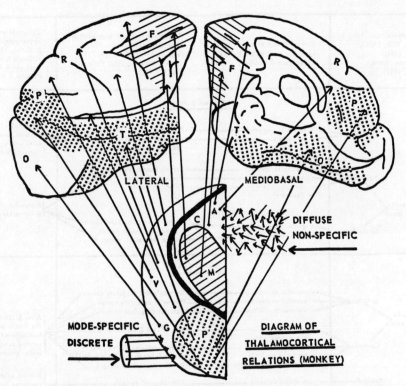

Fig. 7-4. Schematic representation of the projections from the dorsal thalamus to the cerebral cortex in the monkey. The lower half of the figure diagrams the thalamus, the straight edge representing the midline; the upper half of the figure shows a lateral and mediobasal view of the cerebral hemispheres. The broad black band in the thalamic diagram indicates the division between an internal core which receives a nonspecific, diffuse input and an external portion which receives the modality-specific, discrete projection tracts. The stippled and crosshatched portions represent the intrinsic systems: the medial nucleus of the internal core and its projections to the anterofrontal cortex; the posterior nuclear group of the external portion of the thalamus and its projections to the parieto-temporo-occipital cortex. The boundaries of the cortical sectors of the intrinsic systems are not sharp and as yet are not precisely defined—thus this diagram is to be read as a tentative approximation, based on currently available evidence. F, Frontal; R, Rolandic; P, Parietal; T, Temporal; O, Occipital. A, Anterior; C, Central; M, Medial; V, Ventral; G, Geniculate; P, Posterior.

1938; Mettler, 1947; Pribram et al., 1953). The anterior and the central nuclei project to the medial and basal forebrain structures: the anterior nuclei to the limbic areas on the medial surface of the frontal and parietal lobes (Rose, 1927; Waller, 1937; Lashley and Sperry, 1943; Rose and Woolsey, 1948b; Mettler, 1947; Pribram and Fulton, 1954; Pribram and Barry, 1956). The central nuclei project (Rose and Woolsey, 1949; Droogleever Fortuyn, 1950; Powell and Cowan, 1956; Pribram and Bagshaw, 1953; Bagshaw and Pribram, 1953) to the anterior rhinencephalic and closely related juxtallocortical areas and basal ganglia (second rhinencephalic system as defined by Pribram and Kruger, 1954).

Neurobehavioral Studies (Mammals)

The elementary functions in behavior of the ventral and geniculate nuclear groups and their projections to the dorsolateral and posterior cerebral cortex will not be discussed here. Lashley's many studies in vision (e.g. 1942), and those of Klüver (e.g. 1942) and of Harlow and Settlage (e.g. Harlow, 1939; Settlage, 1939) in this modality; the studies of Ruch (e.g. Ruch and Fulton, 1935) and of Zubek (e.g. 1952) in somesthesis; those of Neff and his group in audition (e.g. Jerison and Neff, 1953); and of Patton and Ruch (1944), of Benjamin and Pfaffmann (1955), and of Bagshaw and Pribram (1953) in taste, can be referred to for summaries of this work in animals. Studies in man may be reviewed by referring to the Research Publications of the Association for Research in Nervous and Mental Diseases (1956). Essential to our argument is the demonstration by these studies that a separate thalamocortical system is involved in each of these sensory modalities.

The elementary functions in behavior of the anterior and central nuclear groups and their projections to the medial and basal telencephalon have been delineated only recently. These thalamocortical systems serve behavior which has often been classified as "instinctive," a classification which is acceptable provided the definition of instinct does *not* depend on the characteristic that the behavior is innate. (More will be said below about the appropriate defining characteristic.) Specifically, ablations and stimulations of the medial and basal telencephalon have affected feeding behavior (Pribram and Bagshaw, 1953; Stamm, 1955a; Weiskrantz, 1953); fighting or aggressive behavior (Bard and Mount-

castle, 1948; Klüver and Bucy, 1939; Rosvold et al., 1954; Brady
and Nauta, 1953); fleeing or avoidance behavior (Bard and
Mountcastle, 1948; Klüver and Bucy, 1939; Pribram and Fulton,
1954; Pribram and Bagshaw, 1953; Schreiner and Kling, 1953;
Brady et al., 1954; Weiskrantz, 1956; Pribram and Weiskrantz,
1957); mating behavior (Klüver and Bucy, 1939; Schreiner and
Kling, 1953); and maternal behavior (Walker et al., 1953; Stamm,
1955b). Essential to our argument is the observation that, in contrast to the modality-specific classes of behavior described above,
these behavior patterns are characterized by considerable variability with respect to the concurrent environmental situation—
events in the immediate past must be taken into account in order
to describe the behavior adequately. Thus, a sated animal will react
differently to a food or sex object than will a deprived animal;
whether fighting or fleeing will occur in a social situation will
depend on a multiplicity of yet undetermined antecedent factors
(perhaps amount of total stimulation); maternal behavior is not
elicited in the normal nulliparous organism.

The "intrinsic" posterior and medial nuclear groups and their
projections are of special interest. The morphological data that
the two intrinsic thalamic nuclear groups and their projections
may be assigned to two separate divisions in all mammals (and,
as we have seen, even in nonmammalian tetrapods) suggest a
hypothesis regarding the taxonomy of the behavior served by these
structures. The hypothesis may be stated simply: (a) the behavior
served by the posterior intrinsic nuclei and their projections to
the PTO cortex will share some common and exclusive element
with the behavior served by the remainder of the external thalamic division and its projections: (b) the behavior served by the
medial intrinsic nucleus and its projections to the anterofrontal
cortex will share some common and exclusive element with the
behavior served by the remainder of the internal core of the
thalamus and its projections. Studies generated by this hypothesis
and utilizing the monkey for the most part have been under way
for a decade. They have been detailed in other publications (Fulton, 1951; Pribram, 1955, and in press, a) so that a summary would
be more appropriate for this occasion.

With respect to the posterior group and its projections, both
the morphological and the behavioral facts are overwhelmingly
consistent in support of the hypothesis. Anatomical contiguity

between the posterior nuclei and the ventral group is so intimate in all species that precise definition of the boundaries between them is often difficult (Chow and Pribram, 1956). Contiguity with the geniculate group is maintained posterolaterally in all mammals in spite of a marked ventral rotation of this group and its virtual separation from the rest of the thalamus in primates.

Neurobehavioral studies have shown that damage to the PTO cortex (which derives its thalamic input from the posterior nuclear group) affects the animals' ability to make choices among disparate environmental events, whether that ability has been preoperatively instilled or is investigated by postoperatively administered training procedures (Warren and Baron, 1956; Blum et al., 1950; Mishkin, 1954; Mishkin and Pribram, 1954; Pribram and Barry, 1956). Depending on the location of the damage within the PTO cortex, choices mediated by one or another sense modality are affected; thus far, no effects transcending modality have been uncovered by such experiments. Recent behavioral experiments on man (Wallach and Averbach, 1955) which demonstrate the hitherto unsuspected importance of modality-specific memories may also be mentioned in support of the hypothesis. Thus the element common to the behavior served by the external portion of the dorsal thalamus and its projection to the dorsolateral and posterior cerebral areas is some as yet poorly defined sensory mode-specific "differentiation" factor important to the solution of discrimination tasks.

Evidence contrary to the hypothesis has come entirely from studies on man. Stimulation of the temporal convexity of the cerebrum in patients suffering from epilepsy due to brain pathology and sufficiently severe to warrant surgical intervention has elicited "memories" (Penfield and Jasper, 1954). These findings have been interpreted to mean that the portion of the brain involved in such stimulations serves "memory functions" in general. It is clear, however, that in practically all cases memories in only one modality are elicited in any one patient from any reasonably circumscribed locus, and that the variable pathological involvement of brain tissue makes *inter*patient comparison of data with respect to this problem difficult. Other evidence suggests that certain portions of the PTO cortex may serve intermodality visual-somatic "spatial" orientation in man (Semmes et al., 1955; Humphrey and Zangwill, 1952). The lesions producing such "spatial

agnosia" are, of course, not clearly circumscribed or defined. Nor
has the suggestion that such spatial symptoms may result from a
purely somatosensory defect been adequately explored, though the
findings with respect to the other agnosias (Bay, 1950) urge such
an exploration.

Nonetheless, these data from the clinic serve to sharpen the
focus on the relevance of our problem to the evolution of behavior. Stated succinctly it is this: Does the complexity of man's
perceptual processes (including the language function) evolve
through the development of a supramodality or *association* mechanism or does it evolve through the development of a mechanism
permitting greater *differentiation* within each modality (Gibson
and Gibson, 1955)? Comparative morphology leads me to place
my bet on the latter.

Systematization of morphological and behavioral data regarding
the medial intrinsic nuclei and their projections to the anterofrontal cortex is somewhat more difficult. The morphological
kinship of the medial nuclei with the central (midline and intralaminar) has been pointed out (Rose and Woolsey, 1948b): the
medial nucleus "fuses" with the midline and intralaminar nuclei
"to such a degree that their separation is sometimes artificial."
Contiguity with the anterior nuclei is maintained anterodorsally
in all mammals.

Neurobehavioral studies have shown that damage to the anterofrontal cortex (which derives its thalamic input from the medial
nuclear group) affects the animals' ability to solve tasks in which
correct solution is not determined by the concurrent environment
but depends exclusively upon some prior event (Morgan and
Stellar, 1950; Jacobsen, 1936; Jacobsen and Nissen, 1937; Harlow
and Settlage, 1948; Harlow et al., 1952; Mishkin and Pribram,
1955, 1956). In these tasks sequential behavioral dependencies are
involved and these are implicated irrespective of the modality
which mediates the "prior" event (Pribram and Mishkin, 1956;
Pribram, 1950).

What common element is to be found in the behavior affected
by manipulations of the medial and basal telencephalon (the
projection areas of the anterior and central nuclear groups) and
that affected by manipulations of the anterofrontal cortex? An
answer is suggested by the findings that *both* anterofrontal and
medial and basal cerebral lesions (but not those of the dorsolateral

and posterior convexity) markedly *shorten the duration* of an avoidance reaction (Pribram and Fulton, 1954; Pribram and Bagshaw, 1953; Brady and Nauta, 1955; Pribram and Weiskrantz, 1957). Analysis of the variables important in the deficit produced in the delayed reaction and alternation tasks by the frontal lesion (Meyer et al., 1951; Nissen et al., 1938; Finan, 1942; Mishkin and Pribram, 1955; Pribram, 1950) clearly demonstrates the importance of the animal's reaction to *the signal* which indicates the choice *subsequently* rewarded. The *duration* of this reaction has been shown to be critical (Malmo, 1942). Analysis of the effects on behavior of medial and basal telencephalic manipulations also points to alterations in the *duration* of units in the sequences involved in feeding, fighting and fleeing, mating and maternal behavior (Weiskrantz, 1953; Fuller et al., 1957; Rosvold et al., 1954; Pribram and Bagshaw, 1953; Pribram and Fulton, 1954; Pribram and Weiskrantz, 1957). Thus the element common to the behavior served by the internal core of thalamic nuclei and their projections to the anterofrontal, medial, and basal telencephalon appears to be an as yet poorly defined, nonmodality-specific "durational" factor important to the solution of "sequential" tasks.

The manner in which the mediobasal forebrain structures, which, as we have seen, are characterized by "nonspecific" inputs, affect such a durational factor has been suggested elsewhere (Pribram, in press, b). Essentially, the telencephalon, as well as the diencephalon and mesencephalon, shows a gradient of organization from the ependymal lining outward. This gradient is expressed as the complexity of possible neuronal patterning within a system at any one moment in time. The mediobasal limbic systems of the telencephalon not only are heavily interconnected with the medial diencephalon and mesencephalon but also show functional similarities to these latter systems. Specifically, diffuseness rather than spatial or modality specificity characterizes the relationships of the mediobasal systems and peripheral structures. Activity in the mediobasal systems affects other central neural mechanisms through parallel connections so arranged that different amounts of synaptic delay are interposed in each of the connecting tracts: the result, cumulation of neuronal activity effecting changes of *excitability* of neural tissue, not changes in *momentary* patterns of activity. These changes in excitability are akin to electrotonic, synaptic, and dendritic potential changes rather than to the propagated nerve impulse. Thus, experiments such as the neuropharmacological ones dealing with neural phenomena showing a slow time course may in the immediate future be expected to increase our understanding of the behavioral processes affected by mediobasal system ablations and stimulations: i.e. behaviors categorized as feeding, fleeing, fighting, mating, and maternal.

SUMMARY AND CONCLUSIONS

We have traced the differentiation of the forebrain in nonmammalian vertebrates and detailed some of the constancies in the still more complex differentiation in mammals. We have seen that an attempt to correlate the progressive differentiation of the vertebrate forebrain with a progressive differentiation of the total repertoire of behavior patterns fails to find support in comparative psychological data; on the other hand, one aspect of behavior, i.e. the increasing capacity to make any particular response subject to multiple "sensory" and "motivational" determination, does appear to correlate with the increasing differentiation of the vertebrate forebrain. Contrary to earlier generalizations, which were based on the erroneous assumption that archi- and paleopallial structures were primarily devoted to olfactory processes, current available data are more harmoniously systematized by taking into account the progressive development of these medial and basal forebrain structures as well as the dorsolateral derivatives of the general cortex. The tentative formulation that the medial and basal forebrain structures partake in the increasing evolutionary differentiation of the forebrain finds support in the analysis of mammalian thalamocortical comparative morphology. An internal core of dorsal thalamic nuclei and their projections to the fronto-mediobasal aspects of the telencephalon can be distinguished in all mammals from an external portion of the dorsal thalamus and its projections to the postero-dorsolateral aspect of the telencephalon. The projections of the internal core of nuclei are intimately related to the archi- and paleopallial portions of the forebrain—significantly, however, newer formations such as the medial nucleus and its projection to the anterofrontal cortex develop within this internal core. Thus the classical dichotomy between older forebrain structures and new formations is modified for the purposes of our analysis: a dichotomy more relevant to this discussion is one between an internal or centrally located core of neural systems and an external portion of the forebrain. Each of these portions, the external and the internal, contains both old *and* new formations.

Each of the two major divisions of the forebrain is characterized by its input and by its functions in behavior. The external portion receives a sensory mode-specific input through tracts made up of large, long nerve fibers. These tracts are so constituted as to maintain a topological correspondence between the organization of receptor events and those occurring in the forebrain. The functions of the external portion in behavior have to do with the performance of discrimination tasks. Mode specificity and "differentiation" of cues are involved not only when those sectors which receive the input are studied but also when behavior is affected by manipulations of the "intrinsic" sectors of this external portion.

The internal core of the forebrain receives a nonspecific input through systems made up of fine, short nerve fibers diffusely connected by many synapses. These systems are so constituted as to influence the fluctuating excitability of the forebrain rather than to transmit patterns of signals. The functions of this internal core of systems in behavior have to do with the performance of tasks involving sequential response dependencies for their solution. Changes in the order and duration of the units constituting such a behavior sequence are involved not only when those sectors which receive the input are studied but also when behavior is affected by manipulations of the "intrinsic" sector of this internal core.

This formulation of the data of comparative neurology and comparative psychology proposes the following questions: Have we, in emphasizing the dichotomy between those formations which are represented in most vertebrates and those which are the special acquisition of primates, missed the significance of the equally important findings that in some form or another *all* forebrain structures are represented in all but the most primitive vertebrates; that differentiation does not take place in a "straight line" fashion, but that amphibia show a preponderance of paleopallial formations, reptiles and birds of archistriatal and archipallial structures, while mammals specialize in dorsal thalamus, neostriatum, and general (neo) cortex? Have we, in our preoccupation with the dichotomy between those formations which differentiate in presumably "lower" forms and those which differentiate in primates, lost sight of a distinction in forebrain anatomy which can be discerned in practically all vertebrates and dominates the picture in mammals: viz. the distinction between a core of internally situated forebrain formations and more externally placed systems? Have we, in emphasizing the dichotomy between behavior which is apparently determined by "innate" mechanisms and that which is apparently "learned," confused this dichotomy with an even more interesting distinction between behavior which is inflexibly determined and that which has multiple determination? Have we, in emphasizing the biological aspects of the "motivational" and the environmental aspects of the "sensory" process, missed the taxonomic significance of the difference between behavior involving the sequential dependency of responses and behavior involving discrimination? These are specific questions which can be answered by specific series of experiments and observations. Comparative neurology has a wealth of detailed knowledge which, if sifted with precision, care, and imagination, can form the foundation for hypotheses concerning the taxonomic behavioral schemes so basic to an understanding of the evolution of behavior. There *is* a place in our current scientific endeavors for such a comparative neurology:

> During the past half-century, morphology has seemed to be declining in favor, its problems submerged in the more attractive programs of the experimentalists. Nevertheless, activity in this field has not abated, and now there is a renaissance, the reasons for which are plain. Conventional methods of anatomical research have laid a secure factual foundation, but the superstructure must be designed on radically different lines. Several centuries of diligent inquiry by numerous competent workers have produced a vast amount of published research on the anatomy and physiology of the nervous systems of lower vertebrates; but most of this literature is meaningless to the student of the human nervous system, and, as mentioned at the beginning of this book, its significance for human neurology has until recently seemed hardly commensurate with the great labor expended upon it. The last two decades have inaugurated a radical change, in which we recognize two factors.

In the first place, technical improvements in the instrumentation and methods of attack have opened new fields of inquiry hitherto inaccessible. To cite only a few illustrations, new methods for the study of microchemistry and the physical chemistry of living substance, radical improvement in the optical efficiency of the compound microscope, the invention of the electron microscope, and the application of the oscillograph to the study of the electrophysiology of nervous tissue are opening new vistas in neurology, which involve quite as radical a revolution as that experienced a few centuries earlier when microscopy was first employed in biological research.

A second and even more significant revolution is in process in the mental attitudes of the workers themselves toward their problems and toward one another. A healthy skepticism regarding all traditional dogmas is liberating our minds and encouraging radical innovations in both methodology and interpretation. And, perhaps as a result of this, the traditional isolationism and compartition of the several academic disciplines is breaking down. The specialists are now converging their efforts upon the same workbench, and cooperative research by anatomists, physiologists, chemists, psychologists, clinical neurologists, psychiatrists, and pathologists yields results hitherto unattainable. What is actually going on in the brain during normal and disordered activity is slowly coming to light.

Here the comparative method comes to full fruition, and comparative morphology acquires meaning, not as an esoteric discipline dealing with abstractions but as an integral and indispensable component of the primary task of science—to understand nature and its processes and to learn how to adjust our own lives in harmony with natural things and events, including our own and our neighbors' motivations and satisfactions (Herrick, 1948).

REFERENCES

BAGSHAW, MURIEL, and PRIBRAM, K. H. 1953. Cortical organization in gusta-tion (macaca mulatta). J. Neurophysiol., *16*, 499–508.

BAILEY, P. 1949. Concerning the functions of the cerebral cortex. J. Nerv. Ment. Dis., *110*, 369–78.

BAILEY, P., BONIN, G. V., and McCULLOCH, W. S. 1950. The isocortex of the chimpanzee. Urbana, Univ. of Illinois Press.

BARD, P., and MOUNTCASTLE, V. B. 1948. Some forebrain mechanisms involved in expression of rage with special reference to suppression of angry behavior. Res. Publ., Assoc. Nerv. Ment. Dis., *27*, 362–404.

BAY, E. 1950. Agnosie und Funktionswundel. Monogr. Neurol. Handbuch, Vol. *73*. Heidelberg, Springer.

BEACH, F. A. 1952. The descent of instinct. Presidential address, Eastern Psychological Association.

BENJAMIN, R. M., and PFAFFMANN, C. 1955. Cortical localization of taste in albino rat. J. Neurophysiol., *18*, 56–64.

BLUM, J. S., CHOW, K. L., and PRIBRAM, K. H. 1950. A behavioral analysis of the organization of the parieto-temporo-preoccipital cortex. J. Comp. Neurol., *93*, 53–100.

BONIN, G., and BAILEY, P. 1947. The neocortex of macaca mulatta. Urbana, Univ. of Illinois Press.

BRADY, J. V., and NAUTA, W. J. H. 1953. Subcortical mechanisms in emotional behavior: Affective changes following septal forebrain lesions in the albino rat. J. Comp. Physiol. Psychol., *46*, 339–46.

BRADY, J. V., and NAUTA, W. J. H. 1955. Subcortical mechanisms in emotional behavior: The duration of affective changes following septal and habenular lesions in the albino rat. Ibid., *48*, 412–20.

BRADY, J. V., SCHREINER, L., GELLER, I., and KLING, A. 1954. Subcortical mechanisms in emotional behavior: The effect of rhinencephalic injury upon the acquisition and retention of a conditioned avoidance response in cat. Ibid., *47*, 179–86.

CHOW, K. L. 1950. A retrograde cell degeneration study of the cortical projection field of the pulvinar field in the monkey. J. Comp. Neurol., *93*, 313–40.

CHOW, K. L. 1952. Regional degeneration of the thalamic reticular nucleus following cortical ablations in monkeys. Ibid., *97*, 37–59.

CHOW, K. L., and PRIBRAM, K. H. 1956. Cortical projection of the thalamic ventrolateral nuclear group in monkeys. Ibid., *104*, 57–75.

CHURCHILL, E. P., Jr. 1916. The learning of the maze by goldfish. J. Anim. Behav., *6*, 247–55.

DROOGLEEVER FORTUYN, J. 1950 On the configuration and connections of the medioventral area and the mid-line cells in the thalamus of the rabbit. Fol. Psychiat. Neurol. Neurochirg. Neerl., *53*, 213–54.

FERSTER, C. B., and SKINNER, B. F. 1957. Schedules of reinforcement. New York, Appleton-Century-Crofts.

FINAN, J. L. 1942. Delayed response with pre-delay reinforcement in monkeys after removal of the frontal lobes. Amer. J. Psychol., *55*, 202–14.

FRANZ, V. 1927. Zur tierpsychologischen Stellung von Rana temporaria und Bufo calamita. Biol. Zentralbl., *47*, 1–12.

FULLER, J. L., ROSVOLD, H. E., and PRIBRAM, K. H. 1957. The effect on affective and cognitive behavior in the dog of lesions of the pyriform-amygdala-hippocampal complex. J. Comp. Physiol. Psychol., *50*, 89–96.

FULTON, J. F. 1951. Frontal lobotomy and affective behavior. New York, W. W. Norton.

GALL, F. J. 1807. New discoveries in the functions of the brain: Based on Carlsruhe Lectures, Dec., 1806. Carlsruhe, Müller.

GIBSON, J. J., and GIBSON, ELEANOR. 1955. Perceptual learning: Differentiation or enrichment. Psychol. Rev., *62*, 32–41.

GOLDSMITH, M. 1914. Contribution à l'étude de la mémoire chez les poissons. Bull. Inst. Gén. Psychol., *12*, 161–76.

HALSTEAD, W. C. 1947. Brain and intelligence, Vol. *13*. Chicago, Univ. of Chicago Press.

HARLOW, H. F. 1939. Recovery of pattern discrimination in monkeys following unilateral occipital lobectomy. J. Comp. Psychol., *27*, 467.

HARLOW, H. F., DAVIS, R. T., SETTLAGE, P. H., and MEYER, D. R. 1952. Analysis of frontal and posterior association syndromes in brain-damaged monkeys. J. Comp. Physiol. Psychol., *45*, 419–29.

HARLOW, H. F., and SETTLAGE, P. H. 1948. Effect of extirpation of frontal areas upon learning performance of monkeys. Res. Publ., Assoc. Nerv. Ment. Dis., *27*, 446–59.

HERRICK, C. J. 1948. The brain of the tiger salamander. Chicago, Univ. of Chicago Press.

HUMPHREY, M. E., and ZANGWILL, O. L. 1952. Effects of a right-sided occipito-parietal brain injury in a left-handed man. Brain, *75*, Pt. 3, 312.

JACOBSEN, C. F. 1936. Studies of cerebral functions in primates. I. The functions of the frontal association areas in monkeys. Comp. Psychol. Monogr., *13*, 3–60.

JACOBSEN, C. F., and NISSEN, H. W. 1937. Studies of cerebral function in primates. IV. The effects of frontal lobe lesions on delayed alternation habit in monkeys. J. Comp. Psychol., *23*, 101–12.

JASPER, H. H. 1949. Diffuse projection systems: The integrative action of the thalamic reticular system. EEG Clin. Neurophysiol., *1*, 405–20.

JERISON, H. J., and NEFF, W. D. 1953. Effect of cortical ablation in the monkey on discrimination of auditory patterns. Fed. Proc., *12*, 73.

KAPPERS, C. U. A., HUBER, G. C., and CROSBY, E. C. 1936. The comparative anatomy of the nervous system of vertebrates, including man. New York, Macmillan.

KLÜVER, H. 1942. Functional significance of the geniculo-striate system. In Biological symposia. Vol. 7, Visual mechanisms. Lancaster, Jaques Cattell Press, pp. 253–300.

KLÜVER, H., and BUCY, P. C. 1939. Preliminary analysis of functions of the temporal lobes in monkeys. A. M. A. Arch. Neurol. Psychiat., *42*, 979.

LASHLEY, K. S. 1942. The problem of cerebral organization in vision. In Biological symposia. Vol. 7, Visual mechanisms. Lancaster, Jaques Cattell Press, pp. 301–22.

LASHLEY, K. S., and SPERRY, R. W. 1943. Olfactory discrimination after destruction of the anterior thalamic nuclei. Amer. J. Physiol., *139*, 446.

LINDSLEY, D. B., SCHREINER, L. H., KNOWLES, W. B., and MAGOUN, H. W. 1950. Behavioral and EEG changes following chronic brain stem lesions in the cat. EEG Clin. Neurophysiol., *2*, 483–98.

MACLEAN, P. D. 1949. Psychosomatic disease and the "visceral brain." Psychosomat. Med., *11*, 338–53.

MACLEAN, P. D., FLANIGAN, S., FLYNN, J. P., KIM, C., and STEVENS, JANICE R. 1955/56. Hippocampal function: Tentative correlations of conditioning, EEG, drug and radioautographic studies. Yale J. Biol. Med., *28*, 380–95.

MACLEAN, P. D., and PRIBRAM, K. H. 1953. A neuronographic analysis of the medial and basal cerebral cortex. I. Cat. J. Neurophysiol., *16*, 312–23.

MAGOUN, H. W. 1950. The ascending reticular activating system. Res. Publ., Assoc. Nerv. Ment. Dis., *30*, 480–92.

MALMO, R. B. 1942. Interference factors in delayed response in monkeys after removal of frontal lobes. J. Neurophysiol., *5*, 295–308.

METTLER, F. A. 1947. Extracortical connections of the primate frontal cerebral cortex. J. Comp. Neurol., *86*, 95–117.

MEYER, D. R., HARLOW, H. F., and SETTLAGE, P. H. 1951. A survey of delayed response performance by normal and brain-damaged monkeys. J. Comp. Physiol. Psychol., *44*, 17–25.

MISHKIN, M. 1954. Visual discrimination performance following ablations of the temporal lobe. II. Ventral surface vs. hippocampus. Ibid., *47*, 187–93.

MISHKIN, M., and PRIBRAM, K. H. 1954.

Visual discrimination performance following partial ablations of the temporal lobe. I. Ventral vs. lateral. Ibid., *47*, 14–20.

MISHKIN, M., and PRIBRAM, K. H. 1955. Analysis of the effects of frontal lesions in monkeys. I. Variations of delayed alternation. Ibid., *48*, 492–5.

MISHKIN, M., and PRIBRAM, K. H. 1956. Analysis of the effects of frontal lesions in monkey. II. Variations of delayed response. Ibid., *49*, 36–40.

MORGAN, C. T., and STELLAR, E. 1950. Physiological psychology. 2d ed. New York, McGraw-Hill.

MORIN, F. 1950. An experimental study of hypothalamic connections of the guinea pig. J. Comp. Neurol., *92*, 193.

MORIN, F., SCHWARTZ, H. G., and O'LEARY, J. L. 1951. Experimental study of the spinothalamic and related tracts. Acta Psychiat. Neurol. Scandinav., *26*, 3–4.

NISSEN, H. W., RIESEN, A. H., and NOWLIS, V. 1938. Delayed response and discrimination learning by chimpanzees. J. Comp. Psychol., *26*, 361–86.

PAPEZ, J. W. 1937. A proposed mechanism of emotion. A M. A. Arch. Neurol. Psychiat., *38*, 725–43.

PATTON, H. D., and RUCH, T. C. 1944. Preference thresholds for quinine hydrochloride in chimpanzee, monkey, and rat. J. Comp. Psychol., *37*, 35–49.

PENFIELD, W., and JASPER, H. 1954. Epilepsy and the functional anatomy of the human brain. Boston, Little, Brown.

POWELL, T. P. S., and COWAN, W. M. 1956. A study of thalamo-striate relations in the monkey. Brain, *79*, Pt. 2, 364–90.

PRIBRAM, HELEN, and BARRY, J. 1956. Further behavioral analysis of the parieto-temporo-preoccipital cortex. J. Neurophysiol., *19*, 99–106.

PRIBRAM, K. H. 1950. Some physical and pharmacological factors affecting delayed response performance of baboons following frontal lobotomy. Ibid., *13*, 373–82.

PRIBRAM, K. H. 1955. Toward a science of neuropsychology (method and data). In Current trends in psychology. Pittsburgh, Univ. of Pittsburgh Press, pp. 115–42.

PRIBRAM, K. H. In press, a. Neocortical function in behavior. In Symposium on interdisciplinary research in the behavioral, biological and biochemical sciences. Madison, Univ. of Wisconsin Press.

PRIBRAM, K. H. In press, b. Concerning the neurophysiological correlates of limbic system stimulation. In Symposium on brain stimulation. Houston, Univ. of Houston Press.

PRIBRAM, K. H., and BAGSHAW, MURIEL. 1953. Further analysis of the temporal lobe syndrome utilizing fronto-temporal ablations. J. Comp. Neurol., *99*, 347–75.

PRIBRAM, K. H., CHOW, K. L., and SEMMES, JOSEPHINE. 1953. Limit and organization of the cortical projection from the medial thalamic nucleus in monkey. Ibid., *98*, 433–48.

PRIBRAM, K. H., and FULTON, J. F. 1954. An experimental critique of the effects of anterior cingulate ablations in monkey. Brain, *77*, Pt. 1, 34–44.

PRIBRAM, K. H., and KRUGER, L. 1954. Functions of the "olfactory brain." Ann. N. Y. Acad. Sci., *58*, 109–38.

PRIBRAM, K. H., and MacLEAN, P. D. 1953. A neuronographic analysis of the medial and basal cerebral cortex. II. Monkey. J. Neurophysiol., *16*, 324–40.

PRIBRAM, K. H., and MISHKIN, M. 1956. Analysis of the effects of frontal lesions in monkey. III. Object alternation. J. Comp. Physiol. Psychol., *49*, 41–5.

PRIBRAM, K. H., and WEISKRANTZ, L. 1957. A comparison of the effects of medial and lateral cerebral resection on conditioned avoidance behavior of monkeys. Ibid., *50*, 74–80.

RES. PUBL., ASSOC. NERV. MENT. DIS. 1956. The brain and human behavior. Baltimore, Williams and Wilkins.

ROSE, J. E. 1950. The cortical connections of the reticular complex of the thalamus. In Patterns of organization in the central nervous system. Res. Publ., Assoc. Nerv. Ment. Dis., *30*, 454–79.

ROSE, J. E., and WOOLSEY, C. N. 1948a. Structures and relations of the limbic cortex and anterior thalamic nuclei in rabbit and cat. J. Comp. Neurol., *89*, 279–348.

ROSE, J. E., and WOOLSEY, C. N. 1948b. The orbitofrontal cortex and its connections with the mediodorsal nucleus in rabbit, sheep and cat. Res. Publ., Assoc. Nerv. Ment. Dis., *27*, 210–32.

ROSE, J. E., and WOOLSEY, C. N. 1949. Organization of the mammalian thalamus and its relationships to the cerebral cortex. EEG Clin. Neurophysiol., *1*, 391–404.

ROSE, M. 1927. Gyrus limbicus anterior und regio retrosplenialis. J. Psychol. u. Neurol., *35*, 65–173.

ROSVOLD, H. E., MIRSKY, A. F., and PRIBRAM, K. H. 1954. Influence of amygdalectomy on social interaction in a monkey group. J. Comp. Physiol. Psychol., *47*, 173–8.

RUCH, T. C., and FULTON, J. F. 1935. Cortical localization of somatic sensibility. The effect of precentral, postcentral and posterior parietal lesions upon the performance of monkeys trained to discriminate weights. Res. Publ., Assoc. Nerv. Ment. Dis., *15*, 289–330.

SCHREINER, L., and KLING, A. 1953. Behavioral changes following rhinencephalic injury in cat. J. Neurophysiol., *16*, 643–59.

SEMMES, JOSEPHINE, WEINSTEIN, S., GHENT, LILA, and TEUBER, H. 1955. Spatial orientation in man after cerebral injury. I. Analysis by locus of lesion. Amer. J. Psychol., *39*, 227–44.

SETTLAGE, P. H. 1939. The effect of occipital lesions on visually guided behavior in the monkey. J. Comp. Psychol., *27*, 93.

STAMM, J. S. 1955a. Effects of cortical lesions upon the onset of hoarding in rats. J. Genet. Psychol., *87*, 77–88.

STAMM, J. S. 1955b. The function of the median cerebral cortex in maternal behavior of rats. J. Comp. Physiol. Psychol., *48*, 347–56.

STARZL, T. E., and MAGOUN, H. W. 1951. Organization of the diffuse thalamic projection system. J. Neurophysiol., *14*, 133–46.

STARZL, T. E., TAYLOR, C. W., and MAGOUN, H. W. 1951. Collateral afferent excitation of reticular formation of brain stem. Ibid., *14*, 479–96.

TINKLEPAUGH, O. L. 1932. Maze learning of a turtle. J. Comp. Psychol., *13*, 201–6.

WALKER, A. E. 1938. The primate thalamus. Chicago, Univ. of Chicago Press.

WALKER, A. E., THOMSON, A. F., and McQUEEN, J. D. 1953. Behavior and the temporal rhinencephalon in the monkey. The Johns Hopkins Hosp. Bull., *93*, 65–93.

WALLACH, H., and AVERBACH, E. 1955. On memory modalities. Amer. J. Psychol., *68*, 249–57.

WALLER, W. H. 1937. A cortical lesion causing cell reaction in anteromedial thalamic nucleus. J. Comp. Neurol., *66*, 443.

WARDEN, C. J., JENKINS, T. N., and WARNER, L. H. 1936. Comparative psychology. Vol. *3*, Vertebrates. New York, Ronald Press.

WARREN, J. M., and BARON, A. 1956. The formation of learning sets by cats. J. Comp. Physiol. Psychol., *49*, 227–31.

WEISKRANTZ, L. 1953. Behavioral changes associated with ablation of the amygdaloid complex. Ph.D. thesis, Harvard Univ.

WEISKRANTZ, L. 1956. Behavioral changes associated with ablation of the amygdaloid complex in monkeys: Conditioned avoidance. J. Comp. Physiol. Psychol., *49*, 381–91.

YERKES, R. M. 1903. The instincts, habits, and reactions of the frog. Psychol. Rev. Monogr., *4*, 579–638.

YERKES, R. M. 1904. Inhibition and rein-

forcement of reaction in the frog Rana
clamitans. J. Comp. Neurol. Psychol.,
14, 124–37.

YERKES, R. M. 1905. The sense of hearing
in frogs. Ibid., *15*, 279–304.

YOUNG, J. Z. 1953. The learning system
of octopus. In Symposia on physio-

logical theories of learning. 19th Int.
Physiol. Congr., Montreal, pp. 99–101.

ZUBEK, J. P. 1952. Studies in somesthesis.
II. Role of somatic sensory areas I and
II in roughness discrimination in cat.
J. Neurophysiol., *15*, 401–8.

8

Evolution of Neurophysiological Mechanisms

Theodore H. Bullock

UNIVERSITY OF CALIFORNIA, LOS ANGELES

THOUGH I AVOID saying so in the title of this chapter, in the context of the present symposium it seems certain I am expected to discuss the neurophysiological basis of behavior! Because of the general feeling of this group that candor may sometimes be constructive in the end, I will in fact unburden myself of one or two thoughts on this theme, but essentially they will begin and end with a disclaimer of our ability to contribute fundamentally at present to the real question. Then I shall devote the bulk of my time to an attempt to make some generalizations about the evolution of those physiological mechanisms we do know about, since they have something to do with behavior and may explain a good fraction of it.

What can we possibly say when the questioner, however he phrases it, really asks: "Is there yet assurance that physiological mechanisms will be able to account for observed behavior?" However horrified—whether from the naïveté of the hope or the implied doubt of the mechanistic position—we cannot overlook such a basic question.

To be sure, there is almost nothing easier for the well-read contemporary than to cite recent advances by physiologists using behavioral tests or by psychologists using physiological technics. And in a sense a great deal can be said that is pertinent to, or underlies, or must be kept in mind concerning, or that narrows down the problem of or anatomically localizes some neurophysiological bases for behavior. But at bottom we do not have a decent inkling of the neuronal mechanism of learning or the physiological substratum of instinctive patterns or virtually any complex behavioral manifestation. Indeed, if one considers the other great problems in natural science it seems clear that the gulf between our knowledge of neurophysiology and our knowledge of behavior is at least as wide as any other that confronts us.

This great problem has been on the minds of many, and not only in times past. Both Eccles (1953) and Sherrington (1950), among other physiologists, have recently given full-dress treatments to one aspect of the brain-mind problem and both have given their answer as dualistic. "It is here contended that such a special property [of the cerebral cortex, placing it in a separate category from all the remainder of the matter-energy, or natural world] in outstanding measure is exhibited by the dynamic patterns of neuronal activity that occur in the cerebral cortex during conscious states, and the hypothesis is developed that the brain by means of this special property enters into liaison with mind, having the function of a 'detector' that has a sensitivity of a different kind and order from that of any physical instrument" (Eccles, 1953, pp. 267–8).

Now the first general conclusion I will state here is that this position is not acceptable to all physiologists. It appears to some of them, including myself, a position into which one may be forced by exclusion of alternatives, but we are far from having the evidence to exclude such alternatives. We hesitate, though, when it comes to formulating more tenable proposals in familiar terms.

One way of expressing our faith—and it is just that—is to say that there remain to be discovered new and emergent levels of physiological relations between neurons in masses, which will explain the gaps in our understanding of the phenomena of behavior, and that mind is simply a name for some of these relations or their consequences. It is my understanding that the hydraulic engineer cannot explain the turbulence of the flow of water in a pipe in terms of the known properties of the elementary units, and that the behavior of the atmosphere could not be predicted on our relatively full knowledge of the gases. The concept of emergent properties, believed to inhere in the properties of the lower levels but not readily predicted with an incomplete knowledge, is an old and familiar one. It offers only a refuge, but it does offer that.

We believe then that behavior will be understood in physiological terms one day, but that this day is a long way off. The problems which we cannot yet solve are not only mind and its correlates, e.g. sensation, but learning and complex integrations such as those analyzing input and formulating patterned output. Meantime there is much to be done that is both interesting and significant, and there is always the possibility of stumbling upon one of those new levels of physiological relations among nerve cells.

Having disclaimed that neurophysiology can offer substantial explanations at present of the higher aspects of behavior, I would like to turn to positive aspects and examine certain neurophysiological mechanisms, which doubtless have something to do with behavior, looking for meaningful statements about their evolution.

1. COELENTERATES AND THE NERVE NET

Whenever we think of the evolution of neurological mechanisms the coelenterates come particularly to mind as a strategic group. Here is the lowest phylum of animals living today that possesses a true nervous system; and encompassing as it does the sea anemones, jellyfish, and their allies, it represents a relatively low level of behavioral complexity. The nervous system certainly is different from that of higher animals in being diffuse, that is to say lacking a central nervous concentration. This means a relative autonomy of all parts of the animal, since the sensory, neural, and motor elements necessary for local response are present virtually everywhere. The nerve cells are for the most part isopolar and either multipolar or bipolar, we lack the characteristic monopolar neurons of higher invertebrates and heteropolar multipolars of vertebrates. The sense organs are few and simple. These features are associated with the relative simplicity of behavior but hardly suffice to explain it.

We must look into the functional organization of the nervous system for any real explanation. Here we have come to the remarkable position in recent years that the leading student, C. F. A. Pantin, has opined (1952) that we are probably closer to understanding the behavior of these animals on the grounds of their known nervous organization than any others. Nevertheless, much remains to be learned.

Very briefly, to take the example of the sea anemone: there are a number of muscle sheets—longitudinal, radial, and circular—in the column, in the mesenteries, and in the tentacles and oral disc. Each of these muscle types has a characteristic threshold for the number of nerve impulses per second reaching it through the nerve net to which it will respond, as well as a curve, above this threshold, of response at each frequency. This means that a considerable part of the variety of movements the animal is capable of can be understood in terms of the differential response to different frequencies of arriving impulses in the same nerve net.

Beyond this there is present in certain portions of the nerve net a neuroneural facilitation, that is to say a differential response to different frequencies of arriving nerve impulses, at junctions between nerve cell and nerve cell. Thus the determination of whether an excitation will spread beyond a certain point rests with this property of the synapses. Other parts of the nervous system have junctions which do not require such facilitation but are in the nature of through-conducting pathways. The two types of nerve net can, between them, give us either local response or response at a distance from the site of stimulation. And this response at a distance can itself be confined to certain muscles according to the frequency of the nerve impulses. The frequency of nerve impulses in the net will be determined among other things by the properties of the receptor cells in the epithelia which receive stimulation from the environment. Response to stimulation will therefore depend largely upon and be explained largely by the location of the stimulated receptors and the intensity of their discharge of impulses into the nerve net. In some animals and situations there may be more than two nerve nets (Horridge, 1955), and each may have its own properties with respect to these characteristics.

So far the functions of the nervous system dealt with have been explicable on the basis of familiar mechanisms. There is evidence that the nerve fibers conduct all-or-none impulses of the same general form and duration as the spikes in higher animals, that the junction between nerve cells and muscle elements and the synapses among nerve cells are very similar to some of those known in higher forms. When we add that there is evidence of spontaneous activity in this diffuse nervous system leading to marked changes in the movements and behavior of the animal under apparently unchanging environmental conditions (Batham and Pantin, 1950), we will recognize yet another of the familiar properties of nervous tissue in all groups. This spontaneous activity has been studied in the intact anemone and is characterized by phases or periods of movement of a certain group of muscles, leading to a certain form of external behavior, giving way to quiescence of these muscles and possibly activity of others. An interesting point is that the time scale is very slow—of the order of minutes and hours instead of the milliseconds and seconds characteristic of higher animals—and that similarly stimulation produces long-lasting effects and stimuli spaced many seconds apart elicit response. Thus a stimulus that initiates one impulse in the net every fifteen seconds can alter activity, and strong stimulation during the day may be followed by locomotion during the ensuing night. But the question is just how far the behavior we observe can be explained by the so-called familiar properties.

Conceivably much of the observed spontaneous activity could originate from single loci which all at once break over a threshold and become spontaneous, the discharge being defined by an average frequency over some period. Buck (1954) has recently described vividly the luminescence response of sea pansies—a type of colonial soft coral—to excessive stimulation. After a period of continuous stimulation these colonies begin to luminesce spontaneously instead of only upon stimulation, and the spontaneous waves of luminescence spread from many distinct loci to involve the whole colony. The waves arise so frequently and with such a shifting of loci, and development of new loci that one gains the impression of a frenzied activity. It may last for minutes and then die down. We have called it in the laboratory "berserking," and it cannot but suggest a simple form of focal epilepsy—in the absence of a brain!

However, we cannot feel satisfied that we understand the behavior of corals, sea anemones, or jellyfish. Even if we do not have some of the more complex forms of patterned discharge to explain, we do not seem able to account for all we do see. The loci of origin of the spontaneous discharges in sea anemones are not random; there is coordination of activity in different muscles, and there is a pattern to the recurrence of activity over long periods. We cannot attribute these changes in activity entirely to the environment, and must invoke a form of memory or of slow change of state, accessible to the environment and influenced by previous activity but with intrinsic properties and time course which will determine recurrence apart from the environment. We have no idea of the nature or location of these unknown processes.

2. HIGHER INVERTEBRATES

When we move up to the higher invertebrates, we have evidence of more complex physiological mechanisms. (1) An example is the triggered response, a pattern of effector activity which is determined by built-in mechanisms; the environmental stimulus can only control its occurrence or nonoccurrence and not its pattern. For instance, Hagiwara and Watanabe (1956) have shown that, independent of the nature or strength of the stimulus to the posterior end of a cicada, the reflex production of sound accomplished by muscles in the thorax is at the same fixed frequency. They delivered different numbers and frequencies of impulses into the ganglion containing the neurons which control the sound-producing muscle; recorded the output from the final motor neurons, of which there are two, one for each side; and discovered the fixity of the frequency of their discharge, independent of input. And there are other examples of triggered responses, especially among giant fiber-mediated movements (Wiersma, 1952; Bullock, 1953, 1957). Some of these involve many impulses coming in for a few going out, and some a few impulses coming in and many out.

(2) Besides these cases of a fixed output, which is merely triggered, there are those mechanisms permitting output to vary, depending on the input, but with a bias or amplifying factor which is built in and which may be adjustable according to other parameters of the environment or past history. This is integration, and it may reach a fairly advanced level. Yet we see all this happening in some quite simple situations, such as the neuromuscular junction of crustaceans. Here the output is a function of the input in terms of frequency of arriving nerve impulses, as in the coelenterates, but with a vastly different time scale and with the additional feature that several incoming nerve fibers converge upon the same effector cell, each having a different function between input and output. (3) This function is variable, not only as a result of the past history or the interaction between different incoming pathways but also by the addition of a new pathway, a peripheral inhibitory nerve fiber. When impulses arrive in this pathway, the output measured as a contraction of the muscle is

depressed, depending on the frequency of inhibitory nerve impulses (Katz, 1949; Wiersma, 1953).

Some input-output curves are quite nonlinear, at least in portions of the range; and, although we lack direct measurements, it is easy to imagine that (4) by cascading stages of such nonlinear input-output relations quite drastic consequences can be realized. For example, we can expect sharp step functions, giving, as it were, response in either of two stable manners, with a sharp threshold discriminating between graded degrees of input and labile according to the factors which control the form of the curve in each stage.

We are looking in this section for examples of neurophysiological mechanisms which characterize the intermediate evolutionary levels. We come now (5) to instances of a genesis of patterned discharge which is completely internally determined. The best case thus far demonstrated is the periodic discharge of the cardiac ganglion of the lobster heart (Maynard, 1955, 1956; Hagiwara and Bullock, 1957). This is a neurogenic heart in which the beat is initiated in the ganglion and is not a single, all-or-none response of the myocardium but a partial tetanus whose form is determined by a burst of several score of impulses coming from the nine nerve cells of the ganglion—in sequence and with individual frequencies which are repeated within narrow limits for many beats. The pattern in such a case is accessible both to generalized influence such as the chemical milieu of the blood and the state of inflation of the heart and to influences coming through specific nerves from the central nervous system, both inhibitory and acceleratory. But when these are all in a steady state, the ganglion by itself is capable of generating a periodic repeated complex pattern. It is not yet clear whether this depends upon reciprocal interaction of some neurons back upon those which paced them or can originate in patterned burst of a single cell. But certainly it depends upon the presence of pacemakers and of complex functions of output and input of individual neurons and upon special relations among the properties of the pacemaker or the cells which influence it, preventing continuous discharge and assuring intermittent silent periods. That is, the pendulum which swings between active discharge and silence does not slow down to a low level of continuous firing. We are beginning to learn something of the cellular properties behind some of these examples of integration.

For example, in the higher invertebrates we encounter for the first time—not excluding the possibility of their presence in the coelenterates, to be sure—phenomena such as (6) the graded synaptic potential, which before any postsynaptic impulse has arisen can algebraically add the several incoming presynaptic barrages in a complex way. These incoming barrages are of different value depending upon the pathway and a standing bias. Indeed, so much can be done by means of this graded and nonlinear local phenomenon prior to the initiation of any postsynaptic impulse that we can no more think of the typical synapse in integrative systems as being a digital device exclusively as was commonly assumed a few years ago, but rather as being a complex analogue device which finally converts into a digital output. At least the output is digital in the familiar cases, but as I have suggested before, it is quite possible that the effective output of many neurons is the graded, local event.

There is not space to develop or even illustrate the degrees of freedom which account for the great possibilities of such junctions and therefore of cascaded systems of such interrelations (Prosser, 1950; Bullock, 1952, 1957), but we must name some of them, for these are the actual properties on which most of our knowledge of the evolution of neurophysiological mechanisms is based. Besides (a) facilitation we may see (b) defacilitation or a negative effect of shorter intervals. We may see (c) maintained output with maintained input or (d) adaptation to maintained stimulation or (e) escape from maintained inhibition, both varying according to the intensity and duration of the stimulation. (f) We may see rebound at the end of influx or the absence of rebound. (g) Inhibition can affect disproportionately different parameters of the response; for example, the number of nerve impulses in a burst may be depressed but the frequency of those impulses not depressed. (h) We see various forms and intergrades between subthreshold sinusoidal oscillations and relaxation oscillations which slowly develop to a critical point, then precipitate an event that carries the oscillating level back to a starting point from which another cycle can develop. In still other situations (i) we see slow potentials of the subthreshold sort, which, owing to some protection from being carried back by each impulse to a starting level, are able to determine the initiation of a series of impulses. This is one means of bringing about a one-to-many input-output relation.

The mechanisms, properties, or degrees of freedom of simple

groups of neurons outlined here are capable of accounting for great complexities. Indeed, McCulloch (1951) concluded that a finite population of nerve cells could in fact, with far fewer degrees of freedom, accomplish any conceivable degree of complex behavior. The question is not whether we can imagine a system of neurons of known properties which could accomplish the observed behavior but whether these mechanisms in fact are the only ones responsible and whether the actual brain in any way resembles the conceivable model.

But the point I want to make here is that this variety of properties and of degrees of freedom at the neuronal level has all been demonstrated in simple groups of neurons or single neurons or peripheral junctions in invertebrate animals.

3. More Complex Nervous Systems

If we move up to still more complex systems such as the central nervous system of higher animals where we have vastly more complex behavior to account for, it is significant and interesting that virtually no new neurophysiological mechanisms have been discovered at the level of those just listed. There are a few more cell types, anatomically. There is little that is fundamentally different about the properties of the units. We are uncertain whether there is a really significant difference in the architecture of the assemblages of units, though this remains a distinct hope. At least we cannot say that the architecture is greatly different as between ape and man. (But Sperry, in this volume, reminds us that neurons can be strikingly differentiated chemically and that we cannot rule out a possible correlation between new functional achievement and new chemical cell types.)

A striking case of our thesis that the important properties of the units of the higher nervous systems are already found in the lowest or are of great antiquity instead of being novel is the local and graded response of dendrites which has recently loomed as especially important in understanding the physiology of the cortex of the cerebrum in the mammal. This property or something indistinguishable from it we have seen in the simple ganglia of the invertebrate; and already, in coelenterates, subthreshold stimulation is summated, even with long intervals between stimuli, so that we may assume similar processes are transpiring here. Clare and Bishop (1955) have suggested that there is a stage in evolution of nervous tissue in which no all-or-none propagated impulses but only such graded and decrementally spread events occur. Such a stage has not been found, but it is quite reasonable to compare the properties of the cortical dendrite with those of sensory ramifications of primary sense cells and possibly of terminal branches of axons in at least some presynaptic regions.

Though we cannot point to fundamentally new elements in the neuronal mechanisms of the highest centers, still, it is difficult to assume that their greatly enlarged accomplishments are solely attributable to the great increase in numbers of neurons and interconnections between them, unless this in itself brings on new properties and mechanisms. Many apparently assume as a first approximation that the main factor in increasing behavioral complexity in evolution is the number of neurons—even invoking a kind of critical mass which permits new levels of behavior. I would invite examination of this concept. Consider ants versus grasshoppers; guppies versus tuna; small snails and enormous conchs; mouse and elephant. Even when the brain is not as large in proportion in the larger animals, and even if much of it is increased sensory and motor apparatus, there remains a large absolute difference in interneurons and in the size of higher centers, in favor of the large species. Yet no conspicuous behavioral correlate can be assigned to this. But a mouse, which could hide under the brain of a large shark, has something new. It seems clear that number of neurons correlates with behavioral complexity so poorly as to explain little unless we add as the really essential part that certain kinds of neurons, not now definable, or—what is the same thing—certain kinds of newer properties or consequences of neuronal architecture, are the important substratum of advance. This conclusion does not deny that number of cells and connections contributes to advance, especially in widely separated groups. It does not support or conflict with Rensch's (1956) suggestion for closely related groups.

We do not need to dwell on the evidence that at these new levels of nervous complexity new consequences are achieved, as revealed by physiological tests, to say nothing of ethological criteria. We think of the dramatic results of stimulating localized regions of the mammalian brain, producing subtle emotional expressions or very generalized arousal, ulcers of the stomach or hypersexuality, or appetite for more of the electrical stimulation so that if electrical connections are provided the animal will stimulate itself as though satisfying some drive. In the conscious human subject crude focal stimulation can trigger a vivid experience of a familiar piece of music. There exists much to encourage us to believe that the highest manifestations of behavioral complexity, including learning and memory, insight and altruism, introspection and aesthetic experience, will be accessible to the physiologist's stimulating electrodes.

I would emphasize that exploring the brain with physiological and surgical intervention and behavioral endpoint is one of the greatest and most fruitful areas for investigation in the foreseeable future; and I pay my respects, as an ardent follower, to those pioneers who have already shown us such exciting vistas in this approach, the only approach which seems superficially to be really getting at the no man's land between neurophysiology and behavior (see, for example, Gellhorn, 1953; Adrian, Bremer, and Jasper, 1954; Olds and Milner, 1954; Brady and Nauta, 1955; Pribram and Mishkin, 1956; Morrell and Jasper, 1956).

And yet, having said this, I think we must recognize that these experiments are at present, and as far as we can extrapolate them, likely only to localize the behavioral phenomena in the brain, to indicate more clearly the relative role of different parts of the brain, or to show the accessibility of the behavior to influences applied centrally, as we already know of their accessibility to influences applied peripherally. They can further subdivide and systematize as well as better delineate the kinds of symptomatic phenomena which are represented topographically or are separated from each other in space or in sensitivity to different stimuli, but basically we are not bridging the gap or putting ourselves in the way of encountering new neurophysiological mechanisms.

It is difficult to suggest what dimensions these new mechanisms will have. It seems likely that they will involve newly recognized levels above the single neuron, and hence emergent properties. This is not to say that neuronal mechanisms are adequately known. And it is not meant to distract attention from the great power to explain, inherent in systems of neurons with the many degrees of freedom already known and partly outlined above. But it asserts a challenge still ahead to explain complex integrations like that between cochlear nerve and auditory cortex, cerebellar input and output, lesion- and anesthesia-resistant memory, scanning, attention, set, or the difference between Pribram's discriminative and sequential functions (in this volume).

CONCLUSION

I do not believe that our present physiology of neurons, extrapolated, can account for behavior. The main factor in evolutionary advance is not just numbers of cells and connections. And I cannot believe that a dualism between brain and mind either was there all along from the coelenterates to man or suddenly appeared somewhere in between. The relation between brain and mind evolves in association with a physiological substratum, and hence there is no dualism. Our hope lies in the discovery of new parameters of neuronal systems.

REFERENCES

(Star indicates general background references.)

*ADRIAN, E. D., BREMER, F., and JASPER, H. H. 1954. Brain mechanisms and consciousness. Springfield, Ill., Charles C. Thomas.

BATHAM, E. J., and PANTIN, C. F. A. 1950. Inherent activity in the sea anemone. J. Exp. Biol., 27, 290–301.

BRADY, J. V., and NAUTA, W. J. H. 1955. Subcortical mechanisms in emotional behavior. J. Comp. Physiol, Psychol., 48, 412–20.

BUCK, J. B. 1954. Bioluminescence in *Renilla*, in relation to nerve net physiology. MS.

*BULLOCK, T. H. 1952. The invertebrate neuron junction. Cold Spring Harbor Symposia on Quantitative Biology, 17, 267–73.

BULLOCK, T. H. 1953. A contribution from the study of cords in lower forms. In Ciba Foundation Symposium, The spinal cord. London, Churchill.

*BULLOCK, T. H. 1957. Neuronal integrative mechanisms. In B. T. Scheer, ed., Recent advances in invertebrate physi-

ology. Eugene, Univ. of Oregon Press.

CLARE, M. H., and BISHOP, G. H. 1955. Properties of dendrites; apical dendrites in the cat cortex. EEG Clin. Neurophysiol., 7, 85–98.

*ECCLES, J. C. 1953. The neurophysiological basis of mind. Oxford, Clarendon Press.

*GELLHORN, E. 1953. Physiological foundations of neurology and psychiatry. Minneapolis, Univ. of Minnesota Press.

HAGIWARA, S., and WATANABE, A. 1956. Discharges in motoneurons of cicada. J. Cell. Comp. Physiol., 47, 415–28.

HAGIWARA, S., and BULLOCK, T. H. 1957. Intracellular potentials in pacemaker and integrative neurons of the lobster cardiac ganglion. Ibid., 50, 25–47.

HORRIDGE, G. A. 1955. The nerves and muscles of medusae. II. *Geryonia proboscidalis*. J. Exp: Biol., 32, 555–68.

KATZ, B. 1949. Neuro-muscular transmission in invertebrates. Biol. Rev., 24, 1–20.

McCULLOCH, W. S. 1951. Why the mind is

in the head. In L. A. Jeffress, ed., Cerebral mechanisms in behavior. The Hixon Symposium. New York, Wiley.

MAYNARD, D. M. 1955. Activity in a crustacean ganglion. II. Pattern and interaction in burst formation. Biol. Bull., *109*, 420–36.

MAYNARD, D. M. 1956. Effect of inhibition on interaction in the cardiac ganglion of lobsters. MS.

MORRELL, F., and JASPER, H. H. 1956. Electrographic studies of the formation of temporary connections in the brain. EEG Clin. Neurophysiol., *8*, 201–15.

OLDS, J., and MILNER, P. 1954. Positive reinforcement produced by electrical stimulation of septal area and other regions of rat brain. J. Comp. Physiol. Psychol., *47*, 419–27.

*PANTIN, C. F. A. 1952. The elementary

nervous system. Proc. Roy. Soc. London, series B, *140*, 147–68.

PRIBRAM, K. H., and MISHKIN, M. 1956. Analysis of effects of frontal lesions in monkey. III. J. Comp. Physiol. Psychol., *49*, 41–5.

*PROSSER, C. L., et al. 1950. Comparative animal physiology. Philadelphia, W. B. Saunders.

RENSCH, B. 1956. Increase in learning capability with increase of brain-size. Amer. Nat., *90*, 81–96.

SHERRINGTON, C. 1950. Man on his nature. 2d ed. New Haven, Yale Univ. Press.

WIERSMA, C. A. G. 1952. Neurons of arthropods. Cold Spring Harbor Symposia on Quantitative Biology, *17*, 155–63.

WIERSMA, C. A. G. 1953. Neural transmission in invertebrates. Physiol. Rev., *33*, 326–55.

PART THREE

Categories of Behavior

THE FIRST CHAPTER of this section (Chapter 9) itself provides an introduction to the whole section, which is mainly devoted to a sampling of the tremendous body of data on specific items and kinds of behavior. That chapter also includes an approach to the exceptionally difficult problems of a taxonomy of behavior. Although the involvement of behavior in evolution is pervasive and is emphasized, the discussion makes it implicitly clear that a phylogenetic classification of behavior, in the same sense as that in which we have (or are seeking) a phylogenetic classification of organisms, themselves, is not practicable. There is not the comparatively simple situation of branching lineages in time, but a multiplicity of axes, a multidimensionality, in any full categorization of behavior. Along one of the axes, the main categories proposed are: functional, descriptive, and explanatory. Chapter 10, devoted to food getting, exemplifies a category functional in definition and therefore cutting across other axes, such as the one on which formal aspects may be classified, e.g. by the effectors, receptors, and integrators involved, as likewise suggested in Chapter 9. Chapter 10 demonstrates that within such a functional category as food getting a phylogenetic reconstruction is a definite possibility, although most of the abundant data still await such organization, and conversely that divergence of functional behavior is clearly related to the rise of the higher categories in the

taxonomy of animals. The next example, that of
territoriality as reviewed in Chapter 11, is at present mainly descriptive as categorized along the
functional-descriptive-explanatory axis. There are,
however, many cues toward placing the subject in
the explanatory category. Territoriality further exemplifies the abstraction of one common element
among behaviors so extremely varied and complex
as to include or touch on almost any aspect whatever of behavior among the vertebrates.

Although they are, of course, based on multiple
observations of particular populations, such behavioral studies as those on food getting or territoriality eventually involve trends and generalizations
over broad stretches, all of the vertebrates or the
whole animal kingdom. A different and certainly
no less fruitful approach, developed especially by
the European school of ethology, is by closely detailed study of differences in behavioral complexes
that are species-specific within clusters of closely
related species. Most extensive and perhaps most
interesting are the data on mating or, more broadly,
reproductive behavior in birds, and that subject
is here reviewed in Chapter 12. Explanation is
sought mainly in terms of microevolutionary processes.

Constantly recurrent in the preceding or almost
any other discussions of behavior is the problem of
learning, of its role in various behaviors, and of its
evolutionary status or involvement. Chapter 13,
sometimes provocatively unorthodox, confirms the
general impression of over-all evolutionary increase in learning capacity while denying the existence of truly qualitative changes or marked discontinuities in that aspect of evolution. The nature of
learning is also discussed, and a particular theory of
learning is expounded and defended on evolutionary as well as other grounds.

A final category of behavior that could not be
omitted from any conscientious sampling is that of

social behavior. Some of the peculiar features of human social behavior are deferred to Part V, and some decidedly social types of behavior in other animals have already been discussed, especially in Chapter 12. Chapter 14 seeks to give a taxonomy and frame of reference for use in the evolutionary study of social behavior, and Chapter 15 is devoted to the outstanding examples of nonhuman social behavior, in the social insects, with emphasis on the thorough applicability of general evolutionary principles to this particular field of behavioral evolution.

9

Axes of Behavioral Comparison

Henry W. Nissen [1]

YERKES LABORATORIES OF PRIMATE BIOLOGY

1. THE CATEGORIZATION OF BEHAVIOR

IN THIS and the following six chapters we are to consider, in some detail, the data of behavior. More specifically, we are to examine the constancies and similarities, as well as the larger and smaller differences in behaviors exhibited by animals of diverse sizes, shapes, and internal organization.

A survey of all animal behavior obviously could not be attempted within the scope of a few chapters. Even a comprehensive outline would be either too long or else too sketchy to be at all useful. The compromise solution adopted in these chapters is to sample the area so as to include a variety of behaviors and of animal forms. The many resulting omissions in the materials presented will be obvious. The reader will note, also, that the several topics or chapter headings of this section are not correlative; they vary from discussion of a single behavioral mechanism assumed to be operative in all animals to a detailed consideration of situationally defined behaviors within a single taxonomic category. For a more systematic coverage of the field, the reader might start with one of the standard references, such as Warden, Jenkins, and Warner (1935, 1936, 1940), Maier and Schneirla (1935), or Washburn (1936).

For a phylogenetic comparison of behavior, the problem of classification, of identifying the most meaningful and useful dimensions and descriptive units of behavior, is of basic importance. Indeed, one may say it is *the* problem of psychology generally.

1. Preparation of this chapter was aided by grants from the Rockefeller Foundation and from the Carnegie Corporation of New York.

Various approaches toward a definition of the vectors of mind, the main axes of behavior, have been made, but none of these has been found entirely satisfactory. Some are quite specific and quantitative but cover only a narrow range of behavior. Others are inclusive but are too vaguely formulated to suggest or permit experimental verification. Psychologists are agreed that muscle contractions, or even flexions and extensions, are not the proper descriptive units for their science, and they are likewise agreed that such broad concepts as "intelligence" and the "instinct of self-preservation" are even less useful. But between these extremes there remain many possible bases of classification.

The categories used for comparisons of behavior may themselves be grouped into three classes: (A) functional or finalistic, (B) descriptive, and (C) explanatory, and these are often intermingled as if they belonged in the same universe of discourse. We speak of food getting and reproduction, which are functional classes; locomotion, which is descriptive; and territoriality, social behavior, and learning, which, depending on how they are treated, may be either descriptive or explanatory classes. The functional categories indicate the biological utility of behavior, its purpose in the sense of how it promotes the welfare of the individual and species. They point up the similarities or likenesses of animals. The descriptive and explanatory categories on the other hand stress the means, the mechanisms or processes by which the purposes are achieved; and, in respect to these, animals differ greatly.

Finally, it should be noted that explanatory categories are of several kinds: (C-1) The behavior of a species may be explained in terms of its phylogenetic history. As the behavior of an individual is a function of his heredity plus his individual experiences, so the behavior of a species derives from that of its phylogenetic precursors plus the effects of mutations and selective pressures. (C-2) Behavior may be explained reductively by identifying its neural, hormonal, and other physical substrates. Physiological psychology represents the attempt to derive behavioral phenomena from the established principles of presumably simpler, underlying levels of organization. (C-3) General laws, principles, or mechanisms of behavior, formulated without reference to genetic antecedents or physiological determinants, may be used singly or in combination, to account for any particular instance or aspect of behavior. Such laws and principles may be phrased in mentalistic or operational terms and sometimes take the form of mathematical statements or of models derived by analogy from physics or chemistry.

As Hebb (1949) and others have pointed out, these three kinds of explanation often supplement and correct each other most helpfully, and it may be hoped that eventually they will be integrated into a unified and self-consistent whole. In the meantime, however, one or another type must be adopted as basis for discussion, and at least temporarily a subordinate role assigned to the others. In the present chapter we shall try to indicate how the facts may be ordered under laws or principles derived from the behavioral level of organization—that is under C-3 categories. A few groups of mechanisms, of broad applicability, will be suggested; they should be thought of as first approximations to more specific, experimentally more testable, formulations.

Before resuming the main theme of this chapter, in sections 5 and 6, we devote the next three sections to a consideration of some special features of behavior in the general evolutionary process.

2. The Status of Behavior in Phylogeny and Taxonomy

Common sense makes it obvious that the behavior of animals is a major contributing factor for their survival and, consequently, through the mechanisms of heredity, for the course of evolution. Maintaining favorable relations with the environment is largely a function of behavior. Possessing efficient skeletal, circulatory, digestive, sense organ, and effector systems is not enough. All these must be used effectively in activities such as food getting, reproduction, and defense. Behavioral incompetence leads to extinction as surely as does morphological disproportion or deficiency in any vital organ. Behavior is subject to selection as much as bodily size or resistance to disease.

We say this is obvious, and yet it is mostly an inference. The record of evolution, which is the fossil record, tells us very little about behavior. Bone structures may indicate the manner of locomotion used, and fossil tracks may fill in some details, such as the gait and the speed of locomotion. The form of the teeth, together with contemporary plant and animal fossils, may suggest the kind of food eaten, and this in turn may indicate whether the animal was predaceous, whether it browsed or grazed, and so on.

But even this is largely inference, usually involving analogy with living forms. We do not have, and cannot have, a "phylogenetic psychology" in the sense that we have a phylogenetic morphology. The primary data are lacking. No reporters or cameramen were on hand during the past billion years or so to make a documentary film of "evolution on the march," and nothing less than this could serve our need. Comparative psychology reveals differences of behavior among living animals, but that behavior X, which is relatively simple, preceded behavior Y, which is more complex or more adaptive, is at best a reasonable guess. The best we can do is to borrow paleontological evidence that animal A immediately preceded animal B, that living animals A_1 and B_1 are fairly representative of A and B, and so attempt to reconstruct a phylogeny of behavior.

This limitation on certain knowledge of phylogenetic succession does not deny the validity of behavioral characters, where they are known, for indicating taxonomic relationships. In the absence of geological-paleontological evidence, the data of comparative psychology are no less relevant than are the data of comparative anatomy. As Mayr points out in this volume, behavioral differences and similarities are often more revealing than are morphological ones. Furthermore, it seems just as logical and possible that an adaptive behavior should give selective value to a related structural character as that an adaptive anatomic feature should lend selective advantage to behavior which incorporates or exploits that structure. Obviously genes do not transmit either structures or behavior as such, but instead carry the necessary physicochemical substrates or conditions of these structures and behaviors. There is no a priori reason for supposing that genic variation (and selection) of neural determinants regularly either follows or precedes variation (and selection) of the determinants of structures other than those of the nervous system. Mayr suggests that the question "Structure first or behavior first?" must be analyzed separately in each case. Those instances in which a change in peripheral structure lags behind, or is not followed by, an associated change in behavior, or vice versa, are of course especially conspicuous. However, the possibility of selection for variations in structure and behavior that occur in combination, more or less simultaneously, should not be overlooked.

3. Distinctive Features of Behavior as Adaptive Mechanism

Behavior as a factor contributing to survival differs from other adaptive mechanisms or characters in several respects.

1. Most obviously, it involves a maximum integration of component parts and processes. A change in the color, or color patterning, of feathers, may have intrinsic adaptive value, more or less independent of other characters. But a change in visual acuity is without significance except as it modifies behavior, and this involves also motor and transmissive elements. Behavior always, and without exception, requires the mutually interdependent action of sensory, motor, and integrating systems. Independent functioning of any one of these is almost unthinkable, and at best it could produce only chaotic squirmings, spasms, dreams, or hallucinations. As many students of behavior have pointed out, behavior is a molar phenomenon, as contrasted to the relatively molecular phenomena with which physiologists, for instance, are concerned. This contrast is reflected in the classical definition of behavior as a function of the organism-as-a-whole. The distinction is relative, but it is certainly true that psychology deals with the most complex unit, the highest level of integration, dealt with by any of the so-called biological sciences. And, conversely, it represents the basic unit for all so-called social sciences. Psychology can be thought of as a two-way funnel, into which the biological sciences converge and from which the social sciences diverge (Nissen, 1954).

2. A second feature characterizing behavior as an adaptive mechanism is the variety and changeableness of the forms which it may take. The function of a muscle is relatively constant; its response may vary quantitatively, but its effect is pretty well determined by its locus and insertions. But in behavior, which can only be described or defined in terms of an organism-environment relationship, that muscle may participate in approach to food, flight from danger, mating, or holding an infant. Objectively identical sensory elements or stimuli elicit differing responses, depending on the spatial patterning or temporal sequence of those elements (Tinbergen, 1948). And the identical spatio-temporal patterning of the sensory field may evoke different reactions at different times, depending on the internal state of the organism— its fatigue, degree of deprivation, and hormonal conditions, for

instance. Furthermore, behavior varies with past experience; events which occurred a minute, an hour, a day, a year, or fifty years ago may contribute to the determination of response to the present stimulus situation. In the case of the so-called higher animals, not just one or two such past events but probably hundreds and thousands of them have their influence on present behavior. Considering the large number of determining factors—environmental, intraorganic, and experiential—and the enormously larger number of permutations which are possible among them, the variability of behavior is hardly surprising. By comparison, the functioning of other adaptive characters and mechanisms is relatively simple and constant.

3. Variable and changeable as it is, behavior also manifests some remarkable constancies, namely in its end results. By and large, the activities of organisms lead to rather specific goals, these being such as to maintain favorable relations of the organism to its environment—thermal, chemical, nutritional, mechanical, and so on. The same final outcome (e.g. eating) may follow a sequence of random, trial-and-error responses; a largely innate or instinctual pattern; a learned, habitual sequence; or an "insightful" response. The end result, furthermore, may be viewed either as the final act, often called a consummatory response or unconditioned reflex, or, alternatively, as the attainment of an object or condition which promotes the welfare of the individual or species, such as the ingestion of food or care of the young. Ordinarily, in the environment to which the animal is adapted, these two aspects go together; ingestion of food usually accompanies the act of swallowing. The European ethologists (Lorenz, 1937) contend that the psychological "goal" is the final movement, the *Erbkoordination,* and that this is distinct from the biological goal of getting food into the stomach. However that may be, the high degree of correlation, in nature, between the two aspects of finality, namely the act and its consequence, makes this a problem of subsidiary importance in the context of behavioral evolution.

4. ALTERNATIVES IN ADAPTATION

Within rather wide limits, there are alternative ways of achieving adaptation. The very fact that animals of extremely diverse sizes and shapes, with widely differing organs and organ systems,

exist, and more or less successfully persist, documents this substitutiveness of adaptive mechanisms. It is convenient, in this
connection, to make a distinction between adaptive mechanisms
which concern primarily the internal economy of the organism
and those which determine the relations of the animal to its external environment. The digestive and circulatory systems are
examples of the former, speed of locomotion and acuity of the
sense organs refer to the latter. In general, what is in common
usage called behavior comprises mechanisms for the regulation
of organism-environment relationships, and these are the principal mechanisms available to the organism for this purpose.
Structural features obviously contribute in this respect also—the
thickness and toughness of the integument, for instance, and
whether it is provided with oil and sweat glands, fur, or spines.
Many other anatomical or morphological features are useful—
adaptive, that is—only as the physical substrates of behavior. In
themselves claws and fangs, for instance, are only a drain on the
internal economy of the organism. They, and their associated
muscles, have their biological meaning as contributing elements
in the behaviors of food getting and defense.

Behavior, therefore, may substitute for structural and physiological features, and behavioral limitations may be compensated
for by other adaptive characters or mechanisms. Heavy armor
protects against predators, but so may alertness, speed of flight,
cunning, bluffing, or fighting ability. Modifications in the digestive system may enable the animal to get along with the inferior
diet which is provided by inefficient food-getting behavior.

The general principle of substitutiveness of adaptive mechanisms may be seen also *within* that wide range of phenomena
called behavior. To start with the simple, we have alternative
avenues of sensory contact with the world, and alternative overt
ways of moving and manipulating. All animals are sensitive to certain modalities, but even here poor discrimination in one sense
may be compensated for by high sensitivity in another. Movement
through space can be achieved by one of a variety of effectors, and
"manipulation" is possible by many organs other than the hand.

The most interesting and perhaps the most significant behavioral alternatives, however, pertain to what we loosely call the
central or integrating mechanism. The first order of differentiation or dichotomization in this respect goes by various names,

such as nature-nurture, genetic or innate vs. experiential determination, instinct vs. intelligence, predetermined vs. free behavior, and reflexive and tropistic vs. plastic, docile, or flexible
behavior. Despite the careless and ill-considered way in which
these terms have been applied, and despite the emotional, religious, and moralistic "charge" which they often carry, the distinction is a scientifically useful one. It is a verifiable fact that in some
species behavior is highly uniform from individual to individual,
and that complex activities are executed precisely and with minimum opportunity for learning by imitation, tuition, insight, trial-
and-error, or otherwise. In other species analogous activities—let
us say food getting, shelter construction, and disposal of excre-
ments—may be individually variable, and are demonstrably the
products of learning or experience. The fact that many activities,
formerly thought to be innate or instinctive, have since been
shown to be modifiable does not negate the validity and importance of the distinction, nor does the fact, stressed by Schiller
(1952) and others, that all so-called learned behavior incorporates,
or is based on, genetically determined constituents. The capacity
to learn, to profit by experience, is of course itself inherited;
species and individuals vary both quantitatively and qualitatively
in this hereditary endowment. When the taxonomist says that he
is interested only in that part of behavior which has a genetic
basis, he does not thereby exclude the phenomena of ontogenetic
acquisitions, since these certainly do have an all-important genetic
basis.

(It may actually be that some of the differences between what
we call genetic and experiential determination may reduce to a
difference in degree of readiness to learn. In other words some
animals with a rather limited repertoire of activities learn this
repertoire with extreme rapidity, whereas others with a much
wider potential range of activities learn more slowly. The phenomenon of *Prägung* or imprinting, as seen in geese (Lorenz,
1935), fits this interpretation, as does the extremely slow achievement of even simple locomotion and perceptual ability in the
case of man, who is the "learningest" of all animals. The fact that
adult man seems to learn very rapidly is no argument against this
view, since adult human behavior involves little new learning,
being guided mostly by the application of old learning to new
but similar situations. Generalization, abstraction, transfer, and

transposition are not the same thing as learning, although they may require previous learning. What goes by the name of thinking is mostly a recitation of old habits in a slightly different context; applying the old formula to atoms instead of apples. However this may be, and even if it turns out that all behavior involves a learning component, the species differences in relative importance, amount, and rate of learning are so great that giving the extremes of the continuum different names, such as innate and acquired, is justified and useful.)

5. AXES OF COMPARISON: FORMAL ASPECTS

In accounting for any behavioral event, we must consider both its formal and its motivational aspects. In respect to the former, we ask why this particular environmental situation or stimulus is followed by this particular response. Secondly, we seek to explain the frequency and frequency distribution of the stimulus-response sequence; why it may be almost invariable (as in a reflex), occasional (as in "spontaneous" or trial-and-error behavior), or periodic (as in reproductive, feeding, or other "drive" behavior). That the formal and motivational aspects are closely interrelated is seen especially in the phenomena of learning, where the form of a new behavior—an instrumental act—depends in part on the frequency or probability of a contiguous event or behavior.

The factors responsible for the form of behavior include (a) response or effector mechanisms, (b) receptor mechanisms, and (c) integrative mechanisms. The present section is concerned with these formal aspects of behavior, and especially with the mechanisms of central integration. The following section is devoted to the impulsive or motivational aspects.

a. The rubric of effector mechanisms includes everything that the animal can do, but particularly motor responses which, by muscular contractions, produce movements of the body as a whole or of its parts. A subdivision of motor acts into those of locomotion and of manipulation (which would include such acts as biting, striking, stinging, spitting, throwing, and ramming) is usually made. In some animals the coordinations required by locomotor and manipulative actions are determined almost entirely by inherited organization, whereas in others these motor skills are acquired only by long periods of learning and practice.

Learning capacity usually provides a greater potential scope of differentiated and coordinated movements than does pre-experiential organization.

b. The second group of mechanisms determines the various sense modalities or forms of energy to which the animal is sensitive, the degree of sensitivity in terms of absolute and differential thresholds, and the ability to analyze and synthesize sensory elements.

c. Our third main division, integrative mechanisms, includes a multiplicity of behavioral phenomena which are as yet very poorly understood. Some theorists have tried to subsume them all under a single principle, whereas others have postulated a few or many distinct processes or mechanisms. Our present discussion will consider them under three major subgroups: *perception, learning,* and *reasoning,* which will be taken up in that order.

Analyzing and synthesizing sensory impressions depend first of all on refinements of the sense organs, but are mainly functions of central mechanisms, and thus represent the transition from so-called sensory to cognitive abilities. The bat surpasses man not only in being able to hear minimal intensities of high-frequency tones—which is primarily a sensory difference—but also in responding to the distance and direction of the source, which is a difference in *perception,* involving central integration of sensory elements (Griffin, 1953). A chimpanzee, whose optical apparatus is as good as ours, cannot distinguish among different spatial and temporal patternings of the same visual and auditory elements as well as we can (Spragg, 1936).

Again, animals differ in the genetic basis of their perceptual abilities, some having a small but fairly complete repertoire at birth, whereas others must build up their perceptions in the course of experience. Recent work has shown that in some of the higher animals at least—such as man and the apes—most percepts are products of learning. The newborn chimpanzee does not see, in the ordinary sense of the word; he needs time and practice—some three or four months—to recognize his milk bottle and to differentiate between familiar and unfamiliar faces (Riesen, 1950).

In birds, fishes, and insects, on the other hand, many perceptions seem to be innately organized, and therefore do not have to be learned (Tinbergen, 1951). A given visual pattern, for instance a specific distribution of light on the retina, elicits the same response on early as well as later encounters with that pattern. The ethologists call these innate perceptual organizations "inherited releasing schemata" or *Auslöser*. What these schemata release or elicit are simple inherited movement patterns or motor coordinations, constant for the species, called *Erbkoordinationen* or *Instinkthandlungen*. The innate organization of instinctive behavior may thus comprise three, at least partially independent, integrations: perceptions, motor co-ordinations, and perceptual-motor connections.

A major dimension of difference among animals is the sheer number of percepts and concepts available to the organism. Certain relations, such as "middleness," can serve as a stimulus for some species but not for others (Spence, 1939). In general, it appears that the animals which learn most of their perceptions have a much wider range of potential stimuli—that is, percepts and concepts which may guide their behavior—than do those animals with innately organized perceptions. To put it another way, we may say that intelligence is a function of the number of things or events—colors, odors, tones, pressures, forms, and especially combinations of these in spatial and temporal arrangements (percepts and concepts)—which are or can be stimuli, and of the number of discrete kinds of response that can be made. (Incidentally, just where perceptions leave off and concepts begin is impossible to say; these terms represent quantitative differences on a continuum, to the extremes of which we apply different names.)

Perception, then, comprises one group of integrative mechanisms in which animals differ. Another one is the *learning* of habits, forming new S-R connections or perceptual-motor associations. Such learning is often dichotomized in one or another way: classical vs. instrumental conditioning, for instance. It may be noted in passing that classical, or simple Pavlovian conditioning does not show any significant differences among the diverse species that have been tested (Razran, 1933). Species differences in the S-R connecting process are in (a) the direction and duration of the time interval which can elapse between the association to be made and its direct or signified homeostatic consequences for the organism (Hilgard, 1956), (b) in the speed (required number of experiences) with which such secondary or remote associations can be made (Harlow, 1949), and (c) in the number of habits or associations that can be concurrently functional (Nissen, 1951a).

It may be noted these same factors are effective in the process of acquiring percepts and concepts. Concepts like "color" and "form" are certainly not innate in any organism. They require experience with many forms and with many colors, experiences which are disconnected in time. They furthermore require a responsiveness to the differences among colors and among forms, plus a responsiveness to what is common to colors as contrasted to what is common to forms. Once achieved, the class concepts of color and of form are stimuli which contribute to the determination of behavior. Young and Harlow (1943) have shown that color and form can be stimuli for monkeys, enabling them to solve the generalized conditional matching problem, and more recently this has been shown for one chimpanzee also (Nissen, Blum, and Blum, 1949). This is an extremely difficult and time-consuming achievement for nonhuman primates, and thus far it has not been shown to be within the range of infraprimate capacity.

Our final consideration in respect to integrative mechanisms comprises those processes referred to as abstraction, generalization, transfer, and so on. As good a term as any to embrace all of these is *reasoning*. Some of you might prefer the word "thinking." Without taking time now to elucidate the argument, let me categorically suggest that all reasoning reduces to three processes: responsiveness to identity and to difference, and, thirdly, the balance, or relative weight given to each of these. The child hurt by a knife may thereafter be afraid of all shiny steel objects, of anything resembling a knife—or even of all people, because a person held the knife when he was hurt. This child is responding to identical elements, or similarities, with a vengeance. Another child, similarly hurt, may not learn to be careful with knives generally because other knives are in one way or another different from the particular one that cut him. I once had a chimpanzee whose consistent choice of black versus white was destroyed when the two plaques were moved an inch back from their usual positions. The term reasoning is usually reserved for higher level integrations—that is, for response to similarities and differences among units (percepts and concepts) which are themselves the product of previous organizations of experience. All class concepts require simultaneous responsiveness to identities among members of the class, and to differences between them and members of other classes. The balance between the two we may call sagacity; "judgment" might be an even better term.

In all attempts to characterize the uniqueness of human intelligence, the factor of language, propositional language, is emphasized. The essence of words is that they summarize many past experiences into a manageable unit; that is, they produce or represent a temporal integration of many diverse experiences. The use of words as a tool of thinking or reasoning or problem-solving, therefore, means that a huge number of past experiences are being effective in determining present behavior. Language, or verbal mediating responses, represent an instance of extremely efficient central integration with which we, as educated human adults, are especially familiar. But language does not seem to introduce any really new psychological process; it may be thought of, rather, as an instrumental means or technique which enormously increases the speed and efficiency of processes already present to some extent in nonverbalizing animals. Some problems that we may solve with the aid of language—delayed response, the maze, instrumental and detour problems—animals master without the use of verbal responses.

6. Axes of Comparison: Motivational Aspects

Now that we have summarized in sketchy fashion the formal or cognitive aspect of behavior, it remains to consider the dynamic or motivational side—what impels the organism to behave at all. Much of the confusion and controversy about instinct has arisen, I believe, because of the failure to keep these two aspects separate. The impulsion to do something, to act, is common to all behavior. The random squirmings of the human infant and the execution of a well-trained habit are just as forceful, irrepressible and compulsive as the heliotropism of an insect or the single-minded concentration of the web-weaving spider. The difference between instinctive and learned behavior is in the etiology of the *form* in which the energy expresses itself: innate organization in one case, experience in the other.

The dynamics of behavior seem to be essentially alike in the two cases. They rest, ultimately, on the inherent attribute of all living matter to be sensitive; that is, to be responsive to stimuli. The very definitions of stimulus and response, which are circular, point to this conclusion: an S is something that produces a response, and a response is something that follows an S. The etiology of the connection between this stimulus and that response does not enter into this definition; it may be either innate or learned.

Every S-R has a threshold value; that is, a minimum intensity of S is necessary to evoke R. Some S-R thresholds are chronically low, and then we have a reflex, or tropistic behavior. If the threshold is consistently low because of previous experience or learning, we speak of a conditioned reflex or habit. Other thresholds are variably high and low, and then response is uncertain; it may or may not occur. Or a given S may be connected with a number of R's; when the thresholds of these several S-R's are approximately equal we get so-called random or trial-and-error behavior; the same stimulus situation elicits first one and then another response.

So far we have considered only very simple S-R's which are completed almost as soon as they are started. One of the great puzzles of behavior stems from longer sequences of acts which lead, in one way or another, to a biologically adaptive outcome. Construction of a web by the spider; stalking of prey by the predator; a rat running a maze, at first making many errors but later avoiding all the blind alleys; and the economic behavior of civilized man are examples of such prolonged, drawn-out sequences. By themselves, the earlier or preparatory parts of the sequence have no utility; in and for themselves they make no sense. Only when looked at in toto is the behavior seen to be adaptive. The psychological unit is not a muscle contraction, the extension or flexion of a limb, a turn to the right or left, but rather the whole sequence of acts. It is this unit which, as we say, manifests purpose. And the unit is just as purposive when it consists of a series of innately organized elements, such as those we call instinctive behavior, as when it is the result of repeated experiences in a maze or other problem situation.

These larger units of behavior do not occur at any and all times. The animal has to be in the right mood, or *Stimmung,* as the ethologists say. Or, as the American experimentalists would put it, the animal has to be put on a deprivation schedule; it has to be made hungry, or thirsty, or it must first be made fearful by having a painful experience in the learning situation. Intervals between the occurrences of such units may be fairly short, as in food-getting activities or the defecation ritual of the dog; or they may be quite long, as in the reproductive activities of seasonally breeding animals. We have learned how to change or speed up these intervals—by injecting hormones, for instance. What the hormone does, evidently, is to activate a latent pattern of serial activities. S-R thresholds are lowered—not all thresholds, but specifically those related to the mood or need of the moment. How this differential sensitization occurs is of course very imperfectly understood. In some cases it must be that certain synapses or brain centers are sensitive to chemicals which have no effect, or an opposite effect, on other parts of the brain. In other cases there may be sensory facilitation from peripheral structures on specific central mechanisms. Stimulation from her tumescent perineal area evidently facilitates certain responses of the female chimpanzee to visually mediated stimuli, especially those emanating from a male chimpanzee (Birch and Clark, 1950).

However that may be, the mechanisms by which larger units of behavior are activated seem to be essentially the same, whether the sequence is random activity, trial-and-error behavior with gradual elimination of useless or maladaptive acts, or whether it is a precise, uniform, smoothly executed series which is innately determined or is the result of past learning. The term "drive" has usually been applied only in reference to behavior in which learning is possible or has occurred. With the present interpretation it is equally applicable to instinctive behavior; in either case the term refers to a sensitizing agent, effective over a period of time, which, by differentially lowering thresholds, increases the probability of occurrence of a particular concatenation of acts. The goal or end result of the drive is the same for instinctual as for habitual behavior; it restores the homeostasis whose imbalance activated the sensitizing agent in the first place.

The sensitizing factors or drives that we see expressed in the behavior of most animals are clearly innate, quite independent of experience. When the juices flow, the male seeks out the female and mates; when blood sugar drops, the animal's behavior becomes organized into food-getting activities, whether the form of these is organized innately or by experience.

Now the behavior of man in particular often takes directions and pursues goals which seem to have little or no relation to homeostatic needs or perpetuation of the species. The pursuit of purely intellectual interests, all kinds of artistic endeavor, and the striving toward altruistic, ethical, and religious ideals do not always and directly promote the material welfare of the individual or species. Two kinds of explanation have been proposed for this discrepancy. One explanation assumes that man has more drives than do subhuman animals; in addition to "animal impulses" he has "spiritual" or "higher" motives. That is, man has not only biogenic or viscerogenic drives like other animals but also psychogenic drives. The latter are often thought of as being derived from, or secondary to, the former. Love and affection, altruism and humanitarianism, for instance, are said to stem from the fact that during the long period of human helplessness parents and other people have helped to satisfy the nutritional and other primary drives. In and through this association, it is said, a new, autonomous drive—the social drive—comes into being.

With our present dearth of experimental evidence, this possibility cannot be proved or disproved, but several considerations argue against adopting it as a working hypothesis. First of all, if we start multiplying the number of drives by derivation from primary drives, there is no logical stopping place; we will find ourselves with a list of hundreds of drives and the end never in sight. This is exactly what happened with instincts, and is what brought that concept into disrepute. To postulate a new instinct or a new drive for every new bit of behavior is not to explain it, nor to bring order out of chaos. A second argument is that sensitizing agents, selectively lowering S-R thresholds as in primary drives, have not been identified for the so-called secondary drives. It seems most improbable, furthermore, that such agents, comparable to those provided by the inherited constitution and common to all animals, could be acquired in ontogeny. The third and final argument is that there is a more economical, and I think more plausible, solution.

This alternative locates the source of superficially or apparently nonbiogenic behavior in cognitive rather than in motivational characteristics. It says, in brief, that the complexities and indirections of man's behavior are a function of his superior intellective equipment, which allows him to approach and attain his homeostatic goals more efficiently, and more deviously, than do other animals. Deviousness and efficiency are especially conspicuous in the realm of social interaction, where communication by language, cooperation, specialization and division of labor provide a maximum satisfaction of homeostatic needs with a minimum of effort. According to this view, man's drives are not unique; they are all primary and innate, and are the same as those that motivate all animal behavior. What is unique in human behavior is the much larger number of subgoals, the indirectness of the means by which man attains his ends. Man's intellectual ability to see that the long way around may be the most effective approach, which we call foresight, distinguishes him from other learning animals.

An analogue of foresight is seen in the instinctive web or hive constructions of the arthropods, and especially in some of their reproductive or race-preserving activities. Such activities, with their temporarily remote consequences, are analogous to the long-range planning of man, but the cognitive mechanisms are clearly different.

7. BEHAVIOR AND EVOLUTION

The quantitative differences in perception, learning, and reasoning, or rather the differences in their relative importance for the animal, have significant consequences for evolution. Rigidly fixed responses to innately determined stimulus patterns may be highly adaptive in a stable environment. But if the environment —physical or social—changes, the releasing patterns may be absent or the responses to them may no longer have biological utility. For the individual organism, at least, this is fatal. Thoday's "unit of evolution" can then survive and demonstrate its fitness only by means of genetic variability. Theoretically, such variability can lead in one of two directions. First, it can lead to the selection of a new set of releasers and Instinkthandlungen, adaptive under the changed conditions. The insects perhaps furnish the best illustration of a large number of species, each with a rigid set of innate behavior determinants, and each set being favorable in a different adaptive zone. The other main direction is that which—again via genetic processes and selection—leads toward a genetic constitution that permits *phenotypic* flexibility. In the extreme case, phenotypic flexibility makes the organism relatively independent of the environment; its intelligence allows it to adapt, within limits, to geographically and temporally varying conditions.

One of the more striking evolutionary consequences of intelligent, in contrast to instinctive, behavior, is that it reduces the probability of further speciation. As Mayr (1950, p. 116) has said, "If the single species man occupies successfully all the niches that are open for a *Homo*-like creature, it is obvious that he cannot speciate."

8. THE QUESTION OF PHYLOGENETIC TRENDS IN BEHAVIOR

Simpson (1952, p. 159) has said that "the major (if not the only) nonrandom, orienting factor in the process of evolution is reasonably identified as adaptation." According to this view, linear evolution is determined by the nature of the environment, which gives greater and lesser selective value to one or another direction of deviation from the species average or norm. Both direction and magnitude of possible deviations are, of course, delimited by genetic factors: genic variability and the occurrence of mutations. Within these limits, and in a stable environment or in one changing slowly but consistently in a given direction, there would be selection for a linear series of adaptations. Oriented evolution would likewise be manifested as a species came to occupy adjacent zones or subzones which differed from the original one in a graded series of unidirectional steps. Occasionally, quantitative change in a consistent direction may have survived also the cataclysm of an interzonal shift (Simpson's quantum evolution), but here a given trend would often be obscured, modified, or reversed by major qualitative or discontinuous changes in the pattern of adaptive mechanisms.

The foregoing considerations apply as well to behavior as to purely structural characters, and what we know of the phylogeny of behavior substantiates their implications. If we limit ourselves to sufficiently small sections of evolution, trends in specific behavioral traits can be discerned. Activity increases, a sense organ becomes more or less sensitive, certain effectors become stronger or deteriorate, learning capacity increases, and so on. But as we extend our view to broader segments of the taxonomic range, the plottings of *discrete* behavioral (as of structural) characteristics show great irregularities, discontinuities, and reversals of direction. There is no indication here of a persisting trend in the evolution of behavior.

Nevertheless, as we scan the total range of animal life, and focus especially on its early and end points, the impression remains that there has been some consistency in the direction of behavioral evolution. The primary data, and especially the present status of psychological analysis, are inadequate to the task of satisfactorily substantiating this impression. It may nevertheless be useful to speculate on how evidence for major trends in behavior might be revealed, and the remainder of this section outlines one possible procedure for testing the hypothesis.

A well-known device for smoothing out the irregularities in a complex of individual curves is to pool the data and to draw a single curve representing the averages. (Needless to say, this procedure must be applied with discretion, since it obscures some facts while clarifying others.) I have discussed above the substitutiveness of adaptations; a number of quite diverse mechanisms, as seen in different animals, have essentially the same effect or biological utility. It may be that some orderliness in behavioral evolution will appear if, instead of considering each particular character (or trait, or mechanism) separately, we group together those characters which are behavioral equivalents or alternatives.[2]

The decision as to which mechanisms may legitimately be combined in one class requires a degree of theoretical analysis that at present has only been approximated; the attempt will therefore involve some arbitrariness and guesswork. Technically even more difficult is the assignment of units of measurement by which average "scores" may be obtained for the quantitative comparison of species in respect to a given class of behavioral traits or capacities. This difficulty is exemplified in our first proposed category of "sensory capacity." Since contact with the environment may be had through any of the sense organs, a single index representing the several modalities would permit a meaningful comparison of species having differential capacity in each. It is at once apparent that obtaining such an average score involves the equating of fixed degrees of visual acuity, color vision, auditory acuity, and so on—certainly a formidable undertaking. However, common sense and experience tell us that the several senses *are* roughly interchangeable in bringing us knowledge about our surroundings, and in information theory we already have some indications of how this fact may be quantified.

2. Referring back to the first section of this chapter, it will be noted that we are here proposing a functional (A) grouping of explanatory (C) categories.

The second category of behavioral functions to be grouped on the basis of having similar or equivalent effects is "locomotion." It is assumed that which particular mechanism of locomotion (e.g. swimming, crawling, flying) an animal uses in approaching— or withdrawing—is, for present purposes, irrelevant. Having multiple means of locomoting, instead of only one, however, would add to the score in this category, as would speed relative to distances covered in the animal's vital activities.

A third grouping suggested is "manipulation," in which similar criteria of scoring would be applied.

Sensory and effector capacities set limits to the possible variety and complexity of behavior. The most important differences in the behavior of individuals and species, however, are functions of central integrative mechanisms. How these capacities should be grouped and quantified poses a new set of difficulties.

It has been pointed out previously that sensory organization, motor patterning, and sensorimotor connections may be largely innate or, instead, depend greatly on experience. For present purposes we shall make no distinctions based on the etiology of an organization. A habit is treated as the equivalent of a reflex or tropistic response, an acquired perception is equated with an innate Auslöser, and an Erbkoordination is considered the counterpart of a learned skill. If it is true, as was suggested above, that the potential scope of central organizations is greater when these are determined mainly by experience rather than by inherited patterns of integration, this fact will be reflected in the averaged score of the relevant category.

We do not usually apply the terms "reasoning," "judgment," and "sagacity" to instinctive behavior, but we do recognize in the latter the phenomena of summation, facilitation, inhibition, and prepotency, and these imply similar processes with similar effects. We therefore shall not here attempt to distinguish between (a) a "rational" or "deliberate" choice and (b) a resolution of central interactions determined by innately organized facilitative and inhibitory processes.

For the present, three groupings of organizing functions are suggested: "perception conceptualization," "sensorimotor connections," and "reasoning." In each of these classes the numerical score would represent the sum of incidences tabulated in an extensive survey which included both field observation and analytical experimentation. Although we shall not soon proceed with confidence in quantifying the needed information in this area, it is clear that behavioral science must move in the direction where this becomes possible.

The procedures suggested above would yield, for any species, six scores—one for each of the six named functional categories (sensory capacities, locomotion, manipulation, perception, sensori-motor connections, and reasoning.) [3] A seventh score would represent the average of these six. The final step would be to choose points on the geologic time scale and, on the basis of available scores, to select the most "advanced"—i.e. the highest scoring—species at each of these points. (On theoretical grounds it might be preferable to determine the average, in each category, of all species living at a given time. This possibility is rejected, in part because the selection will have to disregard genera and higher taxonomic levels not adequately represented by living animals, i.e. those for which no reasonable extrapolation from observed behavior can be made, as discussed in the second section of this paper.)

Now the aforementioned impression or hypothesis, that there has in fact been some consistency in the direction of behavioral evolution, would be substantiated if the seventh (average) curve showed a rise from the earliest to latest time points, with no intermediate reversals of this trend. Several subsidiary expectations may be indicated:

1. Curves of each of the six functional categories would show an over-all rise, with few plateaus and very few if any intermediate reversals.

2. Successive points on a curve would represent sometimes the same and sometimes different phyla or lower taxonomic levels.

3. There probably being a positive but imperfect correlation between the six groups of behavior functions plotted, most of the time points would be represented by less than seven different species on the seven curves. One species (man) would be represented on at least four curves at the latest point.

---

3. The total of these six scores provides an index of what I have elsewhere (1954) referred to as the complexity of behavior determination—the sheer number of factors deriving from past and present stimulation which contribute in determining present response.

9. SUMMARY

In the first section of this paper various bases for classifying behavior are reviewed. The status and distinctive features of behavior in adaptation are discussed in the next two sections. It is then pointed out that to a certain extent behavior and structural characteristics may serve as alternatives in adaptation, and that there are often two or more distinct behavioral mechanisms for achieving essentially the same biological result. Particular stress is placed on innate organization versus organization acquired through individual experience as alternative modes of behavioral adaptation.

The principal axes on which individuals and species may be compared in respect to behavior are identified as receptor, effector, integrative, and motivational mechanisms. The most significant phylogenetic differences, it is here concluded, are found in the dimension of central integration or cognitive capacities. The argument is advanced that differences in motivation, especially in the indirection with which goals are approached, derive from quantitative differences in the several aspects of cognition: perception, sensorimotor associations, and reasoning.

In the final section it is suggested that phylogenetic comparisons can be made in terms of classes of related behavioral functions, as well as in terms of discrete mechanisms. Based on six such functional categories, a procedure is suggested for testing the hypothesis that there has been some consistency in the direction of behavioral evolution.

REFERENCES

(Star indicates general background references.)

BIRCH, H. G., and CLARK, G. 1950. Hormonal modification of social behavior. IV. The mechanism of estrogen-induced dominance in chimpanzees. J. Comp. Physiol. Psychol., *43*, 181–93.

GRIFFIN, D. R. 1953. Sensory physiology and the orientation of animals. Amer. Sci., *41*, 209–44.

HARLOW, H. F. 1949. The formation of learning sets. Psychol. Rev., *56*, 51–65.

*HEBB, D. O. 1949. The organization of behavior. A neuropsychological theory. New York, Wiley.

HILGARD, E. R. 1956. Theories of learning. New York, Appleton-Century-Crofts.

LORENZ, K. 1935. Der Kumpan in der Umwelt des Vogels. Der Artgenosse als ausloesendes Moment sozialer Verhaltungsweisen. J. Ornithol., Leipzig, *83*, 137–213, 289–413.

LORENZ, K. 1937. Über die Bildung des

Instinktbegriffs. Naturwissenschaften, 25, 289–300, 307–18, 324–31.

*MAIER, N. R. F., and SCHNEIRLA, T. C. 1935. Principles of animal psychology. New York, McGraw-Hill.

MAYR, E. 1950. Taxonomic categories in fossil hominids. In Cold Spring Harbor Symposia on Quantitative Biology. Vol. 15, Origin and evolution of man.

MAYR, E. 1958. Behavior and systematics. Ch. 17 of this volume.

NISSEN, H. W. 1951a. Analysis of a complex conditional reaction in chimpanzee. J. Comp. Physiol. Psychol., 44, 9–16.

*NISSEN, H. W. 1951b. Phylogenetic comparison. In S. S. Stevens, ed., Handbook of experimental psychology. New York, Wiley, pp. 347–86.

NISSEN, H. W. 1954. Problems of mental evolution in the primate. Human Biology, 26, 277–87.

NISSEN, H. W., BLUM, J. S., and BLUM, R. A. 1949. Conditional matching behavior in chimpanzee; implications for the comparative study of intelligence. J. Comp. Physiol. Psychol., 42, 339–56.

RAZRAN, G. H. S. 1933. Conditioned responses in animals other than dogs. Psychol. Bull., 30, 261–324.

RIESEN, A .H. 1950. Arrested vision. Sci. Amer., 183, 16–19.

SCHILLER, P. H. 1952. Innate constituents of complex responses in primates. Psychol. Rev., 59, 177–91.

SIMPSON, G. G. 1952. The meaning of evolution. New Haven, Yale Univ. Press.

SPENCE, K. W. 1939. The solution of multiple choice problems by chimpanzees. Comp. Psychol. Monogr., 15 (3), 54.

SPRAGG, S. D. S. 1936. Anticipatory responses in serial learning by chimpanzee. Ibid., 13 (2), 72.

TINBERGEN, N. 1948. Social releasers and the experimental method required for their study. Wilson Bull., 60, 6–51.

TINBERGEN, N. 1951. The study of instinct. London, Oxford Univ. Press.

*WARDEN, C. J., JENKINS, T. N., and WARNER, L. H. 1935, 1940, 1936. Comparative psychology. Vols. 1, 2, 3. New York, Ronald Press.

*WASHBURN, M. F. 1936. The animal mind. 4th ed. New York, Macmillan.

YOUNG, M. L., and HARLOW, H. F. 1943. Generalization by rhesus monkeys of a problem involving the Weigl principle using the oddity method. J. Comp. Psychol., 36, 201–16.

10

Food-getting Behavior

Marston Bates

UNIVERSITY OF MICHIGAN

NISSEN, in the preceding chapter of this volume, has called food getting a "functional category" of behavior: equivalent thus to reproduction, dispersal, defense or protection, and the like. Descriptive categories cut right across these functional categories. Social behavior or territoriality, for instance, may facilitate food getting, reproduction, or protection (survival), or all three. And a particular functional category of behavior, like food getting, may involve many kinds of behavioral mechanisms such as stereotyped tropisms, conditioning, and various sorts of learning processes.

Food behavior, like a great many other particular subjects of study, turns out to involve many of the conventional subdivisions of the biological sciences. In the sense that the theory of natural selection depends on competition for food, or competition to avoid becoming food, food behavior is the very essence of this aspect of evolutionary study. The food interrelationships among organisms —food "chains" and food "webs"—are a major preoccupation of ecology. Biological communities and their various sorts of subdivisions are primarily definable and understandable in terms of such food relationships. In studying food behavior, then, we are studying the cement that holds the biological community together. Ecology and comparative psychology are thus concerned with the same subject matter.

Physiology and morphology are also involved. Here we have the old problem of structure versus function: probably a false and misleading dichotomy but firmly embedded in our thinking. The organ systems of an animal carcass are concrete objects that can be handled and described with a vocabulary in which there is a minimum of doubt about the reference of the different word symbols used. Classification can be built up and relationships analyzed with a reasonable degree of "objectivity." In a sense, though, these dead structures that we handle so easily are already abstractions, merely convenient symbols of the functioning organism and its parts. We might be said to fall into the "morphological fallacy" when we treat these dead structures as things-in-themselves.

Any attempt to abstract function from structure is probably equally fallacious, but the physiological fallacy is rarer than the morphological fallacy because function cannot be studied in the absence of the functioning structures. The reverse, however, is all too easy. We can study the evolution of the gut, for instance, through invertebrate phyla, or of mouth parts in the arthropods, with only passing reference to the functional significance of the changes we are describing. A balanced view, a putting together of the functional and structural aspects of evolutionary change, may be easier if, for a while, we try to overstress the functional aspects of the process.

It seems to me that biological studies of function have tended to fall into two categories: those concerned with the processes within the individual organism, and those concerned with the organism as a whole, functioning in its environmental context. The first, "skin in" biology, is usually called physiology. The second, "skin out" biology, is what I would like to call "natural history" though it is perhaps better called "ecology"—Haeckel originally proposed the word to cover the study of "outer phenomena" as contrasted with the "inner phenomena" studied by physiology in the strict sense.

The borders between physiology and psychology have long been blurred. Studies of the inner workings of an animal lead readily outward to studies of the orientation and coordinated functioning of the whole organism—studies of its "behavior," since we generally use this word in a skin-out sense. Yet the analysis of any behavior system soon shows the skin of the organism to be a purely arbitrary line of division across an integrated series of processes, so that skin-out psychology is immediately and intimately involved with skin-in physiology, with sense organ systems, nerve systems, and all of the rest. Thus any description of the system of "food-getting behavior" might start with the behavior governing the environmental orientation of the organism which puts it and keeps it in the context with appropriate food. This general behavior is then

the background for food-getting behavior in the strict sense—
adaptations for seizing prey, for getting at plants, for filtering food
particles from the medium, for penetrating the host. Here the
mouth, as a break in the skin system, in a way symbolizes the breakdown of the skin-out, skin-in division of behavior. Catching, chew-
ing, swallowing form a sequence that can hardly be broken up to
be studied by different branches of science.

Events after the food is caught are generally classed as "digestion" which, with sporadic exceptions, is clearly a "skin-in," physiological process. Yet the digestive enzymes, the gut morphology,
the adaptations with symbiotic micro-organisms, must all be geared
to the nature of the food, the nature of the materials to be digested
—which means also to the external, food-getting behavior of the
organism.

The problem of understanding the evolution of food-getting
behavior thus involves relating materials that are at present widely
scattered among diverse biological sciences. There is an immense
amount of information available, collected from the differing
points of view of these various sciences, but with our present framework of specialization it is difficult to put this together into a coherent account. A general review is, in any case, out of the question
in the present context; the most that can be done here is to indicate
the possibilities.

Food Behavior and Evolution

It is interesting to look at food behavior in relation, on the one
hand, to speciation and, on the other, to the origin and diversification of the major phyletic groups.

In studying speciation, we are apt to be more concerned with
reproductive behavior than with food-getting behavior: we have
come to define "species" in terms of reproductively isolated populations, and the problem of the origin of species thus becomes, in
one sense, the problem of the origin of this reproductive isolation.
There is, of course, no general feeling among students that the
beginnings of population isolation are to be found in diverging
sexual behavior. Subspecific isolation is generally presumed to depend on nonsexual mechanisms, especially on geographical separation, which allows sexual divergence to develop (Mayr, 1942, 1947).
While geographical separation is the best known of the incipient

isolating mechanisms, change in food habits which would bring about ecological isolation has often been suggested. This mechanism would seem especially probable with host-specific parasites and with insects closely associated with particular plant species (Thorpe, 1930; Dethier, 1954).

In general, however, we associate the evolution of food habits not with speciation but with the diversification of groups of species; not with "microevolution" but with "macro-" and "megaevolution." Much of the history of evolution can be looked at, in one way, as the history of the occupation of different adaptive zones (Simpson, 1953, pp. 199–244), and the characterization of these adaptive zones is apt to turn around food (grazing, browsing, capture of large prey, and so forth). Major groups of animals—orders, classes, phyla—are to a surprising extent distinguished by structural or behavioral characters that, in one way or another, turn around food habits. This, among mammals, is reflected in such ordinal names as "Carnivora," or, for that matter, in the word "Mammalia" itself.

The study of the evolution of these major phyletic groups has very largely been concerned with the evolution of their distinguishing structural characters, because these are what we have conveniently at hand for study as fossils. This, however, easily leads us into the "morphological fallacy." What we need, I suppose, are studies of comparative behavior as thorough and as extensive as those of comparative anatomy, so that we can more reliably deduce the behavior when we have only the anatomy. This is not going to be easy, but it seems to me of basic importance if we are to make major advances in our understanding of evolutionary processes.

CLASSIFICATION OF FOOD BEHAVIOR

The problem of behavioral vocabulary, which has been dealt with in various parts of this volume, is very important: we can hardly develop a sound comparative psychology until we have a terminology that enables us to discriminate and compare the significant elements in our systems. It seems to me that at present we are quite a way from this idea. Some particular groups of students, like the European ethologists, have made great progress in developing vocabularies useful from the point of view of evolution, but we are still far from the precision of the anatomists and the systematists. About all that can be done here is to try to outline the nature of the problem.

An early question is the definition of "food." If the word is used in the broadest possible sense, to cover all materials taken by an organism from the external environment and used in metabolism and growth, then water, oxygen and (in the case of plants) carbon dioxide, sunlight and other energy sources would have to be included among the food materials. Oxygen intake is always dealt with separately, under the heading of "respiration." Water is more difficult. In ordinary English usage "food and drink" are contrasting terms; yet in terms of physiology or behavior water can hardly be separated from the other food materials, and ought to be dealt with in the study of "food-getting behavior." The water problems of organisms have, however, many special aspects and, in difficult environments, involve behavioral and physiological adaptations that are rather different from those concerned with food in a strict sense. Thus water is generally and understandably treated as a special topic.

If we leave aside oxygen, water, and (in the case of plants) carbon dioxide and sunlight, we are left with a bewilderingly complex series of materials needed and used by organisms as food. These can be dealt with in terms of component chemical elements, which is not very meaningful because the materials can rarely be utilized in element form and because the list is constantly extended as the role of "trace elements" is more fully understood. Or, more usually, animal requirements are dealt with in terms of proteins, carbohydrates, minerals, and vitamins. But even this is not very helpful for purposes of generalization because of the varying ability of animals to break down complex food materials and to synthesize the sort of compounds needed. Despite the vast literature on nutrition, a great deal remains to be learned about the exact food requirements of different sorts of organisms. (Bourne and Kidder, 1953, have recently surveyed the literature on nutrition.)

It is difficult to draw a line between studies on nutrition and studies of food behavior, because classifications of food habits are apt to be built on kinds of food utilized. Thus in general classifications organisms are grouped as "autotrophic" if they can subsist entirely on inorganic substances (with subgroups of "phototrophic" and "chemotrophic" organisms, depending on the source of energy used for the synthesis of organic compounds); and as "hetero-trophic" if they require organic materials as food. Some organisms, like the green flagellates, can follow either of these basic nutrition patterns: they then have to be treated as a third major group, the "mixotrophic" organisms.

There are numerous classifications of the various sorts of hetero-trophic animal nutrition. These generally involve such words as phytophagous, herbivorous, predaceous, carnivorous, sapropha-gous, omnivorous, parasitic. These words have a general descrip-tive value, but they do not seem to discriminate very sharply de-fined or meaningful categories from the point of view of evolution.

For instance Brues (1946), in his very useful survey of the food habits of insects, distinguishes as basic categories "phytophagous," "carnivorous," "saprophagous," and "parasitic" insects. This is a commonly used classification. Yet the first three terms cover the sort of food materials utilized while the last (parasitic) describes a kind of food behavior. The difficulties of reaching a definition of "parasitism" are notorious—I have sketched some of the problems in connection with the classification of mosquito relationships in another place (Bates, 1949, pp. 186–200). The difficulties and con-fusions that have collected around the different usages of the word "parasite" in a way epitomize the whole classification problem in relation to food-getting behavior.

Ordinarily, when we start out to classify food habits, we think first of the division between "herbivorous" and "carnivorous" ani-mals. This is perhaps because our experience, either as people, or as scientists, is apt to be dominated by those two great groups of organisms, the insects and the vertebrates. Ramsay (1952, p. 7) has remarked that "if one surveys the main groups of the animal king-dom and picks out those which are predominantly and character-istically herbivorous—living on the green tissues (not on the fruit and seeds) of higher plants—one finds himself left with only three. These are the gastropod mollusks, certain orders of insects and cer-tain orders of mammals." The exceptions that come first to mind—among contemporary birds and reptiles—are certainly relatively trivial.

Of course the higher plants, which bulk so large in terrestrial economy, are rather late evolutionary developments. It is never-theless striking that so few animal groups have solved the prob-lem of efficiently utilizing them as food. The herbivorous insects and mammals have certainly been "successful" both in terms of numbers of individuals and of numbers of species. Yet the great bulk of plant material never goes through the animal part of the energy-food cycle so neatly diagrammed in the textbooks. As Ramsay remarks, "if one accepts the classical conceptions of struggle for existence and competition for food substances, one cannot but wonder at the immense resources of food materials which animals apparently allow to slip through their fingers."

A category like "herbivorous," defined as having the ability to utilize the green parts of higher plants as food, may thus have considerable meaning from the point of view of evolutionary study. In this case, the controlling factor in the food habit is the problem of dealing with cellulose—of breaking down the cellulose cell walls of the plant mechanically or chemically. This may involve all sorts of structural, physiological, and behavioral adaptations—including the fascinating business of symbiotic relationships with micro-organisms.

It is more difficult to give "carnivorous" a useful meaning since animals live off other animals in a great diversity of different ways which do not turn on any common problem, comparable with cellulose digestion. "Predatory" would have more meaning as a category because it implies a common problem of catching active food—a problem that has been met with diverse sorts of adaptations in different animal groups. But with "predatory"—and with "herbivorous" in the restricted sense—we are perhaps still dealing with a classification of feeding mechanisms rather than of food materials.

It may well be impossible to build up any sensible or logical classification of the different sorts of food materials used through the animal kingdom. Possible categories are perhaps best dealt with purely as descriptive terms—carrion feeding, fruit eating, seed eating, insect eating, and the like. Within any particular group of organisms we can sometimes trace evolutionary sequences in such food habits, and there may well be a certain parallel orderliness in these sequences in unrelated groups of animals. But it would be an immense—though surely rewarding—task to try to work out generalizations expressing this orderliness.

The concept of "food niche" (Elton, 1927, p. 64) should be mentioned here. This is "the feeding role of an organism in a community" (Allee et al., 1949, p. 516). The niche concept is perhaps chiefly useful in trying to analyze the workings of a biotic community. The use of the concept, however, reveals the remarkably similar roles sometimes played by quite different animals in a given community, and the parallelism in roles among quite diverse communities. Elton points this up with a series of examples: the niche of carnivorous snakes that feed on other snakes; the niche of animals that pick ticks off other animals; the niche of birds that follow herds of mammals to catch insects disturbed by their feet; and so on.

The niche concept need not, of course, be interpreted so narrowly. Our terrestrial herbivores and predatory carnivores could be considered as categories in a food materials series or food-getting mechanism series or as occupying particular niches. Plankton organisms could be considered as forming a niche (Elton calls these "key industry organisms"), and plankton feeders would be another niche, occupied by many diverse kinds of animals with a variety of plankton-gathering mechanisms.

Another kind of classification of food habits would be according to the degree of specialization. A great many animals are able to utilize a wide variety of food materials; others are highly restricted, highly specific in their diet. Whether specific food habits or general food habits are more common among animals has been a matter of some controversy (for references see ibid., p. 517). The matter is of interest in connection with the evolution of food behavior because it involves the question of the plasticity of such behavior.

Certainly such organisms as plant-feeding insects and animal parasites are often highly host-specific, and examples of highly restricted food habits can be found in almost all animal groups. Among insects the terms *monophagous, oligophagous,* and *polyphagous* are often used to describe this aspect of feeding behavior (Brues, 1946, p. 112.) In a somewhat different vocabulary, animals with highly specialized food habits may be called stenophagous, in contrast with euryphagous, or general, feeders. The evolutionary significance of restricted versus general food habits has been discussed by Dethier (1954). A restricted diet seems to represent a specialization, and thus perhaps a "dead end" from the evolutionary point of view, though it has immediate advantages for a species in terms of reduction of competition. Sometimes behavioral food specialization also involves great structural specialization (anteaters come to mind); but sometimes also animals without apparent structural specializations may have highly restricted food habits (as some of the grasshoppers).

Hediger (1950) has stressed the importance of distinguishing between continuous and intermittent feeding habits. This is in part, of course, correlated with the type of food: plankton feeders and herbivores tending to have different food intake timing from, say, predators. The whole topic of food behavior timing has many interesting aspects, as does the related topic of food storage—internal or external.

C. M. Yonge (1928) has proposed a classification of food systems among the invertebrates based not on the nature of the food materials but on the mechanism of feeding. His classification is

I. Mechanisms for dealing with small particles.
   a. Pseudopodial
   b. Ciliary
   c. Tentacular
   d. Mucoid
   e. Muscular
   f. Setous
II. Mechanisms for dealing with large particles or masses.
   A. For swallowing inactive food, e.g. bottom deposits, etc.
   B. For scraping and boring.
   C. For seizing prey.
     i. For seizing and swallowing only.
     ii. For seizing and masticating.
     iii. For seizing followed by external digestion.
III. Mechanisms for taking in fluid or soft tissues.
     i. For piercing and sucking.
     ii. For sucking only.
     iii. For absorption through surface of body.

This is a useful and logical classification of feeding mechanisms when dealing with the whole sweep of the animal kingdom, but it is not very helpful when we look at any particular group, like the insects or the vertebrates. It indicates, however, the lines along which a consistent classificatory scheme of food behavior will probably have to be built, if it is to have wide applicability.

For further discussion, it may be useful to glance briefly at food behavior in two quite different groups of organisms—the insects and the vertebrates.

INSECT FOOD BEHAVIOR

Any discussion of insect behavior gets us at once involved with the problem posed by such words as "instinctive" and "innate." The discussion given by Lehrman (1953), underlining the dangers of a word like "innate," is very persuasive. Clearly, the actual behavior of any organism is the result of potentialities as they have developed in a particular context. But this is equally true of the morphology of any organism. With potentialities and context constant, the resulting behavior (or structure) is constant. But there are great differences among organisms in the ways in which the developmental context—the internal or external environment—can influence the unfolding sequences of behavioral pattern, and we need to have some kind of vocabulary that will reflect these differences. The sort of vocabulary used by Maier and Schneirla (1935) allows recognition of this.

The dangers, however, of words like "instinctive" and "innate" are perhaps no greater than the dangers of the more general word "hereditary." When we say that any trait, behavioral or morphological, is hereditary, we are using a shorthand, since obviously it is only the potentiality for the development of the trait that is inherited. We are perhaps going too far when we throw out such words because they have been or can be misused. I do not think we ought to be afraid of the word "instinctive"—though if we have not the courage to use it we can take cover behind a more neutral term like "stereotyped" when trying to characterize insect behavior.

The vocabulary problem is a tough one. The complicated terminology developed by Fraenkel and Gunn (1940) primarily for insect orientation reactions seemed to me at one time simply obfuscation. Yet we need a finer discrimination than is possible with a wastebasket word like "tropism," and no behavioral vocabulary is anything like as complicated as the vocabulary used by arthropod morphologists, a vocabulary that seems to serve them well. Perhaps we should have no hesitancy in coining technical terms for behavioral elements on the theory that the terms can be discarded when they have served their purpose or if they prove to discriminate elements that do not warrant discrimination.

At any rate, insect behavior, whether called instinctive or

stereotyped, is sufficiently different from vertebrate behavior to make the isolation of homologies very difficult. When we have worked out phylogenies for behavior within the vertebrates and within the insects, perhaps we can start piecing together a grander pattern. But that is hardly possible now.

MACROEVOLUTION IN INSECTS

The definitions of the various orders of insects turn very largely on the presence or absence of wings and type of wing structure, on the kind of metamorphosis, and on feeding mechanisms. Of the twenty-three orders of insects recognized by Imms (1934) in his standard text, in six the mouth parts are modified so that they serve primarily for piercing or sucking rather than biting. Since the structures modified to form sucking tubes are quite different in the different orders, this basic change in insect food-getting behavior seems to have occurred independently several times.

The structural changes in insect mouth parts among the various orders are clearly related to changes in food-getting behavior. The whole complicated business of insect metamorphosis, however, is also related to food-getting behavior. Carpenter (1953), in his discussion of insect evolution, has pointed out that "The immature forms, being very different from the adults, could occupy different environments and feed on different types of food. The tissues of other organisms, both plant and animal, were thus invaded by larval forms as internal parasites, the adult insects remaining free-living and capable of flight." The evolution of insect metamorphosis can thus be looked at in terms of the occupation of different adaptive zones, in Simpson's words—with the zones definable primarily in terms of food and food behavior. Even the third of the major characters used in insect ordinal classification—wings—could be related to food in this indirect sense of contributing to adaptive radiation.

I think, then, that a good case could be made for regarding food behavior as the basic component in the evolution of insect orders. Insect families can also frequently be defined in terms of food behavior; but perhaps even more frequently similar food habits will be shared by several families, or a single family include a considerable diversity of food habits. The mosquitoes (Culicinae) are an example of a subfamily primarily definable in terms of the bloodsucking food habits of the adult female (with the parti-cle-filtering larvae occupying a very different but similarly well-defined food niche). There are mosquitoes with exceptional food habits, but these are easily recognized as secondary modifications.

Food habits seem important in the definition of major groups . in the classificatory hierarchy both in insects and in vertebrates. If one reviews the classification of a primarily marine phylum, like the Coelenterata, this aspect of the classification seems much less striking. I am led to wonder whether this reflects some basic difference in the evolutionary pattern of marine and terrestrial forms—or whether it merely reflects my limited knowledge of marine zoology.

INSECT FOOD BEHAVIOR AT THE SPECIES LEVEL

A great many insects are highly host-specific, and in such cases each species of insect may be associated with a different species of host. Frequently different "races," "varieties," or "strains" of a species are associated with different hosts, and the question arises as to whether shifts in food habits may be one of the primary isolating mechanisms in species evolution. The material bearing on this question has been discussed by Thorpe (1930), Mayr (1942 and 1947), Brues (1946), and most recently and thoroughly by Dethier (1954).

The impression left, after reading these reviews, is that the subject warrants a great deal more investigation. One problem turns around the question as to whether a shift in food habits can ever be the primary cause of a division within a population, leading eventually to the development of two completely inde-pendent (specific) populations. Mayr (1947) has argued per-suasively against the possibility of such "sympatric" speciation. Perhaps some sort of microgeographical or ecological spatial separation is necessary for speciation; but the interesting question remains as to whether a food behavior change is ever the first step leading toward such separation.

Discussion of this tends immediately to involve hypothetical cases, because we simply do not know enough about the genetic control of insect food behavior for concrete discussion. From Dethier's summary of the literature on plant-feeding insects, it is clear that host selection generally turns on a response to some sort of a token cue, perhaps usually olfactory; in many cases the precise chemical or chemical series can be identified. In some cases it is clear that this cue response turns at least in part on what has been called "larval memory" or "olfactory conditioning." In other cases the response seems to be genetically fixed. In experimental attempts to alter host relationships, it often becomes difficult to distinguish the effects of genetic change from those of selection or habituation.

Various evolutionary trends in host relationships have occurred, as Dethier and Brues have shown in their papers on the subject. Highly restricted food habits (monophagy) may be derived from general food habits (polyphagy) and vice versa, though usually, as one would expect, polyphagy seems to be the generalized condition and monophagy the derived.

Brues (1936) has reviewed the wide variety of evolutionary trends that can be demonstrated among insects in food behavior: phytophagy evolving from predation and vice versa; saprophagy from predation or phytophagy, and saprophagy in turn sometimes leading again to predation or plant feeding; and so on through a bewildering variety of combinations. Even parasitism does not seem to be the dead end among insects that it is in the evolution of some other groups of animals. However, insect "parasitism," as Wheeler long ago pointed out, is a very special phenomenon that perhaps ought to be called by a special name; he proposed "parasitoidism."

The evolution of the food behavior patterns of the parasitoid and predatory wasps has been the subject of much discussion. Evans (1953) has summarized this literature insofar as it applies to the spider wasps and he has developed a system of behavior analysis that facilitates comparison among species and that helps in the working out of possible phylogenies. In the parasitoid ichneumons, which may represent the ancestral behavior type, the adult behavior in providing for the larva consists of hunting out the prey and laying an egg on it. This, insofar as it has been analyzed, turns on an apparently rather simple cue response. A few ichneumons sting their prey into temporary paralysis before ovipositing, so that the sequence becomes hunting–stinging–ovipositing. Additional elements may be added to reach the complexity of the majority of the Pompilid spider wasps, in which the sequence is hunting–paralysis–transportation–excavation of cell–oviposition–closing.

Evans uses a symbol system first proposed by Iwata for characterizing these different behavior patterns: C for *claudere,* to close the cell; I for *instruere,* to prepare the nest cell; O for *ovum parere,* to lay the egg; P for *pungere,* to sting the prey; V for *venari,* to hunt. With this system he is able to make generalizations like: "The Pompilidae embrace the ethological types VPTOC (primitive), VPTIOC (basic) and IVPTOC and I'VPTOC (specialized), thus being traceable back to primitive Hymenoptera by way of types VPTO, VPO and VO." This sort of shorthand seems very convenient both for description and analysis, and might well have a wide application in behavioral studies. It at least permits the isolation of unit traits, though it of course is no help in explaining the development of behavioral mechanics of the unit traits themselves.

This, of course, gets us back to the basic problems of the nature of insect behavior, which can hardly be discussed within the scope of this paper. The best short introduction to the enormous literature is perhaps that written by Schneirla (1953).

Vertebrate Food Behavior

The vertebrates show almost as great a diversity in food materials utilized and ways at getting at them as do the insects. Parasitism—in the sense of complete dependence on an organism of another species, with correlated atrophy or impairment of locomotor and sensory functions—is absent from the vertebrates, and this is curious chiefly because it has appeared so frequently as one of the food-getting behavior patterns in other animal phyla. There are, of course, the often-cited males of the deep sea fish, *Photocorynus,* which live attached to the females. Lampreys might be considered parasites in the sense that mosquitoes are parasites. There is the curious South American catfish, the candiru, which squeezes its way into the bodily orifices of other vertebrates, and is sometimes called "the only vertebrate parasite." And cuckoos have developed a way of exploiting their fellow birds that is generally called parasitism. But such cases serve only to illustrate the difficulties inherent in the word "parasitism."

In general, vertebrates are committed to active, food-seeking behavior, and this is perhaps correlated with their generally large body size which requires considerable food for maintenance. It is also correlated with the structure of the vertebrate nerve system with its centralized brain—a system that allows for plasticity or modifiability of behavior and for an increasing dominance of various kinds of learning or habituation processes in behavior.

Evans (1940) studied the relation of brain development in fish to hunting and feeding behavior and found (as would be expected) considerable anatomical variation that could be related to the different developments of sense perception required by differing food habits. The predacious habit, so common among fish, requires acute perception and prompt, efficient motor coordination, which finds reflection in the corresponding brain centers. Such studies, however, still leave us caught in the chicken-and-egg trap of the relationship between development of behavior and development of neural structures. This is a problem of outstanding interest because of the special case of the relationship between the evolution of the human brain and the evolution of human behavior.

The literature on food-getting behavior in various vertebrate groups is enormous, but it has not been covered by any general summary or analysis. The numerous books that have been written on the natural history of particular groups are also apt to be disappointing when examined from the point of view of behavioral evolution, though most such books have chapters on food habits. Thus the food habits of birds have been summarized by Mayaud (1950) and of mammals by Bourlière (1954). Hediger (1950) has many thought-provoking comments to make for his observations of captive vertebrates.

In the literature on evolution, discussion of the topic of "adaptive radiation" is generally really discussion of the evolution of food-getting behavior, though sometimes not labeled as such. Any attempt at summarizing this literature is out of the question here. Many of the well-known studies of Tinbergen, Lack, Lorenz, and others are explicitly dealing with problems of food-getting behavior. The evolution of insular isolates like Darwin's finches and the Hawaiian honeycreepers is particularly apt for illustration of the role of food habits and food relations in adaptive radiation. As an example, the situation with regard to the Hawaiian honeycreepers has been discussed in some detail by Baldwin (1953).

Much of this work is necessarily purely descriptive; yet the processes involved in behavioral evolution can hardly be understood without experimental analysis—the sort of work in which Lorenz and Tinbergen have recently taken the lead. In this connection one is impressed, in reviewing the literature, by the relative neglect of the study of behavioral changes in introduced animals. The deliberate and accidental introductions of animals into new environments provide a series of unplanned but gigantic and interesting ecological experiments which would seem to offer possibilities for all sorts of studies. There are tantalizing glimpses of behavioral changes in such animals, as in the apparent changes in the food relations of the mongoose in various places (e.g. in the Virgin Islands as described by Seaman, 1952). Birds once thought to have been exterminated by the mongoose have started to build up numbers: which would seem to mean a habit change either in the mongoose or in the birds. There is evidence that the mongoose is no longer effective as a rat predator because of changes in the behavior of the rats, leading them to nest high off the ground in the cane fields. But even where such behavioral changes are described, one is left wondering about their possible genetic basis and possible meaning in relation to the various forces that we presume to govern evolutionary processes.

With the vertebrates, and particularly with the mammals, we have a great deal of information about the mechanics of behavior (though detailed studies are curiously restricted to a very few species like the Norway rat and the rhesus monkey); we have an enormous accumulation of natural history observations on habits in the field; we know a great deal about the relation between anatomical structures and habits; and we have a fossil record of many aspects of the changes in anatomical structure. The information on any particular point often seems quite inadequate when we try to interpret it, but the total amount of information still is impressive. Out of all this we ought to be able to build a reasonable synthesis of the evolution of some particular behavioral system, like food getting. The job of putting these bits of information together, scattered as they are among widely separated fields of knowledge, would be great but surely within the range of possibility.

In summary, then, it seems to me that in the vertebrates, in the insects, and perhaps in various other animal groups we have reached a point where attempts at synthesis in terms of behavioral systems like food getting are both possible and desirable. I doubt the advisability at this time of much generalizing across phyla; and I am sure that any synthesis, rather than giving definite answers to the major questions about evolutionary processes, will serve chiefly to provide background for more discriminating future studies. But in that unending chain of observations, experiments, and conceptual schemes which we call science, it seems to me that we have reached the point, in the study of the evolution of behavior, where the greatest need is for the development of conceptual schemes. It is a tantalizing situation. We have a multitude of facts, but they are presently confusing, contradictory, chaotic. Where is the brain to put them in order?

REFERENCES

ALLEE, W. C., EMERSON, A. E., PARK, O., PARK, T., and SCHMIDT, K. P. 1949. Principles of animal ecology. Philadelphia, W. B. Saunders.

BALDWIN, PAUL H. 1953. Annual cycle, environment and evolution in the Hawaiian honeycreepers (Aves: Drepaniidae). Univ. Calif. Publ. Zool., 52 (4), 285–398.

BATES, MARSTON. 1949. The natural history of mosquitoes. New York, Macmillan.

BOURLIÈRE, FRANÇOIS. 1954. The natural history of mammals. New York, Knopf.

BOURNE, G. H., and KIDDER, G. W., eds. 1953. Biochemistry and physiology of nutrition. New York, Academic Press. 2 vols.

BRUES, C. T. 1936. Aberrant feeding behavior among insects and its bearing on the development of specialized food habits. Quart. Rev. Biol., 11, 305–19.

BRUES, C. T. 1946. Insect dietary; on account of the food habits of insects. Cambridge, Harvard Univ. Press.

CARPENTER, F. M. 1953. The geological history and evolution of insects. Amer. Sci. 41 (2), 256–70.

DETHIER, V. G. 1954. Evolution of feeding preferences in phytophagous insects. Evolution, 8, 33–54.

ELTON, CHARLES. 1927. Animal ecology. New York, Macmillan.

EVANS, H. E. 1953. Comparative ethology and the systematics of spider wasps. Syst. Zool., 2, 155–72.

EVANS, H. MUIR. 1940. Brain and body of fish: a study of brain pattern in relation to hunting and feeding in fish. Philadelphia, Blakiston.

FRAENKEL, G., and GUNN, D. L. 1940. The orientation of animals, kineses, taxes and compass reactions. New York, Oxford Univ. Press.

HEDIGER, H. 1950. Wild animals in captivity. London, Butterworths Scientific Publications.

IMMS, A. D. 1934. A general textbook of entomology. New York, Dutton.

LEHRMAN, DANIEL. 1953. A critique of Konrad Lorenz's theory of instinctive behavior. Quart. Rev. Biol., 28 (4), 337–63.

MAIER, N. R. F., and SCHNEIRLA, T. C. 1935. Principles of animal psychology. New York, McGraw-Hill.

MAYAUD, NOËL. 1950. Alimentation. In Pierre Grassé, ed., Traité de zoologie. Tome 15, Oiseaux. Paris. Masson.

MAYR, ERNST. 1942. Systematics and the origin of species from the point of view of a zoologist. New York, Columbia Univ. Press.

MAYR, ERNST. 1947. Ecological factors in speciation. Evolution, *1*, 263–88.

RAMSAY, J. A. 1952. A physiological approach to the lower animals. Cambridge, Eng., Cambridge Univ. Press.

SCHNEIRLA, T. C. 1953. Basic problems in the nature of insect behavior. In K. D. Roeder, ed., Insect physiology. New York, Wiley.

SEAMAN, G. A. 1952. The mongoose and Caribbean wildlife. Trans. 17th North American Wildlife Conference, pp. 188–97.

SIMPSON, G. G. 1953. The major features of evolution. New York, Columbia Univ. Press.

THORPE, W. H. 1930. Biological races in insects and allied groups. Biol. Rev., *5* (3), 177–212.

TINBERGEN, N. 1951. The study of instinct. Oxford, Clarendon Press.

YONGE, C. M. 1928. Feeding mechanisms in the invertebrates. Biol. Rev., *3* (1), 20–76.

11

Territoriality: A Review of Concepts and Problems

C. R. Carpenter

THE PENNSYLVANIA STATE UNIVERSITY

AMONG THE adaptive interactions between animals and their environments which need consideration in a systematic study of behavior and evolution are the complex phenomena symbolized by the term "territoriality." The available information on the subject is limited, unsystematic, and qualitative. Studies and observations of territoriality are largely in the pre-experimental stage. The formulation and testing of hypotheses is merely beginning and many unsolved problems challenge investigation. Principles which can be accepted with confidence and applied to the difficult problems of evolution are not yet available. Nevertheless let us consider some of the available and pertinent data, observations, speculations, inferences, concepts, and elementary theories about territoriality in the context of this symposium. We shall draw on information about vertebrates ranging from the fishes through the nonhuman primates. The invertebrates will not be covered, nor will the complex phenomena of territoriality in human behavior.

HISTORICAL CONCEPTS, 1622–1920

The richest source of historical concepts about territoriality is the writings of those interested in birds and their behavior. Nice (1941) has brought these concepts together in her excellent article on "The Role of Territory in Bird Life." It may be useful to present them briefly here, from the early statement of Willugby in 1622 (Nice, 1933) through the historic formulations of Howard (1920).

Willugby (1678) believed that the male nightingale at "his first coming" occupied or seized a place, which Willugby termed a "Friehold." Into this area "the nightingale would not admit others except its mate." Goldsmith (1774) first used the term "territory" in the following quaint statement quoted by Bates (1950): "the fact is, all these small birds mark out a territory to themselves, which they will permit none of their own species to remain in; they guard their dominions with the most watchful resentment; and we seldom find two male tenants in the same hedge togther." Naumann (1820) sharpened and somewhat extended earlier concepts. He observed that male birds "usually arrive first" in the spring, "seek a breeding place," and "suffer no other pair to nest within a certain distance."

Altum (1868) developed a systematic description of territoriality for birds. His definition has modern connotations: "territory is an area occupied by one male of a species which it defends against intrusion of other males of the same species and in which it makes itself conspicuous." The phrase "in which it makes itself conspicuous" is an anlagen concept for later observations of the functions of singing, display, and aggression. Altum also introduced the idea that birds settle at fixed distances from each other to ensure food for themselves and their young; this ascription of purposive intent to territorial behavior is not absent from more modern descriptions.

Altum debated what enables breeding birds to keep their distance. He observed that large numbers crowd together in preferred areas, while less suitable areas with less food remain unoccupied. The "force" which keeps them apart, he says, "is used by a male as soon as another gets too close during the breeding season." . . . "the interloper is driven to a distance that is determined by the size of the required territory." Altum's explanation is that the birds perceive each other through their songs and when, during the breeding season, male birds get too close together they begin fighting and thus are driven apart. Song and fighting operate together but bird songs are the main means of maintaining necessary separations and ensuring adequate food and territory.

Moffat (1903) suggested that fighting serves to parcel out territories, thus limiting the number of pairs in an area to a fairly constant figure. These adjustments, he held, prevent "indefinite" increase in the population of a species and "condemn" less power-ful individuals to unreproductiveness rather than death. He ar-gued that for any given area the number of breeding pairs and number of young reared would be "exactly the same" for a season regardless of winter mortality. Selection of a territory he believed related to suitability of nesting sites as well as availability of food.

Brewster (1906) gave a full statement of the concepts of terri-toriality, including the ideas of exclusive possession against birds of the same species and sex, tolerance for other species within a territory, and the variations in sizes of territories required by different species of birds. He also observed that territorial pos-session by one bird is "respected" by others, and trespassers retire easily when threatened. The cause of this behavior he thought was "sexual jealousy" since it occurs during the breeding season.

Herrick (1912) emphasized and extended previous concepts on the basis of his study of the herring gull. Observing that the gull community is composed of "family units," he emphasized the so-cial organization factors in the concept of territoriality. The "pre-serve" is "chosen" and "guarded" with vigor. The territories are differentiated into areas around the nest, perch, and feeding area. The "fighting disposition" on which "quarreling" depends "does not lapse" until the young gulls take to the water.

Howard (1907–14, 1920) in his fundamental work on the Brit-ish warblers and his popular book, *Territory in Bird Life,* estab-lished the concept of territory among those interested in the broad fields of animal behavior. He describes territory in behavioral terms. The male "isolates himself, makes himself conspicuous, becomes intolerant of other males (of his species) and confines his movements to a definite area." Howard suggests that cycles of be-havior center around territory. Territoriality serves the function of ensuring a food supply. It ensures mating by providing a focus for activity prior to nest building. It serves to limit the number of pairs of birds which can be accommodated in a limited area, and through fighting ensures that the strong and not the weak shall reproduce. Howard outlined the temporal sequences of ter-ritorial behavior especially in relation to reproduction. It is im-portant to note, finally, that he attributed territorial behavior to an instinctive or congenital basis.

Later concepts of territoriality will be seen to be refinements and extensions of the generic concepts expressed by the above-mentioned men.

Studies of Territoriality

Howard (1929) further emphasized and gave a perspective on territory in bird behavior in his *Introduction to the Study of Bird Behavior*. Meise (1930) reviewed 41 articles on the subject. Probably Heape (1931) was the first to take a broad view of the problems; he extended concepts previously and primarily related to birds, and set the stage for viewing territoriality as part of a broader pattern of movements and adjustments of animals in space. Nice published her first brief study of territorialism among birds in 1933. The next important milestone was Mayr's (1935) translation of Altum's work under the title *Bernard Altum and the Territory Theory*. In 1936 Meise reviewed 66 titles bearing on the subject of territoriality. Nice's comprehensive review of "The Role of Territory in Bird Life" followed in 1941. Picking up the theme where Heape left off, Burt examined "Territoriality and Home Range Concepts as Applied to Mammals" (1943) and again in 1949 he published a short paper on territoriality.

Hediger's superior book *Wild Animals in Captivity*, published in an English edition in 1950 from an earlier one in German, considerably advanced the understanding of territorial behavior of vertebrates. Hediger meticulously and systematically depicts the forms and processes involved in the adjustments of vertebrates, especially mammals, within their objective and subjective Lebensraum. In *The Nature of Natural History* (1950) Bates presents important concepts of territorial adjustments of animals.

Almost for the first time for psychologists, Collias (1951) introduced a very brief review of territorialism into his chapter in Stone's *Comparative Psychology*. Apart from this, the subject, like many other natural history phenomena, has been seriously neglected by comparative psychologists and investigators of animal behavior. Tinbergen (1951) in his *Study of Instinct* touches at many points on principles and processes related to territory.

A monographic report of an international colloquium held in Paris in 1950 on the subject of the Structure and Physiology of Animal Societies, written in French, German, and English and edited by Pierre P. Grassé, was published in 1952. Territoriality is dealt with here by Bourlière in a chapter on "Le territorialisme dans l'organisation sociale des Vertébrés," while Carpenter and Darling also discuss its role. Mayaud (1950) published a chapter on "Territoire" in Grassé's *Traité de zoologie*. Allee (1954), writing on "Animal Sociology" in the *Encyclopaedia Britannica,* gave considerable emphasis to territoriality. He gave special attention to the functional or adaptive values of territorial behavior and social interactions.

The English edition of Bourlière's excellent *Natural History of Mammals* appeared in 1954; descriptions of territoriality occupy a prominent and well-balanced place in this. In his readable book on *Cells and Societies* (1955) Bonner gave descriptions of territorial behavior as he sketched the characteristics of the societies of howler monkeys, fur seals, the red deer, and the beaver.

Carpenter (1958), in the *Handbuch der Zoologie,* weighs the evidence for and against territoriality in primates.

These discussions reflect growing recognition of and interest in understanding the nature and significance of territoriality in animals. They also show a trend toward extending and applying concepts which emerged in the study of bird behavior to a variety of mammals, ranging from fish through rodents to the anthropoid apes. The study of territoriality has become, or is becoming, a regular part of systematic field studies of living organisms. And its special problems are being submitted to controlled experiment.

DEFINITIONS OF TERRITORIALITY

Among the many definitions of territoriality are those of Heape (1931), Noble (1939), Allee (1954), Burt (1943), Hediger (1950), Bates (1950), Carpenter (1952), Kalela (1954), Mayr (1935), Crawford (1939), Tinbergen (1936), and Nice (1941).[1] These definitions are based in great part on bird behavior, and even for this group perhaps do not reflect the complete range of variability of most species. The concepts are especially deficient in descriptions of the main characteristics and variations of the territorial behavior of vertebrates other than birds.

It is clear that those who have studied territoriality have attempted to conceptualize the behavior mainly in two ways: as a spatial or geographic phenomenon and as a behavioral phenomenon. It would seem advantageous to view territoriality primarily as a behavioral system which is expressed in a spatial-temporal frame of reference. The organismic mechanisms, the drives and

1. Exigencies of space have prevented quoting these definitions. Citations are given in the author's logical sequence. (*Editors' note.*)

incentives or motives, and the sensory-response and learning processes are all different aspects of the behavioral systems of territoriality. These are expressed with reference to *loci* in space, and to the topography of habitat areas, as well as to other organisms living in the areas. Behavioral systems change over periods of time. Those which constitute territoriality in animals are so complex, and involve so many adaptive and even nonadjustive mechanisms, that they defy adequate description by condensed definitions. Fully systematic and analytical descriptions are required.

Territorial behavior apparently has great variations. These are related to differences in species and their habits, to seasons and climates, to "population pressures," to social organization, to fluctuations of food supplies, to predation, and many other factors. Hence brief descriptions of territoriality for vertebrates cannot represent accurately the common denominators of the behavior or the kinds and degrees of most variations.

It is clear that those processes which are called territorial behavior are actually *higher order,* complex behavioral systems which are based on a plurality of subsystems. For example, territorial behavior relates to the beginning or terminal phases of migratory responses for those animals which migrate. Also involved is the complex behavior of possession and guarding areas of space. There are many elements of selective and discriminatory responses. Complexes of reproductive behavior relate centrally to territoriality. Attack, encroachment, and defense constitute important aspects of territoriality, and so do challenge, vocalization, song, and other display or signaling activities. These latter, incidentally, are bivalent; they function in birds to repel the males while at the same time they serve to attract females. The vast range of activity concerned with foods and feeding—the search for food, securing, hoarding, and protecting it—are also parts of territorial behavior. Security-ensuring behavioral adjustments are also involved with respect to covers, lairs, dens, nests, burrows, or even places providing merely space and distance. In this connection the dispositional characteristics of wildness reflected in Hediger's concept of "flight distance" and the somewhat similar concept of Carpenter (1958), Fabricius (1954), and others of "tolerance distance" also are included in territoriality. Territoriality is a social phenomenon involving flocks, pairs, groups, and herds. Thus it would seem that the "perceptual-cognitive maps" or behavioral systems of animals, if and when they are charted, will more accurately represent territorial behavior than merely geographic or physical space maps. As stated earlier, these facts lead to the conclusion that territoriality is of the nature of higher order, complex and dependent behavior systems which are organized upon numerous subsystems and behavioral determinants.

CHARACTERISTICS OF TERRITORIALITY IN VARIOUS TYPES OF ORGANISMS

Let us characterize territoriality for different species here as a means of showing its prevalence and variability in vertebrates. We shall examine it in fish, reptiles, birds, rodents, seals, deer, and primates. This will lead to a discussion of its inferred functions and adaptive (survival) values.

Fish

Wunder (1930) experimented with fish in an aquarium of limited space and presumably suboptimal area. He found that the male stickleback would reproduce in its own territory but also would suppress (inhibit) reproduction in other males within close visual distance. When the aquarium was partitioned so that they could not see each other, several males within the same limited space would reproduce. These findings were confirmed by ter Pelkwijk and Tinbergen (1937).

Breder (1934) in an experimental study of cichlid fish concluded that the territorial behavior of fish closely resembles that of birds. Territories are established, nests are built and guarded, and mating occurs within the territory.

Most of the study of fish has been done in aquaria, and except for investigation of migration routes and cycles, studies of territoriality in natural habitats have been few. However, Mayr (1942) reports a study by Rodeheffer (1941) carried out at Douglas Lake, Michigan. Fish were caught and marked, released, and recaptured. Rodeheffer found that of all the fish marked at several locations none was recaptured in a part of the lake distant from the place of original catching and releasing. Mayr also reports that Hart, Tester, and McHugh (1941) have shown localization, perhaps territoriality, in marine fish.

Noble (1938) in his review of sexual selection among fish reports that in different species every male, or spawning couple, occupies a small territory within which no other sexually active fish of the same species are tolerated. Thus the number of spawning couples is limited for a given area. The size of territories indirectly determines the amount of spawn which is laid on an area.

Greenberg (1947) studied the relation of territory to social organization in sunfish. Like others, he found close interaction between territoriality and the dominance order of social hierarchies. Territoriality was prominently displayed even in young sunfish as a basic behavioral substratum to social organization.

Baerends and Baerends–van Roon (1950), like many of the European ethologists, accept territoriality as a fundamental modality of behavior in fishes. They report that larger fish occupy larger territories and have greater tolerance distance.

Fabricius (1951) in experiments on factors influencing the size of territory in Chinese fish of the family Cyprinidae found that males are strongly territorial during spawning. They stay in small areas and defend these by "lateral display" but rarely by fighting. However, fighting may supersede lateral display. In this fish size is not correlated with size of territory. Fabricius also found that bream males in a lake are strongly territorial, and that territories are defended by "splashing reactions." Sizes of territories relate to topography of the lake bottom and the amount of vegetation. Fabricius concluded that amount of spawn can be increased by increasing the number of territories for those fish which exhibit territoriality. Thus he concurs with Breder on this point.

In another aquarium experiment Fabricius (1954) found that when char were introduced into an aquarium they first swam in schools, then displayed and fought. After forty-five minutes to one hour "males defended well-defined territories." The fish swam over its territory and vigorously attacked all trespassers. After three days fish which had not secured territories were driven to neutral zones. Territorial males may during chases cross territories of other males, and they may leave their territories to join females and then return. Territories from which males were removed were occupied by other males. Females like males were observed to occupy definite territories.

These relatively few references support tentatively the broader assumptions held by naturalists that many types of fishes display territorial behavior, especially during the breeding season. Territoriality of schools of fish under natural conditions has not been studied. Information for charting variations in this behavior is not adequate.

Reptiles

The following five references on reptiles deal to some extent with the subject under review: Noble and Bradley (1933), Noble (1934), and Greenberg and Noble (1942) report territoriality for lizards; Evans (1938) reports it for a Cuban species of lizard; and Cagle (1944) describes home ranges, homing behavior, and migration for turtles.

Birds

Since the concepts previously reviewed have predominantly related to birds, the main emphasis will be put on describing variations in the territortiality of different types, and reports on determinants of these variations.

Friedman (1928) studied social "parasitism" in birds with special reference to the cowbird. In birds which parasitize others by laying eggs in the nest of hosts, it might be expected that a change in territoriality would occur. Details need to be worked out, but Friedman developed a theory that bird "parasitism" results from "a weakening of the territorial urge."

Carpenter (1930) studied experimentally the effects of complete and partial gonadectomy on the reproductive behavior of pigeons. Effects on fighting by males in their own nesting areas were studied by introducing males which were unadapted to those nest areas. The bird in its home area regularly won the test encounter even though partially or completely gonadectomized.

Tavistock (1931) challenged the food shortage theory. Many observations reveal that territories are established and defended where food is abundant and widely dispersed. It is possible that territorial behavior is what is currently termed an emergency survival mechanism, which operates regularly but has its survival value only during times of acute food shortage.

Lack and Lack (1933) reviewed the evidence for territoriality. They pointed out that some birds are territorial at times and at other times live in colonies; the great black-headed gull and crested grebe were cited as examples. They observed that fighting is reduced during the period of rearing the young. Finally, they challenged the assumption that territoriality limits the number of pairs of nesting birds in a given area.

The Lacks' viewpoint disagrees with Huxley's report (1933), which concluded: "The pugnacity of the male (and to a lesser extent of the female) is clearly seeing to it that one pair of Swans shall grow where two pairs grew before." The Lacks and Huxley raise the problem of whether species of birds have a territory of rather constant size or there is considerable variation, and if the latter is the case, what causes the variation in territorial ranges and different numbers of pairs in a given area.

Allen (1934) advanced the theory, based on a study of ruffed grouse, that territory, song, display, and fighting "are explainable on the basis of necessity for *synchronizing* the mating cycles of males and females."

Chapman (1935) described a variation of territorial behavior for Gould's manakin in which a number of males cleared "courts" located close together. There may be five to seven "courts" placed 30 to 40 feet from each other. Territorial rights were strictly observed. Females nested apart and separately from males. However, they would come to the males' "courts" and selectively mate with a male. Fighting was not observed among the males.

In her systematic and definitive study of song sparrows Nice (1937) sketches what is perhaps a pattern of territoriality that is widely characteristic of many species of birds. She observed that individual male song sparrows returned to or remained in the same territories from year to year. If another possessed his territory during an individual's absence, he was usually successful in regaining the area.

Nice quotes Vogt (1938) to the effect that the willet is highly territorial and guards the boundary of its domain throughout most of the breeding season, as vigilantly as the passerine birds. Unlike most birds, the willets mate before establishing a territory and then signal its location by "ceremonial flights."

Nice further reports that birds of paradise (Rand, 1940) are apparently monogamous. Males do not establish territories. She gives data on penguins, which as reported by Roberts (1940) show great "emotional *valency*" for areas around the nest. Fighting occurs among birds occupying adjacent territories. Apparently these fights involve both males and females.

Baumgartner (1939) reported on the territoriality of the great horned owl. An owl vigorously excludes others from its range. Baumgartner believes this intolerance to overcrowding importantly affects the density of population. The range of an owl is about one-half mile; and to judge from sounds studied at night, hunting is apparently confined to this range. Trapping, banding, removal to a distance, and retrapping was another method of study used. Owls change ranges after rearing of the young.

Noble (1939) contributed to discussion of the relation of territory to dominance and arrived at several important conclusions: (1) Territories have clear advantages for subordinate animals. A subordinate animal in its own territory can win a fight with a dominant animal. (2) Dominant animals may defend larger territories than subordinate animals. Noble generalizes: "Territory should be sharply divided into different categories. Sexual territory, which is so characteristic of most birds, is, however, found in most egg-laying and nest-building vertebrates. It arises from the sexual interest of the animal in an area suitable for nesting and it functions primarily to test sexual readiness of the opposite sex and to make sexual bonds. Sexual territory is not to be confused with nesting territory which has a different motivational basis, nor with an isolated *retreat* which is defended by many vertebrates against intruders at any season."

Bennett (1940), working on social hierarchy in ring doves, found that males injected with testosterone proprionate enlarged their previously held territories.

Kirkman (1940) studied the black-headed gull by moving nests. Normally the birds never placed nests closer together than 18 inches. When nests were moved experimentally, the behavior of nest owners could be changed to that of nest intruders.

Kendeigh (1941) reported another basic study which was extensive and systematic. He observed the house wrens of a 15-acre plot for 19 years and examined 215 territories, firmly establishing the fact of territoriality for this species and plotting variations of range patterns.

Diebschlag (1941) confirmed previous studies of the house wren, and anticipated others, by pointing out that territory plays an important role in establishing and maintaining peck order dominance in social hierarchies.

Hochbaum (1944) observed that the boundaries of a territory

are the boundaries of the canvasback duck's *tolerance* and vary as this tolerance varies. The tolerance distance is not constant. Territories are larger in sparsely populated than in densely populated areas.

Bain (1949) conducted a field experiment on the great tit relative to home range and dominance. By moving a feeding station nearer or farther from home ranges of birds living in adjacent areas, he was able to alter and reverse dominance relationships.

The most important fact that emerges from reviews of bird behavior is the near universality of some type of territoriality. Nevertheless types and patterns of this behavior show great variance, and much here is not yet known. Furthermore, the field would seem to be ready for productive experimentation to isolate and define the major determinants of territorial behavior in birds.

Rodents

"A Study of Beaver Colonies in Michigan" by Bradt (1938) is a good description of the complex behavior of this animal, including its territoriality. It is well known that beavers build dams, construct houses, and occupy localized areas. Like many animals, they mark the possessed territory, which is elaborately modified, by scent, and use various sound signals to defend the area.

Gordon (1940) found for *Sciurus fremonti,* living in lodge pole pine forest, that these squirrels collected pine seeds and placed them in the center of an area which was guarded by a single animal. Churring corresponded to the song of birds in its use for defending territory. From studies of several species, Gordon concluded that territoriality characterizes the life habits of squirrels.

Evans and Holdenried (1941), studying the ground squirrel *Citellus beecheyi,* concluded that adult males are restricted to small ranges which seldom overlap. Females also remain within their ranges but there is overlapping, sometimes complete, of their territories. Young squirrels range widely and establish territories later. In 1943 these observers reported again, added that some permanent transfers of ranges occur, and concluded: "In summary, observations at the Calaveras Reservoir indicate that many ground squirrels remain within a small area throughout most of their lives."

Linsdale (1946) provides another systematic report on ground squirrels. He confirms territoriality and infers that smell plays a role in identifying territories. "Ground squirrels resemble nearly all other kinds of small mammals in being closely restricted in most of their activity to the near vicinity of their home or nest. Various internal drives send the squirrel from its nest, but normally for only a short distance. The length of its travel is remarkably short when compared with its powers of movement. Moreover, the amount of time spent in travel each day is small. Apparently the nest site is occupied for only a short period though removal to a new site may not be far. . . . When it leaves, temporarily or momentarily . . . the least threat of danger will send it rushing toward its home by the most direct path." Linsdale names some of the drives involved, e.g. food, nest materials, and sunshine, which might activate squirrels. These vary. There are two foci of behavior: the one where activity occurs and one which serves as a refuge. When removed from its home site the squirrel exhibits a stronger drive to return than to find a new one.

Haugen (1942) found that cottontail rabbits have home ranges which average about 140 acres in size during the winter and are reduced to about 22 acres during the breeding season.

Errington (1946) argues for territoriality in vertebrates including rodents and suggests that those without territories in a population are more subject to predation than those with territories. Escape efficiency, it may be noted, could relate to familiarity with the territory (Bates).

For the brown rat, Davis (1948) defines the home range as "an area regularly frequented by an individual." He observes that the scope of behavior or range varies from season to season, with sex and with population density. In his studies and those of his coworkers Davis has used several methods for plotting the range of territories: trapping-marking-retrapping; poisoning; tracking; and feeding dyes which color the feces so that they can be identified. Davis reports that no rat was recovered in the first study more than 65 feet from the place where it was previously captured. No marked animals were captured in adjacent city blocks. In the second study recoveries were made up to 120 feet from point of first capture. Davis concludes: 1) Range of movement is related to harborage and food supply. 2) Rats occasionally shift their home range. 3) Range of the brown rat is seldom more than 100 feet in diameter. 4) Radical changes in the environment may lead to changes in areas occupied.[2]

Davis (1953) made an analysis of home range data from recaptures of the rat. He approached quantitative methods, which are not emphasized in most studies of territoriality. He plotted rats' movements between capture and recapture and applied a formula $fr^x = C$ or $\log f + x \log r = \log C$, where $f =$ frequently of recapture, $r =$ distance, and $C =$ constant. Davis suggested that curves plotted thus may yield a value r which is related in a constant manner (an index) to the size of a home range for a species. He confirmed limited range movements in the rat and reported that males traveled greater distances than females, and that the extent of movement tended to increase with age.

King in his intensive study of the black-tailed prairie dog (1955) gives careful attention to population dynamics, including territorialism. He found that prairie dog towns are organized in limited areas, and as with the ground squirrels, movements in space occur with reference to their burrows. There is cooperative defense of coteries through vocalizations, and the dominant male is most active in defense of the group's area. Movements, however, are not confined to the area of the coterie. The distance traveled varied from 3,000 to 14,000 feet and averaged about 5,000. King analyzed causes of movement, and refers to approach responses between animals, tendency of pups to follow adults, the movement of pups during play, and defense behavior. The greatest distances traveled from the coterie involved males *guarding* the territory. King describes invasions, and surmises the motives to be exploration, search for specific food, a new home site, larger territory, or mates. His thorough descriptions emphasize the close interrelation between social organization and the structure of spatial arrangements in the prairie dog.

Seals

Seals provide yet another excellent example of territoriality in breeding grounds of a migratory animal. The Seal Island colonies described by Darling (1947) and Bartholomew (1952 and 1953)

---

2. One can speculate about the application and extension of this last conclusion to vast geographic changes, including deforestation, which disturb and destroy the social organization and territorial orders of populations of animals. Such disturbed populations may be put under stresses which lead to their extinction.

represent spatial organization as one link in the annual cycle of movement that includes migration. As with many birds, males of the seal colony arrive first on the breeding grounds and take possession of individual territories. It is said that bulls occupy territories held during previous years. Bonner (1955) reports on the basis of his review of the literature: "They may fight for their territory and no doubt there are frequent changes of position." Immature bulls occupy areas apart from mature males which are to possess harems. Arrival at the breeding grounds is ordered apparently in terms both of age or maturity and of sex.

The gigantic struggles prevalent in seal-breeding colonies are well known, but the detailed dynamics of these struggles, the activating drives, the specific incentives, the patterns of actions and reactions over long periods of time deserve further intensive study. It would seem to be clear that territoriality has a central role both as motive and response in the dominance order of breeding-age bull seals. It seems equally evident that in this largely aquatic mammal territoriality is a basic condition for reproductive behavior and colony organization.

Among seals, as in many other territorial animals, it would seem that vocalizations function along with fighting for signaling territorial possessions and for defending them.

The territories of seal-breeding grounds are a complex mosaic, structured in relation to the kinds of animals, their age and sex, and different kinds of behavior appropriate to individuals and subgroups of the colony. There are "hauling grounds" and "breeding grounds." There are places where "bachelors" cluster and areas where pups play. Cows are attracted to cows. The mosaic is indeed complex but it has a functional order. Without this spatial order or territoriality the reproductive processes of seals would be chaotic.

Deer and Ungulates

Darling (1937) has provided in his basic study of *A Herd of Red Deer* and his later report (1952) an example of insightful interpretation of the territoriality of ungulates, especially the deer.

The picture is complex and varies with the seasons. There are definite territories for red deer associated with feeding, and deer are identified with wide regions. Like the elk of North America, the red deer of Scotland spend the summer season in the higher mountains and the winter in sheltered valleys below. The low-land winter ranges are more limited and defined than those of the summer, and herds maintain during the winter more compact, cohesive groups. In major areas hinds and stags are separated except during the rutting season in the fall. Deer restrict their movements to territories. Darling experimented with corn as bait and was unsuccessful in inducing deer to cross a stream which marked the limits of the herd's range.

Darling describes in detail the harem-forming and defending behavior of stags during rut. Here fluid spacing arrangements seem to correspond to the stressful dynamics of sociosexual interactions. During rut, rejected stags explore widely and may go as far as 75 miles from their habitual ranges.

Hinds separate from the herd temporarily during the parturition period.

Darling terms the red deer herd a matriarchal society. This characterization would seem to apply to the entire deer family. Thus, the pattern of territoriality characteristic of these animals is, in all probability, implemented mainly by females.

Writing on the "Social Life in Ungulates" (1952) but with special reference to his vast knowledge of the red deer, Darling observes that territory and sex are related mechanisms of society. Territory, he says, "occurs within the range and is determined psychologically rather than physiologically." He reports that *"defense* (fighting) of group territory among ungulates is not known." He adds, however, that territories result from *choice,* are known (by the occupants), and that this *learned* territory has advantages for finding feed and for strategic purposes. Herds move in response to adverse conditions and they "may combine in the face of common need." Deer territories are well structured by paths, wallows, rubbing trees, and so on. "In September red deer establish rutting territories in the hind territories, usually where rapid movement is possible." A large hind territory is divided into many rutting territories which are near each other. Darling infers that the number and closeness of these territories, and of course the interactions of the animals, stimulate the males especially to vigorous breeding behavior.

Murie published the definitive study of elk, *The Elk of North America* (1951). Their range patterns are similar to those of the red deer. Elk have summer ranges usually in high mountain pastures and winter ranges down on the plains where compound herds sum up to thousands of individuals. There is a spring migration from winter to summer feeding grounds, timed during the calving period of cows, and a dramatic fall migration from summer back to winter ranges. This fall migration coincides with the rutting period, which is characterized by battles of the bulls both with voice and brute force, by harem formation, by defense, and by climactic sexual behavior. Cows dominate and "lead" herds and subherds, except during the rutting season. Ranges and territories are structured by trails, feeding and watering areas, wallows and "day beds," shelters from weather or places where wind gives some protection from flies.

The deer family presents yet another variation of patterning of territoriality for the vertebrate animals.

Primates

What are the characteristics and variability of territorial behavior among primates, if indeed this phenomenon is found to characterize the naturalistic behavior of these cousins of man?

Zuckerman in *The Social Life of Monkeys and Apes* (1932), against the background of Heape's (1931) type of conceptualization, recognized the microterritorial patterns of behavior in the London Zoological Garden as displayed by baboons. He also reported movements within range limits and localized areas of troops of baboons in South Africa.

Carpenter (1934) reported systematic observations of the howler monkeys. One of the first problems he attacked was to identify and plot the movements of a howler clan during about one month's time. Territorial localization of groups was found and used advantageously in making population censuses of howlers living on Barro Colorado Island, Panama. Perhaps censuses would not have been possible either for Carpenter or Collias and Southwick (1952) had howlers not been identifiable in groups and strictly territorial. Observations continued for many months and repeated during different years showed persistence of localizations of the groups.

The territories of arboreal howlers, like those of many other animals, have arboreal pathways; food trees, which change during the seasons; trees where the monkeys rest during the midday and sleep at night; as well as distinct characteristics of the forest, i.e. boundaries between primary and secondary forests or between forest and clearings or the shore of Lake Gatun. Territorial defense behavior consists mainly of special patterns of vocalizations and perhaps very rarely of fighting.

Plots of the movement of howler groups show that they tend to travel toward and away from activity centers of an area. The territoriality is a function of the interactions of activity systems with the physical environment. It would seem that many of these actions and reactions are learned.

Carpenter (1934) confirmed territoriality for spider monkeys and squirrel monkeys in their native habitats of the Coto Region of Northern Panama; charted the distribution of a family of orangutans on the West Coast of Sumatra (1938); and in a monograph on the gibbons of Northern Thailand (1940) gave location and ranges for twenty-one gibbon families.

His intensive studies of territorialism in a rhesus monkey colony transplanted from India to Santiago Island, Puerto Rico, show that organization of the colony's groups proceeded concurrently with the establishment of their territories. One group was territorially dominant over all others and moved occasionally to most parts of the island. By experimentally trapping the males from this group, beginning with the most dominant male, Carpenter demonstrated that territorial range was progressively restricted as the dominant males were removed from the group. Thus, it would seem that dominant animals in groups ensure the extent of territorial ranges just as it has been repeatedly observed that individuals are more dominant and successful in fights when they are in territories to which they are adapted.

Carpenter (1958) has recently reviewed available evidence for and against territoriality in primates. Gilmore (1943) found that cebus monkeys of South America would return to their home ranges when released five to six kilometers away. Haddow (1952) confirms the fact of general territoriality for African monkeys and reports his belief that arboreal trails are *learned* by African monkeys. Haddow questions the negative findings of Buxton (1951), who hired large numbers of natives to observe the "night resting habits of monkeys" and did not find territoriality from plots of the natives' observations. Furthermore, Haddow (1952) confirms Lumsden's (1951) observations that primates occasionally shift their territorial ranges. Specifically Haddow reports: "the writer can place on record an instance where a large band of baboons, which had occupied a certain feeding territory for at least four years, suddenly moved to new ground about one and one-half miles away. After spending about four months in the new area, they returned to their former haunts, where they remained to his knowledge for a further two and one-half years . . ."

Carpenter (1958) summarized his review of territoriality in primates as follows: "Observers who have used adequate methods have confirmed and contributed to the definitions and descriptions of territoriality, that prominent characteristic of primate behavior which involves dynamic interactions with their habitats. Without doubt, as evidence collects, variations of this behavior will be found and the general concepts will be elucidated and made more specific."

Nissen (1951) in "Social Behavior of Primates" writes: "A large band or horde establishes itself within a certain region, ordinarily confiding its activities to that area and stoutly defending its boundaries against encroachment by neighboring bands of the same species. As the size of one horde grows, or its food supply diminishes, it may seek to expand its *Lebensraum* and may come into conflict with adjacent groups."

In conclusion it would seem on the basis of available data that territoriality is as characteristic of primates' behavior as it is of other vertebrates.

INFERENCES ON FUNCTIONS OF TERRITORIALITY

Many naturalists have ascribed functions to territoriality mainly on inferential bases, since controlled experimentation has not yet clearly defined and delineated the area of its possible effects. The following documented inferences should be viewed, therefore, as hypotheses yet to be proven. Nevertheless, the list is impressive and suggests the apparent very great biological significance of territoriality in animal life.

Territoriality:

> Spaces or disperses a species population: Naumann (1820), White (1880), Moffat (1903), Bates (1950), Allee (1954).
> Limits or regulates population by limiting breeding: Moffat (1903), Howard (1920), Huxley (1933), Nice (1941), Allee (1954), Kalela (1954).
> Ensures adequate space per se: Bates (1950).
> Prevents overpopulation: Moffat (1903), Burt (1943).

Exposes elements (nonterritorial) of a population to predation: Errington (1946), Burt (1949).

Affords protection against predation: Errington (1946), Davis, (1948).

Reinforces dominance and selective breeding of the "strong": Howard (1920), Noble (1939), Diebschlag (1941), Carpenter (1942a), Greenberg (1947), Bain (1949).

Is advantageous for subordinate animals: Noble (1939).

Affects rate of gene flow in a population and hence may affect rate of evolution: Burt (1943).

Facilitates establishing of breeding colonies for migratory animals (economy): Carpenter (inferred from data on seals).

Stimulates breeding behavior (rut territories of deer): Darling (1937).

Regulates spawning in fish: Wunder (1930), ter Pelkwijk and Tinbergen (1937), Noble (1938), Fabricius (1951).

Facilitates and perhaps ensures breeding for some species: Darling (1937), Bourlière (1954).

Reinforces dominance statuses: Carpenter (1930), Noble (1939), Diebschlag (1941), Bain (1949).

Reduces sexual fighting and killing: Chapman (1935), Carpenter (1942a), Allee (1954).

Reinforces monogamy: Allee (1954).

Increases inbreeding in groups: Howard (1920), Carpenter (1942a).

Protects nest and young: Herrick (1912), Hediger (1950), Davis (1953).

Reinforces integration of groups: Herrick (1912), Carpenter (1952).

Regulates size of groups: Hediger (1950).

Provides security and defense: Bates (1950), Hediger (1950), Allee (1954).

Provides psychological advantage and favorably affects motivation; territories are learned: Carpenter (1934), Bates (1950), Hediger (1950).

Increases accessibility and availability of food: Altum (1868), Moffat (1903), Howard (1920), Nice (1941), Davis (1948), Bates (1950), Hediger (1950), Allee (1954).

Localizes waste disposal in some species: Hediger (1950).

Reduces stress ("flight distance"): Hediger (1950).

Protects against despotism: Nice (1941).

Protects against interference with orderly nesting cycle: Howard (1920), Nice (1941).

Provides song center for birds: Nice (1941).

Provides attraction area for female (bird) ready to mate: Nice (1941).

Reduces rate of spread of diseases and parasites: Nice (1941), Allee (1954).

Warns away trespassing animals: Schmid (1935).

Inhibits or prevents parasitism: Friedman (1928).

SOME IMPLICATIONS OF TERRITORIALITY
FOR EVOLUTION

Territoriality, which is a complex behavioral system and has wide variations of characteristics for different types of animals, is nevertheless almost universally exhibited in some form from the fishes through the primates. It would seem, therefore, that it has important relationships to the adaptive, selective, and survival mechanisms of animal evolution.

It is assumed that territoriality functions to regulate population dispersal over an area and perhaps indirectly to regulate population numbers. It may be an intermediate factor between food supplies and their availability in amounts needed to sustain a population of a given size. The food supply of an area may be regulated for different segments of a population. Aggressive individuals or groups may reserve to themselves, through the complex mechanisms of territorial behavior, an oversupply of foods, while at the same time denying an adequate supply of food to less aggressive individuals or groups.

In their competitions for territory, individuals and groups pit their strengths or behavioral capacities against others in struggles which determine the basic conditions for survival, especially the opportunities to reproduce, to rear young, and to have access to food. These struggles are tests of "fitness to survive," and with some species many individuals may be killed.

Territorial behavior interacts with the social behavior of animals. Furthermore, social behavior such as mating, herding, grouping provide the necessary conditions for reproduction, including rearing of the young.

The individuals which are excluded from territories and from breeding groups are prohibited, during such separation, from contributing genetically to the population. Territory and social organization, the structure of the population, regulate the flow of genes, thus affecting the characteristics of the "gene pool." Not only are individual gene carriers temporarily or permanently excluded by territorial-group boundaries from breeding, but within groups individuals, especially males, do not have equal probabilities of transmitting their genetic characteristics. For some animal types inbreeding within groups predominates for long periods of time; breeding among organized semiclosed groups occurs through complicated exchanges of individuals from group to group across territorial ranges. These exchanges are importantly affected by the territorial envelopes of the groups which may constitute temporary isolating mechanisms.

An optimal dynamic stability of a population is a favorable

condition for species survival, and the territorial order of the population in an area is an important condition for optimal population stability. Territoriality combined with social organization reduces stress, conflict, pugnacity, and nonadaptive energy expenditure.

On the basis of these assumptions it may be hypothesized that physical-geographic changes which radically disturb the territorial order of a species population may seriously and adversely affect the survival of the species.

It is not, finally, beyond the realm of possibility that the behavioral systems of territoriality may in some species become *hypertrophied* or overdeveloped and hence become nonadaptive. Information on this possibility is lacking for nonhuman animals, and the territoriality of man is another theme which remains to be systematically studied.

REFERENCES

ALLEE, W. C. 1938. The social life of animals. New York, W. W. Norton.

ALLEE, W. C. 1952. Dominance and hierarchy in societies of vertebrates. Structure et physiologie des sociétés animales, *34*, 157–81. Paris, Publ. du Centre National de la Recherche Scientifique.

ALLEE, W. C. 1954 rev. Animal sociology. Encyclopaedia Britannica, 971D–972.

ALLEN, A. A. 1934. Sex rhythm in the ruffed grouse (Bonasa umbellus Linn.) and other birds. Auk, *51*, 180–99.

ALTUM, J. B. T. 1868. Der Vogel und sein Leben. Münster, Niemann (tr. by Ernst Mayr, 1935).

ARMSTRONG, E. A. 1947. Bird display and behaviour. London, Drummond.

BAERENDS, G. P., and BAERENDS–VAN ROON, J. M. 1950. An introduction to the study of the ethology of cichlid fishes. Behaviour, Suppl. 1, 1–242.

BAIN, A. D. 1949. Dominance in the great tit, Parus major. Scottish Nat., *61*, 369–472.

BARTHOLOMEW, G. A., Jr. 1952. Reproductive and social behavior of the northern elephant seal. Univ. Calif. Publ. Zool., *47*, 369–472.

BARTHOLOMEW, G. A., Jr., and HOEL, P. G. 1953. Reproductive behavior of the Alaska fur seal, Callorhinus ursinus. J. Mammal., *34*, 417–36.

BATES, M. 1950. The nature of natural history. New York, Scribner's.

BAUMGARTNER, F. M. 1939. Territory and population in the great horned owl. Auk, *56* (2), 274–82.

BENNETT, M. A. 1940. Social hierarchy in ring doves. II. The effects of treatment with testosterone propionate. Ecology, *21*, 148–65.

BONNER, J. T. 1955. Cells and societies. Princeton, Princeton Univ. Press.

BOURLIÈRE, F. 1952. Le territorialisme dans l'organisation sociale des Vertébrés. Structure et physiologie des sociétés animales, *34*, 199–206. Paris, Publ. du Centre National de la Recherche Scientifique.

BOURLIÈRE, F. 1954. The natural history of mammals. New York, Knopf.

BRADT, G. W. 1938. A study of beaver

colonies in Michigan. J. Mammal., *19*, 139–62.

BREDER, C. M., JR. 1934. An experimental study of the reproductive habits and life history of the cichlid fish. Zoologica, *18*, 1–42.

BREWSTER, W. 1906. The birds of the Cambridge Region of Massachusetts. Mem. Nuttall Ornithol. Club, *4*, 62–3.

BROCK, S. E. 1910. The willow-wrens of a Lothian Wood. Zoologist, *15*, 401–17.

BURKITT, J. P. 1924–26. A study of the robin by means of marked birds. British Birds, *17*, 294–303; *18*, 97–103; *19*, 120–24; *20*, 91–101.

BURT, W. H. 1940. Territorial behavior and populations of some small mammals in southern Michigan. Misc. Publ. Mus. Zool. Univ. Mich., No. 45, pp. 1–58.

BURT, W. H. 1943. Territoriality and home range concepts as applied to mammals. J. Mammal., *24*, 346–52.

BURT, W. H. 1949. Territoriality. Ibid., *30*, 25–7.

BUXTON, A. P. 1951. Further observations on the night resting habits of monkeys in a small area on the edge of the Semliki Forest, Uganda. J. Anim. Ecol., *20*, 31–2.

BUXTON, A. P. 1952. Observations on the diurnal behavior of the redtail monkey Cereopithecus ascanius schmidti Matschie in a small forest in Uganda. Ibid., *21*, 25–8.

CAGLE, F. R. 1944. Home range, homing behavior and migration in turtles. Misc. Publ. Mus. Zool. Univ. Mich., *61*, 1–34.

CALHOUN, J. B. 1949. Influence of space and time on the social behavior of the rat. Anat. Rec., *105*, 28.

CARPENTER, C. R. 1930. Effects of complete and partial gonadectomy on fighting behavior in domestic pigeons. Unpublished data from dissertation research, Stanford Univ.

CARPENTER, C. R. 1934. A field study of the behavior and social relations of the howling monkeys (Alouatta palliata). Comp. Psychol. Monogr., Vol. *10* (2).

CARPENTER, C. R. 1935. Behavior of red spider monkeys in Panama. J. Mammal., *16*, 171–80.

CARPENTER, C. R. 1938. A survey of wild life conditions in Atjeh of North Sumatra, with special reference to the orang-utan. Amsterdam, Netherlands Committee for International Nature Protection, Communications No. 12, pp. 1–34.

CARPENTER, C. R. 1940. A field study in Siam of the behavior and social relations of the gibbon (Hylobates lar). Comp. Psychol. Monogr., Vol. *16* (5).

CARPENTER, C. R. 1942a. Sexual behavior of free ranging rhesus monkeys (Macaca mulatta). I. Specimens, procedures and behavioral characteristics of estrus. II. Periodicity of estrus, homosexual, auto-erotic and non-conformist behavior. J. Comp. Psychol., *33*, 113–62.

CARPENTER, C. R. 1942b. Societies of monkeys and apes. Biol. Symposium *8*, Univ. of Chicago Press, pp. 177–204.

CARPENTER, C. R. 1945. Concepts and problems of primate sociometry. Sociometry, *8*, 56–61.

CARPENTER, C. R. 1952. Social behavior of non-human primates. Structure et physiologie des sociétés animales, *34*, 227–45. Paris, Publ. du Centre National de la Recherche Scientifique.

CARPENTER, C. R. 1954. Tentative generalizations on grouping behavior of non-human primates. Human Biology, *26*, 269–76.

CARPENTER, C. R. 1958. Soziologie und Verhalten freilebender nichtmenschlicher Primaten. Handbuch der Zoologie, Band 8 (Mammalia), Teil 10. Berlin: Walter de Gruyter.

CAUSEY, O. R., LAEMMERT, H. W., and HAYES, G. S. 1948. The home range of Brazilian cebus monkeys in a region of small residual forests. Amer. J. Hygiene, *47*, 304–14.

CHAPMAN, F. M. 1935. The courtship of Gould's manakin (Manacus vitellinus vitellinus) on Barro Colorado Island,

Canal Zone. Bull. Amer. Mus. Nat. Hist., *68*, 471–525.

CLARK, P. J., and EVANS, F. C. 1954. Distance to nearest neighbor as a measure of spatial relationships in populations. Ecology, *35*, 445–53.

COLLIAS, N. E. 1951. Problems and principles of animal sociology. In C. P. Stone, ed., Comparative psychology. New York, Prentice-Hall. Ch. 12, pp. 388–422.

COLLIAS, N., and SOUTHWICK, C. 1952. A field study of population density and social organization in howling monkeys. Proc. Amer. Philos. Soc., *96*, 143–56.

DARLING, F. F. 1937. A herd of red deer, a study in animal behavior. Oxford, Clarendon Press.

DARLING, F. F. 1947. The life history of the Atlantic grey seal. Natural History in the Highlands and Islands. London, Collins. Pp. 217–31.

DARLING, F. F. 1952. Social life in ungulates. Structure et physiologie des sociétés animales, *34*, 221–6. Paris, Publ. du Centre National de la Recherche Scientifique.

DAVIS, D. E. 1953. Analysis of home range from recapture data. J. Mammal., *34*, 352–8.

DAVIS, D. E. 1954. The home range of some Brazilian mammals. Ibid., *26*, 119–27.

DAVIS, D. E., EMLEN, J. T., and STOKES, A. W. 1948. Studies on home range in the brown rat. Ibid., *29*, 207–25.

DEWAR, J. M. 1915. The relation of the oyster-catcher to its natural environment. Zoologist, *19*, 281–91, 340–46, 376–83, 426–31, 458–65.

DEWAR, J. M. 1920. The law of territory. British Birds, *14*, 89–90.

DICE, L. R. 1952. Measure of the spacing between individuals within a population. Contr. Lab. Vert. Biol. Univ. Mich., *55*, 1–23.

DIEBSCHLAG, E. 1941. Psychologische Beobachtungen über die Rangordnung bei der Haustaube. Z. f. Tierpsychol. *4*, 173–87.

DOBZHANSKY, TH. 1941. Genetics and the origin of species. New York, Columbia Univ. Press.

EMERSON, A. E. 1954. Dynamic homeostasis: a unifying principle in organic, social and ethical evolution. Sci. Month., *78*, 67–85.

EMLEN, J. T. 1954. Territory, nest building and pair formation of the cliff swallow. Auk, *71* (1), 16–35.

ERRINGTON, P. L. 1946. Predation and vertebrate populations. Quart. Rev. Biol., *21*, 144–77.

EVANS, F. C., and HOLDENRIED, R. 1941. Field study of ground squirrel (Citellus beecheyi) in relation to sylvatic plague. Proc. Soc. Exp. Biol. Med., *47*, 63–64.

EVANS, F. C., and HOLDENRIED, R. 1943. A population study of the Beecheyi ground squirrel in central California. J. Mammal., *24*, 231–60.

EVANS, L. T. 1938. Cuban field studies on territoriality of the lizard Anolis sagrei. J. Comp. Psychol., *25*, 97–125.

FABRICIUS, E. 1951. The topography of the spawning bottom as a factor influencing the size of the territory in some species of fish. Inst. of Freshwater Res., Drottningholm, *32*, 43–9.

FABRICIUS, E., and GUSTAFSON, K. J. 1954. Further aquarium observations on the spawning behaviour of char (Salmo alpinus L.). Ibid., *35*, 58–101.

FITCH, H. S. 1940. A field study of the growth and behavior of the fence lizard. Univ. of Calif. Publ. Zool., *44*, 151–72.

FRIEDMAN, H. 1928. Social parasitism in birds. Quart. Rev. Biol., *3*, 554–69.

GILMORE, R. M. 1943. Mammalogy in an epidemicological study of jungle yellow fever in Brazil. J. Mammal., *24*, 144–62.

GOLDSMITH, O. 1774. A history of the earth and animated nature. London.

GORDON, K. 1940. Territorial behavior and social dominance among Sciurdae. J. Mammal., *17*, 171–2.

GREENBERG, B. 1947. Some relations between territory, social hierarchy, and leadership in green sunfish (Lepomis cyanellus). Physiol. Zool., *20*, 267–99.

GREENBERG, B., and NOBLE, G. K. 1942. Dominance, social order and territory in the lizard (Anolis carolinensis). Anat. Rec., *84*, 508–9.

HADDOW, A. J. 1952. Field and laboratory studies on an African monkey Cercopithecus ascanius schmidti Matschie. Proc. Zool. Soc., London, *122*, Pt. 2, 297–394.

HADDOW, A. J., SMITHBURN, K. C., MAHAFFY, A. F., and BUGHER, J. C. 1947. Monkeys in relation to yellow fever in Bwamba County, Uganda. Trans. Roy. Soc. Trop. Med. Hygiene, *40*, 677.

HAMER, A. H. 1933. Territorialism and sexual selection. S. African J. Nat. Hist., *3*, 54–59.

HAMILTON, W. J. 1937. Activity and home range of the field mouse Microtus pennsylvanicus. Ecology, *18*, 255–63.

HART, J. L., TESTER, A. L., and McHUGH, J. L. 1941. The tagging of herring (Clupea pallasii) in British Columbia, etc. 1940–41. Rep. Brit. Col. Fish. Dept., 1940: J47–J74.

HAUGEN, A. O. 1942. Life history studies of the cottontail rabbit in southwestern Michigan. Amer. Midland Nat., *28*, 204–44.

HAYNE, D. W. 1949. Calculation of size of home range. J. Mammal., *30*, 1–18.

HAYNE, D. W. 1950. Apparent home range of Microtus in relation to distance between traps. Ibid., *31*, 26–39.

HEAPE, W. 1931. Emigration, Immigration and Nomadism. Cambridge, Eng., Heffer.

HEDIGER, H. 1944. Die Bedeutung von Miktion und Defäkation bei Wildtieren. Schweizerische Z. f. Psychol., *3*, 170–82.

HEDIGER, H. 1949. Säugetier-Territorien und ihre Markierung. Bijdragen tot de Dierkunde, *28*, 172–84.

HEDIGER, H. 1950. Wild Animals in captivity. London, Butterworths Scientific Publ.

HERRICK, F. H. 1912. Organization of the gull community. Proc. 7th Int. Zool. Cong. 1907, Cambridge, Mass.

HESSE, R., ALLEE, W. C., and SCHMIDT, K. P. 1937. Ecological animal geography. New York, Wiley.

HIXSON, G. A. The effect of numbers on the establishment of hierarchies and territoriality in the green sunfish (Lepomis cyanellus). Masters thesis, Univ. of Chicago.

HOCHBAUM, H. A. 1944. The canvasback on a prairie marsh. Amer. Wildlife Inst., Washington.

HOOTON, E. 1942. Man's poor relations. Garden City, Doubleday, Doran.

HOWARD, H. E. 1907–14. The British warblers, a history, with problems of their lives. Cambridge, Eng., Cambridge Univ. Press. 6 vols.

HOWARD, H. E. 1920. Territory in bird life. London, John Murray.

HOWARD, H. E. 1929. An introduction to the study of bird behavior. Cambridge, Eng., Cambridge Univ. Press.

HOWARD, W. E. 1949. Dispersal, amount of inbreeding, and longevity in a local population of deermice on the George Reserve, southern Michigan. Contr. Lab. Vert. Biol. Univ. Mich., Vol. *43*.

HUBERT, L. E. 1947. La faune des grands mammifères de la plaine Ruindi-Rutshuru. Inst. Parcs Nationaux du Congo Belge, Bruxelles.

HUXLEY, J. 1933. A natural experiment on the territorial instinct. British birds, *26*, 270–7.

HUXLEY, J., ed. 1940. The new systematics. Oxford, Clarendon Press.

HUXLEY, J. 1942. Evolution; the modern synthesis. New York, Harper.

IMANISHI, K., and ITANI, J. Report of field observations of Japanese macaque, Macaca fuscata. Private correspondence.

JENKINS, D. 1944. Territory as a result of despotism and social organization as shown by geese. Auk, *61*, 30–47.

KALELA, O. 1954. Über den Revierbesitz bei Vogeln und Säugetieren als population-sokologischer Faktor. Ann. Zool. Soc. Zool. Bot., Fennicae "Vanamo," *16*, 1–48.

KENDEIGH, S. C. 1941. Territorial and

mating behavior of the housewren. Biol. Monogr., *18*, 327–36.

KING, J. A. 1954. Closed social groups among dogs. Proc. Amer. Philos. Soc., *98* (5), 327–36.

KING, J. A. 1955. Social behavior, social organization, and population dynamics in a black-tailed prairie dog town in the Black Hills of South Dakota. Contr. Lab. Vert. Biol. Univ. Mich., *67*.

KIRKMAN, F. B. 1940. The inner territory of the black-headed gull. British birds, *34*, 100–4.

LACK, D. L. 1934. Territory reviewed. Ibid., *27*, 266–7.

LACK, D. L. 1943. The life of the robin. London, H. F. and G. Witherby.

LACK, D. L. and LACK, LAMBERT. 1933. Territory reviewed. British birds, *27*, 179–99.

LEOPOLD, A. 1939. Game management. New York and London: Scribner's.

LINSDALE, J. M. 1946. The California ground squirrel. Berkeley and Los Angeles, Univ. of Calif. Press.

LUMSDEN, W. H. R. 1951. The night resting habits of monkeys in a small area on the edge of the Semliki Forest, Uganda. J. anim. Ecol., *20*, 11–30.

MAYAUD, N. 1950. Territoire. In Pierre Grassé, ed., Traité de zoologie, *15*, 717–29.

MAYR, E. 1935. Bernard Altum and the territory theory. Proc. Linn. Soc. New York, Nos. 45–46.

MAYR, E. 1942. Systematics and the origin of species. New York, Columbia Univ. Press.

MEISE, W. 1930. Revierbesitz im Vogelleben, Ein Umschu, Mitt. Vereins sächs. Ornithologie, *3*, 49–68.

MEISE, W. 1936. Neue Ergebnisse der Revierforschung, Mitt. Vereins sächs. Ibid., *5*, 1–23.

MEYER-HOLZAPFEL, M. 1941. Das Territorium als Grundlage der sozialen Organization bei einer Gruppe von Schwanzbandsalmlern. Rev. suisse zool., *48*, 531–6.

MOFFAT, C. B. 1903. The spring rivalry of birds, some views on the limits to

multiplication. Irish Nat., *12*, 152–66.

MURIE, O. J. 1951. The elk of North America. Washington, Stackpole and Wildlife Manag. Inst.

NAUMANN, J. F. 1820. Naturgeschichte der Vogel Deutschlands. Leipzig.

NICE, M. M. 1933. The theory of territorialism and its development, in fifty years of progress of American ornithology. Lancaster, Pa., pp. 89–100.

NICE, M. M. 1937. Studies in the life history of the song sparrow. Proc. Linn. Soc. New York, *4*, 1–247.

NICE, M. M. 1941. The role of territory in bird life. Amer. Midland Nat., *26* (3), 441–87.

NICE, M. M. 1943. Studies in the life history of the song sparrow. II. The behavior of the song sparrow and other Passerines. Proc. Linn. Soc. New York, *6*, 1–329.

NICHOLSON, E. M. 1935. Territory in the great crested grebe. British birds, *28*, 246–7.

NISSEN, H. W. 1951. Social behavior of primates. Comparative psychology, New York, Prentice-Hall. Ch. 13, pp. 423–57.

NOBLE, G. K. 1934. Experimenting with the courtship of lizards. Nat. Hist., *34*, 3–15.

NOBLE, G. K. 1938. Sexual selection among fishes. Biol. Rev., *13*, 133–58.

NOBLE, G. K. 1939. The role of dominance in the life of birds. Auk, *56*, 263–73.

NOBLE, G. K. and BRADLEY, M. T. 1933. The mating behavior of lizards: its bearing on the theory of sexual selection. Ann. N. Y. Acad. Sci., *35*, 25–100.

PELKWIJK, J. J. ter, and TINBERGEN, N. 1937. Eine reizbiologische Analyse einiger Verhaltensweisen von Gasterosteus aculeatus (L). Z. f. Tierpsychol. *1*, 193–204.

RAND, A. L. 1940. Breeding habits of birds of paradise (Macgregoria and Diphyllodes). Amer. Mus. Novitates, No. 1073, pp. 1–14.

RAY, J. 1678. The ornithology of Francis Willugby. London.

ROBERTS, B. 1940. The breeding behavior

of penguins with special reference to Pygoscelis papua (Forster). British Graham Land Expedition, 1934–1937, Scientific report, *1*, 195–254.

RODEHEFFER, I. A. 1941. The movements of marked fish in Douglas Lake, Michigan. Pap. Mich. Acad. Sci., *26*, 265–80.

SCHMID, B. 1935. Über die Ermittlung des menschlichen und tierischen Individualgeruchs durch den Hund. Z. f. vergl. Physiol., *22*, 524–38.

SCOTT, J. P. 1944. Social behavior, range and territoriality in domestic mice. Proc. Indiana Acad. Sci., *53*, 188–95.

SHOEMAKER, H. H. 1939. Social hierarchy in flocks of the canary. Auk, *56*, 381–406.

SHOEMAKER, H. H. 1939. Effects of testosterone propionate on behavior of the female canary. Proc. Soc. Exp. Biol. Med., *41*, 299–302.

TAVISTOCK, Marquess of. 1931. The food shortage theory. Ibis, *2*, 351–4.

TINBERGEN, N. 1936. The function of sexual fighting in birds, and the problem of the origin of the "territory." Bird banding, 7, 1–8.

TINBERGEN, N. 1951. The study of instinct. New York and London, Oxford Univ. Press.

TINBERGEN, N. 1952. On the significance of territory in the herring gull. Ibis, *94*, 158–9.

TINBERGEN, N. 1953. Social behavior in animals; with special reference to vertebrates. London, Methuen.

VOGT, W. 1938. Preliminary notes on the behavior and ecology of the eastern willet. Proc. Linn. Soc. New York, *49*, 8–42.

VON NOLTE, ANGELA. 1955. Freiland Beobachtungen über das Verhalten von Macaca radiata in Sudindien. Z. f. Tierpsychol., *12*, 77–87.

WHITE, G. 1789. The natural history and antiquities of Selborne, in the County of Southampton. Letter XI. 3d ed. London.

WUNDER, W. 1930. Experimentelle Untersuchungen am dreistachligen Stichling (Gasterosteus aculeatus L.) während der Laichzeit. Z. Morphol. u. Ökol., *16*, 453–98.

ZUCKERMAN, S. 1932. The social life of monkeys and apes. London, Kegan Paul, Trench, Trubner; New York, Harcourt, Brace.

12

The Comparative Study of Species-Specific Behavior

R. A. Hinde

CAMBRIDGE UNIVERSITY

and N. Tinbergen

OXFORD UNIVERSITY

INTRODUCTION. AIMS AND METHODS

Aims

Species-specific behavior is in part the product of evolutionary processes. Likewise, the behavior of a species must influence the course of its evolution. These two interrelated problems—the influence of evolutionary processes on behavior and of behavior on evolution—comprise a large field about which little is yet known. This chapter is concerned mainly with the first, namely how behavior changes in evolution. It is also confined primarily to behavior which is more or less characteristic of the species, and thus discusses only one aspect of the whole problem.

Methods

In studying evolution, the ethologist is in a different position from the morphologist. Direct evidence about the ancestral species, which morphologists can obtain from paleontology, is not available; and ontogenetic evidence has so far been little help, though it may be more widely used in future. Comparison between living taxonomic units is thus the only method available, and this is naturally indirect. However, by comparing the behavior traits of species whose phylogenetic relationships are established, it is possible to make hypotheses about the probable origins of that behavior, and thus about the course of its evolution.[1] In doing this, the ethologist must start by relying on the currently accepted classification of the group he is studying. This is usually satisfactory, but sometimes the results of behavior study clash with the classificatory scheme previously in use. In such cases a reappraisal of all characters, morphological and behavioral, may lead to a revision of the classification. Circular arguments are thus avoided by the same method that is used by comparative morphologists, namely the use of independent sources of evidence about the systematic relationships of the species studied.

Use of the comparative method in studying the evolution of behavior then involves several distinct steps. First, formal similarities in the behavior patterns of the species concerned must be recognized. Since the species are believed to be closely related on other grounds, such similarities suggest that the behavior elements have a common evolutionary origin. However, similarity between behavior elements does not necessarily mean identity,[2] for minor differences between species will occur. Examination of these differences, together with evidence about the causation and function of the behavior elements, enables hypotheses to be erected about which behavior form is the more primitive (i.e. phylogenetically older). This in turn permits hypotheses about the probable origins of the behavior elements, and the differences between their present condition and their probable origin can be described. The result is a tentative description of

1. The use of the comparative method in the study of behavior owes much to the pioneering studies of Whitman (1919), Heinroth (1911, 1928) and Lorenz (1935, 1939, 1941). Among the groups now being studied are salticid spiders (Crane, 1948–50), grasshoppers (Jacobs, 1950; Faber, 1953), mantids (Crane, 1952), *Drosophila* (Spieth, 1950, 1952), spider wasps and digger wasps (Evans, 1953, 1955), fiddler crabs (Crane, 1941), cichlid fish (Seitz, 1940, 1941, 1949; Baerends and Baerends, 1950), sticklebacks (Tinbergen, e.g. 1951; van Iersel, 1953; Morris, in press), ducks and geese (Heinroth, 1911, 1928; Lorenz, 1941), fringilline and cardueline finches (Hinde, 1953, 1954, 1955, 1956, Marler, 1956), old world buntings (Andrew, 1956b), estrildine finches (Morris, in press), and gulls (Goethe, 1937; Tinbergen, 1953; Tinbergen and Broekhuysen, 1954; Moynihan, 1955a; Cullen, in press).

2. The precise meaning to be attached to "similarity" will vary with the nature of the behavioral character and the diversity of the taxonomic group. Since the gaps between the units within a taxonomic group are usually smaller than the gaps between groups, "similar" usually means less different within the group than between the group and other groups. A comparable difficulty of course arises in morphological work and is met in the same way.

the way the behavior has changed in evolution; this is the most that can be expected from descriptive comparative studies.

A knowledge of the probable course of evolution prompts further enquiry as to why evolution has taken that course and not some other. It is thus desirable to know whether the changes are adaptive and can have been brought about by selection. This involves a study of the survival value of the behavior elements and of the interspecies differences, as well as further investigation into the causal and functional relationships between the behavior elements.

Selection of Characters for Study

As in morphology, successful use of the comparative method depends on the selection of the characters to be compared. A major problem is one of level of complexity: how far is the behavior to be analysed before its parts are compared? Both because there is no direct evidence about the behavior of extinct forms, and because convergences are widespread, most of the studies made hitherto have dealt with relatively small behavior elements within groups of closely related species. The conclusions drawn from such studies thus refer at most to microevolution. Although quite complex behavior traits, such as the communal nesting habits of the Crotophaginae (Davis, 1942) and the parasitic habit in cuckoos (Friedmann, 1929), have sometimes been used successfully in comparative work, the results of such studies are often difficult to assess until a further analysis of the characters has been undertaken.

Ultimately it will be desirable to make comparative studies not only of overt behavior but also of the causal mechanisms underlying it. However, since the motor patterns are directly observable, it is these which have been studied most often. Heinroth and Whitman were among the first to point out that species-characteristic movements (the "fixed action patterns") can be isolated from the total motor behavior, and the results obtained by many later workers have confirmed the value of these for comparative work.

One further point about the selection of characters for comparative study must be discussed. All characters of the living animal, behavioral and morphological, are products of environmental factors as well as of inherent potentialities. The student of evolution must therefore always ensure that the differences he is investigating are in fact indicative of genetic diversity and not merely of dissimilar environments. Special care is needed in behavior studies because of the plasticity introduced by learning processes.

In the past, as Lehrman (1953), Beach (1955), and others have pointed out, ethologists have often been too ready to assume that learning does not enter into the development of "instinctive" patterns. (But see also Koehler, 1954). Recently, for instance, it has been shown that an inexperienced ring dove (*Streptopelia risoria*) will not walk up to its chick in order to feed it: this has to be learned (Lehrman, 1955). Similarly, Craig (1912) showed that drinking is not elicited in young doves by the sight of water; the response to the visual characteristics of water has to be conditioned.

On the other hand, the opposite tendency has also occurred: many authors have overestimated the part played by learning and underestimated the widespread occurrence of "unlearned" behavior. To cite but two examples, Sauer's (1956) very detailed observations on *Sylvia borin* show that the complete repertoire of species-characteristic movements and calls is performed by birds raised without their parents. Second, female canaries which have never manipulated anything but fine grain show all the movements of nest building before they have had material to build with, and treat such material appropriately as soon as it is presented. Of course such observations do not show that learning processes do not enter into the development of the elements of the behavioral patterns in question, but only that the species-characteristic patterns develop and are given appropriately in the absence of example or reward.

However, for the present purpose the relevant problem is not whether a given character is independent of learning or not but whether and to what extent behavioral differences between species are due to hereditary differences, that is whether they are innate.[3] This can be decided by raising two species in the same environment: if specific differences persist, then these must

3. Some semantic clarification is perhaps required here. In the past the term "innate" has been applied in ethology to both characters and the differences between characters. Various critics (Beach, 1955; Lehrman, 1953; Spurway, 1953) have pointed out that the application of the term to characters is misleading, since these are the result of continuous interaction between environment and inherent potentialities throughout development. In this paper, therefore, "innate" is applied only to differences (Tinbergen, 1955).

ultimately be due to hereditary differences. For instance, the Heinroths (1928) have given numerous examples of interspecific differences in behavior which persist even in individuals reared in the same artificial environment. To cite another example, great tits (*Parus major*) or blue tits (*Parus caeruleus*) taken from the nest eight days after hatching and reared by hand deal with large food items (e.g. mealworms) by placing them under their feet and pecking at them. The use of the feet appears first, in an incomplete form, at about seventeen days, and learning clearly enters into its perfection. Chaffinches bred from eggs which were hatched and reared for eight days by tits, and subsequently fed by hand, only rarely use the foot in feeding.[4] Thus this difference in the use of the foot is basically hereditary, even though learning plays an important part in its development.

This exemplifies a principal of great importance: many of the differences between species do not lie in the first instance in stereotyped behavior sequences but consist in the possession of a propensity to learn. Thus the production of the species-characteristic song by chaffinches (*Fringilla coelebs*) depends on learning from other singing males, but a chaffinch will not imitate any sound it hears—only those having certain characteristics in common with normal chaffinch song (Thorpe, 1954, 1956; see also Heinroth, 1928; Sauer, 1954). However, although the ontogeny of behavioral characters is as yet largely unexplored, there is a wealth of material showing that interspecies differences in motor patterns of the kind most commonly used in comparative studies are almost invariably innate. On the other hand, differences in responsiveness to releasing stimuli are sometimes due to conditioning and sometimes innate. A check on the relative roles of inherent and environmental factors in the production of interspecies differences is thus even more necessary when comparing responsiveness than when comparing motor patterns.

THE EVOLUTION OF COURTSHIP AND THREAT DISPLAYS IN BIRDS

To exemplify the use of these methods in comparative work we will now consider some of the conclusions reached about the evolution of the threat and courtship displays of birds. Courtship behavior has been much used in comparative studies because

4. Of course the intra-egg environment differed, but even this is presumably ultimately largely under genetic control.

of the relatively stereotyped postures involved and the extent of interspecies diversity.

A Preliminary Causal Analysis of the Displays

It is first necessary to consider some results obtained in the causal analyses of such displays. Recent studies of both fishes and birds have shown that a threatening animal has two incompatible tendencies: to attack its rival and to flee from it. Similarly a courting bird has three incompatible tendencies: to attack, flee from, and behave sexually toward its mate (e.g. Tinbergen, 1952, 1953; Hinde, 1952, 1953). The nature of the behavior shown at any stage in the courtship depends on the strengths and relative strengths of these conflicting tendencies.

Among fishes and birds species differ in the relative importance of these tendencies. In some the male is markedly aggressive to the female throughout the reproductive season (e.g. three-spined stickleback, *Gasterosteus aculeatus,* Tinbergen and van Iersel, in preparation; river bullhead, *Cottus gobio,* Morris, 1954b), while in others he is afraid of her most of the time (e.g. chaffinch, *Fringilla coelebs,* Hinde, 1953; Marler, 1956; zebra finch, *Poephila guttata,* Morris, 1954a). Among many passerines the male is dominant early in the season and the female later, the time at which the change in dominance occurs varying between species: as the relative strengths of these tendencies change, there are correlated changes in the courtship displays (Tinbergen, 1953; Hinde, 1955). In a few species the male's tendencies to attack and flee are relatively insignificant and the courtship is primarily a result of sexual thwarting (e.g. Mexican swordtail, *Xiphophorus helleri,* Morris, 1955). Among fringilline and cardueline finches most of the components (e.g. wing raising, tail spreading, etc.) of the courtship displays are associated with one or the other of these three tendencies. The relations between display components and tendencies are similar in all the species and interspecific hybrids so far studied, and are probably widespread among passerines. The species differences in display thus lie primarily in the relative intensities of components.

The Evolutionary Origin of Display Movements

Comparison of the display movements of related species leads to the establishment of homologies. Behavior elements from the different species can thus be grouped together as having a similar evolutionary origin. Examination of the diversity shown by the homologous elements, coupled with the results of causal and functional analyses, provides indications of the evolutionary origins of the movements. This method has so far revealed three primary sources of display movements. From these the displays as seen today have become elaborated, presumably through the action of selection on genetic variability.

1. Intention movements. These are the preparatory and in-complete movements which often appear at the beginning of an activity; for instance, a bird about to fly crouches, raises its wings and tail, withdraws its neck, and then reverses these movements as it springs off. Many avian displays have been elaborated from such movements (Daanje, 1950).

2. Displacement activities. This term is used here in a broadly descriptive sense for activities which appear at first sight irrelevant in the situation in which they occur; for instance, the bill wiping, preening, and feather movements which often appear during avian courtship (Tinbergen, 1952). Their causation is still poorly understood, but there seems little doubt that many displays have been elaborated from them. In each case the evidence that present-day display postures have evolved from these sources is comparative. Often the display movement can be compared with the unritualized movement as it occurs in the same species. In other cases species can be found in which the evolutionary changes undergone by a particular display movement are relatively slight, and which therefore form a link between the highly elaborated cases and their presumed source.

3. Redirection activities. When the expression of behavior toward the object which elicited it is inhibited, it is sometimes redirected onto another object. Thus the aggressive behavior of the male black-headed gull, elicited by its mate, is often redirected onto other nearby gulls (Moynihan, 1955a, 1955b).

Sometimes a display posture of one type becomes secondarily modified into another. Thus some threat postures, themselves derived from intention movements, have become secondarily modified for courtship. Here the evidence is partly comparative and partly ontogenetic; in the chaffinch the threat behavior of the male toward the female changes gradually into courtship as his sexual tendency increases (Marler, 1956).

Elaboration of Display Movements in Evolution

When the evolutionary origins of the display movements have been provisionally identified, the changes which they have undergone in evolution can be described. Although the precise ways in which intention movements and displacement activities have become elaborated into display are still imperfectly understood, some principles are becoming clear (Tinbergen, 1954).

1. Development of conspicuous structures and further correlation of the movement with the structures. Most display movements show off a conspicuous structure. Although it is often found that a similar movement shows off quite different structures in related species, so that the movement appears to be primary and the structure secondary, there has probably always been a parallel elaboration of structure and movement. Thus among tits (*Parus* spp.) there is a correlation between the degree of elaboration of the "head-up" threat posture and the development of a conspicuous throat and breast coloration (Hinde, 1952). Further, the blue tit (*Parus caeruleus*), in which the head-up posture is relatively inconspicuous, makes much use of a head-forward posture in reproductive fighting, and can raise the cheek feathers in a special way to make this conspicuous (Tinbergen, 1937).

2. Schematization of the movement. Usually the actual nature of the movement itself becomes changed in the course of evolution. The changes which occur have been classified by Daanje (1950) as follows:

a. Exaggeration of certain components of the movement. Thus the magpie (*Pica pica*) makes exaggerated tail movements in display. These represent an elaborated form of the up-and-down tail movements before flight and probably serve as a social releaser.

b. Changes in absolute and relative thresholds of components. This may result in marked accentuation of one component of, for instance, an intention movement of take-off and a virtual suppression of others. Similar changes result in the movement becoming increasingly stereotyped, a given intensity of response being elicited by a wider range of strengths of the eliciting factors. As we have seen, in many finches and other passerines the various components of the displays are linked with one or other of the conflicting tendencies. There have so far been no studies in other groups to determine how far relative changes in the components of the displays are related to changes in the associated tendencies.

c. Changes in the coordination of components. Thus a component of the first stage of taking off (e.g. crouching) may be combined with one from the springing-off phase (e.g. tail lowered).

The above three categories are, of course, to be regarded only as a means of classifying the changes that can be observed. The changes in the mechanisms underlying them are still unknown, and it seems unlikely that the categories have any causal validity. All the changes in the movements and the accompanying structures can be understood as adaptations to the signal functions [5] of the movement; they make it more conspicuous and, in some cases, more different from other movements. The genetic changes involved are undoubtedly rather complex: the displays of cardueline F_1 interspecies hybrids are intermediate between those of the parents (Hinde, 1956a; see also the detailed work of Clark, Aronson, and Gordon, 1954, on Xiphophorin fishes), and most plumage characters conspicuous in display are polygenic (references in Hinde, 1956b).

3. Emancipation. In addition to the changes in absolute and relative thresholds mentioned above, it has been suggested that there are more marked motivational changes such that the movement comes in evolution to be governed by causal factors different from those which governed it originally. Although such changes may be important in some groups (e.g. Lorenz, 1951), their general importance is not yet established. Thus it has recently been suggested that the feather postures of birds, much used in display and always apparently well correlated with one or other of the tendencies underlying it, may be under the same type of autonomic control as when they are used for cooling or warming (Andrew, 1956a; Morris, 1956). Even courtship feeding, which seems to be a clear-cut case of emancipation from parental/juvenile to sexual behavior (for the female may beg while actually holding food in the beak), may in fact be partly

5. The diverse functions which displays may cover, and the ways in which signal movements have been elaborated to serve these functions, have been reviewed recently by Baerends (1950) and Tinbergen (1954).

a secondary result of other (e.g. dominance) changes such that common factors between the parental and sexual situations are introduced.

The Function of Display

Now that we have made a provisional sketch of the evolutionary radiation of display movements within a group of closely related species, it remains to assess their functional significance. Here it is necessary to consider the biological significance both of the differences between a given display movement and its origin and of the differences (and similarities) between the displays of the present-day forms. The principal functions of the displays used in fighting and courtship have recently been reviewed by Tinbergen (1954), and will be mentioned only briefly here:

1. Fighting. Displays reduce the amount of actual combat and help to limit fighting to intraspecific encounters.

2. Courtship. (a) Synchronisation of the behavior of the sexes. This may be long term, involving, for instance, hormonal changes (Craig, 1911; Matthews, 1939), or short term, synchronising the mating activities of the pair. (b) Orientation. Some displays have primarily a guiding function (for instance the song of many passerines, the nest site display of the great tit and other hole-nesting species). The highly coloured patches round the genitalia of many baboons and chimpanzees may guide the male to the female's copulatory organs. (c) Suppression of nonsexual responses. "Submissive" postures in passerines help to suppress the aggressive behavior of the mate. (d) Maintenance of reproductive isolation. Thus sympatric closely related species of birds usually differ markedly in display, color, or song (Huxley, 1942; Skutch, 1951).

As Lorenz has pointed out, all these functions require that the display should be effective in eliciting responses in other individuals. This has led to progressive adaptation for signaling. Apart from this, divergence between species is enhanced by the need for maintaining reproductive isolation. This does not mean, however, that selection acting through the disadvantageous consequences of hybrid pairings is the only cause of evolutionary divergence in displays. Since the various characters of an animal are developmentally, causally, and also functionally interrelated, selection for change in any one character will have repercussions on many others. Thus not all differences in displays are necessarily the product of selection for divergence in the displays them-selves (see below; Hinde, 1955; Mayr et al., 1956; Cullen, in press).

The Extent of Interspecies Differences in Behavior

In general, the behavior of closely related species is more simi-lar than that of distantly related ones. To mention but one exam-ple of this well-known fact, all gulls feed their chicks by regurgi-tating food and presenting it in their bills, carduelines by re-gurgitation into the gape of the young, *Parus* spp. by dropping insects and so forth directly into the gape of the young without previously swallowing them themselves. On the other hand, there are constant differences even between closely related species: thus the alarm calls of all gulls are a series of staccato cries, but the number, pitch, and frequency of the calls varies between species.

The nature and extent of such interspecies differences very often seem to be adaptive. For instance, the motor patterns used in maintenance activities such as preening, bathing and feeding, and in nest building, are closely similar in all carduelines so far studied. All species use the head-forward threat posture, though there are slight interspecies differences in the relative intensities of com-ponents. In song and courtship, however, the interspecies differ-ences are conspicuous, a fact presumably related to their function in promoting reproductive isolation. In general it is in the earlier phases of courtship that interspecies differences are most marked; the female's soliciting posture and the copulatory behavior of the male vary little among species. This suggests that it is these earlier phases of courtship—i.e. pair formation and the immediately sub-sequent period—which are most important in effecting reproduc-tive isolation.

Supporting evidence for this conclusion is given by the fact that if pair formation is forced under conditions of captivity breeding success of mixed pairs between closely related species may be comparable with that of pure species. Similar generalizations could be made for other groups of closely related species. Thus where the motor patterns of courtship, song, and so on play a role in maintaining reproductive isolation there has been selec-tion for interspecies divergence (Huxley, 1942). Usually, however, the color patterns shown off by the displays have diverged more than the displays themselves (Morris, 1954a; Hinde, 1956b); and this in its turn implies that the releasers for courtship behavior have diverged more than the motor patterns. In other spheres, also, the stimuli eliciting the behavior show greater interspecies divergence than the motor patterns. Thus the behavior used in hunting for, catching, preparing, and swallowing food is usually similar in closely related species, but there is seldom much overlap in the kind of food eaten (references in Lack, 1954). However, in cases where one species is exploiting a food niche different from those of its relatives there may also be marked divergence in the method of hunting (contrast, for instance, the avocet, *Recurvirostra avosetta*, with other waders). Interspecies differences in the eliciting stimuli are the rule in other aspects of behavior which have important ecological implications. Often, as with habitat selection, this is probably the direct result of selection for interspecies divergence.

Convergence in behavior can be seen in the feeding behavior of unrelated species exploiting similar niches, for example flycatchers (*Muscicapidae*), drongos (*Dicruridae*), and some American warblers (*Compsothlypidae*); swifts (*Apodidae*) and swallows (*Hirundinidae*). Among display postures, the wide-spread distribution of the head-forward threat among passerines probably indicates that it is primitive and not the result of convergence, but since interspecific disputes over food, roosting sites, and so forth often arise there may have been selection against divergence. Further, since there are selective forces governing the precise way in which intention movements and displacement activities are elaborated into displays, some degree of convergence in the broader features of the displays of unrelated species is to be expected. Among vocal utterances, Marler (1955) has shown that the similarities among the "flying predator" alarm calls of many passerines are probably due to convergence toward a pattern which is difficult for a hawk to locate. Marler also gives an important discussion of many of the selective factors affecting animal calls.

Convergence in color patterns is of course common in predominantly cryptic species. Occasionally unrelated species show some degree of convergence toward conspicuous patterns which are presumably particularly effective in display; e.g. the great tit, Java sparrow (*Padda oryzivora*), and white-cheeked bulbul (*Pycnonotus leucogenys*).

THE USE OF CHARACTERS OF BEHAVIOR IN SYSTEMATICS

In spite of their ephemeral nature, characters of behavior have been used successfully in studies of the systematics of a number of groups. The problems involved are parallel to those entailed in the use of morphological characters.

It is of course necessary to choose characters in which the interspecies differences are innate. Next, the characters must have an interspecies variability suitable for the particular problem. In general, those which have been either markedly conservative or divergent within a group are of little use for assessing relationships within that group, though characters which are conservative within a group may be useful for assessing the relationship of that group with others. For instance, the various *Parus* species all nest in holes and use moss for nest construction, differing in these characters from the other genera frequently included in the Paridae: these characters could thus be used to characterize the genus but would be useless for elucidating relationships within it (Hinde, 1952). Threat postures, and some courtship displays, on the other hand, are very valuable in studying relationships between closely related species or genera but are too divergent for determining relationships between families. The precise patterns of "tail flicks" made by passerine birds when moving through foliage and so forth have proved to be rather conservative within families, and can therefore provide useful evidence in assigning genera to families and in assessing relationships between families (Andrew, 1956c).

As with morphological characters, it is not desirable to use characters which change rapidly and could have been acquired independently in different groups for establishing phylogenetic relationships: when unrelated species acquire superficially similar characters, they may have different origins. However, if the character is analyzed sufficiently, the danger of false homologizing disappears. It is extremely difficult to find characters where there is no danger of convergence. Although, as Lorenz claimed, the courtship postures of birds depend on an "inherited" convention among the members of the species and are thus especially useful for systematic work, even in these movements convergences are by no means absent. There must be some reason for the elaboration of this intention movement other than its being a social signal, and the most effective type of ritualization will depend upon the context. The dangers of being misled by convergent characters can of course be reduced by making comparisons first between species believed to be closely related on other grounds: similarities then found are reasonably likely to be due to homologies.

It is often difficult to assess the systematic significance to be attached to behavioral characteristics because functional relations between characters are frequently more difficult to trace than those between morphological ones (Hinde, 1955). For instance, in passerine birds, selection for territorial behavior, distinctive song, sexual dimorphism in color and behavior, and suppression of male aggressiveness in courtship may all be linked, so that a trend in the direction of one of them will influence the selective advantages of all the others.

An excellent example of the ramifying effects of selection of one characteristic throughout the whole adaptive complex is given by the work of E. Cullen on the kittiwake (*Rissa tridactyla*); we are grateful to her for allowing us to quote her unpublished work. Kittiwakes are the only gulls that select steep cliffs for breeding. This enables them to nest out of reach of both mammalian and avian predators. The following characteristics of the kittiwake are undoubtedly connected with this: (1) They are extremely tame while on the ledges, as shown by their very short fleeing distance and the high threshold of the alarm call. (2) They do not attack predators as other gulls do. (3) They defecate just over the rim of the nest (other gulls walk or fly several yards from the nest), and as a result the nest, though not itself fouled, is extremely conspicuous, the whole rim being white. (4) Neither the eggs nor the chicks are camouflaged. (5) The egg shells are not carried off after hatching, and their white inner surface contributes still more to making the nest conspicuous. (6) The chicks do not run when alarmed, and are thus protected from falling over the cliff. (7) Regurgitated food is not dropped on the ground (nest), so that fouling of the nest is avoided. (Unlike other gulls, which leave the nest soon after hatching, young kittiwakes stay on the nest until fledging.) (8) Prior to building the nest itself, kittiwakes construct a mud platform which broadens and flattens the narrow and often slanting subtrate. This involves collecting of mud and trampling it down by "foot paddling." (9) In a contest over food the young bend the head away from the attacker, instead of either fighting back or fleeing as other gulls do; this head bending stops the attack. The gesture also exposes the black neckband. Neither the movement nor the band is found in chicks of other gulls.

Many of the difficulties involved in the use of behavioral characters in systematics can be avoided by a broad approach: the importance of a knowledge of the natural history of the animal and of the causation and function of the behavior cannot be over-emphasised.

CONCLUSION

We see, then, that the comparative study of behavior can yield the same type of results as comparative anatomy—a tentative description of the course evolution has taken. Furthermore, in both cases the method depends basically on the establishment of homologies, that is the grouping together of elements having a common evolutionary origin. The fertility of the comparative method is, however, enormously enhanced when it is coupled with studies of function and causation. These enable us to distinguish between homology and convergence, give us insight into the origin and later adaptation of "derived" movements, and permit a more accurate description of the true innate differences between species.

All this work, tentative though it may be, provides the necessary basis for an attack on the ultimate problem of the dynamics of behavior evolution. Comparative study itself cannot contribute directly to the solution of this problem, but as a phase of research it is indispensable; it alone can supply us with a formulation of the problems to be solved.

REFERENCES

ANDREW, R. J. 1956a. Some remarks on behaviour in conflict situations, with special reference to *Emberiza* spp. Brit. J. Anim. Behav., *4*, 41–5.

ANDREW, R. J. 1956b. The aggressive and courtship behaviour of certain

Emberizinae. Behaviour, *10*, 255–308.

ANDREW, R. J. 1956c. Intention movements of flight in certain passerines, and their use in systematics. Behaviour, *10*, 179–204.

BAERENDS, G. P. 1950. Specializations in

organs and movements with a releasing function. In Physiological mechanisms in animal behaviour. Sympos. Soc. Exp. Biol., No. 4. Cambridge, Eng., Cambridge Univ. Press, pp. 337-60.

BAERENDS, G. P., and BAERENDS, J. M. 1950. An introduction to the ethology of cichlid fishes. Behaviour, Suppl. 1, pp. 1-242.

BEACH, F. A. 1955. The de-scent of instinct. Psychol. Rev., *62*, 401-10.

CLARK, E., ARONSON, L. R., and GORDON, M. 1954. Mating behaviour patterns in two sympatric species of Xiphophorin fishes: their inheritance and significance in sexual isolation. Bull. Amer. Mus. Nat. Hist., *103* (2), 135-225.

CRAIG, W. 1911. Oviposition induced by the male in pigeons. J. Morphol., *22*, 299-305.

CRAIG, W. 1912. Observations on doves learning to drink. J. Anim. Behav., *2*, 273-9.

CRANE, J. 1941. Crabs of the genus *Uca* from the West Coast of Central America. Zoologica, *26*, 145-208.

CRANE, J. 1948-50. Comparative biology of salticid spiders at Rancho Grande, Venezuela. Ibid., Vols. *33-5*.

CRANE, J. 1952. A comparative study of innate defensive behaviour in Trinidad mantids. Ibid., *37*, 259-93.

CULLEN, E. In press.

DAANJE, A. 1950. On the locomotory movements of birds, and the intention movements derived from them. Behaviour, *3*, 48-98.

DAVIS, D. E. 1942. The phylogeny of social nesting habits in the Crotophaginae. Quart. Rev. Biol., *17*, 115-34.

EVANS, H. E. 1953. Comparative ethology and systematics of spider wasps. Syst. Zool., *2*, 155-72.

EVANS, H. E. 1955. An ethological study of the digger wasp, *Bembecinus neglectus*, with a review of the ethology of the genus. Behaviour, *7*, 287-304.

FABER, A. 1953. Laut und Gebärdensprache bei Insekten. Staatl. Museum für Naturkunde in Stuttgart.

FRIEDMANN, H. 1929. The cowbirds. Springfield-Baltimore, Thomas.

GOETHE, F. 1937. Beobachtungen und Untersuchungen zur Biologie der Silbermöwe auf der Vogelinsel Memmertsand. J. f. Ornithol., *85*, 1-119.

HEINROTH, O. 1911. Beiträge zur Biologie, namentlich Ethologie und Physiologie der Anatiden. Verh. 5 Int. Ornithol. Kongr. Berlin.

HEINROTH, O., and HEINROTH, M. 1928. Vögel Mitteleuropas. Berlin.

HINDE, R. A. 1952. The behaviour of the great tit, and some other related species. Behaviour, Suppl. 2, pp. 1-201.

HINDE, R. A. 1953. The conflict between drives in the courtship and copulation of the chaffinch. Ibid., *5*, 1-31.

HINDE, R. A. 1954. The courtship and copulation of the Greenfinch. Ibid., *7*, 207-32.

HINDE, R. A. 1955. A comparative study of the courtship of certain finches. Ibis, *97*, 706-45; *98*, 1-23.

HINDE, R. A. 1956a. The behaviour of certain cardueline interspecies hybrids. Behaviour, *9*, 202-13.

HINDE, R. A. 1956b. Breeding success in cardueline interspecies pairs and an examination of the hybrids' plumage. J. Genetics, *54*, 304-10.

HUXLEY, J. S. 1942. Evolution: the modern synthesis. London, Allen & Unwin.

IERSEL, J. J. A. VAN. 1953. An analysis of the parental behaviour of the male three-spined stickleback. Behaviour, Suppl. 3, pp. 1-159.

JACOBS, W. 1950. Vergleichende Verhaltensstudien an Feldheuschrecken. Z. f. Tierpsychol., *7*, 169-216.

KOEHLER, O. 1954. Review of Lehrman (1953) in ibid., *11*, 330-34.

LACK, D. 1954. The natural regulation of animal numbers. London, Oxford Univ. Press.

LEHRMAN, D. S. 1953. A critique of Konrad Lorenz' theory of instinctive behaviour. Quart. Rev. Biol., *28*, 337-63.

LEHRMAN, D. S. 1955. The physiological basis of parental feeding behaviour in the ring dove (*Streptopelia risoria*). Behaviour, 7, 241–86.

LORENZ, K. 1935. Der Kumpan in der Umwelt des Vogels. J. f. Ornithol., *83*, 137–213, 289–413.

LORENZ, K. 1939. Vergleichende Verhaltensforschung. Zool. Anz., Suppl. Band. *12*, 69–102.

LORENZ, K. 1941. Vergleichende Bewegungsstudien an Anatinen. J. f. Ornithol., *89*, Sonderheft, 19–29.

LORENZ, K. 1950. The comparative method in studying innate behaviour patterns. In Physiological mechanisms in animal behaviour. Sympos. Soc. Exp. Biol., No. 4. Cambridge, Eng., Cambridge Univ. Press, pp. 221–68.

LORENZ, K. 1951. Uber die Entstehung auslösender "Zeremonien." Die Vogelwarte, *16*, 9–13.

MARLER, P. 1955. The characteristics of some animal calls. Nature, *176*, 6.

MARLER, P. 1956. The behaviour of the chaffinch. Behaviour, Suppl. 5.

MATTHEWS, L. H. 1939. Visual stimulation and ovulation in pigeons. Proc. Roy. Soc. London, Series B., *126*, 557–60.

MAYR, E., ANDREW, R. J., and HINDE, R. A. 1956. Die systematische Stellung der Gattung *Fringilla*. J. f. Ornithol., *97*, 258–73.

MORRIS, D. 1952. Homosexuality in the ten-spined stickleback (*Pygosteus pungitius*). Behaviour, *4*, 233–62.

MORRIS, D. 1954a. The reproductive behaviour of the zebra finch (*Poephila guttata*), with special reference to pseudofemale behaviour and displacement activities. Ibid., *6*, 271–322.

MORRIS, D. 1954b. The reproductive behaviour of the river bullhead (*Cottus gobio*) with special reference to fanning activity. Ibid., *7*, 1–32.

MORRIS, D. 1955. Courtship dance of the swordtail. Aquarist, *19*, 247–9.

MORRIS, D. 1956. The feather postures of birds and the problem of the origin of social signals. Behaviour, *9*, 75–113.

MOYNIHAN, M. 1955a. Some aspects of reproductive behaviour in the black-headed gull (*Larus ridibundus*) and related species. Ibid., Suppl. 4, pp. 1–201.

MOYNIHAN, M. 1955b. Remarks on the original sources of displays. Auk, *72*, 240–6.

SAUER, F. 1954. Die Entwicklung der Lautäusserung vom Ei ab schalldichtgehaltener Dorngrasmücken. Z. f. Tierpsychol., *11*, 10–23.

SAUER, F. 1956. Ueber das Verhalten junger Gartengrasmücken *Sylvia borin* (Bodd.) J. f. Ornithol., *97*, 156–89.

SEITZ, A. 1940–41. Die Paarbildung bei einigen Cichliden. Z. f. Tierpsychol., *4*, 40–84; *5*, 74–101.

SEITZ, A. 1949. Vergleichende Verhaltensstudien an Buntbarschen. Ibid., *6*, 202–35.

SKUTCH, A. F. 1951. Congeneric species of birds nesting together in Central America. Condor, *53*, 3–15.

SPIETH, H. T. 1950. Mating behaviour and sexual isolation in the *Drosophila virilis* species group. Behaviour, *3*, 105–45.

SPIETH, H. T. 1952. Mating behaviour within the genus *Drosophila* (*Diptera*), Bull. Amer. Mus. Nat. Hist., *99*, 401–79.

SPURWAY, H. 1953. Territory and evolution in sticklebacks. Penguin New Biology, *4*, 33–43.

THORPE, W. H. 1954. The process of song-learning in the chaffinch, as studied by means of the sound spectrograph. Nature, *173*, 465.

THORPE, W. H. 1956. Learning and instinct in animals. London, Methuen.

TINBERGEN, N. 1937. Über das Verhalten kämpfender Kohlmeisen. Ardea, *26*, 222–3.

TINBERGEN, N. 1948. Social releasers and the experimental method required for their study. Wilson Bull., *60*, 6–52.

TINBERGEN, N. 1951. The study of instinct. London, Oxford Univ. Press.

TINBERGEN, N. 1952. Derived activities; their causation, biological significance, origin and emancipation during evolution. Quart. Rev. Biol., *27*, 1–32.

TINBERGEN, N. 1953. The herring gull's world. London, Collins.

TINBERGEN, N. 1954. The origin and evolution of courtship and threat display. In A. C. Hardy, J. S. Huxley, and E. B. Ford, eds., Evolution as a process. London, Allen & Unwin.

TINBERGEN, N. 1955. Psychology and ethology as supplementary parts of behaviour. In Group processes, Trans. 1st Conf. Sponsored by Josiah Macy, Jr., Foundation.

TINBERGEN, N., and BROEKHUYSEN, G. J. 1954. On the threat and courtship behaviour of Hartlaubs' gull. Ostrich, *25*, 50–61.

WEIDMANN, U. 1955. Some reproductive activities of the common gull, *Larus canus* L. Ardea, *43*, 85–132.

WHITMAN, C. O. 1919. The behaviour of pigeons. Carnegie Inst. Wash. Publ., No. 257, 1–161.

13

The Evolution of Learning

Harry F. Harlow

UNIVERSITY OF WISCONSIN

1

THERE MUST BE few problems that are more difficult of solution than the problem of the evolution of learning. One difficulty lies in the fact that learning leaves no fossils or remains until we have the scattered indirect archeological evidences associated with the rise of man. Fortunately, however, there still exist representatives of most of the major adaptive types—phyla and classes —providing us with a wide range of animals that may be subjected to psychological test.

Another difficulty lies in existing limitations to a precise classification of the various forms of learning and learning problems into levels of difficulty. Although considerable progress has recently been made along these lines, the puzzle is far from solved; and no one has even attempted to scale the various learning problems or classes of problems in steps of equal difficulty. Furthermore, it is hazardous to compare learning ability among animals independently of their sensory and motor capacities and limitations. Diversity in receptor-effector mechanisms frequently renders exact comparisons of learning between species and genera questionable and poses major problems when we attempt comparisons among orders, classes, and phyla.

The existing psychological-biological data make it quite clear that evolution has resulted in the development of animals of progressively greater potentialities for learning and for solving problems of increasing complexity. No one would question that the problem-solving abilities of man exceed those of the amoeba, even though differences in receptor-effector mechanisms preclude the possibility of direct test. Furthermore, it appears that there have been prolonged geologic periods during which progressively improved learning evolved, and this can be indirectly demonstrated with existing representatives of selected orders, classes, and phyla.

Among the sea-dwelling animals, the scanty data which are existent suggest that the primitive Metazoa, such as some coelenterates (Fleure and Walton, 1907) and echinoderms (Maier and Schneirla, 1935), may have attained an ability to profit from experience that exceeded any capabilities developed in the Protozoa such as the amoeba (Mast and Pusch, 1924) and paramecium (French, 1940; Gelber, 1952). Such evidence as we have on the flatworm (Hovey, 1929) suggests that it stands out as an intellectual giant compared with the most recondite of the Coelenterata (Fleure and Walton, 1907), even though we run the risk that we are looking at intellectual evolution from a worm's eye view. Representatives of the class Oligochaeta of the phylum Annelida (Robinson, 1953; Yerkes, 1912) apparently greatly extended their mental horizons, but the scanty evidence available suggests that they did not attain the level of rationality which we must accord one of the Cephalopoda, the octopus (Boycott and Young, 1950; Schiller, 1949). The learned performances of some of the teleost fishes (Reeves, 1919) probably surpass those of any other nonmammalian marine organism, and it is regrettable that no member of the class Chondrichthyes or the superorder Chondrostei has been subjected to intensive psychological test. Man's interest in the shark has not yet extended to its behavior under higher cerebral control, and the psychology of the sturgeon remains a virgin area for investigation.

The advent of land animals did not result in any sudden superiority of learning capabilities of land over sea vertebrates insofar as can be demonstrated by testing existing representatives of either the Amphibia or the Reptilia. It is doubtful if any amphibian or reptile has demonstrated more complex learning than that exhibited by many teleost fish. This, of course, does not mean that representatives of these two classes did not show adaptive evolutionary changes from those of their fish ancestors, probably the Crossopterygii. It merely implies that there is no conclusive evidence of differential rate in the evolutionary development of learning between the land and the sea vertebrates for the 200 million years extending from the early Devonian to the end of the Cretaceous periods. Some skepticism, however, may be attached to this position in view of the greater development of the cerebral structures in some of the reptiles and the evidence for the beginning of the formation of the cerebral cortex. It is possible that our behavior tests on the turtle have never done justice to it, and that a latent imagination has been obscured by an introverted personality.

It would be an error, of course, to assume that the evolution of intelligence was dormant or delayed from the Cambrian to the Devonian period. During this interval of 200 million years evolution may have progressed from the Echinodermata, which must surely be able to learn even though they have resisted the attempts of biologists and psychologists to demonstrate clear-cut learning (Maier and Schneirla, 1935), to some sharklike form which probably learned some simple problems with ease. Within another 100 million years the goldfish and the turtle evolved, and with them came capability of learning a reasonable range of problems. During the next 100 million years the mammals and the birds may or may not have been making progress in the evolution of learning ability, but progress is by no means unlikely in view of the clear-cut advances that were to be made in the next, and last, 75 million years. It is important to bear in mind that we have no way to scale in anything approaching equal-step intervals the difficulty of various classes of problems, and until this can be achieved on some basis other than intuition and anthropocentrism we cannot judge whether or not the evolution of learning capability has increased or decreased in rate in any 100-million-year block of time, including the last. Whether or not the evolution of learning has increased more rapidly in the last 100 million years than in the 100-million-year blocks preceding, the evolution has been of a nature that greatly simplifies the psychologists' problems of testing and evaluation.

It is interesting to look at the evolution of learning from the anatomical point of view. We make the assumption that learning is primarily a function of the nervous system, or at least that complexity of learning is intimately related to the developing complexity of the nervous system. If we were to examine learning, using the same kind of evidence that we use for assessing locomotion in the evolution of the horse—the anatomical record—we would be struck by a number of facts. Between the Protozoa and the

Coelenterata there must be a vast evolutionary gulf, for the members of the one phylum possess no nerve cells whereas the members of the other do. Between the Coelenterata and Platyhelminthes there must be another separation, but one of lesser magnitude. In both kinds of organisms the mechanisms associated with co-ordination and adjustment is neural, but in the flatworm we find a new kind of organized structure, the cephalic ganglion, and this particular structure and its elaborations are going to characterize all higher nervous systems from here through man. Between the flatworm and the dogfish there is also a gulf, but a lesser one than either of the two previous separations; in this instance we have more neurons and some relatively small changes in their physical elaborations in the forebrain, suggesting an increasing differentiation of their single, basic function. From dogfish to man the separation is very slight: the number of neurons has increased, and the process of structural differentiation has continued. From monkey to man there is essentially no difference other than a very slight tendency to continue the evolutionary trends previously noted.

The very striking fact is that the anatomical record of evolution of the nervous system, including the brain and cerebral cortex, is a continuous and highly orderly process, and there is no evidence that the developmental rate ever suddenly increased, certainly not in the last million years, nor in the last 20 million years, the last 200 million years, or from the beginning of life. The behavioral point of view appears to differ from the anatomical, at least from the human standpoint. Because I have vast respect for anatomy, it is my prejudice that the anatomical point of view is correct, and that, as we become more and more sophisticated concerning the relative difficulty of kinds of learning problems, the learning data relating to evolution will come into accord with those of the anatomy of the development of the nervous system.

Remaining for the time being in the land of speculation, I would like to hazard certain guesses as to how learning evolved. It is my understanding that evolution operates through the selection of different genotypes which differ in their ability to produce adaptive responses to particular environments and to environmental changes, and that the dynamic forces which produce change in gene frequency are mutation, selection, migration, and genetic drift.

One may seriously ask, What is it about learning or improved learning that confers upon organisms some slight advantage which has made possible the selective changes in natural populations that have led to the evolution of the remarkable learning capabilities that characterize the order of primates? Because we look at the world from a Homo sapiocentric point of view, we may attach such importance to learning that we accept as an axiom that learning, all learning, is good and should therefore have survival value. Furthermore, we can all cite many examples in which it would appear self-evident that learning has survival value for the organism. The ability of the sea anemone gradually to differentiate between food and nonfood could confer upon it a slight survival advantage over some other organism of less brilliant intellectual endowments. The capacity to form conditioned escape responses from noxious and dangerous stimuli would appear to have obvious utility even if, by virtue of the slowness of learning, 99 per cent of the organisms perished before the conditioned response was established. The acquired gift of manufacturing weapons is an obvious selective biological gain and appears to have greatly aided a particular species in survival—at least so far.

I have long been puzzled by the fact that the study of animals under laboratory conditions reveals many learning capabilities whose existence is hard to understand in terms of survival value. In the first conference the presentation of the problem to this group engendered considerably more heat than light. As an example, the earthworm can learn a spatial maze, i.e. it can learn eventually to turn right for the reward of a bed of succulent mud and not turn left because of the threat of shock or sandpaper. Under the most idealized laboratory conditions the earthworm solves this task in a faltering and ephemeral way in a few hundred trials (Robinson, 1953; Yerkes, 1912). For more primitive organisms this is a learning landmark; but even so it is hard to see how this feat of learning legerdemain aided the earthworm, or any other animal so endowed, to survive at the expense of less gifted associates.

It might be argued that the earthworm's learning in nature is more efficient than in the laboratory, or that its limited learning is peculiarly adapted to its natural environment and for this reason provides some evolutionary gain. But this is pure speculation, and there are not even the hopelessly inadequate data which naturalists so commonly and gladly provide to give factual support to any such position. The best, not the worst, annelidan learning has been observed by scientists.

I was puzzled for many years as to how the rhesus monkey or chimpanzee developed the capability of solving the complex multiple-sign or conditional problems, including oddity, matching, Weigl-type matching, or the categorization of kinds of stimuli into classes of forms, colors, or—within limits—number (Hicks, 1956; Weinstein, 1955). The observational accounts of these animals make it quite clear that problems of this level of complexity are never solved, indeed, they are never met, in the natural environment. It is superficially difficult to see how a trait which was never used gave to an organism some slight selective advantage over another organism which did not use the trait because it did not have it. Yet such capabilities must have existed in the prehuman primate for some millions of years before the organism developed to the point at which it could put these traits to effective use and convey a clear selective advantage to man.

It can again be argued that those learning capacities essential for complex color categorization by monkeys and apes are used by the same animals in the wild in some manner to provide selective advantage. If this is true, it is something which has eluded, or not been reported or recognized by, the well-trained psychologists and biologists who have gazed patiently at the unending ingenuousness of the social life of monkeys and apes and their adaptations to nature (Bingham, 1932; Carpenter, 1934, 1942a, 1942b; Nissen, 1931).

Since we must accept as fact that evolution is orderly and results from the selection of gradual changes in the gene population, and since an explanation in terms of autogenesis is untenable, it is interesting to speculate how receptive and neural mechanisms underlying learning might have developed and provided selective gain during the process of evolution. It is obvious that the explanation we desire is in terms of orthoselection, and any reasonable explanation of the remarkably orderly and prolonged evolutionary development of learning in whole or in part in terms of allometry should be given full consideration.

That there is an intimate relation between the development of the receptors and the development of the central nervous system may be taken as fact. Indeed, if Parker is correct, the nerve fiber and neuron may have evolved from the primitive receptor cell. The developmental status of the various receptor systems in animals clearly puts a limit upon all animals' learning capabilities, and it is a safe generalization that, from the phyletic point of view, learning potentialities always lag behind receptor potentialities. Thus, there may be fish, and there are likely reptiles, and there are certainly many birds and mammals that have the receptor potentialities to convey all environmental information essential for human-type thought. Yet this particular learning capacity, doubtless like countless other learning capacities, lagged far behind the receptor system's resolving power.

From the point of view of natural selection it is difficult to think of any kind of receptor development which would not result in some selective gain so long as the animal's environment provides an adequate stimulus. Any receptor development, in and of its very nature, demands the development of increasingly complex neuronal systems within the central nervous system and even within the receptor itself. As long as increasingly complex receptor systems provide the organism with slight survival advantages, one can be assured that increasingly complex nervous systems will develop; and as long as increasingly complex nervous systems develop, the organism will be endowed with greater potentialities which lead inevitably to learning.

[From the behavioral point of view the evolution from reception to learning appears inevitable. Reception is progressively aided by the development of mechanisms of sensory search, fixation, and attention. To be efficient, reception involves both differentiation and generalization. Generalization merges into transposition and transfer, and at this point any sharp separation of unlearned and learned functions ceases. The development of a maximally effective receptor system leads to the formation of mechanisms and processes basic to learning or involving learning which directly improve the efficiency of operation of the receptor processes. They are the kinds of mechanisms and traits that should arise from multiple mutations, each mutation providing a slight increment of evolutionary gain.]

Perhaps the most amazing example of convergent development is the evolution of color vision, which has been found in some fishes (Teleostei), some insects, some birds, and most primates. As far as we know, primates are the only terrestrial animals with color vision. In spite of the diversity of forms in which it has evolved, color vision is remarkably similar in all. If one plots a curve showing difference thresholds as a function of wave length, the curves for pigeon and man are almost superimposable. There are no data to suggest that the color vision of man and fish differs in any radical way; and the greatest deviant, the bee, differs primarily in the ability to see into the ultraviolet. It is puzzling, although of course no evolutionary problem, that the primates are the only mammals with hue discrimination. Even more puzzling is the problem of the cat. Granit (1955) has shown that the cat has the retinal structures and functions always associated with color vision, and Lennox (1956) has demonstrated that the cat has in its lateral geniculate body the structures always associated with color vision. But the cat is totally color blind.

The existence of color vision in radically different forms of animals and even radically different forms of eyes must illustrate the adaptive value of a relatively slight modification in receptive capability, at least in the field of visual reception. Color vision must have evolved slowly and must have operated within the principle of orthoselection. There is very scanty evidence from primate data that color vision first consisted of differential response by lemurs (presumably archaic lemuroid forms) in the blue region of the spectrum (Bierens de Haan and Frima, 1930). It is a matter of established fact that, as we go from catarrhine monkey to anthropoid ape to man, the ability to see in the long-wave portion of the spectrum progressively improves (Grether, 1939, 1940). Indeed, if we exclude the spider monkey, learning ability and hue discriminability within the primate order would be almost as highly correlated as learning ability and complexity of cortical structure.

Comparing the learning capacities of fish (Reeves, 1919), honeybees (von Frisch, 1914), pigeons (Hamilton and Coleman, 1933), and primates shows clearly that the evolution of color vision does not of necessity imply an equal level of learning capability. Whether or not there is a high correlation between evolution of color vision and learning ability within a particular class of animals cannot be resolved in terms of the extant data. Color vision has been demonstrated in teleost fishes but has not been tested in any other superorder of fishes. The insects known to have color vision, the bees, have been shown to possess startlingly complex behavior patterns, whether or not these are subject to learned modifications. Recent studies have shown that the pigeon has a wider range of behavioral capacities (Ginsburg, 1957; Reeves, 1919) than had previously been believed, and it is more than possible that the pigeon and other birds are more capable of solving moderately difficult learning problems than many mammals. Finally, the primates as an order are pre-eminent over all other mammals both in terms of their visual capabilities and their capacity for learning.

The assumption that the evolution of learning was dependent in large part upon the evolution of receptors in no way precludes the likelihood that increased learning capability frequently operated as a selective factor during evolutionary development. There are, however, reasons to believe that other factors of great, and perhaps predominant, importance were involved. The process that began to separate the primate order from the other mammalian orders was not an increased learning capacity but the development of the visual mechanisms, which apparently arose as the preprimate ancestral forms adapted to an arboreal life, an adaptation which would provide considerable environmental isolation. It is a striking fact that the brain of the primitive mouse lemur, *Microcebus,* shows the tripartite calcarine fissure and a lateral geniculate body with six distinct layers (Clark, 1934). From our scanty knowledge of more advanced lemurs we may presume that *Microcebus* would show no unusual learning capacities, but the matter remains to be decided by direct test. The brain of *Tarsius* also shows striking development of the visual mechanisms, which, observational evidence suggests, arose independently of any striking gain in learning capacity. Thus, our information about primitive forms favors the view that the remarkably advanced visual system of the primates antedated their pre-eminent learning capacities. It is certain that man's primitive ancestors showed no less early complex development within the visual system, and it is certainly not chance that such a receptive system was antecedent to the development of the human visual cortex.

2

According to present-day theory, evolution takes place by natural selection among multiple mutations, each of which produces some small organismic change. Such a position appears to be at variance with the evolution of learning if we think of learning in terms of our everyday terminology, for the language of learning implies the appearance of rather radical changes in capabilities. The Platonic specter of the national mind is still among us, with the implication that there is some broad gulf separating human and subhuman learning, or at the very least that some set of cumulative changes arose with startling rapidity as man diverged from other higher primate forms.

If we are to explain learning in terms of modern evolutionary theory, there should be continuity from the simplest to the most complex forms of learning. The appearance of a radically new kind of learning at any evolutionary point or period, including that during which man developed, is not in keeping with modern gene theory. Yet we find such an eminent authority as Dobzhansky writing, "Man is not simply a very clever ape, but a possessor of mental abilities which occur in other animals only in most rudimentary forms, if at all" (Dobzhansky, 1955, p. 338).

Dobzhansky falls into the common error of assuming that the particular human traits of language and culture imply the existence of some vast intellectual gap between man and other animals. The probability that a relatively small intellectual gain by man over the anthropoid apes would make possible the development of symbolic language and also culture is given small consideration. It is a common error to fail to differentiate between capability and achievement. Thus, the fledgling swallow a few days before it can fly differs little in anatomical and physiological capacity from the swallow capable of sustained flight, but from the point of view of achievement the two are separated by what appears to be an abysmal gulf.

By comparing selected traits about which we are ignorant, rather than those about which we are informed, one can argue for great intellectual differences between ape and man. We have little knowledge concerning the "aphasia" characterizing monkey and ape, but such little knowledge as we have suggests that the anthropoid ape's language inadequacies basically result from the failure to possess certain unlearned responses (Hayes, 1951). The degree to which it is additionally dependent upon intellectual differences is unknown. The failure of chimpanzees to develop culture may have resulted from some small but critical deficiency in intellectual ability or in specialized unlearned responses such as

those underlying tool construction or nonemotional vocal evoca-
tion. Other nonintellectual factors preventing cultural development may be the lack of social groups of an essential critical size, or
limitations imposed by the physical environment. Knowing nothing about these factors permits unlimited speculation on the part of
the scientist wearied by the research routines required by his field
of specialization.

In contrast with these areas of ignorance there has gradually
developed during the last quarter of a century a rich experimental
literature comparing intellectual performances among many
species within the primate order. No one suggests that more than
a beginning has been made, but such data as are extant question
the assumption that there is a wide intellectual separation between
the human and the subhuman primates. The explanation and
ordering of these data may be done best in terms of a simple classificatory schema.

Many learning problems can be classified effectively in terms of
the complexity of the factors which interfere with successful problem solution. A well-studied learning task of moderate difficulty
is the object or cue discrimination illustrated in Figure 13-1. Two

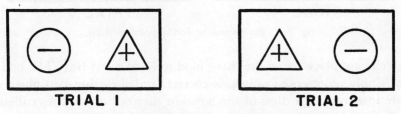

TRIAL I   TRIAL 2

Fig. 13-1. Representative object discrimination trials.

stimuli, such as a triangle and a circle, are placed over the two
food wells of a test tray. One stimulus, the triangle, is consistently
rewarded as indicated by the enclosed +, although it is on the
right side of the tray on trial 1 and on the left side on trial 2. The
position of the triangle varies in an irregular but balanced manner
during the learning trials.

Now it is obvious that on a single correct trial both the triangle
and the position it occupies are simultaneously rewarded, and because a particular position as well as a particular object are rewarded, the nature of the reward is ambiguous rather than differential. During the many trials, however, the triangle is rewarded on

every trial, and each of the two positions, right and left, is rewarded on only half the trials. The inconsistent reward of the ambiguous position cues apparently leads to their elimination, and learning the object discrimination problem may be described as the inhibition or suppression of the positional response tendencies.

From the point of view of the complexity of the ambiguity of cues, the object discrimination problem is relatively simple. Only one condition of ambiguity of reward exists, ambiguity between the object and the position rewarded. This comparatively easy problem can be solved by a wide range of animals, including fish, mice, rats, pigeons, cats, and dogs, as well as monkeys, apes, and men.

The oddity problem involves a single additional condition of ambiguity, and the problem is illustrated in Figure 13-2. Three stimuli, either two circles and a triangle, or two triangles and a

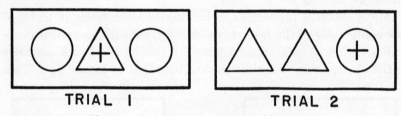

TRIAL 1   TRIAL 2

Fig. 13-2. Representative oddity problem trials.

circle, are placed over the three food wells of a test tray. The odd, or singly represented object, is correct, and the other two objects are incorrect regardless of the position they occupy and regardless of the correctness or incorrectness of any object on any previous trial. Thus, as is illustrated, the triangle may be correct on trial 1 and the circle on trial 2. Now it is obvious that on any particular trial both the position rewarded and the object rewarded are ambiguous. Thus, there are two ambiguous factors in contrast with the single ambiguous condition found in the object discrimination problem. It is hard to believe that solution of a problem involving the addition of a single error factor requires some new "mental ability." From the standpoint of achievement, however, a sudden separation has appeared between various orders. No pigeon, rat, cat, or dog has solved the illustrated oddity problem, even though pigeons (Ginsburg, 1957), rats (Wodinsky and Bitterman, 1953), and cats (Warren, personal communication) are reported to have solved simplified versions of this problem or problems of generally similar type. Furthermore, we are now dealing with a task that is beyond the intellectual capacity of the young child, although data defining the minimal human chronological age level for oddity problem solution are lacking.

A third condition of ambiguity is added in the combined oddity-nonoddity problem. The stimuli are the same as those used in the oddity problem, but the odd or the nonodd object is correct, depending upon the color of the test tray. A green test tray may indicate that the odd object is correct, an orange test tray that the nonodd objects are correct. On any particular trial there are three factors which are ambiguously rewarded—position (right or left), object (triangle or circle), and configuration (oddity or nonoddity). Again, the introduction of an additional condition of ambiguous reward has greatly increased problem difficulty. No subprimate animal has as yet been reported to approach solution of this problem, which can be mastered by monkeys and apes without undue difficulty. Problems of this type can be recognized as components of human mental tests. Although there are no definitive data on the chronological age at which these triple-ambiguity problems can be solved by the child, it is certain that a vast number of human beings, including adults, cannot master problems of this class of difficulty.

Even more complicated problems can, however, be solved by monkeys (Spaet and Harlow, 1943; Young and Harlow, 1943), and apes (Nissen *et al.;* 1948). One chimpanzee solved tasks involving five conditions of reward ambiguity (Nissen, 1951b), and the color-categorizing performance attained by one rhesus subject (Weinstein, 1955) was disarmingly humanoid. Effective reviews of the performances by monkeys on complex learning tasks are available in the psychological literature (Harlow, 1951a, 1951b; Nissen, 1951b).

The particular kinds of problems chosen and the classification selected were not capricious. Problems of the kinds described have been used to measure human conceptual abilities (Goldstein and Scheerer, 1941; Roberts, 1933) and to differentiate normal and brain-injured patients (Weigl, 1941). We have not taken a particular type of test peculiarly adapted to the monkey and used it to test man; we have taken a particular type of test peculiarly adapted to man and used it to test monkeys and apes. If there is any improper comparison in the use of the described tests, it must be unfair to the subhuman, not the human, animal. Be this as it may, the tests clearly demonstrate that defining man as "a possessor of mental abilities which occur in other animals only in most rudimentary forms, if at all" (Dobzhansky, 1955), must of necessity disenfranchise many millions of United States citizens from the society of *Homo sapiens.*

If one appraises factually and unemotionally the learning data of animals on problems ranging in difficulty from object discrimination to effective measures of human conceptualization capabilities, one cannot help but be struck by the intellectual kinship among the phyletic groups being tested. There is no evidence of an intellectual gulf at any point, and there are no existing data that would justify the assumption that there is a greater gap between men and monkeys than there is between monkeys and their closest kin below them on the phylogenetic scale.

As learning and so-called thinking problems become more complex, the number of ambiguities among the problem components increases, and the possible number of extraneous and inappropriate responses increases. All learning and all thinking may be regarded as resulting from a single fundamental operation, the inhibition of inappropriate responses or response tendencies. Since such a position may seem radical, we briefly review the alternative positions taken by modern learning theorists.

All learning theorists can be divided into two groups. One group assumes that learning is the resultant of two opposed mechanisms, which are usually described as excitatory and inhibitory mechanisms, the former strengthening earlier responses or response tendencies and the latter weakening such responses and response tendencies. The advocates of such a theory may be described as duoprocess learning theorists. A converse position asserts that all learning is the result of a single process, either an excitatory or an inhibitory process. Advocates of such a position would be called uniprocess learning theorists. Hebb (1949), for example, appears to be a uniprocess learning theorist favoring an excitatory process.

I have recently presented experimental and theoretical evidence favoring the uniprocess position (Harlow and Hicks, 1957), but contrary to Hebb I believe that inhibition is the single process accounting for all learning. It is presumed that this unitary inhibitory process acts to suppress the inappropriate responses and response tendencies operating to produce error in the problems just described. The nature of inappropriate response tendencies found in the object discrimination (Harlow, 1950) and oddity problems (Moon and Harlow, 1955) has been analyzed in detail. Although I have not yet presented the position formally, I have believed for a number of years that the development of all complex learning of the type described could best be explained in terms of uniprocess inhibition theory.

Having come to this opinion, I was subsequently offered the opportunity of preparing this paper on the evolution of learning. The data on learning by primitive organisms presented for me a new and intriguing problem—investigation of the possibility that the simplest as well as the most complex learning tasks might fit into uniprocess, inhibitory learning theory, that simple as well as complex learning problems might be arranged into an orderly classification in terms of difficulty, and that the capabilities of animals on these tasks would correspond roughly to their assigned positions on the phylogenetic scale. If true, the combined data would present the possibility of ordering all learning phenomena from habituation to abstract thought within a single system in which all differences would be explainable in quantitative terms.

A number of investigators have reported learning in the paramecium; the investigation by French (1940) is typical of the type of function measured, and is the best controlled of the studies. French sucked paramecia into a glass tube .6 mm. in internal diameter and recorded the time required for the animal to swim from the lower end of the tube into its individual culture medium. Ten of the 20 paramecia used as subjects showed significant decrease in escape latency. French observed that during the first few trials these animals would swim back and forth only a few times and then make one long dive to the bottom. These data can be interpreted in terms of learning to inhibit responses extraneous to the culminating response of culture-medium entry. His data show clear-cut inhibition and consequent reduction of activity, and give no evidence for the formation of new associations.

Fleure and Walton (1907) reported learning data for the sea anemone which are also in accordance with a learning theory that stresses inhibition-type learning. These experimenters placed pieces of moist filter paper at 24-hour intervals on the same groups

of tentacles of several sea anemones. At first the paper was carried
to the mouth by the tentacles, but after two to five repetitions of
the stimulus it was rejected by the animals; this habit was retained
for six to ten days for the specific set of tentacles involved. The
nonstimulated tentacles accepted the filter paper even while the
trained tentacles rejected it. The only learning that appears to have
taken place here is inhibition of the original responsiveness to
filter paper. The persistence of the inhibition in a relatively simple
organism is striking.

One of the most comprehensive and best-controlled experiments
on learning in a lower form is the study by Hovey (1929) on the
marine flatworm, genus *Leptoplana*. Hovey produced conditioned
inhibition of the photokinetic response in 17 flatworms by expos-
ing the individual subjects to light for a series of 5-minute periods
and inhibiting progression by tactual stimulation of the anterior
tip of the worm whenever the animal began to creep in response
to light stimulation. The mean number of tactile stimulations
required to inhibit movement steadily declined from 110 on trial
1 to 5 on trial 25; and, even though none of the animals developed
perfect inhibition of the photokinetic response, some subjects
were completely nonresponsive during individual 5-minute test
sessions. Control groups of subjects ruled out the possibility that
the results could be explained in terms of fatigue, light adaptation,
or injury to the snout.

It is perhaps no accident that the first kind of conditioned response to be described in a primitive animal is a conditioned
inhibition of an innate, so-called tropistic response. The learning
consists in learning to inhibit this response tendency.

Robinson (1953) measured the learning by earthworms, *Lum-
bricus terrestris,* of a single-unit T-maze, a spatial discrimination
problem. Robinson's study is selected for presentation because,
though the design and results are similar, it was conducted at a level
of technical elegance surpassing the pioneering investigation by
Yerkes, or the subsequent studies of Schwartz or Heck. He recorded time and errors and traced records of the earthworm's behavior. By preliminary tests Robinson determined the preferred
maze arm for each worm, and learning was measured in terms of
reduction in frequency of entrances into the preferred arm. Partial
entrance into this arm resulted in contact with an electrode and
consequent electric shock; choice of the correct arm led to entry

into a goal box which was also the subject's living box. Robinson's data make it quite clear that the earthworm did not develop any new association between turning into the incorrect alley and shock. Instead, the shock resulted in agitated and excess movements and persistent negative reactions to the stimuli on both the correct and incorrect sides of the junction. These negative reactions were gradually reduced—or, as we would say, inhibited—but the negative reactions even to the stimuli on the correct side of the junction were never entirely eliminated. Robinson's results are strikingly similar to those presented by Hovey despite marked differences in the test situations. There is no sudden emergence of any new association; there is only the gradual elimination or inhibition of the extraneous responses.

Discrimination learning has been reported by Boycott and Young in the octopus (1950). A crab lowered into one end of a tank served as the positive stimulus, and a crab attached to an electrified white plate was used as a negative stimulus. Within 25 trials the octopus came to inhibit response to the negative stimulus in about 85 per cent of the trials, whereas the only change to the positive stimulus was some slight inhibition, but in no case enough to prevent contact. Again, there is no evidence that learning resulted in the strengthening of any response. Indeed, the converse happened: the inappropriate response was almost completely inhibited, and even the appropriate response was partially inhibited.

If one surveys the literature on subvertebrate learning, a single fact stands out in a very unequivocal manner. Learning, all learning which has been adequately described and measured, appears to be the learned inhibition of responses and response tendencies which block the animal or fail to lead it to some terminal response, such as eating or escape from noxious stimulation. Furthermore, it should be remembered that many of these lower animals have reasonably well-developed, synaptic-type nervous systems, and there is no reason from an anatomical point of view to suspect that the nature of learning is going to be altered in any subtle, fundamental manner as we progress to higher forms. The law of parsimony requires, at the very least, that we seek as simple a fundamental explanation of vertebrate learning—including human learning—as is consonant with fact.

The concept of a kind of learning simpler than that of condi-

tioning has been held by other investigators, including both
Thorpe (1943) and Schneirla (1934). Schneirla, for example, describes "habituation learning," defined as learned conformity to
a new situation through generalized adjustments involving inhibition of initial avoidance or shock reactions. This learning is
differentiated from sensory adaptation. It should be kept in mind
that the possibility definitely exists that no fundamental distinction can be made between sensory adaptation and learning, if we
ever reach a level where these processes can be described in biochemical terms.

Ignoring, however, the relationship between sensory adaptation
and learning, I wish to take the position here that there exists no
fundamental difference, other than complexity, between the kinds
of learning listed as habituation learning and the kinds listed as
conditioned response learning—and, for that matter, the kinds of
learning described as reasoning and thinking.

I hold this position in spite of the fact that the Pavlovian-type
conditioned response has been taken by many as the paradigm for
all learning, with the assumption that a conditioned response involves the formation of some new association. This new connection is formed between the conditioned stimulus (CS) and the unconditioned stimulus (US) or between the CS and the UR (unconditioned response), depending upon the psychological learning
school in which you happen to hold club membership. If a CS of
light or sound is presented to an animal, followed by US of shock to
the leg, the animal will—under certain circumstances—learn to
flex the leg to the light or sound. Conditioned response formation
is characteristically described as if a new connection had been
formed. It is, however, obvious that the animal already possessed
the potential capacity to flex the leg to either the light or sound.
There is practically no external stimulus of moderate intensity
that does not have the capability of evoking any and all the postural responses of the body, and this position receives strong support if one considers the ontogenetic development data. Both visual
and auditory stimuli of low intensity can under favorable conditions, even in the adult, elicit exploratory patterns involving all
or any part of the body musculature. From this point of view we
may give serious consideration to the fact that conditioning does
not produce new stimulus-response connections but that it operates
instead to restrict, specify, and channelize stimulus-response po-

tentialities already possessed by the organism. It is entirely possible that a specific visual conditioned stimulus comes to elicit a specific leg flexion response because the presentation of the CS and US in a specific temporal pattern produced inhibition of response to extraneous and distracting external stimuli and inhibition of the other postural responses which the CS was already capable of eliciting.

The description of the learning of the spatial discrimination problem in terms of a uniprocess inhibition theory presents no challenge. A typical spatial discrimination problem involves learning by the animal to choose the right or the left alley of a single-unit T-maze. The common procedure is to give the subject experience on a straightaway unit with food at the end, until the response of running until food is received is thoroughly established. When the animal is transferred to the spatial discrimination problem, this task is automatically learned if the animal inhibits any response tendencies to run down the unrewarded alley and inhibits tendencies to be distracted by extraneous external and internal stimuli.

From spatial discrimination we pass next to nonspatial discrimination learning, also known as object or cue discrimination learning. This kind of learning has been exhaustively tested in the rat with the Lashley jumping box and in the monkey with the Klüver-type test tray. The animal must learn to choose one object, which is consistently rewarded, and not to choose the second object, which is never rewarded. The reader will recognize this as the problem with which we began in the classification of problems in terms of complexity of factors interfering with learning.

Such evidence as exists suggests that the learning of the object discrimination problem may well be explained in terms of inhibition of extraneous and inappropriate responses. Detailed analysis of this problem enabled us to identify four reaction tendencies producing errors (Harlow, 1950), and as these reaction tendencies are inhibited, the percentage of correct responses increases progressively until it approaches 100.

We have been able to carry our analyses of the factors which produce errors to a problem of still greater complexity, the oddity learning problem, and we can see no fundamental theoretical difference between oddity learning and discrimination learning, other than the addition of one or possibly two new error factors

(Moon and Harlow, 1955). The data offer no indication that learning here consists of anything other than the inhibition of response tendencies which interfere with the culminating response leading to reward. We are convinced that we can carry these analyses even further, and we would be very much surprised if there is any fundamental difference in the learning of the oddity problem and the learning of differential equations—other than that of complexity.

Learning by amoeba and learning by man appear superficially to be such basically separable processes that I initially avoided direct comparison. I first chose to select classes of problems illustrating similarities and differences in the abilities of primates and other animal forms known to be gifted in terms of their learning abilities. Then I described the learning abilities of animals, including primitive animals, on the simplest known learning problems. The fundamental similarity between these problems and problems of greater complexity was demonstrated, until we reached the class of problems initially presented in this part of the paper. In spite of the fragmentary nature of research in the evolution of learning, it became obvious that position of an animal in the phyletic scale is related to complexity of problems it is able to solve, and it may be stated that complexity of most of the described problems had been independently defined both on logical grounds and on the basis of ontogenetic development in the higher animals.

The existing scientific data indicate a greater degree of intellectual communality among the primates, and probably a greater communality among all animals, than has been commonly recognized. There is no scientific evidence of a break in learning capabilities between primate and nonprimate forms. Emergence from the ocean to the land produced no sudden expansion of learning ability. Indeed, there is no evidence that any sharp break ever appeared in the evolutionary development of the learning process.

That this is probably true should surprise no one. Indeed, the fundamental unity of learning and the continuity of its developing complexity throughout phylogenesis, or at the least within the development of many major branches of the evolutionary tree, would seem to be in keeping with modern genetic theory.

REFERENCES

BIERENS DE HAAN, J. A., and FRIMA, M. J. 1930. Versuche über den Farbensinn der Lemuren. Z. f. vergl. Physiol., *12*, 603–31.

BINGHAM, H. C. 1932. Gorillas in a native habitat. Carnegie Inst. Wash., No. 426, August.

BOYCOTT, B. B., and YOUNG, J. Z. 1950. The comparative study of learning. In Physiological mechanisms in animal behaviour. Symp. Soc. Exp. Biol., No. 4. Cambridge, Eng., Cambridge Univ. Press, pp. 432–53.

CARPENTER, C. R. 1934. A field study of the behavior and social relations of howling monkeys (*Alouatta palliata*). Comp. Psychol. Monogr., *10* (2) (whole No. 48).

CARPENTER, C. R. 1942a. Sexual behavior of free-ranging rhesus monkeys. I. Specimens, procedures and behavioral characteristics of estrus. J. Comp. Psychol., *33*, 113–42.

CARPENTER, C. R. 1942b. Sexual behavior of free ranging rhesus monkeys. II. Periodicity of estrus, homosexual, auto-erotic and non-conformist behavior. Ibid., *33*, 143–62.

CLARK, W. E. LEG. 1934. Early forerunners of man. Baltimore, William Wood.

DOBZHANSKY, TH. 1955. Evolution, genetics, and man. New York, Wiley.

FLEURE, H. J., and WALTON, C. 1907. Notes on the habits of some sea-anemones. Zool. Anz., *31*, 212–20.

FRENCH, J. W. 1940. Trial and error learning in paramecium. J. Exp. Psychol., *26*, 609–13.

FRISCH, K. VON. 1914. Der Farbensinn und Formensinn der Biene. Zool. Jahrb., Zool. Physiol., *35*, 1–182.

GELBER, B. 1952. Investigations of the behavior of Paramecium aureles. I. Modification of behavior after training with reinforcement. J. Comp. Physiol. Psychol., *45*, 58–65.

GINSBURG, N. 1957. Matching in pigeons. Ibid., *50*, 261–3.

GOLDSTEIN, K., and SCHEERER, M. 1941. Abstract and concrete behavior. An experimental study with special tests. Psychol. Monogr., *53* (2) (whole No. 239).

GRANIT, R. 1955. Receptors and sensory perception. New Haven, Yale Univ. Press.

GRETHER, W. F. 1939. Color vision and color blindness in monkeys. Comp. Psychol. Monogr., *15* (4) (whole No. 76).

GRETHER, W. F. 1940. A comparison of human and chimpanzee spectral hue discrimination curves. J. Exp. Psychol., *26*, 394–403.

HAMILTON, W. F., and COLEMAN, T. B. 1933. Trichromatic vision in the pigeon as illustrated by the spectral hue discrimination curve. J. Comp. Psychol., *15*, 183–91.

HARLOW, H. F. 1950. Analysis of discrimination learning by monkeys. J. Exp. Psychol., *40*, 26–39.

HARLOW, H. F. 1951a. Thinking. In H. Helson, ed., Theoretical foundations of psychology. New York, Van Nostrand.

HARLOW, H. F. 1951b. Primate learning. In C. P. Stone, ed., Comparative psychology. 3d ed. New York, Prentice-Hall.

HARLOW, H. F., and HICKS, L. H. 1957. Discrimination learning theory: uni-process vs. duoprocess. Psychol. Rev., *64*, 104–9.

HAYES, CATHY. 1951. The ape in our house. New York, Harper.

HEBB, D. C. 1949. The organization of behavior. New York, Wiley.

HICKS, L. H. 1956. An analysis of number-concept formation in the rhesus monkey. J. Comp. Physiol. Psychol., *49*, 212–18.

HOVEY, H. B. 1929. Associative hysteresis

in flatworms. Physiol. Zool., 2, 322–33.

LENNOX, M. A. 1956. Geniculate and cortical responses to colored light flash in the cat. J. Neurophysiol., 19, 271–9.

MAIER, N. R. F., and SCHNEIRLA, T. C. 1935. Principles of animal psychology. New York, McGraw-Hill.

MAST, S. O., and PUSCH, L. C. 1924. Modification of response in amoeba. Biol. Bull., 46, 55–60.

MOON, L. E., and HARLOW, H. F. 1955. Analysis of oddity learning by rhesus monkeys. J. Comp. Physiol. Psychol., 48, 188–94.

NISSEN, H. W. 1931. A field study of the chimpanzee. Comp. Psychol. Monogr., 8 (1) (whole No. 36).

NISSEN, H. W. 1951a. Phylogenetic comparison. In S. S. Stevens, ed., Handbook of experimental psychology. New York, Wiley.

NISSEN, H. W. 1951b. Analysis of conditioned reaction in chimpanzees. J. Comp. Physiol. Psychol., 44, 9–16.

NISSEN, H. W., BLUM, J. S., and BLUM, R. A. 1948. Analysis of matching behavior in chimpanzee. Ibid., 41, 62–74.

REEVES, C. 1919. Discrimination of light of different wave-lengths by fish. Comp. Psychol. Monogr., 4, 57–83.

ROBERTS, K. E. 1933. Learning in pre-school and orphanage children: an experimental study of ability to solve different situations according to the same plan. Univ. of Iowa Studies in Child Welfare, 7 (3) (whole No. 251).

ROBINSON, J. S. 1953. Stimulus substitution and response learning in the earthworm. J. Comp. Physiol. Psychol., 46, 262–6.

SCHILLER, P. 1949. Delayed detour response in the octopus. Ibid., 42, 220–5.

SCHNEIRLA, T. C. 1934. The process and mechanism of ant learning. J. Comp. Psychol., 17, 303–29.

SKINNER, B. F. 1950. Are theories of learning necessary? Psychol. Rev., 57, 193–216.

SPAET, T., and HARLOW, H. F. 1943. Solution by rhesus monkeys of multiple sign problems utilizing the oddity technique. J. Comp. Psychol., 35, 119–32.

THORPE, W. H. 1943. Types of learning in insects and other arthropods. Brit. J. Psychol., 33, 220–34.

WARREN, J. M. Personal communication.

WEIGL, E. 1941. On the psychology of so-called processes of abstraction. J. Abnorm. Soc. Psychol., 36, 5–33.

WEINSTEIN, B. 1955. The evolution of intelligent behavior in rhesus monkeys. Genet. Psychol. Monogr., 31, 3–48.

WODINSKY, J., and BITTERMAN, M. E. 1953. The solution of oddity-problems by the rat. Amer. J. Psychol., 66, 137–40.

YERKES, R. M. 1912. The intelligence of earthworms. J. Anim. Behav., 2, 332–52.

YOUNG, M. L., and HARLOW, H. F. 1943. Solution by rhesus monkeys of a problem involving the Weigl principle using the oddity method. J. Comp. Psychol., 35, 205–17.

14

Social Behavior

William R. Thompson

WESLEYAN UNIVERSITY

IN THIS PAPER I shall attempt to analyze social behavior and to examine its relation to evolution, considering it from two points of view: the effect that evolution has had on social behavior and the effect that social behavior has had, or may have, on evolution. Although tied closely together, these are two distinct problems and will be discussed separately.[1] Before going any further, let us look at each of these in more detail.

The influence of evolution on social behavior in the various phylogenetic groups of animals represents essentially a historical problem. It must be attacked by searching for similarities and differences between and within phyletic lines. For example, we may note a fact that has impressed many biologists—the remarkable likeness in the social structures of man and the social insects—and attempt to look for the causes of this similarity. On a more specific level, we may attempt to trace within a certain order, let us say primates, any gradual changes in the complexity and sophistication of social behavior that may occur from the lemurs to the anthropoid apes. It is obvious that in order to deal with such problems effectively we must first have some knowledge of the essential dimensions of the parameter whose evolutionary history we are attempting to follow. Much of this paper will be concerned with an analysis of social behavior so that its evolutionary history may more easily be traced.

While it may be obvious enough that social behavior can have an influence on evolution, the full extent of its importance is perhaps not generally appreciated. It is axiomatic that evolution is due to

1. Since the excellent work of the European ethologists is presented in this volume in the paper of Hinde and Tinbergen, discussion of it is omitted here.

changes in gene frequencies in populations and that these changes
are due, in turn, to the factors of selection, migration, and mutation (Lerner, 1950). As Huxley has indicated (1942), all these factors can readily be determined by what individuals in the population are like and how they relate to each other and to their environment. That social behavior thus influences genetic change
has a great many ramifications, particularly at the human level.
It is true that man can control his own destiny; in a sense, with
man, evolution has outdone itself and has produced a creature
who can cope so successfully with all possible environmental
situations that he need never speciate further. But at the same
time man imposes on himself, by his irrational fears and preju-
dices, by his social institutions and customs, by his class distinctions
and rigid in-groups, many limitations that can change his evolutionary history. We are used to these by-products of human society and take them for granted as the natural state of things. Only
when we consider what the situation might be without them can
we get an idea of their importance and possible influence on the
course of human evolution.

Since space does not permit detail, I will deal only in general
terms and try mainly to suggest a comprehensive breakdown of
social behavior that may be useful in examining its bearing on the
evolutionary problem. For our purposes here social behavior will
be taken to be (a) a process of some kind occurring between individuals that (b) has certain results. The first of these two parts
relates to the problem of communication; the second to the kinds
of communication that can occur between individuals in a group
and the kinds of group structure in which they may result.

The Process of Communication

The first level of social behavior that will be discussed is the
process of interaction, that is, the means by which one individual
can convey certain information to another. This basic problem of
communication is of great importance in the present discussion.

The process of communcation has two main characteristics, as
has been pointed out by numerous writers on the subject (Bierens
de Haan, 1929; Langer, 1942; Révèsz, 1944; Hebb and Thompson, 1954; Mowrer, 1954): (a) Any communication has a certain
form or structure, and (b) it is directed to an audience or to a

recipient. Both these parameters can serve to distinguish human from animal language. The language of man is highly developed, first of all, in that it is syntactic in form (Hebb and Thompson, 1954); that is to say, it involves the combination of two or more representative gestures for a single effect and the use of the same gestures in different combinations for different effects. These combinations usually involve a noun and a predicate, and we call them sentences. Animals are unable to achieve such an order of complexity. They are, for the most part, bound by the immediate sensory environment, while man, in his conceptual and linguistic activity, is not.

Thus bees and ants can announce to the rest of the colony that they have discovered a food source and that the food source has a certain location. But as Mowrer has recently pointed out (1954), this information is limited to what he calls the "thing-sign" variety of sentence. Thus the bee, before she can transmit relevant information by means of a round dance in the case of a near food source, or by a wagging dance in the case of food beyond one hundred meters, must first deliver to the others sugar-water which she has obtained from the source. The behavior of a dog, barking to be let out, is similar. Most dogs sit or stand near the door (the thing), and perhaps scratch at it while they are barking. Their message indicates only some distress that is apparently connected with the door, and that a specific interpretation is placed on it by the dog's master is due to the cleverness of the master and not the dog. Were the animal unable to approach the door at all, it would be unable to convey the requisite information, even to a superlatively clever master, since, in this case, it would need the capacity to use a "sign-sign" type of sentence rather than the thing-sign variety.

Now I think that there is some evidence that in higher forms, and in particular in primates, there is a greatly increased development in intellectual capacity and a tendency for conceptual processes to be freed from the immediate situation. At this level, an animal can often act in one way and think in another—the first dawning of the ability to abstract. This is clearly shown in play and teasing behavior. The aggressive pretenses that mask friendliness, or the friendly pretenses that mask aggression, so evident in the chimp as well as other animals, show an ability to separate a certain type of vocalization or gesture from particular emotional

states (Hebb and Thompson, 1954). Although we can see the beginnings of this capacity in the higher mammals, it is not until we
reach man that a definite threshold is passed and language becomes
completely conventionalized and largely independent of eviron-
ment and emotional states.

The second feature of language is its social function. This has
been stressed by Cooley, Mead, and many others (cf. Swanson et al.,
1952). Mowrer (1954) has recently stated the matter succinctly.
He says: "Language can be regarded as the medium by which
gifts are bestowed on others; we are said to 'give them information'
which they find useful . . . Ontogenetically, the 'selfish' use of
language comes first, and the 'altruistic' use later; perhaps this
was also true historically." This is an intriguing idea and has been
emphasized, at least implicitly, by many interested in the problem
of language phylogeny. To say, for example, that animal language
lacks purposiveness and intentionality as Révèsz (1944) does, or
that it is egocentric rather than allocentric, as Bierens de Haan
(1929) does, is to distinguish it from human language on the basis
of its social function. Indeed, a quick survey of the literature on
the subject will indicate that discussions of language are often
followed or preceded by discussions of cooperation or sociability.

Looked at in this way—as a vehicle for giving something (information) to another individual—language may be said to develop correlatively with cooperative tendencies. It is true, of
course, that in the social insects there are remarkable instances
of behavior that look superficially like cooperation. An example,
the bee wagging dance, has already been mentioned. But in this
case it is significant that a bee that has found food apparently
does not require an audience to receive her information and may
be induced artificially to do her dance—for example, by antennal
stimulation (Birch, 1951). This fact suggests that the communication transmitted is rigidly bound to specific sensory stimuli and
occurs as a reflex action. The language of the bees is not the
language of love.

In the vertebrates we find similar types of communication occurring, sometimes much cruder in form than that of the social
insects and transmitted merely by a general social facilitation. At
the same time, something new appears, namely the increasing
tendency for social awareness of others to play a part in the interaction between animals. That social awareness has an important
relation to language has been stressed especially by G. H. Mead

(1952). Collectively, the many roles taken on by a person constitute what Mead calls "the generalized other." This ability "to be someone else," to take on the characteristic of "the other," he regards as the very core of social behavior and as being uniquely developed in man.

Now while this ability to "be the other" is peculiarly striking in man, it is possible to see at least its beginnings in the lower animals. Köhler (1927), for example, has described what seems to be a true case of empathy in the chimpanzee. Not only is empathy a highly social trait but it is also one that demands a high degree of intellectual development. The empathizing animal must be keenly aware of the other individual and must be able to act as if he were in the place of the second animal, meeting the same environmental situation. Thus empathy demands from the individual the ability to dissociate himself from his immediate, concrete environment and to react to an absent or hypothetical one. In the case noted by Köhler, one chimpanzee watching another reaching for fruit hanging a precarious distance away was able to identify itself with its fellow to such an extent that it made spontaneous reaching movements in empathy with the other animal.

Closely related to empathy, and perhaps presupposing it, are friendship and altruism. Both demand the ability on the part of each member of the pair to put himself in the place of the other and to react and feel as the other does, even though his own environment does not demand the same kinds of reactions. This may often result in considerable personal sacrifice. Observations of what appears to be true friendship in primates have been made by many investigators (Zuckerman, 1932; Nissen and Crawford, 1936; Nowlis, 1941; Nissen, 1951; Birch, 1951). It is not at all certain to what extent genuine friendship appears in other animals, or just at what level in phylogeny it begins. Nevertheless, it does not seem to be the exclusive property of the chimp. A very interesting example of friendship has been observed by McBride (1940) in a very different animal, the porpoise (*Tursiops truncatus*). As McBride and Hebb (1948) point out, the social life of the porpoise is very highly developed, involving clear dominance relationships and quite elaborate epimeletic behavior. In view of the striking brain development of this animal, perhaps this is not surprising.

In general, then, there does seem to be an indication that in

many animals below man intelligence has developed to a point
sufficient for such complex phenomena as empathy and altruism
to appear. It is probable that on these functions true social communication is built. They are by no means simple characters, and
require a high degree of the ability to abstract and to transcend
the immediate concrete limitations of the situation. That is to
say, language probably develops phylogenetically correlatively
with intelligence.

TYPE OF SOCIAL INTERACTION AND GROUP STRUCTURE

On the next level of social behavior we shall discuss the types
or kinds of interactions that may occur between the individuals
in a social group and how these determine the characteristics of
the group. Obviously any attempt to relate social behavior to
evolution involves a primary methodological problem. Before
the different social groups occurring in the various biological
classes can be described and distinguished, it is essential that we
have some means at our disposal of designating empirically the
basic components of a society. We cannot compare groups without
having certain unitary dimensions; and we cannot have unitary
dimensions unless we can find some reliable method of observing
them.

In the social psychology of small human groups, the problem of
describing and classifying social responses has recently been receiving more and more attention, and quite a number of coding
categories have been suggested (Heyns and Lippitt, 1954). Outstanding among the attempts made is that of Bales and his colleagues at Harvard (Bales, 1951).

In Bales' system, responses are classified into three major categories, each including several subtypes, roughly as follows:

1. Social-emotional positive responses, including "giving help
or reward," "showing tension-release or satisfaction," and "passive compliance."

2. Neutral or task-oriented responses, including three types
of attempted answers and three types of attempted questions or
suggestions.

3. Social-emotional negative responses, including "antagonistic
or punitive responses," "showing tension, or withdrawal," "dis-
agreement or passive rejection."

Bales' scheme has been found to work rather well in the analysis of problem-solving behavior of small human groups. It may be discovered, for example, whether differently structured groups differ in the frequency of responses of the different types and how these differences are distributed over time. We can find out whether certain individuals typically make certain types of responses more frequently than other types and also if they make more of one kind than another to particular members of the group. In this manner it is possible to describe in great detail the patterns of social behavior occurring in any group.

For purposes of comparison, another classificatory system suggested by Scott (1945a) for describing the social responses of animals will be examined. He divides social behavior into the following classes: (1) allelomimetic—mutual imitation and facilitation; (2) epimeletic—giving care and attention; (3) et-epimeletic—calling for care and attention; (4) sexual; (5) fighting; (6) shelter seeking; (7) eating; (8) investigation.

As Scott points out, only the first five are directly social. The last three may or may not involve social relationships, depending on circumstances. Eating, for example, may be social when a common food source results in the aggregation of a number of individuals.

It is not an easy task to effect some combination of the categories of Scott and of Bales that will prove practical for observing animal groups in the field. Both authors, however, appear to divide responses roughly into two main types, positive and negative, depending on whether they make for more or less group unity. Thus in Scott's classification allelomimetic, epimeletic, et-epimeletic, and sexual behavior are positive factors in the sense that they tend to bring individuals closer together as a group. On the other hand, fighting and investigation or exploration tend to disperse group members. Eating and shelter seeking may be either, depending on circumstances. Similarly, Bales' categories may be divided into positive and negative, inasmuch as the social responses which they designate may either increase or decrease the homogeneity and uniformity of group climate.

At an empirical level, of course, it will not always be easy to decide whether a response is negative or positive. The sexual courtship of many species, for example the cat, involves a considerable amount of aggressive behavior, as Ford and Beach (1951) have pointed out. Similarly, allelomimetic behavior initially produces tension arousal, which in turn ultimately results in tension reduction, insofar as its final effect is the avoidance of danger. In such cases, it is problematical whether the interactions should be classified as positive, negative, or both. I think that all that can be done at present is to record carefully the complete sequence of actions from beginning to end, much as does the observer using Bales' method on human groups.

To this primary division another classification may be added denoting the type of organism initiating and receiving the interaction, whether male, female, or young. The initiator or the recipient may be a member of the in-group or of an out-group; consequently, we may add a category to cover this possibility. Finally, a division may be provided denoting the type of activity or drive involved in the interaction, whether it be concerned with food, sex, territory, or escape from some noxious stimulus.

This approach may seem rather simple and crude—I do not claim that it is a very good one, or even practicable—but there is no question that something of the sort is necessary if we are to achieve any degree of exactness in our observations and analysis of social behavior in animal groups. Much of the significance of such a model lies in its relation to the next level of social behavior namely, the dimensions of group structure. As I will try to show, these depend completely on the kinds of interactions that occur in the group and the individuals making and receiving them. Five dimensions have been chosen for examination, and each will now be discussed separately.

1. *Size and density.* These two parameters—the number of individuals in a group and their distribution over a unit space—are the most basic and obvious of the dimensions to be discussed, and have received their full share of attention already from geneticists and others interested in population dynamics (Wright, 1921, 1940). Their relationship to social behavior is close and reciprocal. Thus the size and density of a population are dependent to a great degree on such factors as intragroup dominance, aggressiveness, and territory, and these, in turn, are dependent on size and density. For example, population growth in a colony of baboons is limited considerably by the highly restrictive mating privileges accorded to the dominant overlord. Challenges of his rights by unmated males often result in serious, protracted fights that may end in the death of not only many of the males

concerned but also the female over which the battle was initiated (Zuckerman, 1932). Similarly, crowding in colonies of the common term usually results in desertion of nests and increased fighting, with an ensuing increase in mortality rate. The number of birds found dead in a colony has been shown to be in inverse proportion to the size of the territories held. The smaller these are as a result of crowding, the greater the aggressiveness and fighting within the group (Palmer, 1941). In many other species the relation between social factors and population size and density is equally close. In guppies, black bass, voles, and a number of insects, such as the flour beetle *Tribolium,* an increase in population size may lead to such compensatory mechanisms as cannibalism, which regulate numbers within safe limits (Collias, 1951).

As such, these parameters of size and density can hardly be used as a means of delineating or describing phylogenetic levels. In almost any biological classification, great variations in size of groups occur not only between but also within different species and genera. Societies occurring in the primate order illustrate this point amply (Nissen, 1951). In most of these social groups the range in size is so large as to allow little possibility of generalization. It is true that the more primitive genera such as tarsiers and aye-ayes tend to live in pairs or small groups, and that monkeys, both New and Old World, usually live in large bands. But the more highly developed apes again revert to small groups. Either there are no phylogenetic trends with respect to size and density or else they are so complex as to escape ready identification. In any given society they appear to depend on a multiplicity of factors, some purely physical or environmental, others utimately genetic; but it seems unlikely that, in vertebrates at least, there is any systematic relation between particular size or density and particular animal groups.

On the other hand, these parameters have very important effects on the evolutionary fate of populations. For example, as Collias and Southwick (1952) have shown empirically with howling monkeys on Barro Colorado Island, natural selection may operate to favor the maintenance of medium-sized over small or large groups. Both of the latter were found to have disproportionately small numbers of offspring. In a case where populations of different size exist side by side, each representing different gene pools, those in the moderate-size groups will be favored over the others, and any phenotypic characteristics carried by them will have a better chance of being perpetuated. Similar observations made by Calhoun (1952) on a free-ranging colony of rats suggest that too high a population density may have deleterious effects, independently of the amount of food available. Whether such effects are genetic or phenotypic, they can undoubtedly have important evolutionary consequences.

2. *Cohesiveness.* This dimension refers simply to the tendency for the individuals of a certain group to remain in proximity to each other. Another name for it might be "amount of scatter," and, in this respect, it is the psychological counterpart of density.

In terms of the scheme of interaction analysis suggested above, cohesiveness will be given by the total number of interactions in the group over a period of time. In a cohesive group, interactions both positive and negative will be numerous compared to those occurring in a noncohesive group. Thus a group may still have a high degree of cohesiveness even though its members are scattered quite widely, so long as communication goes on between them. For this reason, cohesiveness will be uncorrelated with density up to a point.

In general, cohesiveness varies widely with animal groups. For example, Collias (1950a) has observed in the New York Zoological Park that a group of white-tailed deer showed a particular lack of cohesiveness, scattering widely in their enclosure, whereas a group of nyala antelope usually moved as a compact herd unit. Cohesiveness, in this case, appeared to depend on the amount of intragroup aggressiveness, this being much greater in the first of the two groups mentioned. Aggression need not always be the critical factor, however. In societies of geese and pelicans the same investigator found that the tendency to cohere apparently resulted largely from similarities in coloration or pattern of plumage. Carpenter (1942) has described different degrees of cohesiveness in various monkey groups. Howlers, for example, usually form rather closely knit, cohesive units. Capuchins and baboons, on the other hand, scatter widely in the daytime though they cluster together at night. Spider monkeys apparently scatter even more widely, though, again, they tend to assemble at night. In these cases cohesiveness is governed not only by intragroup antagonisms and the nature of the habitat but also by sexual attractions and familial ties.

Granting such factors as sex and family, however, there is still another more basic cause of cohesiveness. Even individuals which, because of their submissiveness or lack of development, are excluded from the rights of mating and family will tend to stay as close as possible to the other members of the band. Although these isolates receive summary treatment from their fellows, they apparently still find some satisfaction in being associated with familiar individuals. This tendency is especially obvious in birds and has been discussed fully by Emlin (1952). He suggests that cohesiveness is the final product of a balance between positive and negative social responses. For example, in nesting colonies of swallows perching on telephone wires, a great deal of time and effort are taken up in "satisfying both the appetite for companionship and the aversion for crowding." By a continual process of shuffling and reshuffling, the birds gradually establish an optimal amount of cohesiveness. Ten-inch gaps on the wire, for example, are filled centrally with no trouble, while six-inch spaces are avoided generally and their occasional invasion, since it results in too close proximity for comfort, gives rise to aggression. In bird flight, we find the same tendency to cohesiveness that is in evidence in static, roosting groups. Nichols (1931) observed that in a mixed flock of shore birds bunching and wheeling would occur in such a way as to maintain a close proximity between the faster and slower individuals in the group. By these various maneuvers an optimal amount of cohesiveness could be achieved during flight.

The relation of cohesiveness to phylogeny appears to be complex. The tendency for individuals in a group to cohere is found in all social animals from primitive colonial forms to man, but it is difficult to distinguish any real trends. For example, both rat colonies (Calhoun, 1952) and prairie dog towns (King, 1955) are usually divided into smaller local groups, such as "wards" and "coteries," between which there is a reduced incidence of locomotion, and although the division of the prairie dog group is more complex than that in the rat colony, there is perhaps no essential difference between them. Similarly, in Crotophaginae, one of the six subfamilies of cuckoos, Davis (1942) finds a gradual progression (or regression) from pair nesting and pair territory defense in the more primitive genus *Guira* to communal nesting and territory in the species *Crotophaga ani* and *C. sulcirostris*. It is clear that the evolution of group cohesiveness may follow no general rules and be different for different biological groups.

As a causative factor in evolution, the cohesiveness of groups can have an important influence. Strong group cohesiveness is likely to promote better protection of younger or weaker members of the society, as well as better biological "conditioning" of the territory (Allee et al., 1949). Furthermore, in many societies, proximity between individuals may have an even more direct value by providing the social stimulation needed to set off a variety of important reproductive and protective functions. Many bird species, such as the fulmar petrel and the Atlantic murre are stimulated to incubation and mating by the social stimulation involved in moderate crowding (Darling, 1952); and others, such as the arctic skua, show defensive patterns of behavior only under social conditions (Williamson, 1949). In these ways, it appears that the cohesiveness of groups has definite survival value.

On the other hand, too great a cohesiveness, as in the case of crowding, may have deleterious effects. And, in addition, if cohesiveness is so strong that it effectively isolates the individuals in the group from all other groups with whose members crossbreeding might occur, then it may well promote selection and inbreeding, with any evolutionary consequences these may have.

3. *Syntality*. This term (borrowed from Cattell, 1953) is used here to describe the degree to which the members of a group act as a unit, or in concert, in the achievement of some group goal. Although similar to cohesiveness, it may still be regarded as distinct. Thus a cohesive group in which the members stick closely together may act with or without syntality—that is, in unison or individually—when certain circumstances arise. Cohesiveness refers to the fact that group members communicate a great deal; syntality to the fact that the members of the group can act coordinately or cooperatively in meeting some problem that has to be solved, whether this be a sudden stressful situation or merely the everyday task of surviving in a certain milieu. In terms of an interaction analysis, syntality is indicated mainly by the degree to which particular individuals make particular types of social responses over a period of time, especially when danger threatens, and also by the degree to which the group responds to these communiqués.

In vertebrates social roles are less clearly defined than in insects. However, there are some. For example, in reindeer herds some degree of syntality is ensured by the allocation of certain social functions to certain individuals. According to Sdobnikov (Allee et al., 1949), the herd is divided into two main groups—a middle group composed of quiet, peaceable individuals and a "fringe" group that is further divided into a vanguard and side groups of restless, nervous animals. There is also a rear guard of submissive individuals. Thus in a danger situation the fringe animals, by dint of their lower threshold of emotional response, will be able (by social facilitation) to transmit relevant information more readily to the more placid members of the herd. This ensures that a maximum number in the group will react appropriately. Leadership is another role that favors syntality of the group. This is highly developed in some groups, much less so in others. In such species as the red deer (Darling, 1937), Barbary sheep (Katz, 1949), domestic sheep (Scott, 1945b), and goats (Stewart and Scott, 1947), leadership plays an important social function and usually rests with a female. In many other societies, such as the roe deer or baboons, the members of the group are tyrannized rather than led by the most aggressive and dominant male. It is for this reason that Darling (1937) and Allee (1951) have stressed the value of matriarchy in making for true gregariousness and cooperation. Darling has contended that the sociality of the female is "selfless," unlike that of the male, this being always endangered by the "egocentric sex drive." It is interesting to note that in the red deer hind groups there is much more cohesiveness and syntality than in stag companies, which have no apparent leader but only one animal who "may be in a position to bully the rest" (Darling, 1937).

Another factor bearing on syntality in the group is the function of family units aimed at the preservation and rearing of the young. Even within lower phylogenetic levels, in insects, for example, there appears to be some evolutionary development. As Collias (1951) has pointed out, in the primitive forms the mother merely lays her eggs in some location that will prove favorable to the survival of the young once they have emerged. In more advanced forms, however, the mother will remain with the young larvae and protect them. At the highest level, care and raising of the young are often a group project, as in the social insects. In some mammals, such as cats and rodents, the male is associated with the female only during estrus and does not contribute directly to family life. In species such as the red deer (Darling, 1937) or the Alaska seal (Chance and Mead, 1953) the male remains with a number of females, which he protects from other males, during the rutting or mating season; then he returns to the bachelor group, and the young are raised by cooperating female herds. A much higher level of family life is found in some canines (Young and Goldman, 1944) and primates (Zuckerman, 1932; Carpenter, 1942), in which the male and the female may cooperate in raising and guarding the young. Etkin (1954) may be right in suggesting that there is a tendency, phylogenetically, for the family unit to become more and more a well-established feature of the social group, though this may not be very obvious within any particular phyletic lines. It would seem that in the Crotophaginae, already mentioned above, the genus *Guira* shows a better developed family unit than *Crotophaga*, although the first is phylogenetically older (Davis, 1942); while in rodents prairie dogs, with their rather complex social organization (King, 1955), appear to show more group syntality than rats (Barnett and Spencer, 1951). In any biological group a host of different factors, such as physical habitat, food supplies, and sensorimotor equipment may influence group structure and cooperativeness between individuals in the society. These must always be considered when looking for evolutionary trends.

The effects that syntality can have on evolution are more clear. Like cohesiveness, syntality can have survival value, and, in fact, is specifically geared to survival and improvement of group life. A group whose members can coordinate their behavior to the achievement of some group goal has better chances of survival than one whose members act independently. In addition, as Etkin (1954) has suggested, an integrated family life may exert an important selection pressure favoring the development of tool using and language.

On the other hand, while syntality may favor group survival, it may act against individuals, particularly when specialization of roles is extreme. This will certainly be true if cohesiveness is so low that the weaker members, who are concerned only with such functions as nutrition and reproduction, are not continually under surveillance by those members whose main function is protection.

4. *Stability.* The stability of a group, as used here, refers to the

fixity of interindividual relationships within a group, that is to say, the degree to which social interactions between particular individuals remains the same over a period of time. A stable group is one in which the intermember relationships do not change very much. A number of chickens, for example, when put together for the first time, will soon sort themselves out into a rather stable social hierarchy or peck order, as Douglas (1948) and numerous others have shown (Allee, 1951). Pigeon and parakeet groups, on the other hand, are typically unstable and do not have a rigid dominance order but only a loosely defined peck right (Allee et al., 1949). Stability is related to cohesiveness and syntality but is, I think, distinct from them. Thus it is theoretically possible for a group to be low in cohesiveness and syntality but high in stability. The work of Douglas (1948) on hen groups illustrates this possibility quite well. She has shown that a bird may be a member of as many as five different flocks simultaneously and hold a different social rank in each one. A group so composed of absentee members has no cohesiveness or syntality but still has high stability. On the other hand, it is not difficult to imagine a group that is very cohesive and has high or moderate syntality but is very unstable.

Phylogenetically, stability of groups may resemble syntality. In most primitive social groups stability is high in a negative sense, in that these societies are not unstable. At these levels, dominance relations and emotional interactions between particular individuals are probably less important, and there is little problem of social rank. With increasing intellectual and perceptual capacity, however, emotional interaction between particular individuals becomes more noticeable, and competition for social rank and its accompanying priorities emerges. In vertebrate groups we thus find all degrees of stability represented, depending on the ability of different individuals to distinguish each other, their emotional sensitivity, and their ability to remember the outcome of particular encounters. Thus, as Collias (1950b) has pointed out, the stability of bird and mammalian groups is much greater than those of fishes and lizards. Aggressiveness is not any less for this reason, however, in higher social groups; if anything it is greater. But it can be more readily controlled. Because animals come to recognize each individual in the group as distinct from other individuals, they are able to react appropriately with dominant or submissive behavior, depending on their expectations regarding their fellows.

In human societies the stability of groups is ensured in much the same way. For man, although he is a very emotional animal, has the intelligence to find the means of mastering his animosities and fears. Thus it may well be true that increasing stability at the group level reflects rather directly an increasing development of intelligence at the individual level, in that it depends ultimately on the ability of an organism to remember what every individual in the group is like and to react appropriately with certain specified kinds of behavior that convey certain standard kinds of information. This does not mean that capacity for emotionality is therefore less in higher forms. On the contrary, it is probably greater. A baboon society, for example, may appear relatively calm and stable provided the status quo is preserved, but may be completely disrupted for long periods of time by violent fighting when certain circumstances arise that disturb the usual controls exerted by a domanance hierarchy. For the most part, paradoxically, the same factors that make such a degree of emotionality possible also make available the means of controlling it (Hebb and Thompson, 1954).

The evolutionary consequences of stability in groups are important and may be in several directions. Its chief effect is, of course, to reduce the number of aggressive encounters between group members. Scott (1950) has observed, for example, that in three species of grouse—the sage grouse, the greater prairie chicken, and the prairie sharptail—the amount of fighting is inversely correlated with the complexity of social organization. The more clear are the dominance hierarchy and territorial rights, the greater is the stability of the group. These findings are in accord with those of Masure and Allee (1934) on chickens and pigeons and with those of Braddock (1945) on fish (*Platypoecilus maculatus*). In any species having a stable organization, an animal low in the hierarchy and ill equipped to defend itself can avoid the possibly fatal results of combat by giving way gracefully to individuals it recognizes as dominant. Submission may also mean a sacrifice of priority for food and mates, but at least it has a very definite survival value. Because of this, Chance and Mead (1953) have laid considerable emphasis on the ability of an animal to control or delay its aggressiveness in emotion-provoking situations as an evolutionary mechanism, and have suggested it may well reflect increased neocortical development.

5. *Permeability.* This parameter may be defined as the degree to which the members of a group permit the intrusion of strange individuals, and is given by the number of negative interactions to an individual of an out-group. Since it is a group trait which has been studied extensively in many different societies from insect to man, it is of considerable interest in the present connection. At the same time, it seems unlikely that this dimension varies systematically within or between phyletic lines. In almost any biological class there may be found social groups that differ greatly in permeability. For example, among rodents, it appears to be true that different genetic strains react differently to strangers, C57 Blacks, for example, very aggressively, A/Jax rather permissively (Scott and Fredericson, 1951). This difference suggests that permeability represents the expression at the group level of traits that are genetically controlled in the individual. These traits are probably the ability to discriminate strangers from nonstrangers, and degree of aggressiveness. This is indicated quite clearly by King's study (1954) on differences in group permeability between two breeds of domestic dog, the cocker and the basenji. These two breeds are genetically distinct and appear to differ considerably in temperament (Fuller and Scott, 1954). It is interesting that basenjis—a hunting breed and the more aggressive animal—are more rejecting of stranger dogs than cockers and form much more rigid social hierarchies within their own group. The characteristics of the newcomer are also important. As Douglas (1948) has shown, for example, dominant, aggressive hens are usually assimilated much more quickly to an organized group than submissive birds. Curiously enough, in primates, at least, strangers of another species are usually tolerated and allowed to mingle freely with the group, while strangers of the same species are not (Carpenter, 1942). It is possible that this phenomenon is related to sexual dominance, only animals that represent a threat to mating privileges because they are of the same species as the individuals in the group being actively excluded.

While its relationship to phylogeny is vague, permeability may well have an important influence on the course of evolution. In effect, a highly impermeable group isolates itself by excluding individuals which do not already belong to it. This may have the effect of increasing inbreeding, with a subsequent increase in homogeneity and specialization that may be deleterious should environmental conditions change radically. On the other hand, as Collias (1951) has pointed out, low permeability may act to facilitate survival in a species as a whole by permitting closer organization within the group. In flocks of birds, for example, with continually shifting membership, there is more fighting and the average individual gets less food and does not maintain body weight as well as those individuals in a less permeable flock. Furthermore, a certain degree of impermeability may maximize the "fitness" of a species if it results in a number of genotypically distinct inbred lines upon which selection may act (Thoday, 1953).

SUMMARY

In summary, it may be stated that the evolution of social behavior is a broad and complex problem. Although it is not so difficult to see the possible evolutionary effects social behavior can have, it is very difficult indeed to find any obvious phylogenetic trends, with respect either to the structure of groups or to the kinds of interactions occurring in them. It appears to be true that social groups are most highly organized in insects and in man. But the parallelism between the two is superficial, and the organization of each probably depends on different mechanisms. In the social insects evolution has brought about the possibility of intricate social relationships by means of changes in genotype, giving their social life a rigidity that is little susceptible to change. In man, analogous complexity has been achieved more indirectly through the evolutionary development of abstract intelligence and learning ability (cf. Schneirla, 1946). With these abilities come true language and altruism, characters that make possible much more sophisticated social behavior than can occur in insects. In animals between insects and man there is a transition from dominance of genetic mechanisms to dominance of learning mechanisms in determining social behavior. Since neither has definite ascendance at this level, social behavior tends to be rather elementary. At the same time, with increasing ability to abstract, a potential for complex group behavior is gradually built up, culminating in man.

It is perhaps disappointing that at present only such a broad generalization as this can be made. We can but hope that more empirical work will be done on the evolution of social behavior, having as its main aims the exact description and analysis of many social groups in many different species, and the exploration of the manner in which genes produce behavioral characters. Until this is done, little progress will be made.

REFERENCES

ALLEE, W. C. 1951. Co-operation among animals with human implications. New York, Henry Schuman.

ALLEE, W. C., EMERSON, A. E., PARK, O., PARK, T., and SCHMIDT, K. P. 1949. Principles of animal ecology. Philadelphia, W. B. Saunders.

BALES, R. F. 1951. Interaction process analysis. Cambridge, Mass., Addison-Wesley.

BARNETT, S. A., and SPENCER, M. M. 1951. Feeding, social behavior, and interspecific competition in wild rats. Behaviour, *3*, 229–42.

BIERENS DE HAAN, J. A. 1929. Animal language in relation to that of man. Biol. Rev., *4*, 249–68.

BIRCH, H. G. 1951. Social interaction in animal groups. Cybernetics, *8*, 134–72.

BRADDOCK, J. C. 1945. Some aspects of the dominance-subordination relationship in the Fish Platypoecilus maculatus. Physiol. Zool., *18*, 171–95.

CALHOUN, J. B. 1952. Population dynamics. J. Mammal., *33*, 139–59.

CARPENTER, C. R. 1942. Societies of monkeys and apes. Biol. Sympos., *8*, 177–204.

CATTELL, R. B. 1953. New concepts for measuring leadership, in terms of group syntality. In D. Cartwright and A. Zander, eds., Group dynamics. Evanston, Ill., Row, Peterson.

CHANCE, M. R. A., and MEAD, A. P. 1953. Social behavior and primate evolution. In Evolution. Sympos. Soc. Exp. Biol., No. 7. Cambridge, Eng., Cambridge Univ. Press, pp. 395–439.

COLLIAS, N. E. 1950a. Some variations in grouping and dominance patterns among birds and mammals. Zoologica, *35*, 97–119.

COLLIAS, N. E. 1950b. Social life and the individual among vertebrate animals. Ann. N.Y. Acad. Sci., *51*, 1074–92.

COLLIAS, N. E. 1951. Problems and principles of animal sociology. In C. P. Stone, ed., Comparative psychology. 3d ed. New York, Prentice-Hall.

COLLIAS, N. E., and SOUTHWICK, C. 1952. A field study of population density and social organization in howling monkeys. Proc, Amer. Philos. Soc., *96*, 143–56.

DARLING, F. F. 1937. A herd of red deer. London, Oxford Univ. Press.

DARLING, F. F. 1952. Social behavior and survival. Auk, *69*, 183–91.

DAVIS, D. E. 1942. The phylogeny of social nesting habits in the Crotophaginae. Quart. Rev. Biol., *17*, 115–34.

DOUGLAS, M. D. 1948. Social factors influencing the hierarchies of small flocks of the domestic hen: interactions between resident or part-time members of the organized flocks. Physiol. Zool., *21*, 147–82.

EMLIN, J. T. 1952. Flocking behavior in birds. Auk, *69*, 160–70.

ETKIN, W. 1954. Social behavior and the evolution of man's mental faculties. Amer. Nat., *88*, 129–42.

FORD, C. S., and BEACH, F. A. 1951. Patterns of sexual behavior. New York, Harper and Hoeber.

FULLER, J. L., and SCOTT, J. P. 1954. Heredity and learning ability in infrahuman mammals. Eugenics Quart., *1*, 29–43.

HEBB, D. O., and THOMPSON, W. R. 1954. The social significance of animal studies. In Gardner Lindzey, ed., Handbook of social psychology. Cambridge, Mass., Addison-Wesley.

HEYNS, R. W., and LIPPITT, R. 1954. Systematic observational techniques. In ibid.

HUXLEY, J. 1942. Evolution: the modern synthesis. London, Allen & Unwin.

KATZ, I. 1949. Behavioral interaction in a herd of Barbary sheep (Ammotragus lervia). Zoologica, *34*, 9–18.

KING, J. A. 1954. Closed social groups among domestic dogs. Proc. Amer. Philos. Soc., *98*, 327–36.

KING, J. A. 1955. Social behavior, social organization, and population dynamics in a black-tailed prairie-dog town in the Black Hills of South Dakota. Contr. Lab. Vert. Biol. Univ. of Mich., No. 67, pp. 1–123.

KÖHLER, W. 1927. The mentality of apes. 2d ed. New York, Harcourt, Brace.

LANGER, S. K. 1942. Philosophy in a new key. New York, Pelican Books.

LERNER, I. M. 1950. Population genetics and animal improvement. Cambridge, Eng., Cambridge Univ. Press.

MCBRIDE, A. F. 1940. Meet Mr. Porpoise. Nat. Hist. Mag., *45*, 16–29.

MCBRIDE, A. F., and HEBB, D. O. 1948. Behavior of the captive bottle-nose dolphin, Tursiops truncatus. J. Comp. Physiol. Psychol., *41*, 111–23.

MASURE, R. H., and ALLEE, W. C. 1934. The social order in flocks of the common chicken and the pigeon. Auk, *51*, 306–27.

MEAD, G. H. 1952. Language and the development of the self. In G. E. Swanson, T. M. Newcomb, and E. L. Hartley, eds., Readings in social psychology. New York, Holt.

MOWRER, O. H. 1954. The psychologist looks at language. Amer. Psychol., *9*, 660–94.

NICHOLS, J. T. 1931. Notes on the flocking of shore birds. Auk, *48*, 181–5.

NISSEN, H. W. 1951. Social behavior in primates. In C. P. Stone, ed., Comparative psychology. 3d ed. New York, Prentice-Hall.

NISSEN, H. W., and CRAWFORD, M. P. 1936. A preliminary study of food-sharing behavior in young chimpanzees. J. Comp. Psychol., *22*, 383–419.

NOWLIS, V. 1941. Companionship prefer-ence and dominance in the social interaction of young chimpanzees. Comp. Psychol. Monogr., *17* (1), 1–57.

PALMER, R. S. 1941. A behavior study of the common tern. Proc. Boston Soc. Nat. Hist., *42*, 1–119.

RÉVÈSZ, G. 1944. The language of animals. J. Gen. Psychol., *30*, 117–47.

SCHNEIRLA, T. C. 1946. Problems in the biopsychology of social organization. J. Abnorm. Soc. Psychol., *41*, 385–402.

SCOTT, J. P. 1945a. Group formation determined by social behavior: a comparative study of two mammalian societies. Sociometry, *8*, 42–52.

SCOTT, J. P. 1945b. Social behavior, organization, and leadership in a small flock of domestic sheep. Comp. Psychol. Monogr., *18*, 1–29.

SCOTT, J. P., and FREDERICSON, E. 1951. The causes of fighting in mice and rats. Physiol. Zool., *24*, 273–309.

SCOTT, J. W. 1950. A study of the phylogenetic or comparative behavior of three species of grouse. Ann. N. Y. Acad. Sci., *51*, 1062–73.

STEWART, J. C., and SCOTT, J. P. 1947. Lack of correlation between leadership and dominance relationships in the herd of goats. J. Comp. Physiol. Psychol., *48*, 255–64.

SWANSON, G. E., NEWCOMB, T. M. and HARTLEY, E. L., eds. 1952. Readings in social psychology. New York, Holt.

THODAY, J. M. 1953. Components of fitness. In Evolution. Symp. Soc. Exp. Biol., No. 7. Cambridge, Eng., Cambridge Univ. Press, pp. 96–113.

WILLIAMSON, K. 1949. The distraction behavior of the arctic skua. Ibis, *91*, 307–13.

WRIGHT, S. 1921. Systems of mating. Genetics, *6*, 111–78.

WRIGHT, S. 1940. Breeding structure of populations in relation to speciation. Amer. Nat., *74*, 232–48.

YOUNG, S. P., and GOLDMAN, E. A. 1944. The wolves of North America. Amer. Wildlife Inst., Washington, D.C.

ZUCKERMAN, S. 1932. The social life of monkeys and apes. London, Kegan Paul, Trench, Trubner.

15

The Evolution of Behavior among Social Insects

Alfred E. Emerson

UNIVERSITY OF CHICAGO

•

THE SOCIAL INSECTS have long been noted for types of behavior that may be arranged in evolutionary order. They have also contributed to our knowledge of behavioral processes and evolutionary mechanisms. No one type of organism is the best for all aspects of analysis and synthesis of behavior evolution. Insect societies provide the best known material for demonstrating some important points and are inadequate for others.

An adequate interpretation of the evolutionary order of behavioral manifestations among the social insects should find correlative mathematical order of facts from anatomy, physiology, ontogeny (embryology), cytology, genetics, biochemistry, biophysics, taxonomy, ecology, geography, paleontology, and the social sciences in general. Not only are principles and generalizations from these special subsciences often applicable to the behavior of social insects, but some of the principles derived from a study of social insects may contribute suggestions to other fields of study (Emerson, 1954). Some of the attributes of social insects that lend themselves to evolutionary study are listed below.

1. Their behavior is predominantly instinctive and genetically induced, although some associational learning is important in social activity and communication (Schneirla, 1929; von Frisch, 1955a). Organic evolution is a change in time in the genetics of organisms, and the evolution of behavior must deal with inherited behavior. In contrast, the evolution of human behavior is best divided into genetic capacities and social inheritance by means of symbolic communication.

2. Insect societies exhibit emergent group behavior, not just a summation of behavior of individuals. The group behavior is

probably always polygenic. The group system is integrated to a marked degree by its behavior and is a selected unit in evolutionary processes. The individual is always present and important, but has been considerably modified during evolution by its social functions. The group system has many fundamental characteristics of an organism and may be termed a "supraorganism" (Emerson, 1952; Bonner, 1955; also see Schneirla, 1946, for a critical discussion).

3. The group behavior is social, functional, and adaptive (Emerson, 1929).

4. The behavior may be associated with structural characters that are arranged in a phylogenetic order. The evolutionary order of the morphological characters is well substantiated in many instances, and correlations with developmental, ecological, geographical, and paleontological information are established.

5. The cumulative behavior of the group is sometimes expressed in constructions that make precise comparisons possible among closely related species and genera, so that aspects of morphology that lend themselves to evolutionary analysis and interpretation often are paralleled by behavior (Schmidt, 1955a; Desneux, 1956b).

6. The morphological expression of social behavior makes it possible to use terms that heretofore have been applicable to anatomy, physiology, and development. Some of these terms are: taxonomic categories, homology, analogy, symmetry, replication, metamerism, ontogeny, regeneration, fields, gradients, phylogeny, recapitulation, genetic assimilation, vestiges, and homeostasis.

7. The activity of the social insects so modifies the physical and biotic environment that the society has been the focus of biocoenotic evolution incorporating many other species of plants and animals into an interspecies population of relative complexity and evolutionary duration (Seevers, 1957).

Difficulties in the analysis of evolution are due to inadequacies of information about social insects. There is a lack of precise and abundant data on the genetics of behavior, on the details of the function and physiology of the sense organs and central nervous system, and on the individual behavior. The experimental and quantitative data are meager and seldom deal with closely related species and genera. Semantic confusion permeates the literature. Anthropomorphisms, superficial metaphors, and unsound facile generalizations abound.

Behavior and Taxonomic Categories

Homologies of behavior may be correlated with anatomical homologies characteristic of taxonomic categories. These give evidence of continuity through genetic relationships and changes.

Species. Many distinctions of behavior are found among anatomically distinct species, but the role of behavior in speciation is emphasized when the distinctions of behavior are greater than those of structure. The best case that combines slight morphological distinction with great ethological distinction is the pair of ethospecies of termites, *Apicotermes desneuxi* and *A. gurgulifex* (Schmidt, 1955a, 1955b; Emerson, 1956b). The walls of the subterranean nests are perforated by regularly arranged simple ventilation pores or slits running from the surface to the internal inhabited chambers. *A. desneuxi* builds relatively broad scale-like projections on the surface, while *A. gurgulifex* constructs narrower "spouts" or "gargoyles" projecting from the surface. The soldiers of the two species are taxonomically extremely close.

Ethotype. An ethotype is a behavioral race or subspecies with slight taxonomic distinctions. The nests of *Apicotermes angustatus* and *A. kisantuensis* each have two types of slightly different ventilation pore constructions that are probably indicative of instinctive divergence (Desneux, 1948, 1953; Schmidt, 1955a, 1955b; Emerson, 1956b). Each ethotype nest differs from the other in the lining material, the shape of the conduit, and the lip of the conduit.

Genus. All known species of *Apicotermes* construct definitive pores or galleries within the nest walls except the most primitive species (*A. trägårdhi*), whose nest has recently been discovered (Schmidt, 1958). No other genus of termites builds this type of nest. Many species of the genus *Cubitermes* build capped mushroom-shaped nests in the forests and savannas of Africa. The umbrella-like caps function to shed rain from the nest. No other genus of termites makes such constructions. All species of the formicine ant genus, *Polyergus,* are obligatory slavemakers that raid colonies of their ancestral genus, *Formica.* The subgenus, *Rapitiformica,* of the genus *Formica* contains several facultative slavemakers.

Subfamily. The construction of fungus gardens from excrementous material and harvested grass or leaves is a universal behavior of all species of the Macrotermitinae so far examined, with the exception of one genus and species, *Sphaerotermes sphaero-thorax,* which builds what appears to be a nonfunctional vestigial fungus garden (Grassé and Noirot, 1948). The fungus-growing ants of the myrmicine tribe Attini likewise exhibit supergeneric behavior.

Family. All members of the Formicidae are strictly social or social parasites, and all possess wingless workers, except the social parasites in which the worker caste has been lost during evolution. Behavioral distinctions in the family categories are also known for the wasps (Vespidae) and the bees (Bombidae, Meliponidae, Apidae).

Order. The order Isoptera with over 2,000 species arranged in 168 genera and 5 families are all strictly social and all possess a soldier caste, with the exception of two genera (*Anoplotermes* and *Speculitermes*) in which the soldier has been secondarily lost during evolution.

Behavioral reactions between independently evolving taxonomic categories indicate the validity of the taxonomic grouping and the importance of the behavioral functions during evolution. A species of South American ponerine ant, *Termitopone (Syn-termitopone) commutata* is exclusively predaceous upon several species of the termite genus *Syntermes* (Emerson, 1945). The ants attack with characteristic maurauding bands (Wheeler, 1936). *Megaponera foetens* of tropical Africa is another predaceous ponerine ant that specializes on both minute and large species and genera of the fungus-growing termites (Macrotermitinae). The myrmicine genus, *Carebara,* with a number of species in the Old and New World tropics, is exclusively composed of "thief ants" in the nests of two subfamilies of termites that are phylogenetically related (Emerson, 1945). In all cases of social parasitism among the social Hymenoptera, the genus or species seems to have evolved from the host genus or even from the host species. Charles Seevers (1957) gives a detailed and extensive account of the reciprocal evolution of termitophilous aleocharine staphylinid beetles and their host termites. Although the theory of the phylogeny of both termitophiles and hosts is based upon respective homologous anatomical characters, much correlated behavior is known. Physogastry [1] of termitophiles is

1. The swelling of the abdomen or other parts with glandular enlargement. Glandular exudates attract and result in trophallaxis, nutritional exchange that integrates the society.

morphologically discernible and is surely an adaptation to the trophallactic social integration of the hosts. Circumstantial evidence (Emerson, 1955) indicates a Mesozoic origin of mutualistic behavior in termites and termitophilous beetles.

ADAPTIVE RADIATION AND CONVERGENCE OF BEHAVIOR

The supraorganismic social unit integrated by behavior is basic to social evolution (Wheeler, 1911). Darwin, in the *Origin of Species,* recognized the necessity of treating the societal system as an entity, and Weismann (1893) elaborated its significance for the theory of natural selection. Emerson (1939, 1952) has attempted to apply modern concepts of the organism to supraorganismic groupings. Le Masne (1953) gives details of the evolutionary development of trophallactic exchange that integrates eggs, larvae, pupae, and the adult castes of ants.

Sensory communication constitutes the behavioral integration of the social supraorganism (Emerson, 1929). The brilliant observations and experiments on the sensory physiology, learning, and communication within the honeybee society have been summarized by von Frisch (1955a). Recently an evolutionary order of the behavior has been indicated (von Frisch, 1955b). The races of the common honeybee and the four species of *Apis* differ somewhat in the dances performed on the comb by the scouts that communicate direction, distance, amount, and quality of the food source. M. Lindauer has discovered that the foundation pattern of the dance is similar under similar conditions, but that there is a difference in the response to distance. The wagging dance is first seen at distances of about 50 meters from the food source in the "Krainer" bees (*Apis mellifica*), at 7 meters in the Italian race (*A. mellifica*), at 5 in *A. florea*, at 3 in *A. dorsata*, and at 2 in *A. indica*. The dance rhythm also differs somewhat. The dance of the "Krainer" bee is the most rapid, followed by slower rhythms in the Italian race, *A. dorsata, A. indica,* and *A. florea.* The action radius of the species differs, that of *A. mellifica* ranging to a distance of 2 to 3 kilometers and *A. indica* to 800 meters. *A. florea,* with the slowest dance, does not fly farther than 400 meters.

Behavior during the colonizing flight of termites (Emerson, 1933a) has important consequences for the reproductive isolation

of the species. Reproductive isolation produces the branching
of the evolutionary tree and establishes complex genetic patterns in populations. Seasonal reproductive isolation occurs between closely related species of *Reticulitermes* in the same geographic and climatic area. Because mating occurs after the flight,
genes are not readily transferred over water and other barriers of
no hindrance to more vagile animals and plants. For this reason
evolution of termites is markedly correlated with geological
changes in the separation and junction of land masses (Emerson,
1955). The impregnated queens of the various social Hymenoptera may fly long distances over water and other inhospitable
ecological habitats and found their colonies without the male.

Supraorganismic systems have a life cycle of the colony superimposed upon the life cycle of the included individuals. The
evolutionary order of the development of the social colonies is
amply documented. Wheeler (1933) and Haskins and Haskins
(1950, 1951, 1955) have described the foraging activities of the
queen ponerine ants of the genera *Promyrmecia* and *Myrmecia*
of Australia which progressively feed their larvae with food captured at intervals outside the nest. Old females of *Myrmecia
tarsata, M. forficata,* and *M. vindex,* when removed from populous
colonies, revert to the foraging behavior of the young colony-
founding and foraging queens of the ponerine *Amblyopone
australis* which resembles the activities of its rather remote relative, *Myrmecia.* Wheeler assumes that the typical behavior of the
founding queens of the higher ants, which do not leave their incipient nest but feed their young by means of salivary secretions
and regurgitations from the crop, is a later evolution from the
more primitive foraging behavior of the queen. The queens without foraging behavior may live without food for over a year in
experimental colonies. They may eat their own eggs or larvae
and feed their larvae with eggs, larvae, and pupae from the developing colony. The budding of colonies and the invasion of
other colonies by temporary or permanent social parasites must
be considered late stages in the evolution of colony foundation
behavior in the ants.

The colony unit with supplementary reproductives may be potentially immortal. Bodenheimer (1937) indicates a natural senescence or aging of the colony of several social insects, but there
seems to be little evidence or any adequate theory that enables

us to conceive of factors leading to innate senescence of populations aside from the senescence of the individual, which, in the
social insects, might be the irreplaceable queen. Nonreversible
physiological senescence of the individual has no analogy in the
senescence of the colony with constant rejuvenescence through
the reproductive processes.

Development and evolution show relationships that have been
the basis of several important evolutionary concepts. *Palingenesis*
or *recapitulation* has been criticized by some investigators and recapitulation has been considered fallacious by some modern
biologists. Complex gene patterns are selected through the survival
of functional attributes in the adult. The genes affect developmental processes that produce the adult characters, so that all
stages of the life cycle including the genetic base, the developmental sequences, the adult characters, and the functional relations throughout the temporal unitary life cycle are interrelated.
Evolution may be detected in any systemic part or stage with a
partial independence of functions in the spatial organization, the
temporal ontogenetic stages, or the temporal phylogenetic sequences. Gene patterns affecting functions during development
at any stage may be selected, so that relatively recent adaptive
evolution of young stages (*caenogenesis*) may be demonstrated.
If the adaptive function has recently evolved but is expressed in
the adults, we refer to such comparatively recent evolution as
deuterogenesis. A character may appear in an early stage of development that is homologous with a functional character in an
ancestral adult or developmental stage. Such characters may be
reduced or much modified in function during evolution. We refer to the presence of these anciently evolved characters as *palingenesis*. Palingenetic characters may appear in young stages and
be absent in the adult or may be vestigial in the adult. Sometimes
an embryological function may be detected in a palingenetic
character, but in some cases no embryological function is discernible.

Anatomical characters undergo progressive and regressive evolution in some castes of social insects without much modification
of the other castes (Wilson, 1953; Noirot, 1954). Behavior may
be expected to show evolutionary parallels. The adaptations of the
sterile castes of termites are *caenogenetic* because they represent
comparatively recently evolved adaptations of the nymphal stages.

Neotenic evolution is also exhibited by the termites that produce supplementary reproductives with nymphal characters. Neotenic individuals occur in most species of termites, but no termite has lost its alate reproductives. The more recent adaptations of the sterile castes in all the social Hymenoptera are *deuterogenetic,* with the major function occurring only in the postpupal adult. C. D. Michener (personal communication) has evidence that strictly social bees with a worker caste and mass provisioning of the young arose through aggregations of adult females. In the other social Hymenoptera and in the Isoptera (termites), the societal system probably emerged from the parent-offspring relationship or family with progressive feeding of the young. A striking type of deuterogenetic behavior is seen in the worker-like wingless queens of certain ants *(Eciton,* etc.)

In both caenogenetic and deuterogenetic evolution of castes there are numerous structural characters that show a progressive evolutionary sequence toward increased adaptive function and, in contrast, there are likewise many examples of regressive evolution with functionless homologous vestiges of once functional characters. The functionless vestige may occur in one caste and not in another in both caenogenetic and deuterogenetic caste evolution. It seems to be a reasonable hypothesis that physiological thresholds are associated with activation or inhibition during the trophogenic caste determination, with identical genetic composition underlying the capacities to react to physiological trigger mechanisms. The triggers themselves are probably controlled by genes. Otherwise we would not have the phylogenetic enlargement of the "squirt gun" of the nasute soldier, the reduction of the mandibles of the minor soldier while the mandibles of the major soldier remain functional in evolutionary sequences (*Schedorhinotermes, Rhinotermes, Dolichorhinotermes,* with the major soldier lacking in the derived *Acorhinotermes*), the regressive evolution of the worker caste in the social parasites among the Hymenoptera, or the regressive evolution of the pollen-collecting apparatus in the queens of the Apidae. Both behavior and physiology are integrated with anatomy in the evolution of these supraorganismic systems.

Genetic assimilation (Waddington, 1953, 1956) or the "Baldwin effect" [2] (White and Smith, 1956) is an interesting evolutionary

2. The hypothesis that nongenetic adaptive modification of the phenotype may be replaced by genetically controlled modification. See also Mayr, this volume.

change in the mechanism of development. Kerr (1948, 1950a, 1950b) gives evidence of the genetic distinction of queens and workers in species of *Melipona*. The queens of the most primitive species of this genus of bee, *M. marginata*, are heterozygous for two genes (Aa Bb), and the queens of several other species of *Melipona* are heterozygous for three genes (Aa Bb Cc). Males are haploid. Each gene when homozygous in the diploid individual produces a worker. Trophogenic determination of the female castes is the rule in the more primitive bees (Bombidae), in the more primitive genera of the Meliponidae (*Lestrimelitta, Trigona*), and in the domestic honeybee and its relatives (Apidae). Therefore it may be assumed that a genetic substitution that triggers the growth processes—formerly triggered by biochemical and physiological processes only—has occurred in later stages of evolution some time after the phylogenetic origin of the normally sterile worker caste. In this instance the caste determination by genetic mechanisms is secondary to caste determination by trophogenetic mechanisms. In an analogous manner, sex and sex differentiation arose physiologically long before genetic and chromosomal determination of the different sexes occurred. The genetic mechanism infiltrated at a late stage in evolution to trigger the development of the functional adaptations. Of course, the capacity to react to any environmental, physiological, or genetic stimulus is almost invariably based upon a complex genetic pattern that is inherited and itself evolves. But it is clear that an evolutionary feedback occurs through natural selection from the function to the development and genetic mechanisms, and that both the individual organism and the social supraorganism are multidimensional systems incorporating ontogenetic and phylogenetic time with the spatial dimensions.

Melipona shows no differences in size of brood cells, while *Trigona* and *Apis* have distinct queen cells. In *Melipona*, undifferentiated brood cells in which queens are raised are distributed at random in the comb. It seems possible that the behavior of the workers in forming the distinctive cells may assist in the differential trophic treatment and trophogenic development, while the genetic determination makes such differential behavior unnecessary in *Melipona*. It will be noted that feedback mechanisms from behavior may affect the physiology, and feedbacks from genetically induced behavior (instinct) may affect the genetic system in evolutionary time.

Evolutionary divergence or radiation is illustrated by the specifically distinct ventilation pores in the walls of the subterranean nest constructions of the African termite genus *Apicotermes.* Recent papers by Desneux (1948, 1953, 1956a, 1956b), Grassé and Noirot (1954), Schmidt (1955a, 1955b, 1958), and Emerson (1956b) give details of the taxonomic and behavioral relationships. The nests of ten described species are now known and two species each have two ethotypes. The observed order of relationships is surely phylogenetic and provides the best known case of behavior evolution.

Adaptive radiation of nest structures within a genus is well illustrated by the nests of *Amitermes* (Emerson, 1938). This genus is found in both the tropics and warm temperate regions around the world. It is particularly well represented by species in the relatively arid savannas, steppes, and deserts. A few species inhabit rain forests in the Orient and Neotropics. One species, *Amitermes excellens,* is fairly common in the rain forest of British Guiana, and this species constructs orderly rain-shedding finger-like projections of the dirt carton which is thickly plastered on the surface of dead and living trees. These adaptations to heavy rainfall are in sharp contrast to the mound nests or subterranean nests of the same genus constructed by savanna and desert species.

The evolutionary processes leading to adaptation are more complex than the processes resulting in evolutionary loss or reduction of a former adaptation. It is probably a much simpler process to lose social behavior than to acquire such behavior initially (Allee et al., 1949, p. 677). Highly social behavior has evolved independently four times among insects, but it has been lost independently many more times. Evolution of social parasitism with the loss of the worker caste, and loss of independent colony-founding behavior by the queen, has occurred among the Hymenoptera in a number of analogous regressions (Taylor, 1939; Weyrauch, 1937). Examples occur among the wasps, bumblebees, and ants. Brown (1955) lists eleven species of myrmecine parasitic ants and suggests that the majority evolved directly from the host genus and, for some forms, the host species. Wheeler (1928) points out that the evolution of social parasitism requires less adaptive change of behavior when the social relationships of host and parasite are close. Wheeler also thought that the so-called genus *Psithyrus* is polyphyletic and that the resemblances between host and parasite may be homologous rather than analogous, although he and others do not assume the origin of *Psithyrus* species directly from their host species (Reinig, 1935). *Bombus* queens sometimes enter other nests of their own species and the invader may kill the resident queen. *Bombus terrestris* parasitizes *B. lucorum* after killing the *lucorum* queen. These cases suggest the evolutionary sequence of parasitic behavior.

Peculiar behavior is manifested by both the social parasites and the parasitized hosts. *Wheeleriella santschii* queens are adopted by their host worker ants (*Monomorium*) without antagonism, and the host workers later kill their own queen. The queen of an Australian parasitic ant (*Strumigenys xenos*) lives with the host colony (*S. perplexa*) containing host queens without antagonism, but the host workers pay more attention to the parasitic queen than they do to their own (Brown, 1955). A workerless ant (*Labauchena daguerrei*) of Argentina parasitizes the fire ant (*Solenopsis saevissima* var. *richteri*). Four to six queens of the small dealated *Labauchena* mount the back of the large *Solenopsis* nest-mother and cooperate with one another in gnawing off her head. As many as forty-five days may be required for the decapitation. The parasites seem to acquire the odor of the host queen and are not attacked by the host workers. The parasitic queens oviposit during the beheading and the host workers carry off the eggs and raise them. The parasitic queens are not adopted in a definitive manner until the host queen is decapitated.

Cases of robbery of stored honey abound in the literature on bees. One colony may rob the honey of a presumably weak colony of honeybees, and among the Meliponidae (Schwarz, 1948) robbery is fairly common between colonies of the same species and also between species. *Lestrimellita limão* of South and Central America seems to specialize in robbing nests of a few species of its relative, *Trigona,* and may even destroy the occupants and take over the nest. Its workers have regressed pollen-collecting apparatus and seldom have been directly observed on flowers.

A remarkable example of vestigial behavior is afforded by the subterranean nests of *Apicotermes arquieri,* in which nonfunctional plugged pores and circular galleries occur in the nest walls (Schmidt, 1955a). The related *A. occultus* builds nests with no indications of external pores, but vestigial circular galleries are still present. A related but more primitive species, *A. rimulifex,* builds irregular simple ventilation pores in the nest wall that indicate an ancestral type of nest (Desneux, 1956a). This regressive evolution of behavior seems to be correlated with the more porous dry soils of savannas and desert edges.

The convergent evolution of functional analogies in separate phylogenetic branches is indicative of guidance by means of natural selection. Analogous similarity without a possibility of a common ancestor that possessed the character is suggestive of fundamental differences in the genetic basis of the character. Homology, in contrast, is indicative of a shared genetic identity in portions of the gene system. A number of behavioral characters may be considered convergent. Social behavior in the strict sense arose independently in the termites, wasps, bees, and ants. Colony founding by swarming is found in tropical and subtropical wasps in separate subfamilies and in the species of different families of bees living in the tropics.

A striking case of convergence of behavior is seen in the nests of two species of termites belonging to different subfamilies, *Constrictotermes cavifrons* and *Procubitermes niapuensis* (Hingston, 1932; Emerson, 1938; Allee, et al., 1949). Each species constructs a nest on the side of a tree in the rain forest, each builds a series of chevron-shaped ridges above the nest proper on the tree trunk. In each case the ridges angle downward and laterally from the central axis. Each series of ridges functions to divert the water descending the tree away from the nest. As might be expected for analogous behavior, there are a number of details that differ. The rain-shedding ridges of *Procubitermes* are hollow tubes, while the ridges of *Constrictotermes* are solid, more irregular, sharper, and with a slightly gutter-like shape. Another species of *Procubitermes* (*P. undulans*) of the Ituri and Congo forests has a presumably more primitive arrangement of rain-shedding ridges than its congener and probably is an illustration of an earlier evolutionary stage of this homologous behavior pattern (Emerson, 1949).

The fungus-growing behavior of the New World Attini and of the Old World Macrotermitinae is possibly the best known and studied convergent behavior among social insects. Homologous evolutionary sequences among related genera are detectable in the ants and in the termites. And, as would be expected in analogous functions, there is much difference in the types of gardens, the methods of preparing the substrate for mycelial growth, and the care and harvesting of the crops in two such widely divergent insect orders.

Social Homeostasis

Homeostasis is a term coined by the physiologist, Cannon (1932, 1941), and may be defined as self-regulation of optimal conditions of existence (Emerson, 1954, 1956b). "Self" refers to the unit system at any level of integration. "Regulation" involves feedback mechanisms, whether biochemical, biophysical, neurological, or behavioristic, that operate to decrease excess and to increase deficiencies, with a relative stabilization in a comparatively narrow range of fluctuation around an optimum. "Existence" is the development, maintenance, and reproduction of systems at any level. Homeostasis has survival value, so that natural selection guides evolution in the direction of improved homeostasis. The optimum for any given factor may be measured under controlled conditions by functional activity, toleration, and survival. However, optima are not easily measured, and many factors are subtle and have not been investigated. The optimum for one factor is not necessarily the optimum for another, so competitive balance, dominance, and compromise emerge. Regressive evolution of one part may be correlated with the inclusion of the unit in a higher level system. We may find that increased homeostasis of a supraorganism involves regression of former functions in the included lower level unit. For example, one caste of a social insect may have decreased homeostasis of the individual as social homeostasis increases. One species may evolve toward a reduction in certain homeostatic functions as it becomes incorporated into a community system in which there is an increase of ecological homeostasis. Homeostasis often is the maintenance of unbalance, disequilibrium, and asymmetry, as well as the reverse. Functions may be correlated with balance, but they may also be correlated with unbalance, so that "stasis" does not necessarily mean equilibrium. Homeostasis must be considered dynamic and functional. If different incompatible optima are in competition, the system may reduce the degree of conflict by spatial separation in organismic structural patterns, or by temporal separation in periodic functions. The attainment of optimal conditions for all necessities both internal and external is obviously impossible in complex living systems, so perfection of homeostasis is unobtainable in the past, present, or future (see Brian, 1956). Improvement is attainable and seems to be a major direction of evolution, but the realized homeostasis does not eliminate all conflict, competition, death, and extinction. As a matter of fact, there are indications that competition and death are functional at optimal values and are themselves often homeostatically controlled. During evolutionary time adequate homeostatic regulation within a species in a given environment may not be adequate in a changing environment. If the change is slow, the species may keep abreast by evolving new adjustments (Wright, 1932). If the ecological change is rapid, the evolutionary adjustment may be insufficient to keep pace, and the species may become extinct. This is a very brief and oversimplified statement of the principle of homeostasis as it influences evolutionary processes and is influenced by these processes. Obviously the evolution of behavior fits into the concept, and this aspect is particularly well illustrated by the behavior of the social insects, as seen by the following examples.

Brian and Brian (1948) show that bumblebees (*Bombus agrorum*) regulate the time and quantity of brood by an association of egg laying with pupal stages. The authors conclude that there is a fairly sensitive method of regulating the time of appearance and quantity of brood to the capacity of workers to tend it, and that this has evolved in bumblebees.

The well-known "fanning" actions of honeybees and bumblebees at the entrance to their nest is indicative of a control of ventilation and temperature.

Specializations of the reproductive castes, concentrations of eggs and young in "nurseries," and the regulation of fecundity and interindividual feeding are indicative of social homeostasis. These regulatory mechanisms may produce periodicities in most of the social Hymenoptera (Brian, 1957). The slaughter of the drones in the Apidae and Meliponidae is a remarkable behavior regulation controlling excess portions of the colony population and shows that death may be both beneficial and homeostatic.

The intricate social-stimulative effects of trophallactic agents are illustrated by the organization and periodicity of army ant behavior. These have been carefully studied in the field and laboratory by Schneirla (1933, 1938, 1944, 1945, 1947, 1949) and by Schneirla, Brown, and Brown (1954). The last-named authors present an analysis of the microclimatic factors in the environment and in the bivouacs of army ants (*Eciton*) and show that the bivouacs regulate humidity and temperature in such a way as to lessen the risks of the raiding segments of the population. Different species of *Eciton* vary in their bivouac sites. Some are regularly subterranean while others are commonly found in elevated, exposed places. In the species studied, *E. burchelli* had a much greater tendency to nest in arboreal situations than did *E. hamatum*. One may postulate that the mechanisms for homeostatic control of the microclimate have diverged somewhat in the evolution of species within this genus, and produce adjustments to general ecological conditions. Ecological adaptation and behavioral adaptation are correlated in this evolution. The initial factors are difficult to separate in ants living under different ecological conditions, but if the species live together in the same habitat the evolution of the behavior mechanisms may assist in the alleviation of competition between them.

Mounds of *Formica ulkei* modify the microclimate by increasing the mound temperatures and the range of temperatures (G. M. Scherba, in press). Moisture content of the mound is significantly lower than that in the adjacent soil. The distribution of the population within the mound is contagious. The depth of the maximum adult and pupal densities fluctuates in a cyclical fashion through the diel rhythm, and there is evidence that this fluctuation primarily occurs in response to regular temperature changes within the mound. The mounds of this ant therefore may present a range that enables the ants to select optima for variable functions during development and social activities.

Regulation of the food supply is attained by the fungus-growing Attini among the myrmecine ants. Weber (1956) shows that *Trachymyrmex septentrionalis* maintain a pure culture of their fungus despite continuous contamination. Possibly antibiotic and growth-promoting factors are present in the feces and saliva of the workers.

A remarkable homeostatic control over the production and regulation of reproductives has been demonstrated by Lüscher (1952a, 1952b, 1953) in experimental colonies of the termite *Kalotermes flavicollis*.

Termite nests regulate optimal conditions of the individual and social environment (Emerson, 1956a). Nest construction and nest position regulate predation, and this protection is augmented by the soldier caste. Sanitation of the nest is indicative of behavioral homeostasis, and a number of termite species are known that remove their excrement and bury or eat their dead. Regulation of the food supply is shown by the concentration of gathered

leaves or plant parts in storage chambers. Fungus-growing agricultural behavior may be considered a regulation of food supply
that is characteristic of the subfamily of the Macrotermitinae.
Nests that prevent flooding by rainwater have already been discussed. Many nests regulate atmospheric humidity within the nest
chambers (Fyfe and Gay, 1938). Termites as a rule (there are some
exceptions) die rapidly in dry air. Their normally moist chambers
in wood, soil, or constructed nests have probably been a factor in
the regressive evolution of former cuticular protections against
evaporation. Experiments indicate that many species of termites
will move toward moist air when presented with alternatives in
a humidity gradient (Emerson, 1956a). Termitophiles in the nests
also exhibit equivalent orientation to humidity. Differential tolera-
ation to drying has been demonstrated by Strickland (1950). Those
species tested that build definitive nests also orient to high humidities, and it is indicated that the inhabited nest structures
maintain an optimum high humidity. Such regulation through
nest-building behavior allows certain species to inhabit ecological
niches from which they would otherwise be eliminated.

Temperature does not seem to be homeostatic in most termite
nests, but the striking orientation of the nests of *Amitermes meridionalis* in tropical Australia does suggest temperature regulation.
Temperature has an effect upon humidity, so possibly temperature
regulation has evolved through selection toward a homeostasis of
humidity within the nest. Mound nests and arboreal nests probably
have a greater variation in their internal temperature and humidity than the soil at moderate depths below the surface, and
many termites nest in subterranean habitats, coming to the surface
only for foraging and for their colonizing flight. Variations in soil
water must be great in some localities, and mounds probably provide a vertical gradient that allows the population to move up and
down over short distances toward more optimal conditions. By
such behavior they maintain ecological position in a relatively
uniform or narrowly fluctuating environment and ease the problems of maintaining internal individual homeostasis. Social homeostasis of gaseous content of the nest seems to be accomplished by
numerous species of termites. Examples are afforded by the subterranean nests of *Apicotermes,* the mound nests of many species,
and the ventilation "chimneys" of certain species, particularly
among the Macrotermitinae (Lüscher, 1955). Arboreal nests are

typical for some species, notably for a majority of the species of *Nasutitermes,* and the necessity for ventilation may be a partial explanation for their location and the consistency of the walls.

Maintenance of physiological homeostasis in the individual organism may necessitate regeneration of lost parts. Regenerative behavior in the replacement of nests or nest parts maintains social homeostasis (Hingston, 1932; Emerson, 1938, 1956a).

Intraspecific combat and competition are sometimes considered as antisocial (Schneirla, 1946). Although cooperative reactions occur in physiological and behavior systems both within the species and between species, the existence of conflict and combat convinces many biologists and sociologists that there is no universal trend toward cooperation. In the minds of some scientists homeostasis is conceived as resting upon cooperative interactions, and any manifestation of a lack of cooperation is considered to be a refutation of the principle of homeostasis as constituting a general trend in evolution (see Nicholson, 1933). I shall here attempt to reconcile these points of view and to include both conflict and cooperation under a common theory (see Birch, 1957).

Populations that have not evolved together might reach equilibrium after being placed together, but in evolutionary time this equilibrium is almost certain to be influenced by the reciprocal selection pressures set up by the interacting populations. Competition is a very important aspect of natural selection (Park, 1954) and results in much progressive evolution and balanced adjustment. It influences the evolution of improved homeostasis, whether the unit be an individual organism, an intraspecies group, or an interspecies system.

Competition, exploitation, interference, conflict, elimination, and inhibition may be assumed to occur between members of the same caste, between castes in the same colony, between colonies of the same species, and between species with various degrees of phylogenetic relationship and habitat association. Extrinsic and intrinsic influences affect every type of organization. There may be a combination of internal and external factors that attracts and repels individuals and populations with varying intensities and at various times. If repellence dominates, noncontagious distribution results (Emerson, 1956a). If attraction dominates, aggregations and group systems emerge. Periodicities of both the attractive stimuli and the repellent stimuli may be expected. Sexual attraction, responses to food, and responses to rhythms in the environment afford many examples. Temporary dominance of one factor over another independent factor may also be expected under particular physiological and ecological conditions. For example, termites will come into an unfavorable environment to rescue their young when the nest has been broken, but will not appear in the same physical environment if no young are in need of assistance. They will also carry certain termitophiles (*Spirachtha*) into shelters in the same manner as they protect their own nymphs.

Combat between members of the same colony of social insects has been observed rather rarely. Pardi (1948) reports a social hierarchy among female wasps in the polygynous colonies of *Polistes gallicus*, with individual dominance and subordination associated with reproductive capacity and ovarian growth. Elimination of queens by other queens has been observed among various Hymenoptera. In the parasitic ants, the host queen may be killed by her own worker offspring some time after the invasion of the parasitic queen. Combat to the death between supplementary queens of termites has been witnessed in observational colonies (Emerson, 1933b). Although by far the majority of termite nests contain a single royal pair, numerous instances of multiple kings and queens, both primary and supplementary, are known for termites, with obvious tolerance for each other over long periods of time. Experimental production and elimination of supplementary reproductives in colonies of *Kalotermes flavicollis* have been observed and analysed (Lüscher, 1952a, 1952b, 1953).

Talbot (1943) made a study of populations of a single species of ant, *Prenolepis imparis*. She noted two types of foraging activity: (1) exploring, and (2) trailing, after odor trails to large amounts of food were established. No colony maintained a foraging ground territory which it defended against invasion from other colonies, and each piece of ground might be crossed by ants of several different colonies. However, bits of fruit were strictly "private property" for a colony and were defended with fighting if necessary (also see Brian, 1955).

Termites from different colonies usually fight each other when placed together experimentally. The loser is generally killed and later may be buried in excrementous droplets by numerous workers. Colony intolerance and even species intolerance may be experimentally overcome by fusing the colony odors by means of anesthetics or refrigeration and allowing the once antagonistic individuals to recover from immobilization together (Dropkin, 1946). Both colony and species intolerance produced by changeable odors has been described for social wasps, bees, ants, termites and termitophilous beetles.

Interspecies exploitation is strikingly dramatic in robber bees, thief ants, social parasites, and the slave raids of the sanguinary ants (Talbot and Kennedy, 1940; Allee et al., 1949). In these instances there is little question that the adjustment between the species has evolved through natural selection. In general one may expect that the attractions of the nest, the attractions of food, and the repellents in the form of other colonies of the same or different species occupying similar ecological niches may limit the colony territories. There is no doubt that the presence of other colonies of the same species sets up competition that limits the territory of a given colony. There would also seem to be little doubt that social efficiency is associated with optimal colony size, so that competition not only is inevitable but may be assumed to be beneficial at optimal values (Brian, 1953, 1957).

Conflict and competition as well as exploitation of one part by another seem to be present always to a greater or lesser degree within any organism or population system. Behavior is always involved among the social insects. Even without adequate quantitative data, it seems to the author that there is more competition and conflict as one moves from the simpler systems to the more complex and inclusive systems. I should judge there is less unbalanced competition within the cell than between cells, less within an individual organism than between the sexes and siblings, less within the simple family than in the complex family or interfamily system, less within the colony or social unit than between colonies, less between colonies of the same species than between species. There are probably exceptions to such a sequential order, as may be illustrated by the interspecies relations of the myrmecophiles and termitophiles with their hosts or the mutualistic interdependence between cellulose-eating termites and their intestinal cellulose-digesting flagellate symbiotes.

In all of these cases of conflict and competition there is likely to be survival value for defensive adaptations, limited aggression, toleration, and mutualism. When ecologically equivalent species come in contact with each other for the first time through introduc-

tion or experiment, either the competitive endemic species eliminates the other (usual) or it is eliminated (less usual) (Park, 1954).
Species that have lived and evolved together over long evolutionary
periods tend to become more tolerant and evolve methods of decreasing the competition by either spatial, ecological, or periodic
separation (Brian, 1955). The explanation of this trend is to be
found in the fact that conflict and competition are also often associated with mutual interdependence, so that a reduced tendency
to eliminate the competitor may have survival value.

CONCLUSIONS

1. The intraspecies group system is a prime unit in evolution,
without excluding the primacy of other units such as the individual
organism or the cell.

2. The group is often the unit of natural selection leading to
adaptive evolution.

3. The group unit probably exhibits genetic variability by
means of mutation and sexual recombination, and also establishes
complicated genetic patterns by means of reproductive isolation
and selection.

4. Like the organism, the group unit exhibits analogous division
of labor, integration, development, growth, reproduction, homeostasis, ecological orientation, and adjustment. The term supraorganism seems amply justified for the insect society and may also
be applied to other group systems.

5. Behavior is likely to be emphasized in group integration, division of labor, and social homeostasis, as contrasted to the biophysical, biochemical, and physiological mechanisms of proto-
plasmically continuous or contiguous individual organisms.

6. Behavior rests upon physiology, development, and genetics
in varying degrees. The genetic component may be relatively direct in the case of instinct, or indirect through potentials of reaction in associational learning, plastic response, imprinting,
conditioning, reasoning, and intelligence.

7. Genetic behavior is subject to all of the evolutionary processes known for genetic systems in general together with their
physiological and morphological aspects.

8. Behavior mechanisms are predominantly analogous to observed physiological and structural adaptations, but the adaptive

interrelations are so correlated that it must be assumed that the system as a whole in its functional activities forms a web of interactions with many feedbacks.

9. Because of many feedbacks in homeostatic mechanisms, cause and effect are not necessarily linear in the organism or in evolutionary processes. It is incorrect to state that any one attribute of the organism is more basic than another in the functional unit during development or evolution. In other words, the biochemistry of the gene is as much determined by the ultimate functional effects as it determines the subsequent functions. We are obviously dealing with a multidimensional system which incorporates ontogenetic and phylogenetic time with its spatial dimensions.

10. Behavior is as much a part of homeostatic regulation of optimal conditions of existence as is any other aspect of the organism, and social homeostasis is as important a directional trend in the evolution of social systems as is physiological homeostasis of the individual organism.

11. Social insects provide the best proof of adaptive evolution without the possibility of the inheritance of acquired somatic and behavior characters in the Lamarckian sense.

12. Social behavior in the strict sense is found only among social insects and humans. A society is defined as a group that manifests systematic division of labor among adults of the same sex. Most social behavior of insects is genetically determined, while most social behavior of man is culturally determined through symbolic communication (Emerson, 1954). Although this great difference in the basic mechanisms of social evolution lies at the root of the uniqueness of man as contrasted to the social insects, symbols have many functional attributes of genes. Variation, isolation, and selection are operative factors in the evolution of both genetic and symbolic systems. Many significant functional analogues occur in the evolutionary processes and manifestations of the social insects and social man. A careful comparison of the differences and similarities of social evolution may be expected to give us some basic understanding of societies in general.

REFERENCES

(Star indicates general background references.)

*ALLEE, W. C., EMERSON, A. E., PARK, O., PARK, T., and SCHMIDT, K. P. 1949. Principles of animal ecology. Philadelphia, W. B. Saunders.

BIRCH, L. C. 1957. The meanings of competition. Amer. Nat., *91*, 5–18.

BODENHEIMER, F. S. 1937. Population problems of social insects. Biol Rev., *12*, 393–430.

*BONNER, J. T. 1955. Cells and societies. Princeton, Princeton Univ. Press.

BRIAN, M. V. 1953. Brood-rearing in relation to worker number in the ant *Myrmica*. Physiol. Zool., *26*, 355–66.

BRIAN, M. V. 1955. Food collection by a Scottish ant community. J. Anim. Ecol., *24*, 336–51.

BRIAN, M. V. 1956. Group form and causes of working inefficiency in the ant *Myrmica rubra* L. Ibid., *29*, 173–94.

BRIAN, M. V. 1957. Food distribution and larval size in cultures of the ant *Myrmica rubra* L. Physiol. Comp. Oecol., *4*, 331–45.

BRIAN, M. V., and BRIAN, A. D. 1948. Regulation of oviposition in social Hymenoptera. Nature, *161*, 854.

BROWN, W. L. 1954. Remarks on the internal phylogeny and subfamily classification of the family Formicidae. Insectes sociaux, *1*, 21–31.

BROWN, W. L. 1955. The first social parasite in the ant tribe Dacetini. Ibid., *2*, 181–6.

*CANNON, W. B. 1932. The wisdom of the body. New York, W. W. Norton.

*CANNON, W. B. 1941. The body physiologic and the body politic. Science, *93*, 1–10.

CREIGHTON, W. S. 1950. The ants of North America. Bull. Mus. Comp. Zool., *104*, 1–585.

DESNEUX, J. 1948. Les nidifications souterraines des *Apicotermes*. Termites de l'Afrique tropicale. Rev. zool. bot. Afr., *41*, 1–54.

DESNEUX, J. 1953. Les constructions hypogées des *Apicotermes*. Termites de l'Afrique tropicale. Etude descriptive et essai de phylogénie. Ann. Mus. Roy. Congo Belge. Sci. Zool., Série 8, *17*, 1–98.

DESNEUX, J. 1956a. Le nid d'*Apicotermes rimulifex* Emerson. Rev. zool. bot. Afr., *53*, 92–7.

DESNEUX, J. 1956b. Structures "atypiques" dans les nidifications souterraines d'*Apicotermes lamani* Sj. mises en évidence par la radiographie. Insectes sociaux, *3*, 277–81.

DROPKIN, V. H. 1946. The use of mixed colonies of termites in the study of host-symbiont relations. J. Parasitol., *32*, 247–51.

EMERSON, A. E. 1929. Communication among termites. Trans. 4th Int. Congr. Entomol., *2*, 722–7.

EMERSON, A. E. 1933a. The mechanism of tandem behavior following the colonizing flight in termites. Anat. Rec., *57*, Suppl., 61–2 (abstract).

EMERSON, A. E. 1933b. Conditioned behavior among termites. Psyche, *40*, 125–9.

EMERSON, A. E. 1938. Termite nests—a study of the phylogeny of behavior. Ecol. Monogr., *8*, 247–84.

EMERSON, A. E. 1939. Social coordination and the superorganism. Amer. Midland Nat., *21*, 182–209.

EMERSON, A. E. 1945. The neotropical genus *Syntermes*. Bull. Amer. Mus. Nat. Hist., *83*, 427–72.

EMERSON, A. E. 1949. Termite studies in the Belgian Congo. Deux. rapport ann. Inst. Recher. Sci. Afr. Centr., pp. 149–60.

EMERSON, A. E. 1952. The supraorganismic aspects of the society. In Structure et physiologie des sociétés animales. Colloq. int. Centre Nat. Recher. Sci., No. 34, pp. 333–54.

EMERSON, A. E. 1954. Dynamic homeostasis: a unifying principle in organic, social, and ethical evolution. Sci. Month., *78*, 67–85.

EMERSON, A. E. 1955. Geographical origins and dispersions of termite genera. Fieldiana: Zool., *37*, 465–521.

EMERSON, A. E. 1956a. Regenerative behavior and social homeostasis of termites. Ecology, *37*, 248–58.

EMERSON, A. E. 1956b. Ethospecies, ethotypes, taxonomy, and evolution of *Apicotermes* and *Allognathotermes*. Amer. Mus. Novitates, No. 1771, pp. 1–31.

*FRISCH, K. VON. 1955a. The dancing bees. New York, Harcourt, Brace.

FRISCH, K. VON. 1955b. Beobachtungen und Versuche M. Lindauers an indischen Bienen. Bayer. Akad. Wiss., Math.-Nat. Klasse Sonderdr., *10* (Sitzungsb., 1955), 209–16.

FYFE, R. V., and GAY, F. J. 1938. The humidity of the atmosphere and the moisture conditions within mounds of *Eutermes exitiosus* Hill. Pamphl. Australian Council Sci. Ind. Res., *82*, 1–22.

GRASSÉ, P. -P., and NOIROT, C. 1948. Sur le nid et la biologie du *Sphaerotermes sphaerothorax* (Sjöstedt). Ann. sci. nat. zool., *10*, 149–66.

GRASSÉ, P. -P., and NOIROT, C. 1954. *Apicotermes arquieri:* ses constructions, sa biologie. Ibid., *16*, 345–88.

HASKINS, C. P., and ENZMANN, E. V. 1938. Studies of certain sociological and physiological features in the Formicidae. Ann. N. Y. Acad. Sci., *37*, 97–162.

HASKINS, C. P., and HASKINS, E. F. 1950. Notes on the biology and social behavior of the archaic ponerine ants of the genera *Myrmecia* and *Promyrmecia*. Ann. Entomol. Soc. Amer., *43*, 461–91.

HASKINS, C. P., and HASKINS, E. F. 1951. Note on the method of colony foundation of the ponerine ant *Amblyopone australis* Erickson. Amer. Midland Nat., *45*, 432–45.

HASKINS, C. P., and HASKINS, E. F. 1955. The pattern of colony foundation in the archaic ant *Myrmecia regularis*. Insectes sociaux, *2*, 115–26.

HASKINS, C. P., and WHELDON, R. M. 1954. Note on the exchange of ingluvial food in the genus *Myrmecia*. Ibid., *1*, 33–7.

HINGSTON, R. W. G. 1932. A naturalist in the Guiana forest. New York, Longmans, Green.

KERR, W. E. 1948. Estudos sôbre o gênero *Melipona*. Anais Escola Super. Agr. Luiz de Queiroz, *5*, 181–276.

KERR, W. E. 1950a. Evolution of the mechanism of caste determination in the genus *Melipona*. Evolution, *4*, 7–13.

KERR, W. E. 1950b. Genetic determination of castes in the genus *Melipona*. Genetics, *35*, 143–52.

LE MASNE, G. 1953. Observations sur les relations entre le couvain et les adultes chez les fourmis. Ann. Sci. Nat. Zool., *15*, 1–56.

LÜSCHER, M. 1952a. Die Produktion und Elimination von Ersatzgeschlechtstieren bei der Termite *Kalotermes flavicollis* Fabr. Z. f. vergl. Physiol., *34*, 123–41.

LÜSCHER, M. 1952b. New evidence for an ectohormonal control of caste determination in termites. Trans. 9th Int. Congr. Entomol., *1*, 289–94.

LÜSCHER, M. 1953. The termite and the cell. Sci. Amer., *188*, 74–8.

LÜSCHER, M. 1955. Der Sauerstoffverbrauch bei Termiten und die Ventilation des Nestes bei *Macrotermes natalensis* (Haviland). Acta Tropica, *12*, 289–307.

*MICHENER, C. D. 1953. Problems in the development of social behavior and communication among insects. Trans. Kansas Acad. Sci., *56*, 1–15.

*MICHENER, C. D., and MICHENER, MARY H. 1951. American social insects. New York, Van Nostrand.

NICHOLSON, A. J. 1933. The balance of animal populations. J. Anim. Ecol., *2*, 132–78.

NOIROT, C. 1954. Le polymorphisme des termites supérieurs. Ann. biol., *30*, 461–74.

PARDI, L. 1948. Dominance order in

Polistes wasps. Physiol. Zool., *21*, 1–13.

PARK, T. 1954. Experimental studies of interspecies competition. II. Temperature, humidity, and competition in two species of Tribolium. Ibid., *27*, 177–238.

REINIG, W. F. 1935. On the variation of *Bombus lapidarius* L. and its cuckoo, *Psithyrus rupestris* Fabr., with notes on mimic similarity. J. Genetics, *30*, 321–56.

SCHERBA, G. M. Microclimate modification in ant mounds. Amer. Midland Nat. In press.

SCHMIDT, R. S. 1955a. The evolution of nest-building behavior in *Apicotermes* (Isoptera). Evolution, *9*, 157–81.

SCHMIDT, R. S. 1955b. Termite (*Apicotermes*) nests—important ethological material. Behaviour, *8*, 344–56.

SCHMIDT, R. S. 1958. The nest of *Apicotermes trägårdhi* (Isoptera). New evidence on the evolution of nest-building. Behaviour, *12*, 76–94.

SCHNEIRLA, T. C. 1929. Learning and orientation in ants studied by means of the maze method. Comp. Psychol. Monogr., *6* (4), 1–143.

SCHNEIRLA, T. C. 1933. Studies on army ants in Panama. J. Comp. Psychol., *15*, 267–301.

SCHNEIRLA, T. C. 1938. A theory of army-ant behavior based upon the analysis of activities in a representative species. Ibid., *25*, 51–90.

SCHNEIRLA, T. C. 1944. The reproductive functions of the army-ant queen as pace makers of the group behavior pattern. J. N. Y. Entomol. Soc., *52*, 153–92.

SCHNEIRLA, T. C. 1945. The army-ant behavior pattern: nomad-statary relation in the swarmers and the problem of migration. Biol. Bull., *88*, 166–93.

SCHNEIRLA, T. C. 1946. Problems in the biopsychology of social organization. J. Abnorm. Soc. Psychol., *41*, 385–402.

SCHNEIRLA, T. C. 1947. A study of army-ant life and behavior under dry season conditions with reference to reproductive functions. Amer. Mus. Novitates, No. 1336, pp. 1–20.

SCHNEIRLA, T. C. 1949. Army-ant life and behavior under dry-season conditions. 3. The course of reproduction and colony behavior. Bull. Amer. Mus. Nat. Hist., *94*, 1–81.

SCHNEIRLA, T. C., BROWN, R. Z., and BROWN, F. C. 1954. The bivouac or temporary nest as an adaptive factor in certain terrestrial species of army ants. Ecol. Monogr., *24*, 269–96.

SCHWARZ, H. F. 1948. Stingless bees (Meliponidae) of the western hemisphere. Bull. Amer. Mus. Nat. Hist., *90*, 1–546.

SEEVERS, CHARLES. 1957. A monograph on the termitophilous staphylinidae (Coleoptera). Fieldiana, *40*, 1–334.

STRICKLAND, MARGARET. 1950. Differences in toleration of drying between species of termites (*Reticulitermes*). Ecology, *31*, 373–85.

TALBOT, MARY. 1943. Studies of the ant *Prenolepis imparis* Say. Ibid., *24*, 31–44.

TALBOT, MARY, and KENNEDY, C. H. 1940. The slave-making ant, *Formica sanguinea subintegra* Emery, its raids, nuptial flights and nest structure. Ann. Entomol. Soc. Amer., *33*, 560–77.

TAYLOR, L. H. 1939. Observations on social parasitism in the genus *Vespula* Thomson. Ibid., *32*, 304–15.

WADDINGTON, C. H. 1953. The evolution of adaptations. Endeavour, *12*, 134–9.

WADDINGTON, C. H. 1956. Genetic assimilation of the *Bithorax* phenotype. Evolution, *10*, 1–13.

WEBER, N. A. 1956. Fungus-growing ants and their fungi: *Trachymyrmex septentrionalis*. Ecology, *37*, 150–61.

WEISMANN, A. 1893. The all-sufficiency of natural selection. Contemp. Rev., *64*, 309–38, 596–610.

WEYRAUCH, W. 1937. Zur Systematik und Biologie der Kuckuckswespen *Pseudovespa, Pseudovespula*, und *Pseudopolistes*. Zool. Jahrb. Abt. Systematik, Ökol. u. Geogr., *70*, 243–90.

*WHEELER, W. M. 1910. Ants—their structure, development and behavior. New York, Columbia Univ. Press.

WHEELER, W. M. 1911. The ant colony as an organism. J. Morphol., *22*, 307–25.

WHEELER, W. M. 1921. Observations on army ants in British Guiana. Proc. Amer. Acad. Arts and Sci., *56*, 291–328.

*WHEELER, W. M. 1928. The social insects—their origin and evolution. New York, Harcourt, Brace.

WHEELER, W. M. 1933. Colony-founding among ants. Cambridge, Harvard Univ. Press.

WHEELER, W. M. 1936. Ecological relations of ponerine and other ants to termites. Proc. Amer. Acad. Arts and Sci., *71*, 159–243.

WHITE, F. N., and SMITH, H. M. 1956. Some basic concepts pertaining to the Baldwin effect. Turtox News, *34*, 51–3, 66–8.

WILSON, E. O. 1953. The origin and evolution of polymorphism in ants. Quart. Rev. Biol., *28*, 136–57.

WRIGHT, S. 1932. Roles of mutation, inbreeding, crossbreeding and selection in evolution. Proc. 6th Int. Congr. Genetics, *1*, 356–66.

PART FOUR

The Place of Behavior in the Study of Evolution

PRECEDING CHAPTERS have been extensively concerned with the pertinence of evolution to the study of behavior. The strong but artificial barrier that tradition and university organization have erected between psychology and biology needs to be crossed not only in that but also in the opposite direction. It is true that zoologists have long been concerned with the fact that their objects of study do have behaviors. Nevertheless, it has certainly not been sufficiently recognized that comparative psychology is also a branch of zoology and that behavior is an element, essential but often omitted, in the understanding of biological evolution. The next three chapters demonstrate that this is true, with examples in three distinct fields of evolutionary studies.

The existence of species-specific behavior, discussed from a different point of view in Chapter 12, has the corollary that behavior traits may be specific characters in a taxonomic sense. Chapter 16 not only demonstrates the validity and usefulness of that observation but also shows that the whole subject of systematics, with its phylogenetic basis, is illumined when behavior is included with due emphasis.

One of the most crucial elements in the whole evolutionary process is speciation, and the various isolating mechanisms are here of major importance because without them species of common origin cannot become and remain separate, that is, speciation cannot in fact occur. Isolating mechanisms are extremely varied and many of them are not directly behavioral. In Chapter 17 it is pointed out that there is generally a behavioral element in the rise and maintenance of genetic isolation and that behavioral isolation may become predominant when other isolating mechanisms are weak or lacking. Behavior involved in mating has the dual function of promoting in-group mating and impeding out-group mating, and examples demonstrate how highly diverse and intricate may be the various behavioral elements in the latter, isolating function.

Throughout previous chapters it has always been implicit and frequently explicit that behavior is an outcome of the historical process of evolution and subject to the general principles of biological evolution to no less degree than morphology or physiology. Adaptation, a (but not necessarily *the*) universal product and process of evolution, has usually been thought of in morphological and physiological terms. In planning the conferences and symposium it seemed desirable at this point to spell out the fact that behavior is adaptive to the same degree as morphology or physiology and to exemplify behavioral traits that are plainly and specifically biological adaptations. The author of Chapter 18 did this in the conferences, and has included in the latter part of his revised text two detailed examples that may be taken in this way. However, for good reasons given by him, in his final revision he changed the topic and the approach radically. The chapter is now primarily devoted to the definition of adaptation, to the equation of adaptation with organization, and to clarification of the relationship between organization and natural selection. This skillful theoretical treatment of the central problem of evolutionary biology is invaluable, but it is admittedly here somewhat out of place in the sequential development of the book's whole subject. If the editors had anticipated the breadth of this text as finally received and its general theoretical nature, they might have placed it with, or substituted it for, Chapter 1. After consideration they have nevertheless left it where it is, with the feeling that a summing up and redirection of concepts of adaptation, organization, and natural selection are after all not inappropriate following the preceding range of specific topics.

16

Behavior and Systematics

Ernst Mayr

ONE CAN DISCERN two major interests and approaches within any branch of biology, the functional and the evolutionary. Most of the misunderstandings in biology are due to the fact that workers who are interested in only one of these two approaches are incapable of understanding the other approach and express this in intolerance. The normal approach of functional biology is to concentrate on a single zygote (or parts of one) and to ask "How does it operate?" It investigates the how and why of any change occurring in an individual. It deals with growth, differentiation, regulation, and related subjects. Its chief method of research is the experiment.

The evolutionary approach is quite different. It concentrates on the characteristics of organisms and asks "How did they get that way?" Its method is that of historical research, involving comparison and the correct establishment of sequences. It deals with populations, genetic change, selective values, and biological significance. Observation and the analysis of populations are in general the methods equivalent to the experiment of the functionalist, although the experiment also has its place in evolutionary research.

Physiological and population genetics illustrate these two complementary approaches in genetics. In other branches of biology there are comparative embryology and experimental embryology, comparative physiology and cellular physiology, etc. The study of behavior is no exception. This field may be divided into functional or physiological psychology and evolutionary psychology. Until recently the emphasis has been almost exclusively on the physiological aspects of behavior, on the effects of learning and

experience in a single individual, and on the functional relations
between behavior and the nervous system. If an author was interested in "comparative" psychology he compared the performance
of a rat in one kind of maze with that of the same rat in a different
kind of maze. Until recently, studies in the evolution of behavior,
truly comparative psychology, have been incidental and unsystematic.

The spheres of interest of the workers in these drastically different fields of psychology have in the past overlapped very little.
This is one of the reasons why we are so far from having a classification of behavior elements. When speaking of behavior, one
author has in mind various phenomena of learning and conditioning, a second one an analysis of reflexes, and a third one a
comparative study of species-specific movements employed in
courtship or aggression. All this, and more, is behavior, but until
this rather chaotic assemblage of facts is classified, it is difficult
to use it for correlations, such as are indicated in my subject, behavior and systematics.

THE COMPARATIVE STUDY OF BEHAVIOR

Ideally, a comparative study of behavior should include every
single behavior element in all the species of an entire higher
category of animals. A systematic effort to achieve this is at the
present time impossible for two reasons. As stated, no consistent
classification of behavior elements is available, nor is any group of
animals sufficiently well known to permit tracing individual behavior elements or behavior patterns throughout the entire group.

Work in mammals, for instance, deals almost exclusively with
single species in a genus, or at best a few species in an entire
family. Information on birds is more complete owing to systematic work such as that of Tinbergen and associates on various
species of the gull family, of Heinroth and Lorenz on ducks
(Anatidae), and of Hinde and others on finches. Work in fishes has
concentrated on sticklebacks and cichlids, where good comparative work is available. A great deal of information on insects, particularly social insects, has been published, and our information
is building up rapidly. The same is true for grasshoppers as a
result of the work of Faber and Jacobs. The most complete study
of the behavior of any group of related species is that of Spieth on

Drosophila. Much work has also been done on spiders (Crane), fiddler crabs (Crane), slugs (Gerhardt), and other isolated species and genera. Still, not a single complete or even nearly complete inventory of the behavior patterns in a single family of animals is as yet available.

The backward state of the field of animal behavior is, to a considerable extent, due to the former absence of working hypotheses and heuristic schemes. As a consequence, most former work amounted to little more than the accumulation of raw data. It is the particular merit of Lorenz to have provided a set of hypotheses and theories which have tremendously stimulated research in this area. This is a merit which is not decreased even if some of these hypotheses were oversimplifications, or even entirely wrong. The main body of his concepts has been accepted by most students of animal behavior. There is now hope for a synthesis in this field, such as has been achieved recently in the field of evolution.

The comparative method is even more important for the study of the evolution of behavior than for that of morphological features. The conclusions of comparative anatomy can be tested by the paleontologist, who either substantiates or disproves them with the help of fossil material. There is no such recourse for the ethologist, since behavior does not fossilize.

CLASSIFICATION AND THE PHYLOGENETIC METHOD

Evolutionists have frequently expressed their surprise at how little the classification of better known groups of animals was affected by the establishment and acceptance of the theory of evolution. Actually, there should be no surprise, in view of the taxonomic method and the premises of the theory of evolution. Good classifications are based on a multitude of characters, and there is no other probable way to account for two organisms agreeing in the majority of their characteristics than descent from a common ancestor. The phylogenetic method is largely based on this reasoning.

The extension of the phylogenetic method from purely morphological to behavior characters is based on the same consideration. Students of behavior found again and again that species or genera, which had been placed next to each other on the basis of morphological characteristics also agreed or were similar in their behavior patterns. Again this should not have been a surprise, since these forms share a common heritage and since much behavior, particularly species-specific behavior, has a genetic basis. Following the pioneer efforts of Whitman and Heinroth, increasing attention is being paid by systematists to study of the behavior element.

Similarity in behavior between two species, however, does not necessarily mean common descent. The student of behavior, just like the morphologist, must make the distinction between homology and analogy. The decision between these two alternatives is even more difficult for the ethologist than for the morphologist. When in doubt, the morphologist can always fall back on Owen's criterion of homology, that of position. The impossibility of a strict application of this criterion has induced at least one morphologist to deny the propriety of extending the concept "homology" to behavior elements. This would seem an unnecessarily restricted position in view of the modern biological and evolutionary meaning of the term homology. But what criterion can the behavior student use to establish a homology? His method will be the same as that of the pre-Darwinian taxonomist. He will base his conclusions on the sum total of behavior characters. The more behavior elements are consistent with a postulated phylogeny, the greater the probability that the phylogeny has validity.

If the postulate of the equivalence of morphological and behavior characters is correct, then we should find the same phenomena among behavior characters as among morphological ones. There should be nongenetic variation, intrapopulation variation, geographic variation, species-specific characters, group characters, and polyphyletic characters; there should be primitive and advanced characters, and parallel evolution. To be sure, the available evidence is as yet somewhat scanty, but it indicates that all this variation of morphological characters is indeed paralleled by behavior characters. Some of the evidence for this statement will be presented in subsequent sections of this chapter.

From the point of view of usefulness taxonomic characters range between two extremes: those that are so invariable in a large taxonomic group that they are useless for classification, like the two eyes of vertebrates, and those that are either so variable or so easily affected by the environment that they do not even permit discrimination between closely related taxa, like size or color in some animals. Between these extremes are those characters which are constant within a given taxonomic group (species, genus, family) but vary between it and another taxonomic group. There are many behavior characters that fall into this category.

THE UTILIZATION OF BEHAVIOR CHARACTERISTICS IN CLASSIFICATION

The evidence supplied by morphological characters is sometimes ambiguous, and behavior characteristics supply in such cases valuable supplementary information. Some structural characters are very superficial and lead to evidently artificial groupings. If there is a conflict between the evidence provided by morphological characters and that of behavior the taxonomist is increasingly inclined to give greater weight to the ethological evidence. This has led to a number of recent improvements in the classification of certain groups of animals. The following may be selected from a large number of cases:

1. Three European species of grasshoppers, *Parapleurus alliaceus, Mecostethus grossus,* and *Ailopus thalassinus,* used to be classified with the subfamily Acridinae on the basis of morphological characters. However, Jacobs (1953) found that these three species agree in various behavior characteristics much better with members of the subfamily Oedipodinae, and subsequent analysis has revealed some morphological characteristics which support this shift.

2. The crag martins (*Ptyonoprogne*) have been customarily placed near the bank swallows (*Riparia*) or even been united with this genus. Mayr and Bond (1943) pointed out that the nesting habits of the two kinds of birds differ drastically and suggested that the crag martins be placed near the barn swallow group (*Hirundo*) because, like the latter, they build a nest from pellets of mud while the bank swallow digs tunnels into sand banks. The new taxonomic placement is supported by the voice of these swallows, and by concealed white spots on the tail feathers of crag martins, a sign stimulus also found in *Hirundo* but not in *Riparia.* This case illustrates how even the slightest clue must be utilized to determine relationships in a group as morphologically uniform as are these swallows. The same has been shown by Lack (1956) for the family of swifts.

3. Studies by Heinroth (1911) on the behavior of ducks yielded many results at variance with the accepted classification, which was based on morphological characters. Using this ethological information as well as additional characters (including the color of the downy young), Delacour and Mayr (1945) proposed a radically new classification. In this the diving ducks were split into two groups, fresh-water divers (pochards) and sea ducks; the mergansers (*Mergus*) were associated with the golden-eyes (*Glaucionetta*); the wood duck (*Aix*) removed from the river ducks (Anatini), etc. These findings have been largely confirmed by subsequent investigation. Where modifications were proposed (e.g. separation of the eider group and the merganser group), the reasons again were in part the result of behavior studies.

4. In a recent reclassification of finchlike birds, Tordoff (1954) associated the genus *Fringilla* (chaffinch and relatives) with the New World finches. Andrews and Hinde (1956) were able to show, however, that *Fringilla* agrees in its behavior much better with the Old World finches (Carduelinae), and Mayr (1956) came independently to the same conclusion on the basis of morphological criteria.

In all the stated cases a species, a genus, or a group of genera was shifted from its traditional place in the zoological system to a new position as a result of the study of behavioral criteria. The new arrangement was subsequently confirmed in all these cases by new or re-evaluated morphological evidence.

BEHAVIOR ELEMENTS AS TAXONOMIC CHARACTERS

Taxonomic characters have a dual function (Mayr, Linsley, Usinger, 1953). They have a diagnostic value (permitting the discrimination between similar taxa) and they have an associative value (permitting the grouping together of related taxa). A few examples, listed in the next two sections, will show that behavior characters share these characteristics with other taxonomic characters.

1. Behavior Characters in Taxonomic Discrimination

In a number of recently described cases, a study of behavioral attributes permitted much finer taxonomic discrimination than was possible with the use of morphological criteria. A few examples of this may be mentioned.

The conventionally recognized family of titmice ("Paridae") of the ornithologists has no morphological characters that would permit further subdivision. Yet the nest building habits indicate that the so-called family is a somewhat artificial assemblage of four, perhaps not closely related, groups of birds. The first comprises the true titmice (*Parus* and relatives), which apparently always nest in hollow trees or other cavities. The second group consists of the long-tailed tit (*Aegithalos*), the bush tit (*Psaltriparus*) and related forms, which build an oval nest with lateral entrance in bushes and trees, and which are very social birds; all members of this group have essentially the same habits and call notes. The third group consists of the penduline titmouse (*Remiz*) and its relatives, which build a peculiar retort-shaped nest of plant down worked into feltlike consistency (the nest being similar to that of some flowerpeckers, Dicaeidae); and finally the bearded titmouse (*Panurus*), which builds a stick nest with a lateral entrance and which by this and other habits is unmasked as belonging to the babbler family (Timaliidae). The study of behavior thus not only indicates that these four groups of genera are not very closely related but also provides clues for the proper placing of some of the forms.

The weaver finches (Estrildidae) have always been considered one of the groups of weaver birds (Ploceidae), and some of the older authors did not even separate them in a distinct subfamily. Steiner (1955), however, presents evidence, most of it derived from the study of behavior, to show that these two groups of seed-eating birds of the Old World tropics are not related (Table 16-1).

A study of the method employed by various groups of grasshoppers in cleaning their antennae has confirmed the justification of giving them family status. Gryllidae, Tettigoniidae, and other groups with long antennae clean them with the help of their maxillae. The Acrididae place a leg on one antenna and clean the antenna by pulling it through between leg and substrate. The Tetrigidae (and this is one reason why this group of genera is placed in a separate family) clean the antennae by stroking them with the legs, and the latter in turn by pulling them through the mouth (Jacobs, 1953).

Behavior characters have proven particularly useful in distinguishing morphologically very similar species, the so-called "sibling species." This is true for sibling species in many genera of animals (Mayr, 1948). For example, in a study of the wasp *Am-*

TABLE 16-1

Character	Estrildidae	Ploceidae
1. Nest	A globular structure of small twigs or grass stems with lateral entrance.	Usually a finely woven structure, often hanging from twigs.
2. Pair bond	Tightly knit, often lasting through years.	Either no pair formation, or polygamy, or a pair bond of short duration.
3. Parental care	Nest building, incubation, feeding of young jointly done by both parents.	Most parental duties performed by the female alone.
4. Tail movements	Lateral	Vertical
5. Courtship posture	Stiff upright, with wings pressed against the body. Stereotyped repetition of song strophe.	Excited courtship dances with wing fluttering and occasional display flights. Noisy chatter.
6. Incubation	From first egg on; young hatch with daily intervals.	After completion of clutch; young hatch simultaneously.
7. Tongue, gape, and throat of nestlings	With peculiar species- or genus-specific pigment spots and papillae.	Without markings or papillae.
8. Feeding of nestlings	Take regurgitated food from the crop of the parent.	Normal food begging. Parents feed with the bill.
9. Begging of young	Without wing flutter.	With wing flutter.
10. Nest hygiene	Droppings of young not removed.	Droppings of young removed by parents.

mophila campestris Adriaanse (1947) noticed that some individuals had a behavior pattern which agreed with previous descriptions, others had an aberrant pattern (Table 16-2). The latter turned out to be a new species (*A. adriaansei*). In several other cases behavior gave the first clue to the discovery of sibling species. In the North American fireflies of the genus *Photuris*, Barber (1951) discovered several sibling species on the basis of the number, timing, and coloring of the flash signals. For further examples see Evans (1953).

2. Behavior Characteristics in Taxonomic Grouping

Behavior characters are taxonomically useful not only for the separation of taxa but also in giving clues as to the relationship of taxa of uncertain taxonomic position. The interesting group of desert birds called sand grouse (*Pterocletidae*) has downy young which greatly resemble young grouse (*Tetraonidae*). For this rea-

TABLE 16-2

Ethological Character	campestris	adriaansei
Nest hole filled with material from	a quarry	flown in
Choice of food	sawflies	caterpillars
Sequence of egg laying and provisioning	First egg, then prey	First prey, then egg
Breeding season	Earlier, ending in August	Later, until middle of September.

son, these birds were long considered to be one of the families of gallinaceous birds. Comparative anatomists, however, discovered some structural features allying the sand grouse with the pigeons. A behavior character strongly supports this assignment. While all other birds when drinking water scoop it up with their bills and then let it run down into their stomachs by lifting head and neck, pigeons have a very different drinking behavior. They stick their bills into the water and simply pump it up through the esophagus. The fact that sand grouse are the only other group of birds with this behavior strongly reinforces the anatomical findings which place them next to the pigeons.

Another case is the family of bowerbirds (Ptilinorhynchidae). All the eight genera of this fascinating family are rather different from each other in color, and on the basis of morphological criteria they were variously separated into three to five subfamilies. However, Stresemann (1953) and Marshall (1954) showed that previous classifications were artificial and that on the basis of bower construction the following three subdivisions could be recognized: (a) stagemakers and catbirds (*Ailuroedus, Scenopœëtes,* and perhaps the poorly known *Archboldia*), (b) Maypole bower builders (*Prionodura, Amblyornis*), and (c) avenue bower builders (*Sericulus, Ptilonorhynchus, Chlamydera*). Subdivisions (a) and (b) have white eggs, (c) has colored eggs with a highly characteristic pattern of streaking. The absence of bower building in *Cnemophilus,* always considered a bowerbird, resulted in anatomical investigation which showed that it is actually a bird of paradise.

The relationship of the spider wasps (*Pompilidae*) is another problem solved with the help of ethology. On morphological grounds they are so distinctly set off from other wasps that they are not placed in any of the major families. Yet a study of the behavior traits of this family leaves no doubt that they were derived from bethyloid-scolioid stock and have evolved independently of other stocks of wasps (Evans, 1953). The following combination of behavioral characters defines the family, according to Evans, as clearly as any comparable set of morphological characters: (1) All utilize spiders as larval food. (This occurs, of course, also in some other families, as in the mud daubers). (2) All stock the nest cell with a single paralyzed prey (a habit otherwise exhibited principally by certain Scolioidea and Bethyloidea). (3) In transportation to the nest, the spider is seized in the wasp's mandibles and dragged backward over the ground (some Bethylidae and Ampulicidae share this behavior, some Pompilidae lack it). (4) To close the nest the female wasp pounds down the earth with the apex of the abdomen, or in mud users uses it as a trowel for manipulating the mud (other mud daubers use the mandibles and legs for this purpose). (5) The nest is often prepared after the prey has been taken (as with many Bethylidae).

In all the cited instances, behavior characters have established previously unknown relationships or have confirmed one that had previously been only tentatively established. It is important to stress that there are many behavior traits, such as the method of drinking of pigeons and sand grouse, which are characteristic for entire higher categories (genera, families, orders, or classes). All the available evidence indicates that in their genetic basis as well as in their phylogenetic history such characters are completely equivalent to morphological characters which have a similar taxonomic distribution.

Polyphyletic and Analogous Characters

The systematist must be aware at all times of the shortcomings of the phylogenetic method. Similarities between two kinds of organisms do not always prove common descent. The same behavior may occasionally be acquired independently in unrelated or distantly related forms. A "rattle flight" has evolved not only in some grasshoppers of the subfamily Oedipodinae but also in unrelated genera of Acrididinae (Jacobs, 1953). Small species of gulls (Moynihan, MS) and small herons (Meyerriecks, MS) tend to utilize aerial displays much more commonly than large species, regardless of relationship.

Parallelisms and analogies are particularly common in all types of behavior that are strictly functional, such as food getting or locomotion. Birds which have similar food habits such as those which crack seeds (Emberizidae, Fringillidae, Ploceidae, Estrildidae, Psittacidae, etc.), which prey on mice and other small vertebrates (hawks, owls), which feed like flycatchers (Tyrannidae, Muscicapidae, Todidae, even some Alcedinidae, etc.), which feed on nectar (Trochilidae, Nectariniidae, Meliphagidae), and which have otherwise similar feeding habits, show many similarities mistakenly considered as indicating relationship. The same is true for birds with similar locomotion, as diving (grebes, loons, *Hesperornis*), running (ostrich, emu, rhea, moa), wading (storks, cranes, flamingos, shore birds), hawking (swallows, Artamidae, swifts, nightjars), and so forth.

Perhaps one reason for the slowness of getting behavior characteristics used in systematics is that early authors, from Aristotle to about 1700, did actually use behavior (and associated adaptations) largely as the basis of their systems of classifications. Unfortunately, however, they emphasized food getting and locomotor behavior, which among birds and mammals are, on the whole, of rather low taxonomic value. This disappointment had to be thoroughly forgotten before behavior could again assert its rightful place in systematics.

The Variability of Behavior

The philosophical basis in much of early science was typological, going back to the *eidos* of Plato. This implies that the "typical" aspects of the phenomenon can be described, and that all variation is due to imperfect replicas of the type, all variants being, in the terms of Plato's allegory, "shadows on a cave wall." Such typological thinking is still prevalent in most branches of physics and chemistry and to a considerable extent in functional biology, where the emphasis is on the performance of a single individual. The typological concept has been completely displaced in evolutionary biology by the population concept. The basis of this concept is the fact that in sexually reproducing species no two individuals are genetically alike, and that every population is therefore to be characterized only by statistical parameters such as means, variance, and frequencies. In virtually all major controversies in the history of evolutionary theory, the argument was between a typologist on one side and a student of populations on the other.

Genetic variability is universal, a fact which is significant not only for the student of morphology but also for the student of behavior. It is not only wrong to speak of *the* monkey but even of the behavior of *the* rhesus monkey. The variability of behavior is evident in the study not only of such a genetically plastic species as man but even of forms with very rigid, stereotyped behaviors such as hunting wasps. The Peckhams (1898) give a delightful description of such behavior differences between individuals of the wasp *Ammophila urnaria:* "While one [individual] was beguiled from her hunting by every sorrel blossom she passed, another stuck to her work with indefatigable perseverance. While one stung her caterpillar so carelessly and made her nest in so shiftless a way that her young could only survive through some lucky chance, another devoted herself to these duties not only with conscientious thoroughness, but with an apparent craving after artistic perfection."

Whitman emphasized as early as 1899 "The clocklike regularity and inflexibility of instinct . . . have been greatly exaggerated. They imply nothing more than a low degree of variability under normal conditions . . . close study and experiment with the most machine-like instincts always reveal some degree of adaptability to new conditions." One would like to have more precise information on the nature of this variation: How variable is a given behavior within a single population? How much variation is there from population to population within a species? Finally, one would like to know what portion of the variability is due to non-genetic modification.

"Innate" is of course only the reaction norm, which has a more or less wide range of phenotypic expression. The term innate is meaningful only if it is interpreted epigenetically (rather than preformistically!). This is fully understood by the geneticist who states that a certain flower color or the presence of wing veins are "inherited." The fact that the tendency to hoard is "innate" in the Norway rat is not negated by the fact that certain treatments or experiences may reduce this tendency or obliterate it altogether. Most mammals cannot be induced to hoard no matter what treatment they get. The time has come to stress the existence of genetic differences in behavior, in view of the enormous amount of material the students of various forms of learning have accumulated on nongenetic variation in behavior. Striking individual differences have been described for predator-prey relations, for the reaction of birds to mimicking or to warning colorations, for child care among primates, and for maternal behavior in rats. It is generally agreed by observers that much of this individual difference is not affected by experience but remains essentially constant throughout the entire lifetime of the individual. Such variability is of the greatest interest to the student of evolution, and it is to be hoped that it will receive more attention from the experimental psychologist than it has in the past.

From the evolutionary point of view, there is an interesting conflict between two opposing selective forces. One selects that behavior which is "optimum" for the species and places a premium on uniformity of behavior within the species. The other favors variability as a means of preserving evolutionary plasticity. The most important mechanisms maintaining genetic variability of populations are perhaps geographic variation and gene flow.

The study of morphological characters has shown that the differences between species are often foreshadowed by minor or incipient differences between geographic races. The study of such geographic variation has shed a great deal of light on the origin of taxonomic characters and of new species. Studies of this sort with respect to behavior are at the very beginning. However, there is evidence for geographic variation of song in birds and in grasshoppers. In some species of the bee genus *Halictus* some geographic races are solitary while others are colonial (Michener

1953a). The begging posture of young mockingbirds of the genus *Nesomimus* in the Galapagos Islands is supposed to vary between islands. The difficulty of this field is that most behavior studies are made at a single locality, while geographic variation in behavior can be demonstrated only if the behavior of different, geographically segregated, populations of the same species is investigated.

THE PHYLOGENETIC ORIGIN OF NEW BEHAVIOR

There are at least two different possibilities for the acquisition of a new behavior pattern by a species.

1. The new behavior may have a genetic basis right from the beginning. Since much behavioral variability is correlated with the genetic variability of the species, any factor affecting the gene content of the species may also affect behavior. Some of this may happen as an incidental by-product of genes selected for very different properties. Some of the behavioral variability described above may have this source.

2. A new behavior is at first a nongenetic modification of an existing behavior, as a result of learning, conditioning or habituation, and is replaced (by an unknown process) by genetically controlled behavior.

The study of a new behavior "fashion" might be very revealing. When titmice in England acquired the habit of opening milk bottles, it was observed that the technique was highly variable (Fisher and Hinde, 1949).

Daanje, Hinde, and other ethologists have pointed out that in birds much instinctive behavior seems to have started as intention movements or as displacement activities. Indeed, what is an intention movement or a displacement activity in one species may be incorporated into the courtship repertoire in a related species. The genetics of this process are still completely obscure. This is one of the few evolutionary phenomena where the "Baldwin effect" [1] might have played a role, although the behavior, after its incorporation in the courtship, is in a different neural "environment" than it was previously. How such a change of neural tie-up may be achieved is still quite puzzling.

1. The hypothesis that a nongenetic plasticity of the phenotype facilitates reconstruction of the genotype.

A thorough study of individual variation of behavior is perhaps the most promising approach to the problem of the origin of new behavior. Typological concepts have, in the past, retarded the analysis. There was a search for specific mutations producing specific new behavior patterns. It is much more likely that most kinds of behavior have a multiple genetic basis. This hypothesis is supported by the observation that much of the behavior of interspecific and intergeneric hybrids is somewhat intermediate between that of the two parental species.

Even more important for an understanding of the origin of behavior than a balanced concept of mutation is the proper consideration of natural selection. There is nearly always a dynamic balance between opposing selective forces, as clearly evident, for instance, in the case of the so-called "superoptimal" stimuli. The study of these various selective forces, even though they were already considered by Darwin, is still in its infancy. Indeed the whole subject of the evolutionary origin of new behavior and the remodeling of behavior by natural selection is a much neglected field. The study of entire populations would seem to be the most promising approach toward a solution.

New Behavior and Morphological Structures

[In the days of mutationism a heated controversy went on as to whether behavior precedes structure or vice versa. The mutationists postulated that mutation caused structural changes and that the organism then developed the behavior which best permitted it to cope with the new structure. This purely typological approach was, of course, in error. We now know that the matter is much more complex. When it comes to structure we have to specify whether we are dealing with the structure of the nervous system or the structure of peripheral organs which facilitate or emphasize behavior. On the whole it seems correct to state, as Lorenz has emphasized, that behavior movements often precede phylogenetically the special structures which make these movements particularly conspicuous.] Many birds raise the feathers of the crown or hind neck and bow their heads toward females or competitors. However, only in a limited number of species have long crests developed which emphasize these movements. Likewise in grasshoppers there is a widespread intention movement of flexing the legs prior to jumping. However, only in a limited number of higher groups has this movement been incorporated into courtship and led to a conspicuous coloration of those parts of the legs that are shown or to the development of sound organs which produce sound during the repeated flexing of the legs. Yet it is obvious that without legs this movement could not have been made at all, just as wing displays in birds would be impossible without the prior presence of wings. Likewise all behavior depends on certain structural components in the nervous system. It is now obvious that there is no general answer to the question, "Structure first or behavior first?" Each case must be analyzed separately, to determine all of its components.

TRENDS IN THE EVOLUTION OF BEHAVIOR

The student of evolution is not satisfied merely to prove that evolution has occurred and to reconstruct phylogenies, he also wants to know whether it is possible to make generalizations concerning the course of evolution and to express observed regularities in the form of "rules" or "laws" with wide applicability. It would be very satisfying if this could also be done for the evolution of behavior. "Instincts, like corporeal structures, may be said to have a phylogeny . . . The main reliance in getting at the phyletic history must be comparative study" (Whitman, 1899). Such a study is now being conducted by Tinbergen and his associates for various species of gulls. They find that hostile and courtship movements are essentially homologous in all species of the family but may differ in relative frequency, intensity, and specific form. A movement which is hardly noticeable in one species may be a conspicuous component of the courtship of another species. Similar comparative studies on birds, with similar results, have been carried out by Lorenz (1941, 1952) for ducks (Anatidae), by Meyerriecks (MS) for herons (Ardeidae), by Hinde and associates for finches (Hinde), by Morris and associates for weaver finches (Estrildidae), and by Whitman (1919) himself for pigeons. Along the same line is much work cited in the bibliography, such as that on cichlids (Baerends and Baerends, 1950), on grasshoppers (Jacobs, 1953), on *Drosophila* (Spieth, 1952) and on various hymenopterans (Evans, 1953; Michener, 1953; Iwata, 1942; Lindauer, 1956), to mention merely a few.

Differences between closely related species, particularly in birds and also in *Drosophila,* are often largely quantitative. In other cases completely new components are found. Some of the most clear-cut behavior differences exist among closely related species of wasps. Evans (1953) describes six differences between two similar species of spider wasps of the genus *Anoplius* (Pompilidae). Although their nests are in close proximity they differ in the area where they hunt, in the choice of their prey, in the storing of the prey during nest digging, in the place on the prey where the egg is deposited, in the feeding of the adults, and in wing movements. While *A. semirufus* holds its wings quiet during hunting, *A. spiculatus* vibrates them incessantly. The differences between two sibling species of *Ammophila* have been described above (Table 16-2). One species provides its larvae with caterpillars, the other with sawflies. It is not to be assumed, however, that the choice of food is always necessarily a very plastic character. As has long been known and recently again summarized by Beaumont (1952), whole groups of predatory wasps have specific prey. For instance, *Sphex* hunts grasshoppers, *Ammophila* caterpillars, *Sceliphron* spiders, and *Podium* roaches. Among the tribe Larrini species of *Larra* catch mole crickets while species of *Liris* take true crickets. In another tribe of the subfamily *Larrinae,* namely the Miscophini, there is great variability of prey: *Solierella,* orthoptera and hemiptera; *Miscophus,* spiders; *Lyroda,* crickets; and *Nitela,* aphids. There may be an exceptional species in most of these genera, such as *Ammophila campestris.*

Students of evolution have long indulged in constructing phylogenetic trees, on the basis of morphological characters. Where such constructions are based on fossil material, they tend to have a degree of reality. Where they are merely based on degrees of morphological complexity, they are usually pure speculation and often demonstrably wrong. The wishful hope that no secondary simplification has occurred is not always fulfilled. Attempts to reconstruct behavior phylogenies face the same difficulties as similar attempts of the morphologist. Yet their value is not to be minimized and such reconstructions have a considerable heuristic value. Evans (1953), for instance, has reconstructed the development of behavior in Pompilidae from the simplest to the most complex and derived pattern. Desneux (1952) has traced the probable development of "architectural styles" in the nests of termites

of the African *Apicotermes* group. In the hive bees of the genus
Apis a number of living species permit a reconstruction of the
evolution of the dancing behavior (von Frisch, 1955). In the
courtship behavior of *Drosophila* one can discern certain evolutionary trends (Spieth, 1952), as in the bower building of bower-
birds (Marshall, 1954).

Students of vertebrates and particularly of mammals are aware
of a broad phylogenetic trend toward an increased role of the
higher centers of the brain at the expense of purely instinctive
behavior. No other type of behavior has been studied as intensively as cortex-centered behavior in the primates and in man.
It must not be forgotten, however, that, taking the animal kingdom as a whole, this is a very exceptional type of behavior. Similar
trends are found in some groups of birds (Corvidae, Sturnidae,
Psittacidae), but the enlarged central nervous system of even the
most advanced insects is not in this category.

"An instinct may sometimes run through a whole group of
organisms with little or no modification" (Whitman, 1899). An
analysis of behavior differences among species, genera, and higher
categories, such as was presented in the preceding sections, shows
that in addition to very conservative types of behavior (drinking
in pigeons and sand grouse!), there are some which change rapidly
in evolution. It would be intriguing to find out whether or not
different components of behavior have different rates of evolution.
This indeed seems to be the case.

Among the many components of behavior two stand out: (1) the
ability to react selectively to specific objects and (2) the specific
actions of which the behavior consists. This may be illustrated for
the case of predatory wasps: (1) The object is the spider, the
caterpillar, or the sawfly larva. (2) The action consists of grasping
and stinging. Both (1) and (2) may and do change in the course
of evolution, but it seems that in the majority of cases the action
(the pattern of locomotion) is more stereotyped, less plastic than
the choice of the object. Wasps of many different genera may have
a rather stereotyped stinging movement, but the prey that is stung
may vary from species to species or from genus to genus. In pollen-
collecting bees there may be great similarity in pollen-collecting
equipment and method, yet each species or genus may have a
decided preference for the pollen of specific flowers. This species
specificity of food preference has an obvious selective value since

it will reduce competition for food among species and perhaps permit a denser occupation of the habitat.

In the courtship of birds likewise, the courtship movements seem much more conservative than the "releasers" which elicit them. Many responses to special components of the environment are either learned during the lifetime of the individual or have the earmarks of recent evolutionary acquisition. For instance, the "following response" of young ducks consists of very stereotyped movements; the object of the response may be learned by imprinting.

Since the choice of an object, the reaction to a stimulus, is determined by a perception pattern, it can be suggested that the locomotory components of behavior patterns tend to be more conservative in evolution than the perceptual. This is a working hypothesis which seems worth further testing.

SUMMARY

1. There is a close correlation between behavior patterns and systematics.

2. Some behavior elements are very conservative and thus very useful in the reconstruction of phylogenies.

3. Reaction to stimuli from the environment seems to change more easily on the average than innate movements.

4. There is probably more genetic variability in behavior than is generally recognized.

REFERENCES

ADRIAANSE, A. 1947. *Ammophila campestris* Latr. und *Ammophila adriaansei* Wilcke. Ein Beitrag zur vergleichenden Verhaltensforschung. Behaviour, *1*, 1–34.

ARMSTRONG, E. A. 1947. Bird display and behaviour. New York, Oxford Univ. Press.

ARMSTRONG, E. A. 1950. The nature and function of displacement activities. In Physiological mechanisms in Animal behaviour. Symp. Soc. Exp. Biol., No. 4. Cambridge, Eng., Cambridge Univ. Press, pp. 361–84.

BAERENDS, G. P. 1950. Specializations in organs and movements with a releasing function. In ibid., No. 4, pp. 337–360.

BAERENDS, G. P., and BAERENDS, J. M. 1950. An introduction to the study of the ethology of cichlid fishes. Behaviour, Suppl. 1, vii + 242 pp.

BARBER, H. S. 1951. North American fireflies of the genus *Photuris*. Smithsonian Misc. Coll., *117* (1), 58 pp.

BASTOCK, M., MORRIS, D., and MOYNIHAN, M. 1954. Some comments on conflict and thwarting in animals. Behaviour, *6*, 66–84.

BEAUMONT, J. DE. 1952. La valeur systématique des caractères éthologiques. Rev. suisse zool., *59*, 306–13.

BERLAND, L. 1943. Les classifications des naturalistes confirmées par l'instinct. Rev. sci., *81*, 59–64.

CRANE, J. 1949. Comparative biology of salticid spiders at Rancho Grande, Venezuela. Pt. IV. An analysis of display. Zoologica, *34*, 159–214.

CRANE, J. 1952. A comparative study of innate defensive behavior in Trinidad mantids (Orthoptera: Mantoidea). Ibid., *37*, 259–93.

DAANJE, A. 1951. On locomotory movements in birds and the intention movements derived from them. Behaviour, *3*, 48–98.

DAVIS, D. E. 1942. The phylogeny of social nesting habits in the Crotophaginae. Quart. Rev. Biol., *17*, 115–34.

DELACOUR, J., and MAYR, E. 1945. The family Anatidae. Wilson Bull., *57*, 3–55.

DESNEUX, J. 1952. Les constructions hypogées des *Apicotermes* termites de L'Afrique tropical. Ann. Mus. Roy. Congo Belge. Tervuren, Série in 8° Sciences zoologiques, *17*, 9–120.

DREES, O. 1952. Untersuchungen über die angeborenen Verhaltensweisen bei Spring-Spinnen (Salticidae). Z. f. Tierpsychol., *9*, 169–207.

EVANS, H. E. 1953. Comparative ethology and the systematics of spider wasps. Syst. Zool., *2*, 155–72.

EVANS, H. E. 1955. An ethological study of the digger wasp *Bembecinus neglectus*, with a review of the ethology of the genus. Behaviour, *7*, 287–303.

EVANS, H. E., LIN, C. S., and YOSHIMOTO, C. M. 1953. A biological study of *Anoplius spiculatus autumnalis* (Banks) and its parasite, *Evagetes mohave* (Banks) (Hymenoptera, Pompilidae). J. N. Y. Entomol. Soc., *61*, 61–78.

FABER, A. 1929. Die Lautäusserungen der Orthopteren. I. Z. Morphol. u. Ökol., *13*, 745–803.

FABER, A. 1937. Die Laut- und Bewegungsäusserungen der Oedipodinen. Z. wiss. Zool., *149*, 1–85.

FABER, A. 1953. Laut- und Gebärdensprache bei Insekten. Orthoptera I. Stuttgart, Ges. Freunde Mus. Naturkunde.

FABRICIUS, E. 1954. Aquarium observations on the spawning behaviour of the burbot, *Lota vulgaris* L. Rep. Inst. of Freshwater Res., Drottningholm, *35*, 51–7.

FISHER, J., and HINDE, R. A. 1949. The opening of milk bottles by birds. British Birds, *42*, 347–57.

FRIEDMANN, H. 1949. The breeding habits of the weaverbirds. A study in the biology of behavior patterns. Ann. Rep. Smithsonian Inst. for 1949, pp. 293–316.

FRIEDMANN, H. 1955. The honey-guides. Bull. U.S. Nat. Mus., *208*, vii + 292 pp.

FRISCH, K. VON. 1955. Beobachtungen und Versuche M. Lindauers an indischen Bienen. Sitzungsber. Bayer. Akad. Wiss., Math.-Nat. Klasse., 209–16.

GERHARDT, U. 1929. Zur vergleichenden Sexualbiologie primitiver Spinnen, insbesondere der Tetrapneumonen. Z. Morphol. u. Ökol., *14*, 699–764.

GERHARDT, U. 1934–1941. [Studies on Limacidae], Ibid., Vols. *27, 28, 30, 31, 32, 34, 35, 36, 37*.

GRUHL, K. 1924. Paarungsgewohnheiten der Dipteren. Z. wiss. Zool., *122*, 205–80.

HALL, C. 1951. Psychogenetics. In S. S. Stevens, ed., Handbook of experimental psychology. New York, Wiley.

HEINROTH, O. 1911. Beiträge zur Biologie namentlich Ethologie und Psychologie der Anatiden. Verh. 5 Int. Ornithol. Kongr. Berlin, 1910, pp. 589–702.

HEINROTH, O. 1930. Über bestimmte Bewegungsweisen der Wirbeltiere. Sitzber. Ges. Naturforsch. Freunde, Berlin, pp. 333–42.

HINDE, R. A. 1952. The behaviour of the great tit (*Parus major*) and some other related species. Behaviour, Suppl. 2, x + 201 pp.

HINDE, R. A. 1953. The conflict between drives in the courtship and copulation of the chaffinch. Behaviour, *5*, 1–31.

HINDE, R. A. 1955. A comparative study

of the courtship of certain finches (Fringillidae). Ibis, *97*, 706–45.

HINDE, R. A. 1956. Ibid., *98*, 1–23.

IWATA, K. 1942. Comparative studies on the habits of solitary wasps. Tenthredo, *4*, 1–146.

JACOBS, W. 1953. Verhaltensbiologische Studien an Feldheuschrecken. Beiheft 1, Z. f. Tierpsychol., 228 pp.

JAMESON, D. L. 1955. Evolutionary trends in the courtship and mating behavior of Salientia. Syst. Zool., *4*, 105–19.

KESSEL, E. L. 1955. The mating activities of balloon flies. Ibid., *4*, 97–104.

KRUMBIEGEL, I. 1938. Physiologisches Verhalten als Ausdruck der Phylogenese. Zool. Anz., *123*, 225–40.

LACK, D. 1956. A review of the genera and nesting habits of swifts. Auk, *73*, 1–32.

LINDAUER, M. 1956. Orientierung bei indischen Bienen. Z. f. vergl. Physiol., *38*, 521–57.

LORENZ, K. 1941. Vergleichende Bewegungsstudien an Anatinen. J. f. Ornithol., *89*, Erg. Band *3*, 194–294.

LORENZ, K. 1951–2. Comparative studies on the behaviour of the *Anatinae*. Tr. of Lorenz, 1941; tr. by C. H. D. Clarke, Avicult. Mag., *57*, 157–82; *58*, 8–17, 61–72, 86–93, 172–83.

LORENZ, K. 1952. Die Entwicklung der vergleichenden Verhaltensforschung in den letzten 12 Jahren. Verh. Deutsch. Zool. Gesell., Suppl. 17, pp. 36–58.

MAIDL, F. 1934. Die Lebensgewohnheiten und Instinkte der staatenbildenden Insekten. Wien, 823 pp.

MAKKINK, G. F. 1936. An attempt at an ethogram of the European avocet (*Recurvirostra avosetta* L.) with ethological and psychological remarks. Ardea, *25*, 1–62.

MARSHALL, A. J. 1954. Bower-birds. Their displays and breeding cycles. Oxford, Clarendon Press.

MAYR, E. 1948. The bearing of the new systematics on genetical problems. The nature of species. Advances in Genetics, 2, 205–37.

MAYR, E., ANDREWS, R. J., and HINDE, R. A. 1956. Die systematische Stellung der Gattung *Fringilla*. J. f. Ornithol., *97*, 258–73.

MAYR, E., and BOND, J. 1943. Notes on the classification of the swallows, Hirundinidae. Ibis, *85*, 334–41.

MAYR, E., LINSLEY, E. G., and USINGER, R. L. 1953. Methods and principles of systematic zoology. New York, McGraw-Hill.

MICHENER, C. D. 1953a. Problems in the development of social behavior and communication among insects. Trans. Kansas Acad. Sci., *56*, 1–15.

MICHENER, C. D. 1953b. Life-history studies in insect systematics. Syst. Zool., 2, 112–18.

MORRIS, D. 1954a, The reproductive behavior of the zebra finch (*Poëphila guttata*), with special reference to pseudofemale behaviour and displacement activities. Behaviour, *6*, 271–322.

MORRIS, D. 1954b. The courtship behaviour of the cutthroat finch. Avicult. Mag., *60*, 169–77.

MOYNIHAN, M. 1954. Some aspects of reproductive behavior in the blackheaded gull (*Larus ridibundus* L.), and related species. Behaviour, Suppl. 4.

MOYNIHAN, M., and HALL, F. 1956. Hostile, sexual, and other social behavior patterns of the spice finch (*Lonchura punctulata*), in captivity. Behaviour, 7, 33–76.

PECKHAM, G. W., and PECKHAM, E. G. 1898. On the instincts and habits of the solitary wasps. Wisc. Geol. Nat. Hist. Surv. Bull., No. 2, 245 pp.

PETRUNKEVITCH, A. 1926. The value of instinct as a taxonomic character in spiders. Biol. Bull., *50*, 427–32.

RAU, P. 1942. The nesting habits of *Polistes* wasps as a factor in taxonomy. Ann. Entomol. Soc. Amer., *35*, 335–8.

REED, C. A. 1946. The copulatory behavior of small mammals. J. Comp. Psychol., *39*, 185–206.

REGEN, J. 1913. Über die Anlockung des Weibchens von *Gryllus campestris* L. durch telephonisch übertragene Stridulationslaute des Männchens. Pflügers Arch. ges. Physiol., *155*, 193–200.

REGEN, J. 1926. Über die Beeinflussung

der Stridulation von *Thamnotrizon apterus* Fabr. Männchen durch künstlich erzeugte Töne und verschiedenartige Geräusche. Sitz. Ber. Akad. Wiss. Wien, *135*, 329–68.

RICHARDS, O. W. 1927. Sexual selection and allied problems in insects. Biol. Rev., *2*, 298–364.

SCHMIDT, R. S. 1955. The evolution of nestbuilding behavior in Apicotermes. Evolution, *9*, 157–81.

SCOTT, J. P., and FREDERISSON, E. 1951. The causes of fighting in mice and rats. Physiol. Zool., *24*, 273–309.

SEITZ, A. 1940–1. Die Paarbildung bei einigen Cichliden. Z. f. Tierpsychol., *4*, 40–84.

SPIETH, H. T. 1947. Sexual behavior and isolation in *Drosophila*. I. The mating behavior of species of the *willistoni* group. Evolution, *1*, 17–31.

SPIETH, H. T. 1949. Sexual Behavior and isolation in *Drosophila*. II. The interspecific mating behavior of species of the *willistoni* group. Ibid., *3*, 67–81.

SPIETH, H. T. 1951. Mating behavior and sexual isolation in the *Drosophila virilis* species group. Behaviour, *3*, 105–45.

SPIETH, H. T. 1952. Mating behavior within the genus *Drosophila* (Diptera). Bull. Amer. Mus. Nat. Hist., *99*, 395–474.

STEINER, H. 1955. Das Brutverhalten der Prachtfinken, Spermestidae, als Ausdruck ihres selbständigen Familiencharakters. Acta 11 Congr. Int. Ornithol., Basel, pp. 350–5.

STRESEMANN, E. 1953. Spielplätze und Balz der Laubenvögel. J. F. Ornithol., *94*, 367–8.

THORPE, W. H. 1954. Some concepts of ethology. Nature, *174*, 101–5.

TINBERGEN, N. 1948. Social releasers and the experimental method required for their study. Wilson Bull., *60*, 6–51.

TINBERGEN, N. 1951. The study of instinct. Oxford, Oxford Univ. Press.

TINBERGEN, N. 1952. "Derived" activities; their causation, biological significance, origin, and emancipation during evolution. Quart. Rev. Biol., *27*, 1–32.

TINBERGEN, N. 1953a. Fighting and threat in animals. New Biol., *14*, 9–24.

TINBERGEN, N. 1953b. The herring gull's world. London, Collins.

TINBERGEN, N. 1954. The origin and evolution of courtship and threat display. In J. Huxley, A. C. Hardy, and E. B. Ford, eds., Evolution as a process. London, Allen & Unwin, pp. 233–50.

TORDOFF, H. B. 1954. A systematic study of the avian family Fringillidae based on the structure of the skull. Misc. Publ. Mus. Zool. Univ. Mich., No. 81.

WEIDMANN, U. 1951. Über den systematischen Wert von Balzhandlungen bei *Drosophila*. Rev. suisse zool., *58*, 502–11.

WEYRAUCH, W. 1939. Zur Systematik der paläärktischen Polistinen auf biologischer Grundlage. Arch. Naturg. (Neue Folge), *8*, 145–97.

WHITMAN, C. O. 1899. Animal behavior. In Biological lectures delivered at the Marine Biological Laboratory at Woods Hole in 1898, pp. 329–31.

WHITMAN, C. O. 1919. The behavior of pigeons. Posthumous works of Charles Otis Whitman. Carnegie Inst. Wash. Publ., No. 257, Vol. *3*, xi + 161 pp.

ZIMMERMAN, K. 1956. Gattungstypische Verhaltensformen von Gelbhals-, Wald-, und Brandmaus. Zool. Garten (N.F.), *22*, 162–71.

ZIPPELIUS, H. M. 1949. Die Paarungsbiologie einiger Orthopteren-Arten. Z. f. Tierpsychol., *6*, 372–90.

17

Behavior and Isolating Mechanisms

Herman T. Spieth

UNIVERSITY OF CALIFORNIA (RIVERSIDE)

THE INDISPENSABLE FACTOR in the origin and maintenance of race and species is isolation. This concept has been enunciated by various workers, and its reality demonstrated both theoretically and experimentally as well as by observational deductions.

Divers data indicate that various types of factors operate as isolating mechanisms between Mendelian populations. Simply put, this means that one or more mechanisms serve to prevent interbreeding of the members of separate Mendelian populations.

The types of isolating mechanisms have been classified and discussed by various authors, including Huxley (1942), Mayr (1942), Carter (1951), Dobzhansky (1951). For orientation purposes these mechanisms are reviewed briefly here.

Interbreeding obviously cannot occur between different populations if they are separated by an intervening area which neither population can cross or inhabit. Such populations are geographically or spatially isolated and are termed allopatric in distribution. If, however, the populations are sympatric—living concurrently in the same area—they still can be effectively isolated by factors such as (1) seasonal isolation: the individuals are sexually functional at different times; (2) mechanical isolation: there is physical noncompatibility between the sexual parts; (3) ecological isolation: individuals of the populations are restricted by biological needs to specific and different habitats of the same area; (4) behavioral isolation: the individuals respond in such a manner to the stimuli they receive from individuals of the opposite sex belonging to other Mendelian populations that mating does not occur; (5) hybrid inviability: F_1 hybrid zygotes are produced but they are inviable; (6) hybrid sterility: the F_1 hybrids that are produced are sterile individuals, unable to produce normal functional sex cells.

Anyone who has collected and observed animals in their normal habitat knows that at any given time there are usually a considerable, often large number of species that are found living as sexually mature individuals within a relatively restricted area, for instance in a meadow, a small pond, or even a suburban yard. It is tacitly assumed that the majority of these species never will attempt to court and mate with each other. Thus, houseflies and stable flies live together and yet do not mate, or, to give a ludicrous example, a deer and a mountain lion never court each other and attempt to mate. Such organisms are so phylogenetically distinct that they are never expected to court each other, and yet it must be admitted that it is the behavior of the individual organisms that causes them to avoid even the beginnings of such actions as might lead to mating. As Thorpe (1950) has pointed out, this type of behavior is related to, if not dependent upon, the fact that the individual organism tends to take avoiding or self-protective action to (1) a wide range of stimuli likely to be signals for danger, especially any moving object, (2) any stimulus or situation which is strange, and (3) any stimulus at an unusually high intensity.

Two examples will indicate how this type of behavior operates.

When wounds occur on certain deciduous trees, sap flows, and in these wet areas bacteria, yeasts, and molds grow. To such spots numerous organisms are attracted, including various species of *Drosophila*, which feed and mate here. The drosophilid males, in addition to feeding, also vigorously investigate, i.e. make physical contacts with other drosophilids, courting the females of their own species and "fighting" with the males. They ignore or avoid other larger and smaller Diptera such as bluebottle flies and fungous gnats. Slow-moving beetles move about without causing any obvious reaction on the part of the drosophilids, and ants are merely avoided or ignored. Even large wasps do not greatly disturb the activities of the drosophilids, although they are given a wide berth. However if a bird, such as a sapsucker, alights upon the spot, there is immediately a frantic exodus of the insects.

May flies, or ephemerids, give a parallel example. These insects gather in groups for aerial nuptial dances, typically in the late afternoon or early evening. The males repeatedly fly upward and then volplane downward, while the females fly through such a swarm of males on a level pathway of flight. A male will see a female above him and immediately fly upward, grasp her and attempt copulation. At times, however, other insects such as caddis fly (Trichoptera) and stone fly (Plecoptera) adults will also fly into the same area. Now and then a male ephemerid will be seen pursuing a caddis fly of about the same size as the May fly females. The stone flies, however, have a characteristic flight that is very different from that of the May fly females, and the male ephemerids never attempt to grasp one of them. If a dragonfly enters the area the ephemerids scatter, or if one sweeps a net through the swarm they fly upward and away. Examples of this type are known and could be cited for numerous organisms from diverse phyla of animals.

There is, however, one particular aspect of general behavior that should be noted. Often numerous individuals of diverse species are seen in close proximity yet seeming wholly indifferent to each other. Thus a number of different species of birds may be seen feeding near together; several species of insects move about together on a slime flux with seemingly no concern for each other; different species of fishes may be found swimming about in a restricted area. Such reactions often occur even though the members of one species may be actively engaged in courting activities.

Whether this response by avoidance or indifference is innate or learned is not known certainly in most cases. In many instances if learning is involved it must be of the imprinting type. For example, the May fly male normally lives only for twenty-four hours and engages in only one nuptial flight. Regardless of the ontogeny of the avoidance and ignoring reactions, the behavior seems not only to serve as an isolating mechanism but also to guard the organism against the numerous dangers that constantly beset it while allowing the individuals to carry on their normal activities without incessantly responding to each and every other organism in the immediate vicinity.

Although isolation is necessary for maintaining the integrity of species, it is a truism that, for bisexual organisms, fertilization of the ova is also necessary if the population is to remain in existence. This automatically means that individuals of opposite sexes must synchronously produce ripe germ cells and place them in such a situation that the sperm can travel through a liquid medium and enter the ovum. This is achieved in many marine organisms (Thorson, 1950), including most Actinozoa, several Polychaeta, the Lamellibranchiata, most primitive Prosobranchiata, and nearly

all Echinodermata, by the dumping of the gametes into the surrounding water. Sometimes (*Sargartia troglodytes, Patella coerula,*
and other Prosobranchiata, and *Toxopneustes variegatus*) the
sexual products are not shed unless the individuals of the two
sexes are in close proximity.

As Mayr (1942) has shown, two factors are involved in the reproduction of such marine organisms. First, a complex of environmental factors results in a physiological readiness for production
of the mature sexual products. Second, one or a few individuals
reach such a high degree of sexual readiness that they spontaneously shed the sexual products. Usually it is a male that first reaches
such a peak of readiness, and the materials shed serve as a stimulus
to other individuals, both male and female, to spawn. Spawning,
once initiated, becomes epidemic for the entire population of the
species in the vicinity. Thorson (1950) reports that the females of
some species will never shed their eggs unless the active sperm of
males of the same species are in the surrounding water.

No information is available as to the exact stimulus that causes the
first individual or individuals to spawn. Perhaps it is a combination
of internal and external factors to which the animal responds. Obviously, once spawning is started the remaining individuals in the
vicinity that possess sexually mature germ cells are responding to
the material, i.e. sperm or accompanying substances, that has been
dumped into the water. As Mayr (1942) notes, it is certainly possible and even probable that the various stimuli may act as isolating mechanisms and be just as specific as the apparently more complex and obvious courtship behaviors of many terrestrial organisms
such as birds, mammals, and insects. Experimental data unfortunately are lacking, and we can only conclude by inference that
such behavior in marine organisms serves as an isolating mechanism.

In terrestrial animals, and many marine and fresh-water animals
also, physical contact between two individuals of opposite sexes is
generally necessary to ensure the transfer of sperm. This means
that somehow two individuals of opposite sexes must be appropriately stimulated and must respond correctly so that they select
each other from the welter of individuals that are to be found in
the area. The union thus formed may be of fleeting duration or
it may persist for a period, in some cases throughout the adult
life of the individuals.

It is amazing that the individual existing in a constantly hostile and dangerous situation—in which the normal response is flight or defense or at least indifference to a multitude of other living organisms—should also possess a behavioral pattern which enables it correctly to select another individual from among all those potentially possible in its environment and willingly make the intimate physical contact necessary for reproduction. Obviously, this must occur if the species or population is to remain in existence, and we tend to take the fact for granted.

Types of Mating Behavior

Scientific literature abounds in descriptions of how organisms behave during mating, and many of the patterns are complex and spectacular. The mating behavior of many, perhaps most, Mendelian populations is, however, to the human observer's eye relatively simple and of short duration. In the simplest form one individual, usually a male, approaches another individual and attempts to copulate. If the second individual is a receptive female of the same Mendelian population the union is successfully consummated.

Thomas (1950) studied the mating behavior of three species of coprophagous *Sarcophaga, S. knabi* Parker, *S. fuscicauda* Bottcher, and *S. albiceps* Meigen, which along with species of *Chrysomyia, Lucilia,* and other flies assemble and feed upon human feces in China. Mating typically occurs after feeding, when both sexes are gorged. The male initiates the process by mounting another individual, then vibrating his wings violently and attempting to hook the terminalia under the posterior end of the abdomen of the other fly. The males are indiscriminate in their selection and may mount a *Lucilia,* a male *Sarcophaga,* a female of another species of *Sarcophaga,* and so on, until the proper female of their own species is found. Apparently the selection of a receptive mate is purely by trial and error. Such mating behavior is typical of numerous species of organisms, especially many of the arthropods and some of the vertebrates. Even though it is obvious that this type of behavior involves stimulus and response on the part of both partners it is, from the human point of view, difficult of analysis. Biologists therefore have tended to devote more energy to the study of those organisms, particularly the larger ones such as fish, reptiles, birds, mammals, and some arthropods, that typ-

ically display complex mating behaviors, which offer more opportunity for observation, experimentation, and analysis.

The complex mating behaviors of various organisms seem to
differ from that of *Sarcophaga* in the accretion of specific new
elements upon the basic type. Four factors seem responsible for
the evolution of these new elements. They can be stated as follows:

1. Before any courtship can occur, two sexually mature individuals of opposite sexes must find each other, and obviously an organism cannot search an unlimited area for a mate. It is here that the
responses of the individuals to the environment serve as a helpful
adjunct, and thus the individuals are not uniformly and evenly distributed through the environment but rather are clumped together.
The sort of area that the male cockroach prefers is also preferred by
the females and represents a very small fraction of the total environment. Numerous species, however, have individuals scattered over a
much wider area, and in many instances special mechanisms have
evolved for bringing the sexes together. Thus while the diurnal
butterflies and most diurnal Diptera find their mates while feeding
or flying about, the females of the nocturnal moths produce odors
that attract the males, and the female mosquitoes make sounds
which attract and guide the males. The crickets and their relatives,
as well as most of the frogs, also produce sounds, but in these cases
it is the males whose sounds attract the opposite sex.

Roth and Willis (1952) note that the courtship of *Blattella
germanica* is similar in many respects to that of certain tree crickets
of the genus *Oeocanthus,* except that the male cricket employs
sound to attract the female while the male roach does not. Many
of the male birds, "fastened to" their territories, be they large or
small, utilize sound to bring the females near. In all of these instances only one of the participants is being stimulated by the actions of the other. Thus the male moth receives a stimulus, the
odor from the female, but the female receives no stimulus until
the male actually reaches her. The female bird hears the advertising song of the male, but he must await her arrival to be himself
stimulated. This, then, is a sort of prologue to the primitive type
of mating behavior. Such procedures have evolved independently
in many groups, and while we can postulate that originally they
were selected for and elaborated upon in order to bring individuals
together, they have now been completely incorporated into the
mating behavior. That they also serve as isolating mechanisms is

shown by the fact that birds which possess advertising songs produce fewer hybrids in nature than do birds such as the ducks, which
depend upon visual stimuli.

2. Many vertebrates establish territories which they defend.
Such territories may be permanent or may be established only for
the duration of the breeding season. In the latter case the male
typically first establishes and defends the territory, but after pair
bonds have been formed between a specific male and female the
area is defended by both individuals. In organisms that establish
territories—for example many fish, numerous reptiles, most birds
and mammals—there occur during the mating period three elements of behavior, commonly called drives, that are of significance
in the evolution and functioning of the courtship pattern. These
drives are (a) the sexual or mating, (b) fleeing or escape, and (c)
aggression or fighting. Clearly all three of these are mutually antagonistic; and, as Morris (1955) has shown, they result in a three-
point conflict in each individual at the time of courtship. Nevertheless, courtship and successful mating must occur if the Mendelian population is to stay in existence. Lorenz, Tinbergen, and
many others in their studies on the ethology of numerous animals
have thoroughly investigated these drives and their resultant interactions (see Tinbergen 1951, 1954). From the interaction of
these and, of course, of other drives which are not pertinent to the
present discussion, there have resulted certain derived activities
such as displacement actions, intention movements, and threat
postures which have become ritualized and integral components
of the behavior of each species of animal. Once established, these
serve as isolating mechanisms, particularly because they increase
the complexity of the mating pattern and also tend to extend the
length of the courting period. If the reciprocal actions and responses of the courting individuals do not "fit," then the final
acts of copulation will not be reached.

3. Some animals, for example spiders, do not show territoriality
and are rapacious carnivores. The three drives listed above seem
to exist in them, and there apparently have evolved—at least in
those spiders that possess effective visual mechanisms—complex,
extended forms of mating behavior which are analogous to those
displayed by the territorial vertebrates.

4. Some species of animals form gregarious assemblages at the
time of courtship. Thus the fiddler crabs of the genus *Uca* dwell

in colonies, and often colonies of several species coexist in the same restricted area (Crane, 1941). Numerous individuals of various species of *Drosophila* collect together for limited periods of time upon feeding areas of small size and engage in courtship and feeding. During the breeding season the males of the Lek birds gather upon communal breeding grounds. Analysis clearly shows that the evolutionary as well as the functional forces that create such assemblages are diverse for the various groups, but still a parallelism seems to exist in the mating behavior of all these groups in that (a) the males are promiscuous, i.e. do not form pair bonds that persist after copulation, and will mate with more than one individual during a breeding season; (b) the males' mating displays are hypertrophied compared to those of males of related but nongregarious species.

Some birds that are gregarious at the time of the breeding season do not, however, display these hypertrophied sexual characteristics, but in such cases, for instance herring gulls and cliff swallows, the individuals form pair bonds and the males are not promiscuous.

Two other general aspects of mating behavior should also be considered.

1. In many birds pair formation often precedes actual insemination by a considerable time, and during this time specific ceremonies may be repeated many times between the two individuals of a pair. Apparently these serve both to maintain pair formation and to synchronize the production of the ripe gametes. Two sorts of factors of course are involved in the synchronization of the sexual activities of the two sexes: (a) the physical environment, including such factors as temperature, available food, length of day, and so on, and (b) the effect of the individuals of the two sexes upon each other. Most animals, especially those that display the basic or primitive type of mating behavior, depend almost exclusively upon the physical environment factors for synchronization, but for some species, especially birds and mammals, interindividual actions are of importance in synchronizing the gonadal products. Such ceremonies, of course, can and apparently do serve as isolating mechanisms.

2. There is the question of sex recognition. A drosophilid male, for example, cannot tell the sex of another individual until it has actually tapped the stranger and he or she has responded. Usually

a scuffle develops between two males, but neither is injured. With spiders, however, the individuals are capable of injuring each other, and definite response patterns have evolved, threat patterns that enable two individuals to recognize each other. Many birds also, especially the males, have specific structures that permit sex recognition, for instance the flicker's moustache and the colored undersurface of his tail. These features play no part in isolation of the species.

SEXUAL BEHAVIOR OF CLOSELY RELATED SPECIES

Although there are many descriptions of the behavior of individual species, there is little information available on the comparative behavior of closely related species. Few investigators have studied the behavior, especially the mating behavior, of all the known species of a given genus or family. It has been done for some birds and for a few insects and spiders. Such studies take a great deal of energy and time, for one must become intimately acquainted with the individual species througout their life spans. On the basis of the evidence accumulated to date, it seems clear that the more closely related the species the more similar are the behavioral patterns. Thus in *Drosophila* all the species that are known to be extremely close relatives have observably identical mating behavior. To put it another way, there are species of *Drosophila* that can be differentiated on the basis of structure and other characteristics but cannot be differentiated by means of their observable mating behavior. On the other hand, it is clear that as the species diverge phylogenetically, as determined by structure, ecology, distribution, etc., the observable mating behavior also diverges so that species from different species groups and subgenera exhibit different mating behavior. It is to be expected that eventually exceptions to this generalization will be discovered, but it can be rather confidently expected that such exceptions will be rare. In general it can be anticipated that very closely related species of all organisms will display very similar mating behavior. This does not mean that if there are only two species in a genus they will necessarily have similar behavioral patterns, for even if they are the only two representatives of the genus they may be evolutionarily more distinct than any two members of another genus that contains numerous species.

It so happens that some species which have observably similar mating behavior live in the same area, that is, they are sympatric and yet at the same time maintain their identity and therefore represent isolated populations. Two questions immediately arise: How are these populations isolated? Does behavior play any part in keeping them isolated? Perhaps a consideration of concrete examples will give some indication of the answers to these questions.

Smith (1953) in Canada has studied two closely related species of the lepidopteran genus *Choristoneura*. One, *Choristoneura pinus*, seems restricted during the larval stage to the jack pine. The other, *C. fumiferana*, has caterpillars that live primarily on balsam fir but also are to be found on white spruce, black spruce, and tamarack. The host trees of these two species are often found in the same area. The adults are winged and fly about, the males seeking the females; in the laboratory the males of both species will court the females of either species. Under laboratory conditions cross-mating between the species produces viable fertile off-spring. The males also have visibly identical courtships. Further, the males will attempt to mate with dead or etherized females of either species.

In nature no hybrids of *Choristoneura* have ever been found. A careful study of the two species shows that normally *C. fumiferana* emerge as adults during the first two weeks of July, and that a day or so after the last *C. fumiferana* has been seen the first *C. pinus* adults appear. Also, although both species mate during the afternoon or evening, *C. fumiferana* mates a couple of hours earlier. There is however very broad overlap in mating time.

In 1952 Smith found an area at Blue and Indian Lakes, Ontario, where the seasonal isolation broke down, and as a result both species appeared at the same time in the same area. Careful study of these populations resulted in the observation of 246 copulations during the period when virgins of both species were present, of which none represented an interspecific cross. This represents a typical example of what biologists expect of such sympatric sibling species pairs: normally various isolating mechanisms such as ecological and seasonal barriers serve to keep the species isolated, but when these break down the behavioral barriers are completely, or almost completely, effective even though they appear to be ineffective under the artificial conditions of the laboratory.

The species *Drosophila pseudoobscura* and *D. persimilis* represent another such pair. In nature *persimilis,* which occurs from Vancouver Island and central British Columbia to south-central California, and from the Pacific to the eastern slope of the Sierra Nevada and Cascade ranges, is almost totally sympatric with *pseudoobscura,* but since the latter has such an extensive range (from southern Canada to Guatemala) most of its population is allopatric with *persimilis.* Dobzhansky (1938 and 1951) and his associates, Mayr (1945, 1946a, 1946b), and others have studied these two species intensively and found that, in areas where they are sympatrically isolated, the isolation between the two species is maintained by a number of factors such as (1) somewhat different habitat preference, with *D. persimilis* being found in the cooler, moister niches and *D. pseudoobscura* in the warmer, drier niches; (2) some differences in food preferences; (3) different diurnal periods of maximum activity; (4) behavioral isolation. The first three mechanisms are not completely effective, as shown by the fact that Carson (1951) found both species feeding and breeding side by side in the same slime flux on the black oak *Quercus Kellogii.* Dobzhansky concluded that "the absence of interspecific hybrids in natural habitats is due chiefly, if not entirely, to sexual isolation." It should be added that during the summer of 1953 a hybrid was recovered by Dobzhansky (personal comm.) in nature. Further, it is known that when interspecific mating takes place in the laboratory fewer sperm are transferred than would be true in intraspecific crosses, that the F_1 males are sterile, and the F_1 female progeny from backcrosses have reduced vigor.

Recent investigations show that both of these species will court and mate freely when enclosed in a small cell that can be observed under a binocular microscope; and to date hundreds of courtships and matings, both inter- and intraspecific, have been observed. The courtships and matings are identical except that the average duration of copulation is somewhat longer in *pseudoobscura* than in *persimilis* under approximately similar conditions. By observation it is impossible to tell what species or combination of species is in the observation cell at any particular time since the insects' actions appear identical. The ontogeny of the mating behavior of both species is as follows:

When the flies first emerge from the pupal case the young males will not court, nor are the young females attractive to older males. Emergence typically occurs in the morning. When the males of both species are 12 hours old they will occasionally court older females but are unable to achieve coition. At 24–28 hours old they court the females but are still unable to achieve intromission, though they attempt it. At about 32 hours males of both species can successfully achieve coition. The females for their part are not attractive to the males until they are approximately 24 hours old. At this age, although the males court them, the young females will not accept, and continue to refuse until the *pseudoobscura* females are 32–36 hours old and the *persimilis* females 44–48 hours old. Since the drosophilids assemble on the feeding and mating grounds for two periods each day—one in the early morning and the other in the late afternoon—it can be concluded that the young *pseudoobscura* females emerging on the morning of day 1 will probably mate during the evening of day 2. Also, they will be courted on the morning of day 2 but will not accept the males' overtures. The young *persimilis* females will not accept until they are 48 hours old, or on the morning of the second day after they have emerged. Dobzhansky's data on mating pairs collected in the wild seem to substantiate this conclusion, since his evening collections contained 280 pairs of *pseudoobscura* and 25 of *persimilis,* while the morning collections contained 65 pairs of *pseudoobscura* and 25 pairs of *persimilis.* A female of either species mates more than once during her life and after the first time such a mating may occur during either morning or evening. Also, the young males have tried to mate before they are able actually to inseminate a female, and the young females have been courted before they were willing to accept any male.

Various authors (Dobzhansky, 1938; Mayr, 1945, 1946a, 1946b; Koopman, 1949) have shown that these two species will hybridize rather readily in the laboratory, but in every case virgin individuals were utilized that were at least 4 days old. On the assumption that the flies in nature did not hybridize because they had somehow acquired the ability to discriminate before they were sexually mature, experiments were run in which individuals of both sexes and both species were put together a few hours after they had emerged. By using *persimilis* flies homozygous for the eye mutation orange and *pseudoobscura* flies homozygous for glassy, it was readily possible to see if the offspring were hybrids. The hybrids always appear as wild-type flies since the mutations are recessive and on different chromosomes. The very young adults were placed together in half-pint jars with suitable food, allowed to live, mate, and lay their eggs. The offspring of these flies were then counted to see if hybrids had been produced. In 6 experiments 2 individuals of each sex and each species were tested, or a total of 8 individuals. From these 6 experiments no hybrids were produced. In 14 experiments 4 of each sex and species were used. One of the 14 experiments produced hybrids. In 15 experiments 8 of each species and sex, or a total of 32 parents, were placed in the rearing bottles. Two of these bottles produced hybrids. Out of a total of 38,347 F_1 individuals, only 117 were hybrids. This represents 0.3 of 1 per cent, and is considerably lower than Koopman's results from population cage experiments. It can reasonably be assumed that, out of the 392 females of both species utilized, only 3 individuals mated with the wrong male. It also seems relatively safe to assume that the isolation had been enhanced by the fact that the individuals had matured together.

This is substantiated by the following data. A series of single pair matings were made by placing a male and female together in shell vials with food. In vials 1–5 the individuals were *persimilis* male and female; in vials 6–10 *persimilis* male and *pseudoobscura* female; in vials 11–15 *pseudoobscura* male and *pseudoobscura* female; in vials 16–20 *pseudoobscura* male and *persimilis* female. All of these individuals carried the eye mutants mentioned above. At the end of five days males 1–5 and 11–15 were exchanged. Thus the females that had been paired with a male of their own species now found themselves with a male of another species. This situation was maintained for seven more days and then the original males were returned. Numbers 6–10 and 16–20 were treated in like manner, but in these the females had spent the first five days with a foreign male and now from days 5 to 12 found themselves with their own male. On the twelfth or thirteenth day the foreign males were returned. The results of these experiments are shown in Tables 1–4. The x marks indicate the first appearance of eggs. The upper or top line whenever present indicates the presence of hybrid offspring, and the figure just above the line gives the actual number of hybrid individuals. The drosophilid female copulates a number of times during her life span; unless she does so she exhausts her sperm supply and produces infertile eggs. The *persimilis* females that matured with their own *persimilis* males (Table 17-1) never accepted the *pseudoobscura* males—and laid a considerable number of infertile eggs during days 10, 11, and 12. In comparison 4 of the 14 *persimilis* females that matured with *pseudoobscura* males (Table 17-2, Nos. 36, 39, 40, and 60) did sometime or other during the experiment engage in an inter-specific mating. Specimen 60 is unique in that the *persimilis* which should have been introduced on the fifth day was lost (all specimens were transferred from vial to vial without etherization) and therefore the female was stored in "solitary" from the fifth to twelfth day, when the original *pseudoobscura* male was returned. This female had originally accepted the *pseudoobscura* male's overtures and apparently did so again, since she produced hybrid offspring throughout the experiment and a single insemination would not have supplied sufficient sperm for this continual production of fertilized eggs. The *pseudoobscura* females showed much less sexual isolation to the *persimilis* males than did the

TABLE 17-1. PERSIMILIS ♂ X PERSIMILIS ♀

Experiment #	pseudo. ♂ intro.					persim. ♂ ret.										
Days	1	2	3	4	5	6	7	8	9	10	11	12	13	14	15	16	17	18	19	20
1				x												
2				x												
3				x												
4				x												
5				x												
21				x												
23				x												
24					x											
41					x											
43					x											
44					x											
45					x											

x indicates first appearance of eggs. Dotted line indicates hybrid offspring. Solid line indicates nonhybrid offsp *persimilis* to the *pseudoobscura* males (see Tables 17-3 and 17-4). The data from these four sets of experiments clearly show (1) the well-known fact that *pseudoobscura* displays much less isolation to *persimilis* than does *persimilis* to *pseudoobscura;* (2) that the females of both species will immediately accept their own male as soon as they are able to, even though under duress they had accepted the male of the other species; (3) that the *persimilis* female, once she has been fecundated by a *persimilis* male, will not accept a *pseudoobscura* male.

Additional information of a somewhat similar nature is presented in Table 17-5. In these experiments two wild stocks, both derived originally from the same locality, were used. Eight females were placed with four males in a half-pint jar with food, and after a number of hours or days the females were sacrificed in order to determine whether they had accepted the males' over-

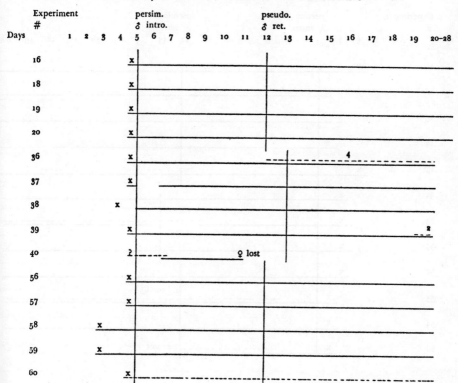

TABLE 17-2. PSEUDOOBSCURA ♂ x PERSIMILIS ♀

Experiment # (Days)	1	2	3	4	5 persim. ♂ intro.	6	7	8	9	10	11	12 pseudo. ♂ ret.	13	14	15	16	17	18	19	20–28
16					x															
18					x															
19					x															
20					x															
36					x											4				
37					x															
38				x																
39					x															2
40					2						♀ lost									
56					x															
57					x															
58			x																	
59			x																	
60					x															

x indicates first appearance of eggs. Dotted line indicates hybrid offspring. Solid line indicates nonhybrid offspring.

tures. The data are self-explanatory and clearly indicate the differences in the responses of the two species under these non-choice conditions.

Haskins and Haskins (1949 and 1950) have elucidated a somewhat similar pattern in the poeciliid fishes. Three species, *Lebistes reticulatus,* the guppy, *Micropoecilia parae* and *Poecilia vivipara,* all live together in the shallow waters of Trinidad streams. All males are brightly colored, but the females are dun colored, and, to the human eye, resemble each other. No intergrades have been found in nature, but *P. vivipara* $\times$ *L. reticulatus* has produced hybrids in the laboratory. The fish are viviparous, and insemination is accomplished by the male transferring a spermatophore by means of his gonopodium. Haskins and Haskins have clearly shown that the males of *L. reticulatus* can be conditioned to different mutant females (see Tables 17-6 and 17-7). However, when

TABLE 17-3. PSEUDOOBSCURA ♂ X PSEUDOOBSCURA ♀

Experiment # (Days)	1	2	3	4	5	6	7	8	9	10	11	12	13	14	15	16	17	18	19	20-
				persim. ♂ intro.								pseudo. ♂ ret.								
11			x																	
12				x																
13			x																	
14				x																
15			x										36					2		
31				x																
33				x												13				
34				x																
51				x																
53				x										63						
54				x																
55				x			61					♀ lost								

x indicates first appearance of eggs. Dotted line indicates hybrid offspring. Solid line indicates nonhybrid offspri the male (Table 17-8) is given a choice between a mutant of its own species and a normal *M. parae,* which to the human eye looks much more like the typical wild *Lebistes* female than does the *Lebistes* mutant, it quickly learns to choose the mutant.

In summary, the evidence would seem to indicate that in the two *Choristoneura* species the mating behavior is completely innate while in the *Drosophila* species *pseudoobscura* and *persimilis* and also the poeciliid fishes it must be partially innate and partially "learned." One can also speculate that *persimilis,* which is sympatric throughout its entire range with its sibling species *pseudoobscura,* has had selective pressure operating in the direction of the production of a high degree of sexual isolation. This involves intensification of discriminating ability to such a degree that the *persimilis* females are, so to speak, "wary" of their own males. The result is that even under no-choice conditions (Table

TABLE 17-4. PERSIMILIS ♂ X PSEUDOOBSCURA ♀

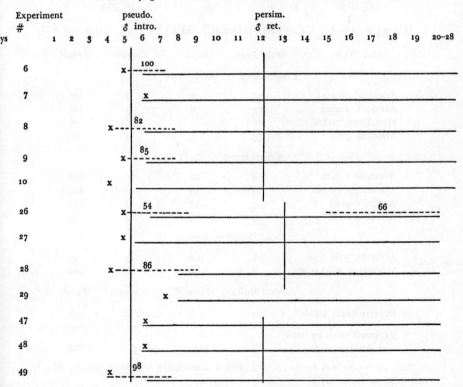

x indicates first appearance of eggs. Dotted line indicates hybrid offspring. Solid line indicates nonhybrid offspring.

TABLE 17·5

Age-Hours	Number	% Fecundated	% Nonfecundated
	Pseudoobscura ♀ x ♂ St. Helena		
40–50	62	100.0	0.0
	pseudoobscura ♀ x persimilis ♂ St. Helena		
40–50	62	6.5	93.5
50–60	45	2.2	97.8
65–75	27	49.0	51.0
	persimilis ♀ x ♂ St. Helena		
44–50	101	52.4	47.6
50–60	18	66.6	34.4
68–75	32	87.5	12.5
70–80	16	100.0	0.0
	persimilis ♀ x pseudoobscura ♂ St. Helena		
70–80	63	0.0	100.0
90–100	72	0.0	100.0
6½ days	16	0.0	100.0
8½ days	21	9.5	90.5

TABLE 17·6. "CONDITIONED" MALES, AS SHOWN *

Male Type	Wild Type	Gold	Cream	Total
	Conditioned to Wild Type			
Armatus, cream	92	2	6	100
Armatus, cream	91	0	9	100
Maculatus, cream	87	7	2	96
Armatus, gold	95	5	0	100
	Conditioned to Gold			
Armatus, cream	9	87	10	106
Maculatus, cream	104	14	7	125 [a]
Armatus, gold	5	73	23	101
Armatus, wild type	9	74	22	105
	Conditioned to Cream			
Armatus, wild type	6	6	13	25
Maculatus, wild type	8	8	84	100

	Total Males	"Correct"	"Incorrect"	Total
Experimental totals	10	710	248	958
Expected totals on basis of chance contacts		319.4	638.6	958

[a] This exception was further tested with a diminutive wild-type female. The results were confirmatory.

* From Haskins, C. P. and Edna F. (1950).

17-5) one does not find 100 per cent fecundation until the females are 70–80 hours old, even though they become sexually receptive at about 48 hours of age. In comparison, the *pseudoobscura* females are much more easily stimulated to the point of acceptance

TABLE 17-7. RELATIVE CHOICE EFFICIENCY OF MALES "CONDITIONED" TO WILD TYPE AND TO OTHER BODY COLORS *

"Conditioning"	"Correct"	"Incorrect"	Total	
Wild type	1,319	172	1,491	Experiment
Wild type	497	994	1,491	Theoretical
Other	708	549	1,257	Experiment
Other	419	838	1,257	Theoretical

Total contacts recorded: 2,748
Total males observed: 125

* From Haskins, C. P. and Edna F. (1950).

of the males' overtures and by the time they are 40–50 hours old have, under no-choice conditions, all become fecundated.

Data from other groups of organisms, although less extensive and detailed, are similar to those just discussed. Roth and Willis (1952 and 1954) have made elegant studies of various species of cockroaches, belonging to a number of different genera. The sig-

TABLE 17-8. RELATIVE CHOICE EFFICIENCY OF WILD-TYPE LEBISTES MALES "CONDITIONED" TO WILD-TYPE FEMALES BETWEEN FEMALES OF M. PARAE AND MUTANT LEBISTES *

Sixteen males of wild-type Maculatus stock, twice backcrossed to wild stock from the Arima River, Trinidad, taken from wild-type mass culture. Exposed to one wild female of *M. parae* and one female of Maculatus Cream, domestic stock, taken from mass culture of Maculatus Cream

Elapsed Time from Introduction	Contacts with M. parae	Contacts with Maculatus Cream
Day of introduction (n)	49	26
n + 1	2	23
n + 7	2	98

Length (snout to base of caudal fin) of *M. parae* female: 25.0 mm.
Length (snout to base of caudal fin) of *Lebistes* female: 24.0 mm.

Weight of *M. parae* female: 0.35 g.
Weight of *Lebistes* female: 0.31 g.

* From Haskins, C. P., and Edna F. (1950).

nificant findings are (1) that the courtships are similar in related species, (2) that the individuals are able to distinguish between stimuli received from their own species and those from others, (3) that the substances which produce the stimuli are somewhat similar but differ either quantitatively or qualitatively, (4) that the males of *Blatta germanica* can be conditioned by experience and are less discriminating if they lack experience with their own females.

Spiders display mating patterns that are in many aspects parallel to the behavior of the cockroaches. Kaston (1936) found that males of certain piasurid and lycosid species are stimulated by an ether-soluble substance which occurs over the female's body, is produced by immature individuals of both sexes, but disappears entirely from the mature male. Crane (1949) investigated in detail the behavior of a number of salticid species. Unlike the nonterritorial, noncarnivorous roaches, the spiders possess both courtship and threat displays. By using models and actual specimens Crane determined that no male of *Corythalia xanthopa* would display to a spider or model with a frontal area more than five times or less than one-third the male's size. Further, the use of cardboard models showed that the shape of the model must approach normal if the male was to respond readily. Crane also found that "in general, any A-tone male would initiate appropriate display before any moving male or female that showed a few sign stimuli roughly similar to those of its own species. The females presumably because of the chemical factors were close relatives; the males, in inter-male display, had to conform in appearance only. The heterosexual pairs of species which displayed regularly to each other, under unconfined laboratory conditions, were the following: *Corythalia chalces* and *C. fulgipedia; Plexippus paykulli* female and *Eustiromastix* sp. male; any two species of *Phiale*."

These displays did not terminate in insemination of the female since she would refuse the male sometimes before copula could be achieved. Further, when individuals of their own species were presented to a pair of mismatched displaying spiders, attention would promptly be turned to the newcomer by the appropriate displaying individual.

Among the amphibians the mating behavior of the frogs and toads has received considerable attention. Jameson (1955) has recently summarized the known facts and has shown that, although the basic pattern is the same throughout the group, many variations and differences do exist among the various species. Thus at least twelve different types of amplectic claspings have been described for the different species, ranging from pelvic to cephalic. Nevertheless, closely related species do have very similar mating behavior. That the isolating mechanisms between closely related species of frogs and especially toads break down occasionally is well authenticated by both field collections and experimental studies. Blair (1941), studying *Bufo americanus*, *B. terrestris*, *B. fowleri*, and *B. woodhousi*, found that wherever the species overlapped geographically some intermediate individuals appeared in the populations, and these were similar to the hybrids he was able to produce in the laboratory. Later work by Volpe (1952) and Cory and Manion (1955) on *B. americanus* and *B. fowleri* confirmed Blair's findings and showed that (1) the calls of the males were different; (2) *B. fowleri* preferred grassland areas; (3) *B. americanus* chose woodland areas; (4) the males of *B. americanus* when congregated in the breeding ponds were active and attracted to disturbances in the water, while *B. fowleri* males were scattered about the ponds and tended to remain hidden and quiet when disturbances in the water occurred; (5) typically *B. americanus* finished its breeding period before *B. fowleri* started breeding. Apparently, although behavioral isolating mechanisms do exist, the main isolating mechanisms are ecological in nature and the hybrid populations that now exist in various areas are primarily due to man's modification of the environment.

Careful investigation of the mating behavior of some species of frog has shown that sufficient behavioral differences exist to prevent interspecies insemination. Thus Noble and Aronson (1942) were able under experimental conditions to cause cross amplexus and oviposition between *Rana pipiens* and *R. clamitans*. The *R. pipiens* female followed her normal pattern of oviposition while the male *R. clamitans* reacted in his characteristic manner, and since these reactions resulted in the cloacae never approximating each other, the genital products of both, although they were shed at the proper time, never came into contact and the eggs were sterile.

Bragg (1944 and 1945) concluded that "even though all species of *Scaphious* follow a generally similar pattern of breeding, they are quite effectively sexually isolated even when breeding in the same pools." While several interacting factors play their parts, the two principal ones are (1) differences in details of how males secure females, and (2) the attraction of calls of the males for females of the same species.

The various examples listed above could be replicated in any group of organisms that has been adequately studied, and the particular ones given have been selected merely to show how behavior operates in diverse types of organisms as an isolating mechanism.

DISCUSSION AND SUMMARY

The full gamut of mating behavior as displayed by animals presents a vast and amazing array of seemingly quite different patterns ranging from apparently simple ones that endure for very short periods of time to extremely complex and spectacular ones that extend over a remarkably long time. This confusing welter of mating behavior can be roughly classified into a number of different types as follows:

1. *Sedentary aquatic type.* The individuals of both sexes under the stimulus of environmental factors simultaneously reach a stage of sexual readiness. One or a few individuals (typically a male) spontaneously spawns, and the sexual products then stimulate all other individuals to release their gonadal products epidemically.

2. *Basic type.* The individuals of both sexes simultaneously reach sexual readiness due to the influence of environmental factors, and then one individual, apparently invariably a male, seeks out and by trial and error attempts to copulate with an appropriate and receptive individual. This type of mating behavior is unspectacular, quite difficult of analysis, and is in need of careful investigation. The individuals involved form only fleeting liaisons for the period of insemination; the male is usually promiscuous and mates with more than one individual during his life span, while the female may or may not be promiscuous. The male apparently approaches the other individuals because of his sex drive, but little is known about the mechanism whereby he can and does, under the influence of the sex drive, approach a certain individual but avoid or flee from other organisms. The female for her part can reject or accept the male's attentions, and the response is often made on the basis of what appears to be merely momentary

physical contact between the two organisms. If the female refuses or if the male has mistakenly approached a male or an individual belonging to another closely related species, the separation of the two individuals may involve vigorous physical action; but typically it does not result in injury to either individual since attack behavior seems lacking in such organisms. Apparently the male is merely inhibited by the stimulus he receives from the nonreceptive individual. Spurway has suggested to Bastock and Manning (1955) that "inhibitory stimuli in sexual behavior will be characteristic of non-aggressive animals." This basic pattern is characteristic of many invertebrates, especially the arthropods, and some vertebrates, particularly the amphibians.

An extension or variation of this basic pattern is the production by one sex, usually the male, of special stimuli such as sounds, odors, or obvious display of special ornamentation that attract the receptive individuals of the opposite sex. Once the individuals are close the basic pattern operates in typical fashion. This pattern is typical of many insects, such as sound-producing Orthoptera, scent-producing Lepidoptera, and so on.

Finally it should be noted that some organisms, for instance certain species of birds like the spruce grouse, certain birds of paradise, and others, have secondarily returned to this pattern of mating behavior.

3. *Territorial type.* Organisms that maintain territories at the time of mating seem to differ from the basic type in that pair bonds of some duration are formed, and in that they possess strong aggressive or fighting and escape or fleeing drives at the same time that they exhibit the sexual drive. The interaction of these three drives results in complicated and often spectacular mating behavior. In many of the species that follow such a pattern, specific and unique recognition ornamentation and movements have evolved. This type can be further subdivided, as shown by Lorenz (1935) and Tinbergen (1939), although they do not designate the major type as territorial. This type of mating behavior is primarily exemplified by vertebrates that establish territories during the breeding season, and has been evolved from the basic type.

4. *Predatory nonterritorial type.* The same three drives that operate at high intensity in the territorial type also are found in many spiders and perhaps a number of other carnivorous nonterritorial species. In these there has apparently evolved a type of

mating behavior, including unique recognition ornamentation and movements, parallel to those found in the territorial type. Threat postures, derived movements, and all the other complex behavior so clearly found in the territorial type are also found in this type.

5. *Lek type*. This type is characterized by the facts that (1) the males carry on their mating behavior at a special restricted area, where they gather together in number. The females may normally be present with the males or may be attracted to the area; (2) the males are promiscuous; (3) the mating behavior is complex and often extends over a considerable period of time. Typical examples are the crabs of the genus *Uca*, the various Lek birds, and insects such as *Drosophila*. Analysis of the behavior of such organisms shows that this group is an artificial assemblage derived evolutionarily from other types. Thus the Lek birds have apparently evolved from typical territorial types, while the *Uca* and *Drosophila* behavior has been derived from the basic type. The curious fact is that there is apparently great parallelism in the mating behavior of all these organisms. It is to be expected that further investigations will uncover examples that will be found to be intermediate in varying degrees between the extreme Lek type on one hand and the basic and territorial types on the other. In fact, some cockroaches such as *Periplaneta americana* seem to represent an intermediate type.

Any classification is to some extent artificial for the simple reason that the mating behavior is an integral part of the total behavioral fabric of any given species of animal. Mating behavior, therefore, is to some extent unique for each species, and can be completely analyzed only by considering the evolutionary history of the specific animals concerned. It may in some cases, but certainly not the majority, be compounded from the resultants of the sexual drive plus other drives such as escape, aggression, feeding, etc.

The mating behavior serves two separate but reciprocal functions: (1) the successful consummation of bringing the gonadal products of opposite sexes of the same Mendelian population together, and (2) the isolation of the gonadal products of a particular Mendelian population from those of another foreign population. Behavior may serve the major role for the latter function but is often also aided by other isolating mechanisms.

In addition, mating behavior may serve other secondary but related functions such as (1) synchronization of gonadal production, (2) orientation of the individuals and (3) suppression of nonsexual actions on the part of individuals of the opposite sex. The special actions that accomplish these additional ends also secondarily have been interwoven into the isolation mechanism.

Clearly, therefore, mating behavior serves an important role in the isolation of Mendelian populations. Observation and analysis of those behavioral elements that operate as isolating mechanisms show that closely related Mendelian populations invariably display quite similar behavior; in fact, the gross overt actions of closely related species are often more nearly similar than are the structural characteristics. However, such Mendelian populations displaying "identical" courtship patterns are reproductively isolated by behavioral differences that must operate at the sensory level. Often such populations exist sympatrically and depend solely or primarily upon mating behavior as an isolating mechanism. In such instances it seems most reasonable to assume that these populations had at some previous period in their history been separated spatially, that the differences that now isolate them must have arisen then, and that the populations have subsequently come together again.

CONCLUSIONS

1. Individuals of phylogenetically widely divergent species that are simultaneously sympatric and sexually mature respond to each other with an avoidance reaction such as is elicited by strange or strong stimuli. This automatically prevents even the beginning of courtship.

2. Individuals of phylogenetically closely related species universally show similar mating behaviors, and these may or may not be effective isolating mechanisms.

3. Behavioral isolation between closely related sympatric species is usually only one of the isolating mechanisms that normally function between closely related species, but it is often the most effective one of the series.

4. Behavioral isolating mechanisms that function effectively when the species is dwelling in its normal habitat may break down

when the individuals are transferred to a new and different environment.

5. Behavioral isolating mechanisms are typically innate, but in some forms also contain "learned" elements.

6. We can perhaps best explain the origin of the behavioral isolating mechanisms that exist between closely related sympatric species by assuming that they arose when the Mendelian populations were geographically isolated and that they have been reinforced by selection when the two populations became sympatric.

REFERENCES

BASTOCK, M., and MANNING, A. 1955. The courtship of Drosophila melanogaster. Behaviour, 8 (2–3), 85–111.

BLAIR, W. P. 1941. Variation, isolating mechanisms and hybridization in certain toads. Genetics, 26, 398–417.

BRAGG, A. N. 1944, 1945. The spadefoot toads in Oklahoma with a summary of our knowledge of the group. Amer. Nat., 69, 517–33, and 70, 52–72.

CARSON, H. L. 1951. Breeding sites of Drosophila pseudoobscura and Drosophila persimilis in the Transition Zone of the Sierra Nevada. Evolution, 5 (2), 91–6.

CARTER, G. S. 1951. Animal evolution. London, Sidgwick & Jackson.

CORY, L., and MANION, J. J. 1955. Ecology and hybridization in the genus Bufo in the Michigan-Indiana region. Evolution, 9, 42–51.

CRANE, J. 1941. Crabs of the genus Uca from the west coast of Central America. Zoologica, 26, 145–208.

CRANE, J. 1949. Comparative biology of salticid spiders at Rancho Grande, Venezuela. Pt. IV. An analysis of display. Ibid., 34, (4), 159–214.

DOBZHANSKY, TH. 1951. Genetics and the origin of species. New York, Columbia Univ. Press.

DOBZHANSKY, TH., and HOLLER, P. C. 1938. An experimental study on sexual isolation in Drosophila. Biol. Zentralbl., 58, 589–607.

HASKINS, C. P., and HASKINS, E. F. 1949. The role of sexual selection as an isolating mechanism in three species of poeciliid fishes. Evolution, 3 (2), 160–9.

HASKINS, C. P., and HASKINS, E. F. 1950. Factors governing sexual selection as an isolating mechanism in the poeciliid fish Lebistes reticulatus. Proc. Nat. Acad. Sci., 36 (9), 464–76.

HUXLEY, J. S. 1942. Evolution, the modern synthesis. London, Allen & Unwin.

JAMESON, D. L. 1955. Evolutionary trends in the courtship and mating in Salentia. Syst. Zool., 4 (3), 105–19.

KASTON, B. J. 1936. The senses involved in the courtship of some vagabond spiders. Entomologica Americana, 16, 97–167.

KOOPMAN, K. 1949. Natural selection for reproductive isolation between Drosophila pseudoobscura and Drosophila persimilis. Evolution, 4 (2), 135–48.

LORENZ, K. 1935. Der Kumpan in der Umwelt des Vogels. J. Ornithol., 83, 137–213 and 289–413.

MAYR, E. 1942. Systematics and the origin of species. New York, Columbia Univ. Press.

MAYR, E. 1946a. Experiments on sexual isolation in Drosophila. VI. Isolation Between D. pseudoobscura and D. persimilis and their hybrids. Proc. Nat. Acad. Sci., 32 (3), 57–9.

MAYR, E. 1946b. Experiments on sexual isolation in Drosophila. VII. The nature of the isolating mechanisms between Drosophila pseudoobscura and

Drosophila persimilis. Ibid., *32* (5), 128–37.

MAYR, E., and DOBZHANSKY, TH. 1945. Experiments on sexual isolation in Drosophila. IV. Modification of the degree of isolation between *D. pseudoobscura* and *D. persimilis* and of sexual preferences in *D. prosaltans.* Ibid., *31* (2), 75–82.

MORRIS, D. 1955. The causation of pseudofemale and pseudomale behaviour; a further comment. Behaviour, *8* (1), 46–56.

NOBLE, G. K., and ARONSON, L. R. 1942. The sexual behavior of Anura. I. The normal mating pattern of *Rana pipiens.* Bull. Amer. Mus. Nat. Hist., *8* (Oct. 5), 127–42.

ROTH, L. M., and WILLIS, E. R. 1952. A study of cockroach behavior. Amer. Midland Nat., *47* (1), 66–129.

ROTH, L. M., and WILLIS, E. R. 1954. The reproduction of cockroaches. Smithsonian Misc. Coll., *122* (12), 1–49.

SMITH, S. G. 1953. Reproductive isolation and the integrity of two sympatric species of *Choristoneura* (Lepidoptera: Tortricidae). Canad. Entomol., *85* (4), 141–51.

THOMAS, H. T. 1950. Field notes on the mating habits of *Sarcophaga* Meigen (Diptera). Proc. Roy. Entomol. Soc. London, Series A, *25* (Pts. 7–9), 93–8.

THORPE, W. H. 1950. The concepts of learning and their relation to those of instinct. In Physiological mechanisms in animal behaviour. Sympos. Soc. Exp. Biol., No. 4. Cambridge, Eng., Cambridge Univ. Press, pp. 387–408.

THORSON, G. 1950. Reproduction and larval ecology of marine bottom invertebrates. Biol. Rev., *25*, 1–45.

TINBERGEN, N. 1939. The behavior of the snow bunting in spring. Trans. Linn. Soc. N. Y., *5*, 1–95.

TINBERGEN, N. 1951. The study of instinct. London, Oxford Univ. Press.

TINBERGEN, N. 1954. The origin and evolution of courtship and threat display. In A. C. Hardy, J. S. Huxley, and E. B. Ford, eds., Evolution as a process. London, Allen & Unwin.

VOLPE, E. P. 1952. Physiological evidence for natural hybridization of *Bufo americanus* and *Bufo fowleri*. Evolution, *6* (4), 393–406.

18

Adaptation, Natural Selection, and Behavior *

Colin S. Pittendrigh

PRINCETON UNIVERSITY AND THE ROCKY MOUNTAIN
BIOLOGICAL LABORATORY

THE WRITER'S assigned task in this symposium was to discuss behavior as adaptation. Both the concepts involved suffer from vagueness, that common affliction of biological terms; and the simple proposition that behavior is adaptive has been found either too trite to merit explicit discussion or too profound for brief treatment. The main problem in a short paper, in fact, has been to avoid a mere recital of platitudes; and this has been faced, if not overcome, by changing the objective. Two considerations have ultimately dictated the change. First is the view that in a symposium such as this the primary goal should be a mutual clarification of concepts and problems; the evolutionist and the student of behavior should explicate what they offer and what they ask each other. Second is the belief that adaptation cannot be properly understood outside the context of evolutionary process. The most useful course for me has therefore been to attempt a brief explication of adaptation as an evolutionary phenomenon. Some major points are then illustrated by reference to two general studies of insect adaptation in which behavior has played an essential role.

A third consideration supports my decision to go over—even partially—the old ground of adaptation as an evolutionary problem. Like the equally vague term "competition" (cf. Birch, 1957), adaptation has not received the explicit attention it merits in the large modern literature on evolution. Leaders in the modern phase of evolutionary thought, mostly geneticists and systematists,

* Previously unpublished observations reported in this paper were made with the support of grants from the American Philosophical Society, the National Science Foundation, and the Eugene Higgins Fund at Princeton University.

seem in retrospect to have been preoccupied with the dynamics of population diversification at a highly abstracted level; they have been preoccupied, in fact, with speciation and isolating mechanisms. It is true that speciation involves (surely always) the development of new adaptation, but to leave it at that is not enough. There are quite fundamental aspects of the adaptation problem that transcend the short-range processes of population diversification and reflect a long historical chain of transient opportunities and conjunctures of opportunity as the truly creative agent responsible for contemporary biological organization. It is pertinent in this connection to note that our most valuable explicit discussions of the origin of adaptation have recently come from a biologist (Simpson, 1944, 1949, 1953) whose attention has been focused on the historical record of life.

1. ON ADAPTATION IN GENERAL

Adaptation: Teleonomy versus Teleology

A number of writers (see e.g. Medawar, 1951 and Sommerhof, 1950) have noted that the words "adapt" and "adaptation" have several meanings even in ordinary usage. It will be useful to note the commonest of these.

1. Adaptation has been described as the relationship between the organism and its environment. This usage can produce and has produced some confused thinking. It leads to statements like the following being treated as equivalent: "Organism X is fit for environment Y"; "Environment Y is fit for organism X." [1] My objection is that this usage obscures the fundamental asymmetry of the relationship, the fact that the essential nonrandomness of adaptation is due entirely to the organism's (not the environment's) capacity to accumulate and retain information both phylogenetically and ontogenetically. The word "adaptation" should be restricted to discussion and description of the organism.

2. Perhaps the commonest use is exemplified by statements like the following: "The size and surface contours of the premolars and molars in *Equus* are adaptations to grazing." "The capacity of bees to analyse polarization patterns in the sky, their possession of a chronometer, and their capacity to communicate information to other bees are all adaptations serving the nutrition

1. Cf. the title of L. J. Henderson's great book, *The Fitness of the Environment.*

of the colony." The word "adaptation" here denotes some feature of the organism—morphological, physiological, or behavioral—which serves a proximate end (food getting, escape, etc.) that the observer believes he can discern fully by direct observation and without reference to the history of the organism.

Adaptation is also used to refer to those processes whereby the state of adaptation (meaning 2) is achieved. Even here there are two meanings to be sharply distinguished.

3. In the statement "*Apodemus* adapts to high altitudes by producing more red cells" reference is made to the process of acquiring adaptation within the life span of the individual. The capacity to adapt in this way—sometimes called somatic adaptability—is itself an adaptation in the sense of meaning 2. The concept of somatic adaptability covers all those processes like general homeostasis, habituation, antibody formation and, conspicuously, learning whereby the organization (information content) of the individual is heightened with respect to some new environmental situation. But somatic adaptation (meaning 3) takes place without change in the information content of the genotype.

4. On the other hand statements like "Some equids adapted to grazing conditions in the Miocene" imply a change in the genotype. Reference is being made to a historical process spanning many generations; it is the process whereby adaptation (meaning 2) is developed.

These four contextual definitions, while they do not exhaust its meanings, serve to introduce the essential features of adaptation. They all connote that aura of design, purpose or end-directedness which has, since Aristotle, seemed to characterize the living thing, to set it sharply aside from the nonliving. It is the connotation of adaptation—not the multiplicity of its denotations—that has been its greatest burden in the history of biology. For adaptation as a genuine scientific problem was obscured up to 1859 by its association with Aristotelian teleology; and since 1859 it has had a hard time shedding a guilt acquired by that former association.

It is idle, perhaps, to seek discrete beginnings in the growth of any science, biology included; but a strong case could be made for claiming the hundred years from 1760 to 1860 as the gestation period of the life sciences. This case would contend that adaptation is the central and most stubborn biological problem as well as the most characteristic feature of the living thing. It would point to Buffon (ca. 1760) as the beginning: his *Natural History* contains two of three elements essential to the modern understanding of adaptation. He spurned final causes as not materially efficient; and he introduced the historical or evolutionary principle into biological explanation. The first step was not, to be sure, new with him; and he never fully grasped the second step, for his vision of life's history was that of degeneration from pristine perfect types. But the whole tenor of his discussion, especially of the hog, is pointed toward the proper view. It is to Darwin a hundred years later that we owe the third and most important element in what we might call the biological enlightenment. This element, natural selection, is important not so much as the driving force behind the historical process Buffon glimpsed; its overwhelming significance is that it offered, for the first time, a program for the explanation of adaptation that was entirely free of teleology and thus conformable with the dominant scientific conceptual scheme—that of physics.

It is, I believe, worth while to recall these simple historical facts because in 1859 the concept of adaptation was by no means finally clarified, nor rescued from the disrepute of teleology. Indeed it reached perhaps its lowest ebb of respectability about fifty years or more after *The Origin of Species;* and the causes of this disrepute are instructive. The concepts of adaptation and natural selection are so interwoven that it is impossible to misunderstand one without doing violence to the other, and at the turn of the century neither was well understood. Adaptation was still not free of an air of perfectionism which in earlier writers like Paley had demanded "an intelligent, designing mind"; and Darwin's real meaning was obscured by clichés of survival and struggle. The overestimation of adaptation was altogether too much for the current misunderstanding of selection. One has the impression that in the apparent absence of an acceptable (nonteleological) explanation for its origin many students solved the problem of adaptation by nearly denying its existence. Biologists for a while were prepared to say a turtle came ashore *and* laid its eggs, but they refused to say it came ashore *to* lay its eggs. These verbal scruples were intended as a rejection of teleology but were based on the mistaken view that the efficiency of final causes is necessarily implied by the simple *description* of an end-directed mechanism.

Today the concept of adaptation is beginning to enjoy an improved respectability for several reasons: it is seen as less than perfect; natural selection is better understood; and the engineering physicist in building end-seeking automata has sanctified the use of teleological jargon. It seems unfortunate that the term "teleology" should be resurrected and, as I think, abused in this way. The biologist's long-standing confusion would be more fully removed if all end-directed systems were described by some other term, like "teleonomic," in order to emphasize that the recognition and description of end-directedness does not carry a commitment to Aristotelian teleology as an efficient causal principle.

The following sections attempt to clarify adaptation in terms of its origin by selection.

Adaptation as the Total Organization of a Living System

In attempting to go beyond contextual definition of adaptation the close relationship—if not identity—of organization and adaptation becomes clear. Organization is universally recognized to be characteristic of life as evidenced by the general use of "organism" for living system. But like adaptation, organization has been an intuitive and vague biological term. The following two points offer a useful approach to its more exact discussion: (1) all organization is relative and end-directed; and (2) the converse of organization is randomness.

There is no such thing as organization in any absolute sense, pure and simple. Organization is always relative, and relative to an end; it differs from mere order in this respect. The organization of an army is relative to the end of defeating an enemy; and doing so, moreover, in a particular environment of terrain, weapons, and political system. A room may be organized with respect to relaxation—or, perhaps, to work which may demand a different organization. Certainly neither a room nor an army can be organized with respect to nothing. The importance of this point for the student of living systems is that he cannot lightly assert they are organized without being prepared to face the question: "with respect to what are they organized?" There simply is no meaning to the word organization that will safeguard him against this question which so many biologists evidently sought to avoid. And there is little excuse for avoiding the simpler wording: "To what end is the living system organized?" Thus to say that living things are organized is to say they are adapted. It is only the vagary of usage that has so far protected "organization" from the fatal connotation of "teleology." Neither term in fact necessarily implies teleology but both do imply teleonomy.

The second point is that organization is nonrandomness; it is the converse of disorder or randomness. An organization is an improbable state in a contingent—a Gibbsian—universe; and as such it cannot be merely accepted, it must be explained. Organization implies, in modern terms, an information content.

The concept of information as negative entropy has been developed in recent years by engineering physicists concerned with communications networks and the design of automata. It promises to be a useful addition to the biologist's language permitting a new and potentially quantitative way of discussing all the so-far vague and ill-defined notions of *complexity, organization, and adaptation that are, in last analysis, recognized by virtue of their nonrandomness.*[2] The idea of information is the idea of the instructions necessary to specify one particular configuration out of an ensemble of many configurations that are, physically, equally probable. The fidelity with which the improbable organization of fly or rosebush is reconstructed in each new generation is possible only by virtue of transmission from the parent of that information in the genotype, that inherited message, which specifies the constructional steps that comprize development.

This twofold approach to biological organization is useful in several ways. By identifying organization and adaptation the latter concept is put in proper perspective. The study of adaptation is not an optional preoccupation with fascinating fragments of natural history; it is the core of biological study. The organism is not just a system some features of which may or may not be adaptive; the living system is all adaptation insofar as it is organized. Moreover it is still not enough to say that the organism is a "bundle of adaptations" (Huxley, 1942), for this is to imply that organization is an additive phenomenon and that discrete adaptations can be isolated from the system. We must anticipate that, by identifying adaptation with organization, the abstractions necessary for our usual ways of thought will do violence to the real nexus of meanings; the organisms' ends will be served in complex ways unamenable to simple description.

The approach to adaptation as organization is also useful in

2. See e.g. Quastler (1953).

defining the errors committed by balking at a teleonomic description of the turtle. The refusal to admit that the turtle came ashore
to lay its eggs was intended as a pious assertion that a causal
analysis was the only proper course open to the biologist. But it is
clear now that no organization—living or nonliving—is ever fully
explained by a causal analysis of its operations. The physicist,
since Gibbs, demands explanation of the origin of the organization. Thus the causal analysis of turtle motions leaves two fully
meaningful questions unanswered: (1) What is the goal of turtle
organization (including the subsidiary goals of constituent features)? (2) What is the origin of that information which underlies
and causes the organization? A student in Princeton described the
earlier insistence on exclusively causal analyses with the cliché
"Newton or bust." And this puts it well insofar as Gibbs was left
out.

Before proceeding with the implications for adaptation it is
perhaps worth noting another terminological difficulty that arises.
Several writers have recently given explicit attention to the three
lines of explanation open to the biologist and have called those
that arise from our two questions just noted *functional* and *evolutionary* respectively, using *causal* for the other mode. "Causal"
has many overtones, some of which are righteous, carrying the
implication of nonteleological. It might, therefore, be better to
replace the expression "causal explanation" with "physiological
explanation," and avoid the possible overtone that "functional"
and "evolutionary" explanation are antithetic to "causal." For
those features of life at any horizon in time which demand functional and evolutionary explanation have developed by a process
that is itself fully causal in the sense of being free from teleology.
Another way of putting this is to say that an exclusively causal
explanation of life is possible but only if organisms are not abstracted from their concrete history.

Of the two "new" questions we must ask about organizations
like the turtle, the second is crucial: "What is the origin of that
information which underlies and causes the organization?" The
second law of thermodynamics exacts, as it were, a general pay-
ment from the universe in the form of a loss of information, an
increase in disorganization; and we might accordingly restate our
question as follows: "How has the information content of the
genotype accumulated in face of the universal tendency to maxi-

mize entropy?" The only general answer to this question is that outlined by Darwin: natural selection. Selection, as Fisher put it, is a device for generating a high degree of improbability. And, accordingly, it is by understanding the nature of natural selection that we get our best insights into the nature of the adaptive organization it generates.

Natural Selection and the Nature of Adaptation

A key factor in the earlier misunderstanding of selection was the unhappy accident that Darwin himself used the terms "struggle for existence" and "survival of the fittest" as convenient clichés for the process of natural selection which he himself nevertheless saw—at least at times—more clearly as differential reproduction. The clichés of struggle and survival, even for the professional biologist, have focused attention on secondary aspects of the historical process whereby genetic information accumulates. They have focused it on individuals—and it should be on populations; they have focused it on the avoidance of death (perpetuation of the individual)—and it should be on reproduction (perpetuation of the genotype).

For the most part it is only since 1930—beginning with Haldane's and Fisher's books—that selection has been freed of the nineteenth-century emphasis on struggle and survival, and has been seen primarily as a process of differential reproductive success. The very existence of living organization is dependent in the first place on its unique capacity to duplicate itself; more precisely on its capacity to duplicate, and hence perpetuate, the information—the inherited message of the genotype—that specifies itself. The genotype is a phylogenetic memory store; what it gains it preserves and perpetuates by duplication. It is the dependence of long-term perpetuation on the duplication process that generates organic evolution and gives it that unique character of heightening organization with respect to reproductive success. As novelty is thrust into the inherited message by mutation and recombination, there is a slow net gain by the population gene pool of information with respect to reproductive efficiency. Alternative versions of the inherited message make larger or smaller contributions to the ancestry of future generations in proportion to their effect on the efficiency of the genotype to perpetuate itself by reproduction. If we need a cliché it should be not "survival of the

fittest" but "the eventual predominance of the most efficient re-
producer."] When Samuel Butler, that sharp critic of Darwin,
remarked that "a hen is only an egg's way of making another egg,"
he may have spoken more profoundly than he thought. For in a
very real sense the developed organism is no more than a vehicle
for its genotype. At least it is from such a perspective on the hen—
as only handmaid to the egg—that we get our best insights into
the nature of its adaptive organization. Procurement of food and
avoidance of death are proximate ends in relation to which many
aspects of the hen's organization are directed. But they are not
ends in themselves; these ends (and the fragments of organization
that serve them) have been perpetuated because they are in turn
necessary means to the supreme end of reproduction, which is the
sole agent of perpetuation.

The nature of natural selection as differential reproductive success between contemporary genetic alternatives merits continual
re-emphasis because of the light it sheds on problems of adaptation. And familiar as this view of selection may be, its implications
for adaptation are commonly overlooked. It implies that adaptation demands the historical context of becoming and a comparative approach for its evaluation. It implies that adaptation is a
relative matter in many senses; that it cannot be discussed in
absolute terms; and specifically that adaptation cannot be recognized with a criterion of necessity—for—viability. The necessity-
for-viability criterion of adaptation could be called the refrigerator
fallacy, following Huxley's apt analogy: it amounts to saying that
refrigerators are of no use to us today because our grandparents
did well enough without them. The refrigerator fallacy goes with
the older view of selection as being a matter of survival and regards selection as competent to explain only what is essential for
survival. It finds much of life's organization—like the behavior
of bowerbirds, or the plumage of birds of paradise—to be baroque
in the sense of exceeding what appears, a priori, to be functionally
adequate. And what it overlooks is precisely the real nature of
selection. It misses the point that genotypes cannot escape (although they may come to minimize) those processes of mutation
and recombination that force novelty into the genetic message;
and that, just as surely, genotypes cannot escape having that novelty processed by selection. Thus it is inevitable for the organization of living systems to exceed the functionally adequate and

attain an elaboration that is, in a sense, baroque. The refrigerator fallacy would have us believe that mammalian organization is not adaptive because it evolved in spite of the fact that reptilian ancestors were fully viable. Mammalian organization evolved not because its constituent features were a unique and indispensable solution to the problems of land life but because in a historical succession of environmental opportunities mammalian features rendered organisms that possessed them the more efficient reproducers among the alternatives which the then current genetic alternatives realized.

It is pertinent here to emphasize the necessity for a comparative approach in evaluating the adaptive meaning of contemporary forms. The organization developed and perpetuated by selection is always dependent on the genetic variation that the population genotype can mobilize. In a later section it is shown how the comparative study of *Drosophila pseudoobscura* and *D. persimilis* was essential for gaining what little understanding we now have on the adaptive meaning of their behavior. In deciding whether or not the photonegative response of *pseudoobscura* is adaptive with respect to the low humidity conditions of its typical environment, it is quite beside the point to remark on the fact that *D. azteca* successfully occupies roughly the same environment in spite of being photopositive. The significant comparison is with that species (*persimilis*) from which *pseudoobscura* has diverged, both being descendants of a common ancestral population. *D. pseudoobscura,* or its parent species, could well have occupied its present range before evolving the photonegative response that is now one of its conspicuous adaptive features. But once variability permitting photonegativism was mobilized, it was inevitably exploited insofar as it rendered the insects concerned better vehicles of their genotypes than those insects in the same species which lacked it.

Adaptation is thus relative to past genetic alternatives realized by the population, as well as to the particular environment the population inhabits. And since the environment is itself continually evolving we are surely confronted in many contemporary forms with organization that is, as it were, an adaptive anachronism; much of the organism must have evolved as adaptation to conditions—and in terms of genetic potentialities—long since past.

Another feature of the selection process which has significant consequences for adaptation is its opportunistic nature. Differential reproduction as the sole arbiter of biological success is indifferent to the nature of the feature which increases efficiency of reproduction. The consequences of this are among the commonplaces of biological generalization. A given problem—a given pattern of selection—is met by a multiplicity of different solutions in different (and even in the same) organism. As will be seen in a later section of this paper *D. pseudoobscura* has responded to selection stemming from desiccation hazards in a host of complementary ways, such as waterproofing of the cuticle, timing its activity, and behaving hygropositively and photonegatively. In the geographic race of *pseudoobscura* from the most adverse environment we have sampled we anticipated adaptive specialization to the extreme environment, but we could not anticipate that all features bearing on water conservation would necessarily be emphasized. In fact this particular race (No. 306, see below) in our collection does not possess the cuticle most resistant to desiccation, nor is it the most hygropositive. But it is quite spectacularly the most photonegative. There are many ways of skinning a cat—or of minimizing desiccation; and the realized way depends on the contingencies of past genetic opportunity.

The opportunistic nature of natural selection is something more, however, than its indifference to the precise manner in which functional needs are served. It is the nature of a historical process full of contingency. Space precludes an adequate discussion of the way in which the interplay of physical, ecological, and constitutional opportunity (cf. Simpson, 1953) creates a net historical opportunity which in turn dictates how the opportunities afforded by the prevailing genetic variance shall be exploited. This net historical opportunity largely controls the direction and pace of adaptive evolution. It is, however, from such an understanding of selection that we eventually perceive adaptive organization in its true light: not as Paley's perfection demanding an intelligent designer, but rather as a patchwork of makeshifts pieced together, as it were, from what was available when opportunity knocked, and accepted in the hindsight, not the foresight, of natural selection. Organisms are literally historical creatures; and the study of adaptation—of their organization—must become in part at least a historical analysis. It must attempt to unravel the historical succession of ecological and constitutional opportunities that generated the present system. It might be argued that behavior as adaptation is simply not open to this historical viewpoint because the paleontologist has only "structure" to work with. This is of course wrong. In this volume Romer has shown us what the structure–function type of analysis can be made to yield when the paleontologist reflects on the history of behavior. But, more importantly, the comparative method applied to modern forms is as fruitful of historical insights in the case of behavior as it is known to be elsewhere. This is well shown here in the chapter by Hinde and Tinbergen and in the classical studies of Heinroth, Lorenz, and Tinbergen. Analyses of the major features of animal behavior along historical lines are a task far beyond the scope of a single paper; they are a task to which the whole symposium must address itself. The remaining sections of this paper are restricted to a brief description of behavior of a low level of complexity as part of the total adaptation in some *Drosophila* and *Anopheles* species. This brief description nevertheless serves to illustrate some of my general points.

2. Behavior as Adaptation in Drosophila pseudoobscura and D. persimilis

Adaptive Divergence in Water Relations

In the following discussion macrodistribution refers to gross geographic distribution on a continental scale; mesodistributions are between adjacent woodland types (e.g. oak vs. cedar) on a scale of yards to a mile; microdistributions are within a woodland on a scale of inches to feet (e.g. precisely where an insect rests on a tree).

The macrodistribution of these two forest drosophilids in North America is well known (Dobzhansky and Epling, 1944). For present purposes we need only note the generally more northerly distribution of *persimilis* compared to *pseudoobscura,* and the fact that as its range extends southward into California *persimilis* becomes predominantly an upland form. In brief, *persimilis* occupies the colder and wetter end of the macrodistributional range. In the Sierra Nevada of California the two species occur together. Here a study of their distributions spatially (as between two immediately adjacent woodlands, one oak and the other cedar) indicated that there was a similar differential in their mesodistributions; the *persimilis* population (compared to *pseudoobscura*) was heavily weighted into the moister and colder woodland (cedar) (Pittendrigh, 1947, unpublished observations).

In laboratory work subsequent to the field study, we have focused our attention on the adaptive differentiation of the two species in their water economy (Pittendrigh, Hooper, Boyer, and Atwood, 1957). A general problem which both species face is water conservation, aggravated by their small size and the highly unsaturated atmospheres they normally exploit. Their total adaptation to this problem involves a host of distinct features some of which are anatomical, others physiological, and still others behavioral.

Physiologically the feature we have studied most is resistance to desiccation due to cuticular transpiration. The geographic races and species involved differ markedly in the rate at which

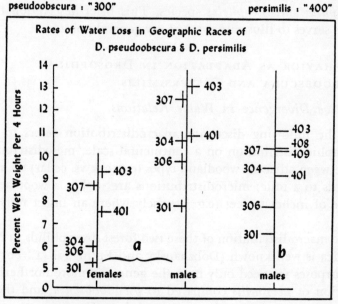

Fig. 18-1. The adaptive difference in rate of water loss between *Drosophila pseudoobscura* and *D. persimilis*. From Pittendrigh, Hooper, Boyer, and Atwood, 1958.

Water loss is expressed as per cent wet weight lost per 4 hours by samples of flies maintained at 0% RH and 21° C. Standard errors are indicated with each value plotted. Males lose water faster than females; and *persimilis* races (400 numbers) lose water faster than *pseudoobscura* races (300 numbers). *a* and *b* are results from two distinct sets of experiments.

they lose water, evidently as a function of differences in cuticular lipids. As was expected, the four races of *pseudoobscura* which we have studied lose water less rapidly than do the *persimilis* races (Fig. 18-1). It is, however, the behavior of the flies which is our principal concern.

Behavioral Adaptation to the Daily Cycle of Atmospheric Moisture Conditions

The 24-hour cycle in the desiccating power of the atmosphere is obvious and well known; and in relation to this cycle many insects, including our drosophilids, have evolved behavior patterns that supplement their anatomical and physiological adaptation. The most conspicuous of such behavioral adaptations is the rigorous control exerted on the time of day at which the adult emerges from its puparium. This is a highly critical event in the life of the fly; at the time of eclosion it is very susceptible to desiccation, and its wings commonly fail to expand properly in low humidities. It is, therefore, of the utmost importance that eclosion be forbidden in the hot, dry midday. It is in fact restricted to the cool and moist time near dawn (cf. Pittendrigh, 1954) (Fig. 18-2).

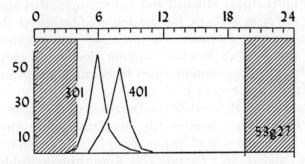

Fig. *18-2.* Adaptive difference between *Drosophila pseudoobscura* (race 301) and *D. persimilis* (race 401) in time of emergence from the pupal case on July 27, 1957 (53g27). Abscissa: time of day in hours; dawn at 4 A.M., sunset at 7:30 P.M. Ordinate: emergence activity per hour in per cent of the day's total activity. Both species eclose in the generally moist period following dawn, but *pseudoobscura* activity is even more restricted than *persimilis'* to the moister hours.

Although this piece of behavior is adaptively related ultimately to the moisture conditions near dawn, it is proximately controlled by entirely different variables. It is controlled by a temperature-independent 24-hour interval timer (or clock) whose phase is appropriately synchronized with the external cycle of physical change. Even the synchronization of clock and external cycle is not brought about by the adaptively significant variable, moisture; it is effected by the dark-light transition at dawn, which is not only reliable in its timing but well perceived. The ultimate target time for the fly is dawn on day 2; to emerge at dawn on day 2 irreversible processes have to be initiated several hours earlier when the external environment (in the middle of the night) is devoid of reliable time markers. This initiation time is identified by an endogenous time measurement from zero hour at dawn of day 1. The points of general interest to the student of adaptation are clear enough; the adaptive end is achieved in a most devious way, exploiting well-perceived tokens (light) for poorly perceived correlates (cf. Pittendrigh, 1958. This paper is still in press).

The mature flies are also confronted with the adversity of extreme desiccating conditions during the middle of the day, and again meet this problem with behavioral adaptation. Their flying, feeding, and sexual activity is virtually entirely restricted to the moist periods near dawn and sunset. Here the behavior pattern is evidently largely mediated by direct response to the condition of the external environment, and there is a suggestion (Dobzhansky and Epling, 1944; Mitchell and Epling, 1951) that again light intensity serves as a token for the less well-perceived (but ultimately significant) moisture. However, we have obtained clear evidence that in adult flies their 24-hour clock again plays a role in identifying the appropriate times in morning and evening; see Roberts (1956) and Fig. 18-3.

The same kind of behavioral adaptation to the daily cycle of atmospheric moisture is especially clear and noteworthy in another pair of closely related insects, *Anopheles (Kerteszia) bellator* D. and K., and *A. (K.) homunculus* Komp (bromeliad-breeding mosquitoes of South American rain forests), which I will return to later in this paper. *A. homunculus* has higher humidity demands than *bellator,* as evidenced by its geographic distribution and other details (cf. Pittendrigh, 1950a, b, c). Both anophelines, like the drosophilids, restrict their activity as adults principally to the dawn and sunset hours. The declining activity through the midday and its rise in the later afternoon follow the humidity regime closely. In the case of these anophelines interspecific adaptive differentiation in behavior is very clear: (1) *homunculus*

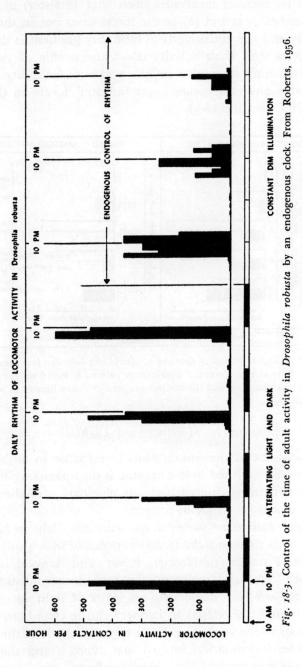

Fig. 18-3. Control of the time of adult activity in *Drosophila robusta* by an endogenous clock. From Roberts, 1956.

comes to its evening maximum even later (moister) in the evening than *bellator;* and (2) as the forest dries out in the middle
of the day and the entire vertical humidity gradient is depressed,
both species shift their activity down the profile of the forest,
thus maintaining themselves in the optimum humidity zone. *A.
homunculus* always occupies lower (moister) levels on the forest
profile (Figs. 18-4 and 18-5).

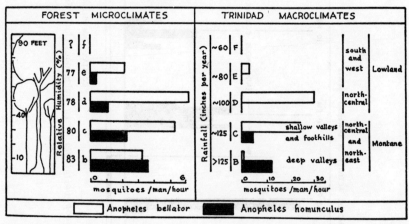

Fig. 18-4. The higher humidity demand of *Anopheles homunculus,* compared with
A. bellator. The same differential distribution pattern is found on the geographic
gradient of macroclimates and the vertical gradient of microclimates in forest. From
Pittendrigh, 1950a.

Adaptive Responses to Moisture and Light

The behavior of the drosophilids in response to moisture and
light is briefly outlined below because it documents well the need
for the comparative approach in the elucidation of the adaptive
meaning of a given behavior pattern.

We have studied responses to moisture and light in laboratory
choice-chamber systems, the technical detail of which will be given
elsewhere (Pittendrigh, Hooper, Boyer, and Atwood, 1958). In
both cases (light and moisture) the procedure consists basically
of scoring "choices" made between pairs of light intensities or
relative humidities offered in two-way choice chambers. The humidity response is very complex in the sense both of the number
of variables (information inputs) that affect it and the manner
in which it is executed. The choice is affected by sex, age, water
balance, time of day (as given by 24-hour clock), light intensity,

and temperature. At least two distinct sets of moisture receptors are involved: the antennae contain receptors that evidently function as evaporimeters (perhaps exploiting the normal temperature sensillae), and the major thoracic bristles are also receptors (presumably functioning by hygrometry). Dry preferences are effected almost entirely by an orthokinesis, while in the selection of wet conditions a strong angular velocity component is involved in the

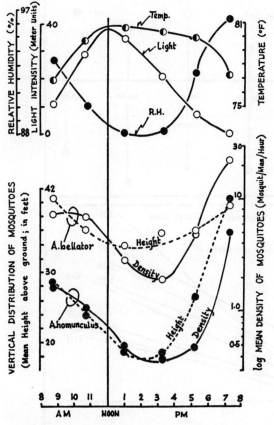

Fig. 18-5. The adaptive difference between *Anopheles homunculus* and *A. bellator* in the daily cycle of total feeding activity and its vertical distribution. The curve of mosquito activity, in general, follows the humidity curve; but *homunculus* maintains, throughout the day, a lower (wetter) distribution and rises to its evening peak (also ascending the forest) at later (wetter) hours than *bellator*.

response. *The organism is exploiting all relevant information sources bearing on the desiccating power of the environment; and responding in a complex fashion also.*

We had expected in comparing the responses of *pseudoobscura* and *persimilis* to find adaptive differences that would explain the mesodistributions observed in the Sierra Nevada. Thus we expected to find *persimilis* selecting moister and darker alternatives than *pseudoobscura*, because, on the average, *persimilis* habitats (on mesoscale) are wetter and darker. We found, however, to our complete surprise, that all the geographic races of *pseudoobscura* we studied selected moister conditions than *persimilis* (Fig. 18-6).

Our first reaction to this result was to view it as a "pathology" of response due to the "artificial" conditions utilized in the labo-

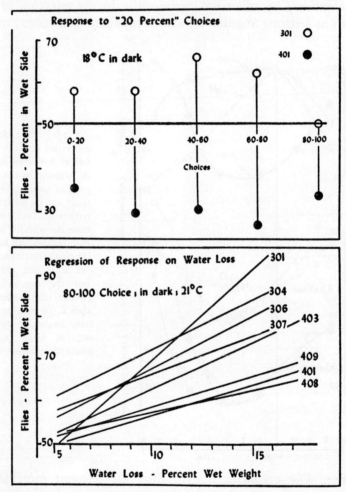

Fig. 18-6. The adaptive difference between *Drosophila pseudoobscura* (several races numbered in the 300's) and *D. persimilis* (several races numbered in the 400's) in their response to humidity choices.

The upper figure shows that in five different choices covering the whole humidity range pseudoobscura (race 301) showed a "wetter preference" than the *persimilis* race (401) collected from the same neighborhood (Mather, California).

The lower figure plots the regressions of response on water balance (expressed as water loss). The response becomes "wetter" the more desiccated the fly; but at all levels of water balance the *pseudoobscura* races manifest a "wetter preference" than *persimilis*.

ratory. This reaction was due of course in part to our strong anticipation of the converse results; but it was also due to our knowledge of the complexity of the system we were studying. I have already listed the array of variables that affect the response. Some of these affect it so strongly as to change its sign. And, moreover, the sign of the effect, as in the effect of light on the humidity response, may be different in the two species; *pseudoobscura* can be made to go from a weak, wet response in the dark to a dry response by turning on the light, while in *persimilis* a similar treatment transforms a dry response into a wet one. Again, for some time we could elicit nothing but a universal dry response out of all our insects *because,* so it turned out, we were carefully agitating the flies, to re-randomize them, in between successive observations. Eventually we discovered that our vigorous agitation was eliciting a special response—presumably a kind of alarm reaction—that overrode the response otherwise characteristic for the strain, sex, age, light intensity, and water balance being studied.[3] It was for reasons such as these that we suspected initially that the stronger hygropositivism in *pseudoobscura* was an "artificial" result; that the behavioral system in the flies had evolved in relation to a particular combination of conditions that we were still not reproducing in the laboratory; and that hence the full adaptive organization of the behavior was still eluding us. We still think that this is a danger constantly confronting the laboratory student of behavior; but fortunately results from a study of light responses lead us to an entirely different position. It seems clear now that the stronger wet preference in *pseudoobscura* is adaptively meaningful and reflects the normal difference in behavior as it occurs in the field.

Drosophila responses to light have been fairly extensively studied, using *D. melanogaster,* which is a classical example of a strongly photopositive insect. Our assumption (Pittendrigh, Hooper, Boyer, and Atwood, 1958), shared by many drosophila workers who routinely "use" the phototactic response to clear *pseudoobscura* from bottles and population cages, was that both *persimilis* and *pseudoobscura* would be, like *melanogaster,* photopositive. At best we anticipated that *persimilis* (exploiting darker woodlands; mesoscale) might be less photopositive than *pseudo-*

3. We are inclined to suspect that this "shake-dry-response," as we call it, may account for the surprising commonness of dry preferences reported in other studies of insect humidity preferences.

obscura. It turns out that *persimilis* is indeed less photopositive than *melanogaster,* but *pseudoobscura* to our surprise is a strongly photonegative insect (Fig. 18-7). The clean-cut difference between the species holds up at all light intensities and temperatures and water balance. It is interesting that in both species the response

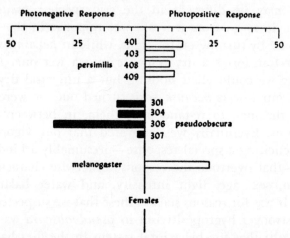

Fig. 18-7. The adaptive difference between *Drosophila pseudoobscura* and *D. persimilis* in their choice of alternative light intensities. Data were obtained with a black Y-tube; flies enter the stem of the Y down whose two arms lights are shone after passing through neutral filters of different density. The flies' response is plotted as the excess over 50% found in the darker arm (photonegative response) or lighter arm (photopositive response). The photonegative behavior of *pseudoobscura* is clear. Data for *D. melanogaster* given for comparison. From Pittendrigh, Hooper, Boyer, and Atwood, 1958.

changes (increasing a photonegative reaction in *pseudoobscura* and tending toward that reaction in *persimilis*) as the temperature rises or water balance deteriorates. This is an obviously adaptive qualification of the response, supporting the interpretation that the reaction to light is part of the adaptive complex directed at maintenance of water balance. Light again is acting as a well-perceived token for the less well-perceived humidity conditions. And again we are confronted with behavior in *pseudoobscura* that indicates a greater "concern" in this species to avoid the more unfavorable (*qua* desiccating conditions) alternative offered to it.

It became clear from our light experiments that the behavior we were studying was not concerned with *causing* the mesodistribution differentials (as between adjacent oak [lighter, drier] and cedar [darker, wetter] woodlands). Rather the behavior patterns are adaptive *consequences* (in evolutionary perspective) of the difference in distribution. Forced by other variables (still to be clarified) to occupy the drier end of the mesodistribution scale, *pseudoobscura* has been under heavier selection pressure to choose the moistest microniches available to it within its generally dry woodlands. On the other hand, *persimilis*, being restricted to generally wetter and darker woods has not been so severely obliged to seek the moistest niches (microdistribution scale). This new interpretation moreover immediately clarified another surprising datum which we had shelved for some time: we had been perplexed by the fact of *pseudoobscura*'s emergence activity's being even closer to dawn than that of *persimilis* (Fig. 18-2). Here again is a behavior pattern adaptively oriented to the moisture regime, less accentuated in the species from the moister woodland.

The student of behavior, more than the evolutionist, may be surprised at the extent of the inherited differences in behavior between the geographic races, within our species. These differences —at least the major ones—are, like the net interspecific difference, adaptive. The geographic race of *pseudoobscura* from the most adverse environment sampled is No. 306 from the hot and dry San Joaquin Valley at the foot of the Sierra Nevada. It is quite clearly the most photonegative of all the races. On the other hand, strain 307 is the most *persimilis*-like of all our *pseudoobscura* strains not only in its light response but also in its reaction to moisture and in its resistance to desiccation. This is of special interest to the evolutionist for the following reasons. Strain 307 was collected at 8,000 feet in the vicinity of Dr. Simpson's home in the New Mexico Rockies. Here it is in an ecological zone (the Transition) closely comparable with that in the Sierra Nevada from which strains 301 and 304 were collected. *D. persimilis* is present in the Transition Zone of the Sierra Nevada and competes with *pseudoobscura* 301 and 304; *persimilis* is, however, entirely absent from the whole Rocky Mountain chain, where the moister end of the mesodistribution scale is therefore more available to *pseudoobscura* than in the Sierras. Here then in strain 307 from the Rockies there is a minimization of those compensatory adaptations that are forced on Sierra *pseudoobscura* by its restriction (ultimately due to *persimilis* competition) to drier woodlands.

The most general point emerging from the present data, and worth re-emphasis on closing this section, is the fact that without the comparative approach we could not hope to discern the adaptive status of the behavior in either species. Nor without knowledge of *both* the light and the humidity responses could we be nearly so confident that we understood the adaptive meaning of either.

3. ADAPTIVE BEHAVIOR IN ANOPHELES (KERTESZIA) SPECIES

Behavioral Basis for the Coexistence of
A. homunculus *and* A. bellator

I propose now to discuss briefly some aspects of behavioral adaptation in the two rain forest anophelines, *Anopheles (Kerteszia) bellator* D. and K. and *A. (K.) homunculus* Komp, to which I referred briefly in an earlier section. These two mosquitoes and all but one of the other members of the anopheline subgenus *A. (Kerteszia)* breed exclusively in the interfoliar water of bromeliads. The epiphytic bromeliads in rain forest retain a well-defined demand for high light intensities that reflects their early evolution as terrestrial plants in deserts (Pittendrigh, 1948). Consequently, the flora in which the anophelines breed is concentrated markedly into the upper, highly illuminated, canopy levels of the forest (Fig. 18-8). *A. (Kerteszia)* spp. are correspondingly canopy species in their typical rainfall zones. However, where the anophelines

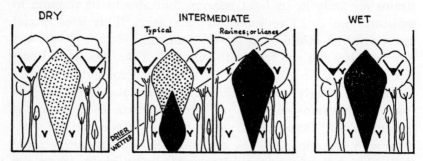

Fig. 18-8. The vertical distribution of bromeliads and anophelines in different rainfall zones in Trinidad, B.W.I. (from Pittendrigh 1950c). Large bromeliads (plotted as large V's) are found only in the canopy; small bromeliads (plotted as small v's) are present in the canopy and are the only plants in the lower, darker levels of forest. Vertical distributions of *A. bellator* (stipple) and *A. homunculus* (solid black) are shown in three rainfall zones: wet, intermediate, and dry. In the intermediate zone the *homunculus* vertical distribution remains high only in a few ravines and heavily liana-covered patches of forest that are wet and dark; in general, it is depressed by the low general humidity and is thereby divorced from the large bromeliads in the canopy.

spread out on the geographic scale into drier areas, their vertical range in the forest becomes depressed. They move downward on the gradient of forest climate to meet their overriding demand for adequately high humidity. This downward shift in dry geographic zones tends to divorce the mosquito from its main breeding ground in the canopy. When, as in the case of *homunculus,* the dry end of one species' range is the optimum for a competing sister species (*bellator*) this downward movement is a severe setback. Thus in central Trinidad (British West Indies) where *homunculus* penetrates the rainfall range of *bellator* it is ostensibly at an adaptive disadvantage because its moisture requirements give it far less access to the main canopy flora of bromeliads than *bellator* (flying higher because of lower humidity demands) enjoys (Fig. 18-8). Indeed the coexistence of *homunculus* with *bellator* in such circumstances is a mystery until one discovers the two behavioral adaptations that give *homunculus* the necessary specialization to avoid elimination in unequal competition with its sister species for the bulk of the flora in the canopy.

There are a few bromeliad species in Trinidad which have penetrated the lower (moister and shadier) levels of the forest. It so happens that in Trinidad (as against South Brazil for example; vide Pittendrigh, 1950c) these are all small species holding about 30 cc. of water, the exposed surface of which is very small and inaccessible because of overhanging leaf blades. Experimental study of the ovipositional habits of both *bellator* and *homunculus* (Pittendrigh, 1950b,c) showed that the latter was better able than *bellator* to oviposit in these small plants of the lower forest levels. The difference between the species is not large, and the adaptive meaning of *homunculus* oviposition habits would again not be evident if we lacked *bellator* for comparison (Fig. 18-9).

The adaptive specialization permitting *homunculus* to coexist with *bellator* in this isolated (island) area of overlap is thus strictly behavioral and has evolved under competitive pressure from *bellator,* which has clear superiority in utilizing the large bromeliads in the canopy. The evolution has exploited the local opportunity afforded by the fact that the lower moist and shady levels are occupied nearly exclusively by small bromeliads. The details of the *bellator-homunculus* behavior differential have not been studied directly. It is however in the highest degree likely that it devolves on the space required for the ovipositional act (Pit-

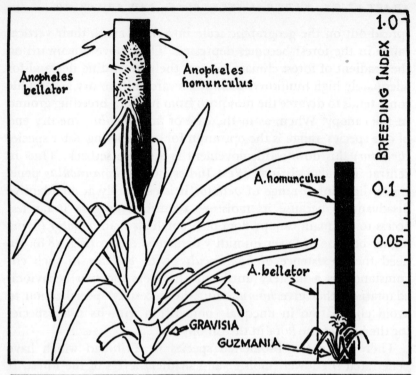

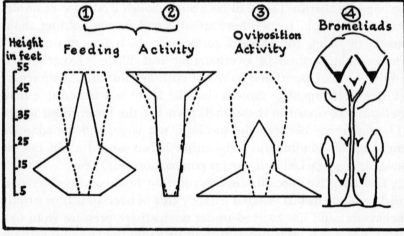

Fig. 18-9. Behavioral adaptations in *Anopheles homunculus* bearing on its poor access to the canopy in most of Trinidad (from Pittendrigh 1950b and 1950c).

The upper figure compares the relative utilization of large (*Gravisia*) and small (*Guzmania*) bromeliads by *A. bellator* and *A. homunculus*. Utilization of the large plant is taken as 1.0 for both insects; utilization of the small plant is plotted as a "breeding index" (decimal fraction of *Gravisia* utilization) for the two mosquitoes. *A. homunculus* makes more use of the small plant from the lower forest levels.

The lower figure plots the vertical distributions of *bellator* (dashed line) and *homunculus* (solid line) activity in forest. The vertical distribution of feeding activity is given in (1) and (2) for afternoon and evening respectively; (3) gives the over-all vertical distribution of oviposition activity; (4) shows the comparable vertical distribution of large bromeliads (large V symbols) and small bromeliads (small v symbols). It is clear that *homunculus* restricts oviposition to lower levels than it has physiological access to; and that these are the levels populated exclusively by small bromeliads, in the exploitation of which *homunculus* is superior to *bellator*.

tendrigh, 1950c). Mosquitoes often demand a considerable stretch of uninterrupted water surface in order to oviposit successfully, as Russell and Rao (1942) showed for *Anopheles culifacies* in India. In the evolution of species of *Anopheles* (*Kerteszia*), exploiting, as they have the small and obstructed surface of water in bromeliads, one of the adaptive adjustments must have been in respect to the ovipositional "dance." In *homunculus* this tendency has reached its limit, so to speak. I have seen *homunculus* oviposit while it sat still on the bromeliad leaf at the edge of the minute "pond" in between the leaves of a bromeliad.

The elimination of a dance and willingness to utilize small, confined surfaces are not the only adaptive specializations in *homunculus* behavior that have evolved in relation to the particular environment in Trinidad. *A. bellator*'s feeding and ovipositional ranges on the vertical moisture gradient are, to all intents and purposes, identical. *A. homunculus*, however, restricts its oviposition to much lower levels than it needs to in terms of its moisture demands: its vertical feeding range is extended into much higher levels than it chooses to oviposit in. The adaptive meaning of this is clear; having gained superiority over *bellator* in the exploitation of the bromeliads that inhabit the lower levels, it now restricts its ovipositional activity to these regions (Pittendrigh, 1950c) (Fig. 18-9).

Exploitation of a Behavorial Opportunity

The behavior of these anophelines in breeding leaves the observer forcefully impressed with the extent to which distributions may be controlled by behavorial convention rather than physiological necessity. In experimental breeding plots (Pittendrigh, 1950b) in the forest we found that neither species would lay eggs in dishes or cut bamboo filled with bromeliad water and its usual microflora and fauna. Immediately adjacent bromeliads were laid in regularly; and the dishes and bamboos were wholly adequate, in the sense that larvae placed in them developed normally. Evidently the only reason they were not exploited was the absence of cues in the form of the bromeliad leaf: cut bromeliad leaves placed in a "vase" of bamboo elicit oviposition when none occurs without them (Pittendrigh, 1945; unpublished observations).

In a group like *A.* (*Kerteszia*) where, as I believe convention in breeding behavior is so important in controlling distribution and abundance, the evolution of a new behavioral convention may often assume just as great, or greater, importance than new physiological competence such as food or moisture requirements. *A. (K.) bambusicolus* is the one species of *A. (Kerteszia)* known that does not breed in bromeliads. However, far from being primitive, its behavior suggests strongly that the new adaptive zone it has entered—intact bamboo internodes perforated by minute beetle holes that permit the collection of water inside the internode—was opened to it by virtue of the general *A. (Kerteszia)* willingness to enter restricted apertures and oviposit on small water surfaces. Here convention opens up an entirely new and poorly exploited adaptive zone.

REFERENCES

BIRCH, L. C. 1957. The meanings of competition. Amer. Nat., *91*, 5–18.

DOBZHANSKY, TH., and EPLING, C. 1944. Contributions to the genetics, taxonomy and ecology of *Drosophila pseudoobscura* and its relatives. Carnegie Inst. Wash. Publ., *554*, 1–183.

DOWNS, W. G., and PITTENDRIGH, C. S. 1949. Malaria transmitted by bromeliad breeding Anophelines. In M. F. Boyd, ed., Malariology, Vol. 2, ch. 29, 736–48. Philadelphia, W. B. Saunders.

HUXLEY, J. S. 1942. Evolution, the modern synthesis. London, Allen & Unwin.

MEDAWAR, P. B. 1951. Problems of adaptation. New Biol., *11*, 10–27.

MITCHELL, D. D., and EPLING, C. 1951. The diurnal periodicity of *Drosophila pseudoobscura*. Ecology, *32*, 696–708.

PITTENDRIGH, C. S. 1948. The bromeliad-anopheles-malaria complex in Trinidad. I. The bromeliad flora. Evolution, 2, 58–89.

PITTENDRIGH, C. S. 1950a. The ecoclimatic divergence of *Anopheles bellator* and *A. homunculus*. Ibid., *4*, 43–63.

PITTENDRIGH, C. S. 1950b. The quantitative evaluation of Kerteszia breeding grounds. Amer. J. Trop. Med., *30*, 457–68.

PITTENDRIGH, C. S. 1950c. The ecotopic specialisation of *Anopheles homunculus;* and its relation to competition with *A. bellator*. Evolution, *4*, 64–78.

PITTENDRIGH, C. S. 1954. On temperature independence in the clock system controlling emergence time in Drosophila. Proc. Nat. Acad. Sci., *40*, 1018–29.

PITTENDRIGH, C. S. 1958. In press. Perspectives in the study of biological clocks. In Perspectives in marine biology. Berkeley, Univ. of Calif. Press.

PITTENDRIGH, C. S., HOOPER, G. B., BOYER, D. D., and ATWOOD, R. 1958. Adaptive behavior in *Drosophila pseudoobscura* Frolowa. *MS* in preparation.

QUASTLER, H. 1953. Essays on the use of information theory in biology. Urbana, Univ. of Illinois Press.

ROBERTS, S. K. de F. 1956. Clock controlled activity rhythms in the fruit fly. Science, *124*, 172.

RUSSELL, P. F., and RAO, T. R. 1942. On relation of mechanical obstruction and shade to ovipositing *Anopheles culifacies*. J. Exp. Zool., *91*, 303–29.

SIMPSON, G. G. 1944. Tempo and mode in evolution. New York, Columbia Univ. Press.

SIMPSON, G. G. 1949. The meaning of evolution. New Haven, Yale Univ. Press.

SIMPSON, G. G. 1953. The major features of evolution. New York, Columbia Univ. Press.

SOMMERHOF, G. 1950. Analytical biology. London, Oxford Univ. Press, pp. 1–207.

PART FIVE

Evolution and Human Behavior

IN ANY DISCUSSION of behavior the old question
of instinct *versus* learning arises, in one form or
another and in various more or less equivalent
terminologies. This book is no exception; several
of its authors have discussed the supposed dichotomy. All the objections and difficulties that have
come to adhere to the word "instinct" have been
cited, and yet there is clearly a consensus (as there
was in the conferences without complete unanimity)
that there *is some* distinction here and that with
suitable disclaimers and explanations the old labels
may apply as well as any. When one turns, as we
now do, to the subject of human evolution and human behavior, a related although not quite identical dichotomy at once leaps to all minds: in any
aspect of human behavior we have to take account
of biological and of cultural aspects that are somehow, if only vaguely, to be distinguished. It cannot,
to be sure, be maintained that the whole behavior
of other animals is "biological" and that man's
ancestors started with a "biological behavior system" on which a wholly different and new "cultural
behavior system" was later superimposed. Nevertheless human behavior does clearly combine elements—and we may as well call them "biological"
—that are phylogenetically older, more widely
shared with others in the animal kingdom, and as a
rule more obviously related to (not necessarily
rigidly determined by) genetic factors, with other
elements—and almost everyone recognizes them

under the term "cultural"—that are on the whole of more recent origin, more specific to man, and comparatively independent of biological inheritance. The study of specifically human behavior must therefore give preponderant emphasis to its cultural elements, but much of its complexity is due precisely to the fact that these are not two separate behavioral systems but are inextricably interwoven into one.

The biological elements of the system are especially considered in Chapter 19, which compares man and other primates and stresses behavioral concomitants of the origin and early history of the human species. It is pointed out that there has been an accretion of hereditary changes in which successive, new behavior patterns can even be correlated with functional, morphological units in the skeleton. Chapter 20 might be considered antiphonal to Chapter 19. In it culture is seen as essentially a biological adaptation, and yet one with its own quite special processes of accumulation and transmission. It is insisted that all evolution involves progress and that cultural evolution continues prior progress in (partly) different ways and to new heights. Conditions believed necessary for that progress are considered, and the dilemmas of stability *versus* change, diversity *versus* unity are exemplified in the headlong cultural evolution of the modern world.

The syncretism of human biological and cultural evolution has, plainly enough, both analogues and homologues elsewhere in the animal kingdom, but nowhere does it produce such ambivalence as in man, the anxious animal, as psychologists see him in Chapter 21. Sexuality, aggressivity, and acquisitiveness, the dimensions chosen by the authors for the major part of their analysis, have deep evolutionary roots. In the human species they are shown to be complexly projected into cultural milieus where they can as well be maladaptive as adaptive, and where the resultant conflicts are as yet far from resolved.

Finally in Chapter 22 the cultural determination of human behavior is considered from an anthropological point of view. Earlier attempts at evolutionary interpretation of the subject fell into disrepute or became sterile, but the desirability of such an approach is now again evident and its possibility is demonstrated. The nature and processes of cultural changes, reversible and irreversible, are discussed, and the cumulation of cultural experience, as affected by gradations of recognition and techniques of transmission, is studied in some detail, with a striking and explicit example in a group that has undergone radical cultural evolution in our own day.

19

Evolution of Human Behavior

S. L. Washburn and Virginia Avis

UNIVERSITY OF CHICAGO

HUMAN NATURE is the foundation upon which cultures must build, and it has long been recognized that the attainment of human biological status was a necessary prerequisite for the development of an elaborate way of life. The factors differentiating between the human way of life and that of the ape are bipedal locomotion, the use of tools, and numerous functions of the brain, especially speech. The tremendous importance of these has been emphasized for a century, having been well described in Huxley's *Man's Place in Nature*. Since the conditions surrounding the origin of man have been greatly clarified by recent fossil discoveries and new techniques of dating and analysis, the main part of this paper will be taken up by a consideration of the interrelations of locomotion, tools, diet, and intelligence.

However, much of human behavior is shared with many other primates, and a general view of the origin of human nature from an evolutionary point of view must describe these features held in common as well as those which differentiate man. For example, stereoscopic color vision, though shared with many other primates, is an important determinant of human behavior. Since the general features of human evolution have been repeatedly described, they have been put into tables here with comments under each section; thus the emphasis will instead be on the origin of those features differentiating man from ape. Before we examine the tables, however, it is well to remember that supporting evidence for the various statements is of very different caliber. For example, the characteristics of the teeth are preserved and can be studied directly, but the probable diet of fossil forms can only be inferred from the dentition, skull, and habitat plus a knowledge of living monkeys and apes. In addition, many of the features most important to the study of behavior do not fossilize at all and can be included in the table only as reasonable guesses from the study of living primates. The reconstruction of muscles has been criticized as "hypothetical," but the evolution of man can be understood only with the aid of imaginative reconstruction. The actual course of evolution was that of a succession of adapting populations, and the phylogenetic explanation of man's nature is the understand-

TABLE 19-1. REPRODUCTION AND GROWTH

	Monkeys a	Apes b	Man
Reproduction			
Menstrual cycle	Yes	Yes	Yes
Female receptive during estrus	Yes	Yes	Female receptive at most times (essential to monogamous family)
Breeding season	None	None	None
Single offspring with great maternal care	Yes	Yes	Yes
Growth			
Rate	Slow	Slower	Slowest
Maturity	2–4 years	8 years	14 years
Male full grown (i.e. socially dominant)	7 years	12 years	20 years
Period of infant dependency	1 year	2 years	6–8 years

a. Old World monkeys, primarily *Cercopithecus*.
b. Orangutan, gibbon, gorilla, and, *primarily*, chimpanzee.

ing of the sequence of adaptive radiations in which man's ancestors took part. It is unfortunate that there are not many more primate fossils so that the history of this group could be understood in detail. However, many of the living forms have changed far less than has man, so that comparative anatomy, ecology, and psychology can enrich our interpretations of the bones.

In general, human reproductive behavior is shared with many other primates, that of monkey, ape, and man having much in common and contrasting greatly with that seen in primitive mammals. Man's distinctive features are the loss of a sharply defined estrus period in the female and the prolongation of the growth period. Both are important determinants of behavior. When estrus is present, the female in heat mates with several males, and the limitation of male sexual activity found in all human societies presupposes that the female is usually receptive. Among

TABLE 19-2. SOCIAL GROUP

	Monkeys	Apes	Man
Size of Group	30 with much variation (to over 75 in baboons)	Same (gibbons exceptional: family only)	Larger
Grooming	Yes	Yes	Yes
Adult males dominate and protect	Yes	Yes	Yes
Canines in male	Very large	Very large	Small
Adult males provide food	Never	Never	Major responsibility (related to tools and the carnivorous habit)
Territory	Very small	Very small	Very large
Shelter	None	Temporary nests	Shelters, houses; clothes; fire
Sounds	Few	Few	Speech

apes, only female gibbons (who have long canines and are almost as large as the males) are capable of competing with the adult males on nearly equal terms; this, coupled with the very low sexual drive in the males, is apparently the biological basis for the gibbon family organization (Carpenter, 1940).

Two notes of special comment are necessary regarding the period of dependency of the human infant, long even when compared with that of the great apes, which grow quite slowly by comparison with most mammals. First, in monkeys and apes the infant is able to cling to the mother's hair without aid although it may receive help from the mother for the first few days. The human infant has nothing to which to cling. It seems extremely improbable that this degree of dependence could be evolved without devices to help the mother carry the baby. The human brain is approximately 400 cc. at birth, or larger than that of many adult apes and within the range of variation of adult australopithecines.

It is primarily during the first eighteen months of postnatal life that the human brain achieves its great size, and the prolongation of the rapid fetal growth rate is probably correlated with the general helplessness of the human infant. If the extreme slowness of human development in the first year is related to the enormous postnatal increase in brain size, it is probable that the difference in rate of maturation of man and ape developed entirely after the use of tools. Other evidence will be presented to show that this is indeed the case.

By the time an ape or monkey is weaned and food no longer provided, it is able to live by its own efforts. This is not the case with man. Hunting, the use of tools to obtain food, and food preparation all mean a very much longer period of dependency for the human child, even at a quite primitive level. As compared to the ape, cultural dependency is added to biological dependency.

There is no evidence of any general trend toward, or groups larger than, those of baboons until after the use of tools. Well-made tools, belonging to clearly defined traditions, date back through second interglacial times, and their makers were probably intelligent enough to be organized in much larger and more complex groups than those seen among living monkeys and apes. Man was certainly hunting at an even earlier time (second glacial times), so there must have been some 200,000 years during which men were living a hunting, tool-using, fire-making, complex life before men anatomically like ourselves appeared. With the latter came human societies having music, dancing, and art, all of which have existed for at least 30,000 years.

TABLE 19-3. SPECIAL SENSES AND BRAIN

	Monkeys	*Apes*	*Man*
Sense of smell reduced	Yes	Yes	Yes
Primitive muzzle lost	Yes	Yes	Yes
Tactile hairs lost	Yes	Yes	Yes
Stereoscopic color vision; fovea active by day	Yes	Yes	Yes
Reduction in size and loss of mobility of external ears	Yes	Yes	Yes
Brain	Large	Larger	Largest
Sounds	Few	Few	Speech

Large canines in the male cannot be related to diet as the males and females eat the same things and the males do not provide food. They are probably related to dominance in, and protection of, the group, both of which functions were gradually replaced in early human societies *by tools*.

In primates the great change in the special senses apparently came between the prosimians of the Eocene and later forms, since those of monkey, ape, and man are very similar. The latter three all receive the same sensory impressions and explore the world with hands rather than with muzzle, but the larger brained forms have greater memory, foresight, insight, and power of abstraction. It is, however, in the association areas that the human brain is especially enlarged; this shows most clearly in the case of speech. Baboons and chimpanzees, for example, can make a great variety of sounds, some of which convey general information, but those sounds are few in comparison with man's, and speech in even a simple form is confined to man. Apes can be taught to associate quite a few sounds with meaning but they are (with minor exceptions) incapable of producing words themselves. It can be

TABLE 19-4. LOCOMOTION, POSTURE, AND MOVEMENT

	Monkeys	*Apes*	*Man*
Locomotion	Quadrupedal	Brachiating	Bipedal
May lie on	Side	Back	Back
Sleep	Sitting comfortably	Lying	Lying
Wrist	Abduction and adduction little and in both mid-carpal and radiocarpal joint	Much more; in radiocarpal joint	Much more; in radiocarpal joint
Forearm	Supination approximately 90°	180°	180°
Shoulder	Moderately mobile	Very mobile	Very mobile
Stretching of arms	Forward	To side	To side
Arm muscles	Big extensors	Big flexors	Big flexors
Thumb	Small, but used	Small (used less?)	Large; great use
Movement	Rapid	Slow	Slow
Viscera	Adjusted to quadrupedal position	Adjusted to up-right position	Adjusted to up-right position

seen, therefore, that the difference between ape and man is in the brain, not in the production or hearing of sounds. Although intelligence is a complex matter, depending on the structure of the brain as well as on its size, it appears that human behavior is impossible with less than approximately 800 cc. of cranial capacity, and that it normally requires much more than that.

The principal differences between monkey and ape lie in the locomotor skeleton, the former keeping the proportions and movements of a small arboreal quadruped while all ape arm and trunk muscles are modified for swinging under branches (brachiation). Man shares these bone-muscle-joint-action complexes with the ape (Loth, 1931). The proportions of the trunk of man and ape also are similar (Schultz, 1950); and the arrangement of the viscera—heart, lungs, small intestine, colon, etc.—is much alike.

In the preceding tables and comments the attempt has been made to summarize briefly some of the information on monkeys, apes, and man which might be useful in the study of the origin of human behavior. It will be seen that many important functional complexes (special senses, most aspects of reproduction, etc.) are shared by all three groups. Because of this, their evolutionary origin must be sought among the prosimians, probably prior to the Oligocene period. Man shares the characteristics of his arms only with the apes and is unique in his brain and way of locomotion. This view of man is put somewhat differently in the accompanying picture, in which the human body is shown divided into three functionally distinct areas each of which has acted surprisingly independently during the course of evolution. The arms and trunk are seen to be the least changed part of our locomotor system—that part which we share with the apes. The bipedal complex developed millions of years later. Finally, the head is shown as that part of us which attained its present form last of all.

It has long been possible to see how the arboreal way of life preadapted an ape in special senses, intelligence, reproductive behavior, motion of arms and trunk, structure and disposition of the viscera, and form of teeth for life as a human precursor. But until recently the lack of fossils of very primitive men made it impossible to do more than guess, in a general way, how a bipedal, tool-using hunter emerged from an arboreal, vegetarian ancestor. Theories of human evolution were further complicated by the fact that some *Homo sapiens* fossils were supposed to be of great antiquity, and many scientists believed that men essentially like ourselves had lived throughout the Pleistocene and perhaps well back in Pliocene times. The discovery of the australopithecines, extremely primitive hominids of early Pleistocene age, and the discrediting of numerous *sapiens* fossils (see Vallois, 1954) for which great antiquity was claimed, have simplified the probable picture of man's origin, suggesting a greater importance for tools

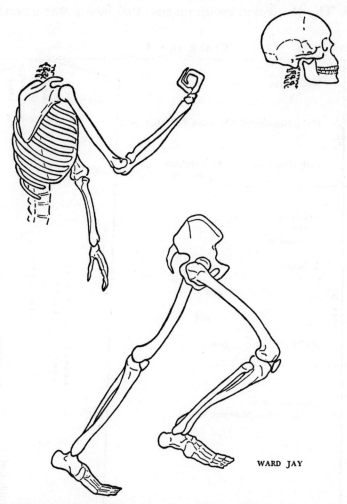

WARD JAY

Fig. 19-1. Diagrammatic representation of the human skeleton showing the three major functional divisions which evolved at different rates and which are surprisingly independent during their evolution.

as a cause of much of what is distinctively human. Probably all the Hominidae were tool users and all men from middle Pleistocene time on fabricated tools according to well-defined traditions (Oakley, 1951, 1954, 1956).

Table 19-5 gives a brief listing of human fossils and tools known from the same levels. The men of Mauer and Pekin were using tools, and it is clear from the great site of Chou-kou-tien that these men were fully bipedal, with femora in the range of variation of living man; they were hunters and fire users, with very primitive skulls. The Java-Pekin group suggests that men whose postcranial

TABLE 19-5 *

	Fossils	Tools	
LATE PLEISTOCENE	Modern man Classic Neanderthal, Rhodesian, Solo, Mt. Carmel Early Neanderthal Fontechevade (*sapiens?*) - - - - - - - - - - -	BLADE TOOLS — Elaborate and specialized; regional variety, rapid change	

MIDDLE PLEISTOCENE	Steinheim and Swanscombe
	
	Ternifine
	
	              Pekin
	
	                    and
	
	Mauer Java
	- - - - - - - -
		HAND AXES, FLAKES AND CHOPPERS
		
		PEBBLE TOOLS
			Improvement Standardization

EARLY PLEISTOCENE	*Australopithecus* (Sterkfontein, Makapan, Taung)		Utilization

* Prepared with the aid of R. B. Braidwood, F. Clark Howell, and Kenneth P. Oakley.

skeletons were essentially like our own had an average cranial capacity of only 900–1,000 cc. or approximately halfway between the brain size of living apes and living man.

The origin of man and his way of life must lie further back, in the early Pleistocene. Near the end of the early Pleistocene there are pebble tools, but it is uncertain what forms of man made them. It is quite possible that the men represented by the earliest Java skull, the Mauer jaw, the two jaws called "Meganthropus," and the last of the australopithecines all belong to this time. Archaic types may have lived beside true men for a considerable period of time and both may well have been making tools. However this may be, tools must have been used long before stones were deliberately fashioned in a way recognizable today. It is because the australopithecines *may* represent such a tool-using (but not stone-fashioning) animal living in Villafranchian times well before any of the fully bipedal, large-brained men that the examination of these animals is critical to any theory of the actual origin of our behavior. These remarks will be confined to the specimens from the earlier deposits (especially Sterkfontein) because the earlier forms seem less specialized in the dentition, more like men of the middle Pleistocene, and seem to be early enough to be actual ancestors of the later forms.

The australopithecine ilium is remarkably like that of later men (Clark, 1955; Mednick, 1955). After examination by the senior author of the original specimens of the pelvis and sacrum from Sterkfontein, through the generosity of Dr. J. T. Robinson, the writers feel that these can only be reconstructed as belonging to a bipedal animal. This view has been criticized (Zuckerman, 1954), but the human ilium is a very specialized, peculiar bone. The australopithecine ilium resembles that of man in those very features which make possible the upright posture and in which man differs from *all* other mammals. The fragments of femur support the bipedal interpretation, but there are some features which are not fully human (especially in the ischium and size of the femoral head). It is for these reasons and those outlined in detail by Mednick that the writers feel that these forms were not as efficient bipeds as man. If some of the australopithecines were ancestral to the early men, there was considerable evolution in the pelvis during the lower Pleistocene. Once the femur had attained the large head and great length (characteristic of all men from Java-Pekin on), evolution in the locomotor system seems to have ceased, or produced only minor adaptation and racial variation. It is possible that the australopithecine pelvis represents an unstable condition 80 or 90 per cent along the way from ape to man. In any case, the pelvis seems to us to prove that these hominids were bipeds, so we must find to what extent they already had the other human characteristics: tool using, large brain, and hunting.

There have been several reports suggesting that the australopithecines used tools of bone. The specimens so far found have been unconvincing. It has also been claimed that the australopithecines killed other animals, but again proof is lacking, and the australopithecines may have been the game rather than the hunter. However, there is indirect evidence which strongly suggests that these creatures were using tools. Man and the australopithecines are differentiated sharply from the apes and monkeys in the size of the canine teeth. Measurements on the unworn canines of some apes and monkeys are given in Table 19-6. It can be seen from the figures that the canines are long, project far beyond the premolars, and that those of males are much longer than those of females. In the australopithecines and man the canines project so little that they wear off flat like incisors and there is no sex difference in size (Robinson, 1956). As discussed earlier in this paper, large canine teeth are associated with fighting, not with diet. This being true, the great reduction of these teeth in male australopithecines implies that the teeth were no longer important for this purpose. Since these South African forms were plains-living, could not have taken refuge in trees, and probably did not run even as well as man does, it seems quite probable that they were using tools. The pelvis proves they were upright, with hands free, while the small canines suggest that fighting was no longer done with the teeth.[1]

The brain of the australopithecines was small by human standards, the cranial capacities of the best preserved skulls giving a range of only about 450 to 600 cc. That these small estimates of capacity are correct is supported by the fact that the foramen for the internal carotid artery is no larger than that of apes. These

1. Tools undoubtedly made by man have just been found in the Sterkfontein deposit (J. T. Robinson, personal communication). It is as yet uncertain what form of man made these tools. Oakley (1957) believes that the tools were made by australopithecines.

Table 19-6. Length of Unworn Canine Teeth in Old World Monkeys and Apes[1]

Name of Animal	No. of Specimens	Upper Canine Height Mean	S.D.[2]	Upper Canine Projection Mean	Range	Upper Canine Width Mean	Range	Length Molar Series Mean	S.D.	Index 100x Canine Ht./Molar Series Mean	S.D.
Cercopithecus (C. aethiops)	8 ♂♂	21	2	14	(13–17)	8	(7–8)	19	1	113	7
	10 ♀♀	13	1	8	(7–9)	6	(5–6)	18	0.5	74	5
Cercocebus (C. albigena)	8 ♂♂	20	1	12	(11–13)	9	(8–10)	21	0.4	93	6
	9 ♀♀	11	0.4	4	(3–5)	6	(6–7)	20	1	53	3
Baboon (Papio doguera)	10 ♂♂	40	4	31	(23–41)	15	(13–17)	38	4	105	10
	7 ♀♀	15	2	8	(6–9)	9	(8–10)	35	2	43	5
Rhesus (Macaca mulatta)	10 ♂♂	24	3	14	(12–17)	9	(8–11)	24	1	97	11
	11 ♀♀	10	1	4	(3–5)	6	(5–6)	23	1	44	6
Colobus (C. polycomos)	10 ♂♂	21	2	12	(10–16)	10	(9–11)	22	1	94	12
	10 ♀♀	16	3	8	(6–10)	8	(7–9)	22	1	71	12
Gibbon (Hylobates lar)	10 ♂♂	19	2	12	(12–14)	8	(6–9)	17	1	111	11
	10 ♀♀	16	1	10	(9–13)	7	(6–8)	17	1	92	8
Orangutan (Pongo pygmeus)	11 ♂♂	31	2	16	(12–21)	17	(15–19)	38	1	82	8
	12 ♀♀	20	2	8	(4–10)	13	(12–15)	34	2	58	5
Chimpanzee (Pan sp.)	14 ♂♂	26	3	13	(9–15)	14	(13–17)	31	2	82	9
	13 ♀♀	18	2	9	(6–14)	12	(10–13)	30	1	60	5
Lowland gorilla (Gorilla gorilla)	15 ♂♂	35	3	18	(14–23)	21	(18–25)	46	3	75	8
	13 ♀♀	19	2	9	(6–11)	14	(13–19)	43	2	45	5

1. Measurements were taken by F. Clark Howell and the senior author on *unworn* teeth from specimens at the American Museum of Natural History, U. S. National Museum, Chicago Natural History Museum, Harvard Museum of Comparative Zoology, and Johns Hopkins University (Laboratory of Physical Anthropology).

2. S.D. = standard deviation.

capacities are within the range of variation of living apes, and the mean for the australopithecines may be approximately half that of Pekin man. If these forms were tool users, it appears that tool use requires far less brain and intelligence than tool making according to defined traditions. Examination of the fossil record, of the tool-using behavior of living apes, and the behavior of microcephalic human beings all suggest that tool use requires much less brain than does speech and might have started as soon as the hands were freed from locomotor functions. Oral traditions essential for complicated human society probably were not possible with less than 700 or 800 cc. of brain, and there is no likelihood that elaborate traditions of tool making are possible at lesser capacities, although simple pebble tools might well be. Therefore it seems probable that the origin of tool making, speech, and complicated cultural traditions lies toward the end of the early Pleistocene and that these aspects of human behavior are correlated with the change from some animal such as *Australopithecus* to the primitive men of the early middle Pleistocene.

Although it is relatively certain that the australopithecines were small-brained bipeds, the questions of diet, possible hunting habits, and use of tools are much more difficult and debatable. Man is clearly distinguished from all living monkeys and apes by being much more carnivorous, hunting and killing large animals. These habits are certainly characteristic of all the genus *Homo,* are present by the time of Pekin man, and are dependent on the use of tools. Human fingernails and teeth will not tear the thick hide of large antelopes or deer, and man had to have tools before he could utilize such animals for food. From the evolutionary point of view it is most unfortunate that the form of the teeth gives so little information about diet unless the specialization is extreme. Although the dentition of the chimpanzee and gorilla are similar, their dietary requirements are very different. If the dentition, stomach, and viscera are moderately generalized, as in man, chimpanzee, and many monkeys, a considerable variety of diets seems to be possible, and the degree to which the basic vegetarian diet is supplemented cannot be inferred from anatomical evidence. The extent to which early man was carnivorous must therefore be inferred from the presence of tools and from the broken bones in his living sites.

The possibility that the australopithecines might have been

hunters deserves examination. Ground-living monkeys, whether macaques, baboons, or vervets, all eat insects, and most if not all apes and monkeys eat eggs and nestling birds. Baboons spend a lot of time digging for both vegetable and insect food. The use of tools of even the simplest sort would greatly increase the quantity and variety of food available. Once the hands were free so that an especially useful stick or stone might be carried from place to place and used repeatedly for digging, crushing, and tearing things open, the way would be open for adding to the diet. However, it should be remembered that hunters in the tropics actually subsist chiefly on vegetable food, and that the first tools were probably used to extend the quantity and variety of this rather than to obtain meat. Our belief is that the australopithecines probably were mainly vegetarian but had begun to supplement their diet with more animal food than is characteristic for the apes. However, the human carnivorous habit apparently depends on tools to such an extent that these forms cannot have been hunters to the same extent as Pekin man. Much of this is pure speculation, however, and definite proof of the food habits and diet of the australopithecines must await further discoveries and excavation.

Hunting as an important activity (in contrast to the eating of eggs, nestlings, and insects) had three important effects on human behavior and human nature: psychological, social, and territorial. Man takes pleasure in hunting other animals. Unless careful training has hidden the natural drives, men enjoy the chase and the kill. In most cultures torture and suffering are made public spectacles for the enjoyment of all. The victims may be either animal or human. This behavior is strikingly similar to that of many carnivores, and no parallel behavior has been observed among wild primates; in fact, our whole conception of wild and tame is a reflection of the human hunting attitude, with the feeling that it is normal for animals to fight and flee. If one watches baboons in one of the great African game reserves, one sees that they move unconcernedly among a great variety of animals, and it is only when larger carnivora appear that the animals react as they do to man.

Hunting not only necessitated new activities and new kinds of cooperation but changed the role of the adult male in the group. Among the vegetarian primates, adult males do not share food. They take the best places for feeding and may even take food from less dominant animals. However, since sharing the kill is normal behavior for many carnivores, economic responsibility of the adult males and the practice of sharing food in the group probably result from becoming carnivorous. The very same actions which caused man to be feared by other animals led to more co-operation, food sharing, and economic interdependence within the group.

The living apes and monkeys inhabit small territories (Carpenter, in this volume). No migratory forms are known, and groups are very localized. Even baboons seem to move no more than two or three miles from their sleeping place, and one soon learns to locate a group of gibbons or forest-dwelling monkeys in the same bit of forest, often in particular trees. The acquisition of hunting habits must have been accompanied by a great enlargement of territory, since the source of food was now more erratic and mobile. For example, a pack of African wild dogs today ranges over a vastly wider area than do baboons. Whether early man scavenged from the kills of the big carnivores, followed herds looking for a chance to kill, drove game, or followed a wounded animal, his range of operations must have been greatly increased over that of arboreal apes.

The world view of the early human carnivore must have been very different from that of his vegetarian cousins. The interests of the latter could be satisfied in a small area, and other animals were of little moment, except for the few which threatened attack. But the desire for meat leads animals to know a wider range and to learn the habits of many animals. Human territorial habits and psychology are fundamentally different from those of apes and monkeys. For at least 300,000 years (perhaps twice that) carnivorous curiosity and aggression have been added to the inquisitiveness and dominance striving of the ape. This carnivorous psychology was fully formed by the middle Pleistocene and it may have had its beginnings in the depredations of the australopithecines.

This view of human evolution attributes to tool using a dominant role in both cultural and later biological evolution. If one views the first stage in human evolution (possibly represented by such forms as *Australopithecus*) as the development of bipedal locomotion followed by invasion of savannahs and plains by an ape, all subsequent human change is increasingly dominated by the use of tools. Increase in brain size resulted from the new selection pressures stemming from tool use. Speech, made possible by the larger brain, was correlated with a complicated technological tradition; and the larger and more complicated society was made possible by the larger food supply. Human hunting depended on tools, and hunting brought about greater mobility, the use of clothing, the conquest of the Arctic by a tropical animal, and so the peopling of the New World. Increase in brain size was associated with a slowing of the growth rate and a much greater period of dependency. This changed the social life, establishing long-term social relations. Thus the hunting life changed man's psychology and the way of life of the human group.

In stressing the tremendous importance of tools in the latest phases of man's evolution and in considering the later phases of biological evolution as understandable only in terms of concomitant cultural progress, one must not forget that the animal which became a biped was preadapted for developing the human way of life. The arms which were freed from locomotor functions were the long, highly mobile arms of an ape. The brain was large and inquisitive, adapted to control the hands in delicate and complicated movements. Stereoscopic color vision gave a rich picture of the world, and perhaps an omnivorous diet gave an interest in everything. The animal could make many sounds and some of these had meaning. Facial expression conveyed a wealth of additional meaning. It is no accident that of the many animals which have become bipedal only man has become a tool maker. Man's way is built on the ape's way, and just as there are many things which are new and uniquely human, so are there many more which are ape-like and monkey-like. As one looks back over the complex and multiple adaptive radiations of the primates, one can see the succession of ways of life which made possible lemurs, monkeys, apes and, finally, a biped. After this adaptation came the use of tools, the hunting habit, increase in intelligence and, finally, the animal we know as man.

REFERENCES

(Star indicates general background references.)

CARPENTER, C. R. 1940. A field study in Siam of the behavior and social rela-tions of the gibbon (*Hylobates lar*). Comp. Psychol. Monogr., Vol. *16*.

*HOOTON, E. A. 1942. Man's poor relations. New York, Doubleday, Doran.

*HOOTON, E. A. 1946. Up from the ape. New York, Macmillan.

*LE GROS CLARK, W. E. 1934. Early forerunners of man. Baltimore, William Wood.

LE GROS CLARK, W. E. 1955. The fossil evidence for human evolution. Chicago, Univ. of Chicago Press.

LOTH, EDWARD. 1931. Anthropologie des parties molles. Paris, Masson.

MEDNICK, L. W. 1955. The evolution of the human ilium. Amer. J. Physical. Anthrop., *13* (2), 203–16.

OAKLEY, K. P. 1951. A definition of man. In Science news. Harmondsworth, Eng., Penguin.

OAKLEY, K. P. 1954. Skill as a human possession. In History of technology, Vol. *1*. Oxford, Clarendon Press.

OAKLEY, K. P. 1956. Man the tool-maker. London, British Museum (Natural History).

OAKLEY, K. P. 1957. Tools makyth man. Antiquity, *31*, 199–209.

ROBINSON, J. T. 1956. The dentition of the Australopithecinae. Transvaal Museum, Monogr. 9. Pretoria.

*SCHULTZ, A. H. 1950a. The physical distinctions of man. Proc. Amer. Philos. Soc., *94* (5), 428–49.

SCHULTZ, A. H. 1950b. The specializations of man and his place among the catarrhine primates. Cold Spring Harbor Symposia on Quantitative Biology. Vol. *15*, Origin and evolution of man. Lancaster, Science Press.

VALLOIS, H. V. 1954. Neandertals and prae-sapiens. J. Roy. Anthrop. Inst., *84* (2), 1–20.

*YERKES, R. M. 1943. Chimpanzees. New Haven, Yale Univ. Press.

*YERKES, R. M., and YERKES, ADA W. 1929. The great apes. New Haven, Yale Univ. Press.

*ZUCKERMAN, S. 1933. Functional affinities of man, monkeys and apes. New York, Harcourt, Brace.

ZUCKERMAN, S. 1954. Correlation of change in the evolution of higher primates. In J. Huxley, ed., Evolution as a process. London, Allen & Unwin, pp. 300–52.

20

Cultural Process and Evolution

Julian S. Huxley

LONDON, ENGLAND

YOU HAVE invited me, a biologist, to give my views about the central subject matter of cultural anthropology, and indeed of human history. If you ask a representative of one branch of science to express his views on the main subject matter of another, you cannot expect more than the fruits of his immediate reactions to a new landscape of fact and idea. This is all I can offer—a series of obiter dicta, doubtless colored by my biological knowledge and ideas. However, they will at least show how your subject looks to an outsider; the attitude will help to arouse opposition and stimulate discussion, and may perhaps serve as a broad background against which individual contributions may appear in a better perspective.

As I see it, culture in the anthropological sense is neither an entity nor a principle: it can only be treated as a type of process. It is not just the sum or even the organization of all "artefacts, socifacts, and mentifacts," but constitutes a self-reproducing and self-varying process whereby the pattern of human activities is transmitted and transformed in the course of time.

As organisms are what evolve in the biological phase of evolution, so cultures are what evolve in its psychosocial or human phase. To put the matter baldly, biological species, with their bodies and their physiological functions, confront the environment with organized systems of self-reproducing matter and its products: the human species does so with organized systems of self-reproducing mind and its products, superimposed on the constituent biological organisms.

In general, cultures are not so highly organized nor so specifically adapted as organisms. Indeed, in the present state of our knowledge, a culture is best envisaged merely as a system of human activities and products which happens to survive and be transmitted and so to possess continuity in time. Cultures will accordingly always be in some degree "adapted" in the narrow sense of being suitably related to their immediate environment. However, since the rate of cultural change can sometimes be rapid, and since a cultural group can unconsciously or deliberately alter its environment, the concept of adaptation as applied to cultures must include a suitable relation to change, both to changes in themselves and to changes in their environment.

It should be noted that this dual concept of adaptation—adaptation to long-term survival as well as to immediate success—has recently been found necessary in biology also.[1] Thus certain types of genetic system permit accurate, immediate adaptation; but they do so at the expense of reserve variability, so that environmental changes (as of climate) may cause their extinction. For continuing success, a compromise has to be reached between the immediate advantages, conferred by inbreeding, of accurate adaptation to the present environment, and the long-term advantages, conferred by outcrossing, of extra variability (and therefore less accurate present adaptation) as a reserve against possible future environmental change. On a still more extended time scale, extreme specialization will also reduce potential variation; so that specialized products of one biological type are likely to be extinguished in competition with the products of a biologically higher type (as happened with most groups of reptiles in favor of mammals in the late Mesozoic).

Cultures, too, though not so highly organized or so fully integrated as higher organisms (as is obvious when one looks at, say, American or British culture today), do of course show some degree of organization or pattern. Cultural organization too necessarily stands in some relation with social organization.[2] However, the relation need not be either close or exact. Thus in classical times the Greeks shared a common culture but were socially organized in the form of separate and often competing or conflicting city-states. A similar situation exists in modern Europe, with the existence of competing or conflicting nation-states within a single

1. See e.g. C. D. Darlington, *The Evolution of Genetic Systems*, Cambridge, England, 1947.
2. I am using social organization in the broad sense, to include political organization.

cultural framework. In other cases, as with ancient Egypt, the boundaries of the culture and the social organization are essentially coterminous; even then, however, cultural and social organization cannot be equated.

Cultures, like organic types, also show differentiation or diversification, usually on a geographical basis. Thus, to take an obvious case, European culture (or civilization—for from the broad anthropological point of view one can only define civilization as culture at a certain high level of technological and social organization) is differentiated into main subcultures, such as Latin, Germanic (Nordic), and Slavic, and these again into subsectors, such as French, Italian, Portuguese, and Spanish within the Latin subculture. Here again the cultural and social boundaries need not coincide: the obvious example is that of Switzerland, in which Latin (French) and Germanic (German) subcultures (as well as others) coexist.

To return to our central topic, I would suggest that the adaptiveness of cultures is best considered as a problem in relatedness, and that the essential relation is the relation between the form and pattern of the culture and what I may, perhaps provocatively, call the group's current vision of destiny. Under this head I would include the current knowledge, ideas, assumptions, and beliefs, often unconscious or only partially conscious, concerning human nature as embodied in the particular group, the nature of the environment, and the relations between the two. It is often, but I believe falsely, stated that cultures are *determined* by their environment —climate, geography, fauna and flora, and resources. It is of course true that they are *related* to the environment, but the relation is not a simple one. It is conditioned by the knowledge which men have about the environment, by the skills which they have developed for coping with it, and by their ideas and attitudes concerning it and themselves.

This applies even to the exploitative aspects of culture, the human activities concerned with getting a living from the environment. In Arabia the same environment which conditioned the development of a nomad culture in the pretechnological Semitic population is now beginning to support a culture based on the exploitation of oil resources, which in previous periods were unsuspected and even if they had been known could not have been utilized for want of technical skill. Similarly, the technical skills of horse training and horse breeding, when introduced by Europeans to the North American continent, completely transformed the culture of the Plains Indians.

Perhaps the most striking examples are those like North America and Australia, where the same environment has provided the basis for cultures at radically different levels of knowledge, skill, and organization. The cultural contrast is most extreme in Australia; but it should be remembered that the high level of white culture could never have been established there without the introduction of domestic animals and plants, of technological skills and their products, and of ideas and attitudes, from other regions. All such examples, of course, emphasize the great importance of culture contact and cultural diffusion in the genesis, development, and transformation of cultures during the process of cultural evolution.

The suggestion that cultures are essentially related to the current vision of human destiny can now be amplified. The most important factor in progressive long-term cultural evolution appears to be knowledge or, to use a more general term, awareness. In this, two elements are involved. One is the quantitative amount and accuracy of factual knowledge, and of its application in the form of skills and technology; the second is the way in which knowledge and awareness are organized, whether in explicit concepts and ideas, in esthetic and ritual expressions, or in conscious or unconscious beliefs, assumptions, attitudes, and general approach. I would emphasize that any over-all progressive trend in cultural evolution can only be detected when the process is looked at on the largest possible time scale. On smaller time scales what is detected is recurrence, as by Toynbee and Spengler, or limited advance or specialization, as in histories covering limited areas for limited periods.

The basic difference between man and other organisms is that human experience can be cumulative over the generations. This clearly applies primarily in the sphere of knowledge, its organization and its practical applications; but increased and better organized knowledge will eventually affect social structure, political organization, attitudes, belief systems, and modes of expression. We must, however, remember that social, political, and ideological organization, once established, can in their turn affect the central process of accumulating and organizing knowledge: the general change-resisting properties of ancient Egyptian civilization, and the ideological opposition of the Church of Rome to scientific advance in many fields, are examples.

From the evolutionary point of view, the most important characteristics of a culture concern cultural stability (self-reproduction) and cultural change (self-transformation). Some degree of stability is of course necessary, and some degree of change is probably inevitable. But, broadly speaking, cultures can be classified into two main types: those which promote stability and resist change, and those which encourage or at least permit change. And this difference is associated with different views or assumptions about destiny. Thus most primitive cultures are adapted simply to securing their own continuance in conditions which are assumed to remain constant.

In general, savage societies accept the continuance of their environment and of their methods of making a living from it; and the rituals (*rites de passage,* hunting or agricultural magic, etc.) and the ethicosocial systems (taboos, kinship and marriage systems, etc.) are designed to give cohesion and continuity to the cultural group. High civilizations may continue to be stability-centered—e.g. ancient Egypt, or historical China with its ancestor worship and reliance on tradition. At the other extreme we have that modern phenomenon: cultures focused on the idea of transforming themselves and the environment, and relying on science and the scientific method, which itself is consciously based on the idea of increasing the amount and improving the organization of knowledge.

There are of course a number of intermediate cases. Sometimes the idea of change becomes operative in one department of life, for instance in nations which become obsessed with the idea of increasing their size or their power by military conquest, though they may be stability-centered in other ways, e.g. in their religion or ideology: ancient Assyria provides a crude example, and the classical Roman Empire a more elaborate one. In the politico-religious sphere, Islamic expansion resulted in a conscious and explosive transformation, but since then socially and intellectually Islam has been stability-promoting and tradition-ridden, resistant to change. Or the idea of intellectual and artistic discovery may become powerful, as in classical Greece. In this case, freedom and change were consciously sought in the ideological sphere but (owing to various peculiarities of Greek culture) not emphasized in technology and the application of scientific knowledge.

In other cases, notably in the French and Russian Revolutions, what may be called the millenary notion of change has been operative: the idea that a violent revolutionary change could and would initiate a new, better, and definitive stable system. This has always proved deceptive, for the simple reason that the process of change, whether in the biological or the psychosocial sphere, does not operate in this way. Though revolutionary periods may occur in which change is particularly rapid and old systems are largely destroyed, evolutionary change is always a dialectic process, in which stability, even if reached, is reached slowly and gradually. Furthermore, man's cultural evolution is so near its beginning that it is now quite impossible to envisage the possibilities before it, and especially to envisage any definitive stable state.

There is also the frequent phenomenon of what has been picturesquely (though not very correctly) called cultural fossilization. This often occurs when culturally important ideas or attitudes become embodied in an organized institutionalized system: the cultural inertia of such a system, together with the powerful vested interests which it creates, will usually promote resistance to social and cultural change. Obvious examples are the institution of absolute monarchy based on the concept of Divine Right, and that of the Roman Catholic Church based on the authoritarian assumptions of revelation and dogmatic certitude; but the phenomenon has been widespread in all periods and places. The fundamental cleavage is between the assumption of continuing stability, leading to backward-looking cultures based on tradition, and that of possible change, especially change for the better, including quantitative change in knowledge and qualitative change in ideas, leading to factual discovery and ideological revaluation and so to technological and social transformation.

When we envisage the matter of cultural adaptedness in the broadest possible way, we see that the basic problem is that of adapting cultural systems to the facts of the evolutionary process in all its sectors, including the progressive realization of new and desirable possibilities. Regarded in this light, the development of change-promoting cultural systems is seen as itself an increasingly adaptive and progressive evolutionary trend. Various steps in this trend can then be recognized. There was first the discontinuous or sporadic appearance of change-promoting elements in various cultures, the most notable being the already mentioned rise of the spirit of free inquiry in classical Greece.

Continuity of the trend has only become apparent since the transition between the Middle Ages and the Renaissance in the 15th century. It began with the idea of geographical discovery, which was soon complemented by that of historical discovery, or if you prefer, the rediscovery of ancient knowledge. Then came the idea of scientific discovery, in the 16th century largely confined to mathematics and astronomy, but soon extended to other branches of "natural knowledge." In the 17th century, thanks in the first instance to Bacon, the idea of scientific discovery was generalized in the concept of scientific method. This was a truly revolutionary event, leading to the supersession, in field after field of study, of backward-looking tradition by the idea of forward-looking attitudes and research. The former inevitably and sometimes consciously resisted change; the latter inevitably facilitated and sometimes deliberately encouraged it.

Rapid cultural change, especially if also progressive, usually stems from the discoveries or achievements of exceptional individuals, but will not operate effectively except in a group receptive to the notion of change and technically and professionally equipped to apply the new discoveries and ideas. As Kroeber has shown, the effective manifestation of the gifts of exceptional individuals is elicited by the cultural environment. The effective application of their achievements is then made possible through the activities of less exceptional individuals in the cultural group. For rapid progress, both an adequate supply of exceptional individuals and also an appropriate culture and an adequately educated community are necessary. It should be stressed, however, that the role of the individual in evolution has increased in importance, not only in the passage from biological to cultural evolution but also in that from stability-promoting to change-promoting cultures.

The promotion of change need not imply the abandonment of the ideal of stability, but it does imply the replacement of a static concept of stability with a dynamic one: the ideas of stability and change tend to become combined in the ideal of integrated process —the moving equilibrium of an ordered transformation. This is the eventual step; in earlier stages the ideal of a stably integrated but directional process was lacking, and change, at least change in certain aspects of a culture, might be regarded as desirable per se, and little attention paid to its direction or to its effects on other aspects.

Before this eventual step could be taken, the fact of evolution had to be discovered. With this, the change-promoting method of science revealed the fact that nature itself was not, as had been previously assumed, a static mechanism but a dynamic process, a process of orderly or at least comprehensible self-transformation. In the heady intoxication generated by this discovery, together with the spectacular results of the practical application of scientific knowledge, a misconceived and oversimplified idea of the change-promoting process arose: the myth of universal and inevitable progress was born.

It remained to clarify and extend the concept of evolution, and to apply scientific method to the study of man, including his values and his history. This has brought us to a fresh critical point. We now are beginning to see the whole of reality as a unitary process of evolution (though comprising three distinct sectors or phases), and man as the agency by means of which that process is becoming self-conscious and could become consciously purposeful. Evolutionary progress, both in the biological and the human sector, is now seen as a fact, but as occurring only rarely and by no means inevitably: from being a myth, it is becoming a subject for scientific study. From a slightly different angle, we may say that cultural evolution, i.e. evolution in the psychosocial phase, can now be seen as an extension of biological evolution, but with its own peculiarities of method and results, and "progress" and "advance" can be profitably redefined as processes leading to greater realization of desirable possibilities.

As our analysis of the evolutionary process in general, and of evolutionary progress in particular, becomes more accurate, as our knowledge of them becomes fuller, and as our application of that knowledge grows more efficient, a new and decisive increase in the adaptedness of culture will have been taken. Human culture will be not merely purposefully but also adaptively change-promoting: the type of change which it sets itself to achieve will become increasingly adjusted to the realities of the actual process, including both its limitations and its possibilities. Man's vision of his destiny will become more closely adjusted to the facts of destiny; and the direction in which he consciously steers will become increasingly "right"—in other words, will have more long-range adaptedness. This statement is not, as some may think, uncritically optimistic. I believe it to be a reasonable extrapolation from past human history. In any case, it is optimistic only in the long run: any such process will take a long time, and will be subject to many temporary and local setbacks. But pessimism is the result of incomplete knowledge or of too short a view: any general or long-run pessimism is contradicted by the facts of evolutionary progress in the past.

So far, I have only been considering what may be called directional adaptedness: the better adaptation of cultures to the process of cultural change, so as to permit that change to be as progressive as possible. It now remains to consider diversificational adaptedness: the adaptation of different cultures or subcultures to local conditions, including of course their history, traditions, achievements, and existing organization, as well as the conditions of their physical and biological environment, resulting in greater variety in cultural evolution.

With the increase of communications, population pressure, economic interdependence, and interpenetration and culture contacts of all sorts, the maintenance of satisfactory cultural diversity is becoming increasingly urgent as a practical problem: with the obvious and inevitable trend toward world unity in all spheres, it will speedily pose itself as a basic theoretical problem. Just as the basic theoretical problem in the sphere of directional adaptedness is the reconciliation of stability with change, and their synthesis in a moving but integrated equilibrium, so in that of diversificational adaptedness the basic theoretical problem is the reconciliation of uniformity with diversity, and their synthesis in a system of variety-in-unity. This appears to me as one of the most important fields for cultural anthropologists and social scientists to explore at the present time. Here I can merely give a few examples to illustrate its nature and its importance.

In general, when cultures differing in level of scientific and technological advance come into contact, the less advanced are more affected. But the result differs widely in different cases. Sometimes the less advanced culture simply disappears, as has happened with that of the Australian aborigines over much of Australia, and seems destined to happen to many tribal cultures in Africa. Sometimes it persists in modified and partial form as a subordinate factor in an invading culture, as with the pre-Columbian elements in much of Latin America; or elements of it persist subterraneously in the basement, so to speak, of the new culture, as with witchcraft and magic in medieval Europe or with voodoo and similar practices in the West Indies today; or it may persist, though with considerable transformation, as an overt but minor factor in the new culture, as with the Maoris in New Zealand. Or it may be eroded or even degraded by the infiltration of cheap, mass-produced goods, as in too many Asian areas today; or by that of new but imperfectly assimilated ideas, as too often when missionaries impose Christianity on primitive peoples. In this last case, new and alarming ideological systems may arise, as with various of the nominally Christian sects in black Africa.

It is an empirical fact that primitive cultures react in very different ways to contact with more advanced cultures. Some are exceedingly fragile and go to pieces under the impact; others are tough and are capable of assimilating suitable new elements while preserving their basic identity and continuity and their essential values. Here is an important field for urgent study.

Sometimes the preservation of less advanced cultures has depended on historical and geographical accident. Thus the barbaric but highly organized cultural systems of the kingdoms of West Africa were saved from destruction at the hands of Moslem (Fulani) invaders from the north by the tsetse flies of the forest zone, which killed the horses on which Fulani military success depended. In general terms, the problem that now faces the world in this sphere is how to ensure that the contact between more developed and less developed cultures (especially as regards technological and industrial techniques but also in regard to political, social, and religious ideas) should have the maximum of desirable effects and especially the minimum of undesirable ones. Or the problem can be formulated in a more restricted way: how desirable elements of advanced scientific and technological culture may penetrate into "underdeveloped" areas without destroying what is good and desirable in the recipient cultures. The usual tendency is for cheap, mass-produced goods from outside (and, after industrialization, from inside) to cause the decay of craftsmanship and the creative arts; for population increase consequent on improved death control to disrupt the social and economic system; for industrialization to create a depressed urban proletariat cut off from local cultural tradition; and for the overready adoption of ideas and idea systems from advanced cultures (e.g. democracy, Christianity, Communism, self-determination, etc.), leading to meaningless slogans, unworkable political systems, nationalist touchiness, and so on. Ideas and idea systems can rarely be imported and maintained intact, and in point of fact usually become more or less seriously distorted and degraded in an alien and unprepared cultural environment, resulting in an undesirable hybrid culture.

When racial (ethnic) differences as well as differences in cultural level are involved within a single political area, the problem may become highly complex. Thus in South Africa the drawing off of male Bantu labor, notably for the mines, is causing a radical deterioration of the social setup in the reserves, while at the same time it is creating a detribalized Bantu proletariat in the cities. And the coexistence of a dominant white minority with a subordinate Bantu majority, with all the fears, conflicts, and cultural clashes that it involves, has led to the formulation of the unworkable and theoretically undesirable cultural principle of racial *apartheid,* and to a potentially explosive political situation.

When the two racial-cultural groups reproduce at markedly different rates, further difficulties arise. Thus in Fiji the immigrant Indian population not only has work habits, cultural background, and attitudes to education quite different from those of the native Fijians, but is multiplying so much faster that it will shortly be in the majority [as this book goes to press, already is]. It is indeed clear that attitudes toward family planning and population control are becoming important elements in the world's cultural setup.

The problem may be illustrated with reference to two cultures with which I have a slight personal acquaintance. India is a large and powerful but in many respects underdeveloped independent state which has deliberately embarked on the task of modernizing itself, not only scientifically, technologically, and industrially but also socially (e.g. in regard to the untouchables and the depressed classes and the large tribal elements in the population) and politically (e.g. in regard to constitution, political democracy, and administration). Modernization has to be superposed on a traditional culture, inevitably dependent on agriculture, and involving such important elements as caste and the village system; pervasive nondoctrinal and nonecclesiastical religion ranging up to great spiritual heights from the depths of essentially magic and sometimes barbaric rituals, rigid taboos and a kaleidoscopic polytheism, and including veneration both for cattle and for holy poverty and meditation; a newborn nationalism of a very particular kind; and various legacies of Gandhi's influence, such as a belief in nonviolence and satyagraha, in the superiority of hand over machine production, in the desirability of prohibition and the undesirability of birth control. It has to be carried out in an environment whose agricultural resources have been impoverished by erosion, deforestation, and bad methods of cultivation, and with a population which is largely undernourished, already excessive, and still rapidly increasing. The picture is further complicated by the existence of strong and often mutually hostile religious minorities, by considerable ethnic differences, and by great linguistic diversity.

Among the resultant practical problems I may mention the following: How to increase the well-being, the competence, and the productivity of the villager while maintaining his satisfactions and without undermining the stability of the village system. How to introduce scientific ideas and methods without either destroying the entire framework of traditional beliefs and practices or introducing a grave cleavage of thought between different sections of the population. Conversely, how to do away with the bad effects of what are essentially superstitions such as belief in the sanctity of cattle, or in the merit of suttee, without damaging the general spiritual framework of Indian life, or provoking violent reactions. In the most general terms, the problem is how to induce the common man and woman to want and to work for desirable change in a desirable way. I am sure that this can be accomplished; but it will not always be easy. On one hand, there is a massive inertia and resistance to change; on the other there is a dawning awareness, even among remote illiterate villagers, that science is somehow making possible a freer life and a greater well-being. But this awareness is still mainly on the mythical level: the limitations in the way of quick scientific application, the need for slow, rational advance in place of magical or millenary wish fulfillment, are not yet apparent. Here as elsewhere the proper organization of public awareness is a prerequisite for desirable change, and right education is an essential key to progress. Truly desirable change can never be wholly imposed from outside; it must be essentially a self-generating process.

Then there is the problem of how to reconcile the potent new idea of democratic equality with the facts of biological and social inequality and the inevitable limitations of opportunity. Here the distortion of the idea of democracy has introduced new difficulties. For instance it is perfectly obvious that there are now many too many college and university students in India. Many are destined to fail; there are not nearly enough positions for the remainder; and meanwhile professors and lecturers are grossly overworked and the standards of teaching and research are being depressed. But any suggestion that colleges and universities should restrict their intake of students is met by the statement that this is impossible because it would not be "democratic."

Finally there are the problems of national unity and of international integration. In both these fields an exaggerated nationalism and an understandable but unfortunate reaction against anything British are creating difficulties. English is the only language that has ever been shared by all the different regions of India; and it is the language which is far and away the most able to help India to advance in all international fields, notably in science and learning. Yet because of the prevalent nationalist spirit it has been decreed that Hindi, though normally spoken only by a minority of the population, shall become India's official language; and, though it lacks many scientific terms and though its adoption will make interchange of scientific and other ideas more difficult, it has been decreed that it shall become the medium of instruction even at the highest educational level. Recently there has even been a recommendation that an Indian national calendar should supersede the Gregorian calendar, which would introduce still further difficulties. These last examples show how important it is, from the standpoint of cultural adaptedness, to distinguish between the sectors where uniformity is desirable and those where variety is desirable.

My other example is Bali. This differs from India in many ways, notably in being a small, dependent portion of a definitely underdeveloped state and in being inhabited by a homogeneous cultural minority (Hindu instead of Moslem like the rest of Indonesia). It is probably unique in that, with insignificant exceptions, the entire population engages in and finds satisfaction from creative activity of some sort or another—music, dance, drama, celebrations of various sorts, decoration, carving, painting; even the normal heavy tasks of agricultural labor are clothed with cultural satisfactions, in the shape of communal rituals of various kinds.

The resultant "cultural democracy" is obviously something very vital and very desirable. Meanwhile, however, Bali is already being exposed to a flood of cheap and often esthetically nasty mass-produced goods; health leaves much to be desired; and in many fields educational standards are low. The Indonesian Government is taking measures to improve health and is introducing education of essentially Western type (with Western uniforms for the children); and it has permitted the entry of Christian missionaries (there is even a Roman Catholic bishop in Bali). Bali is not at the moment overpopulated. But as health measures succeed the death rate will drop; and unless birth control is not merely permitted but encouraged, population will soon outrun food supply. Then population pressure will result in increased pressure toward technical efficiency and industrialization.

In Bali the major conflict is a straightforward one between two desirable ends—the maintenance of a creative cultural democracy on the one hand, and on the other better health and greater intellectual and scientific enlightenment. Desirable ends may have certain undesirable consequences—e.g. overpopulation as the result of improved health; and the situation is further complicated by the intrusion of alien elements under the cloak of freedom— mass-produced industrial products under that of freedom of trade, missionaries under that of freedom of belief. If the Balinese come to feel that their creative activities are in any sense inferior or stand in the way of the better health and education that they rightly desire, the resultant change will be a retrograde step in cultural evolution. Here again it is apparent that compromise is necessary, but the precise nature of the most desirable type of compromise must be determined in relation to local circumstances. Unfortunately speed is also necessary; changes of various sorts are already rapid, and if not corrected may quite unbalance the entire culture. In such a situation, it is eminently desirable to consult real experts —those who have studied and thought deeply about similar problems elsewhere. They will undoubtedly make mistakes, but their mistakes will certainly not be as serious as those made by local politicians in a hurry.

It would be possible to prolong this disquisition to almost any length. There are obviously many interesting points which I have not discussed. There is the long-term nonadaptedness of certain cultural trends—some (like unchecked militarist expansion or addiction to the idea of world dominance) being manifestly in the long run self-defeating; others, like a belief in one's own intrinsic racial superiority, manifestly untrue; still others, like overexploitation of resources, self-limiting. There is the notion of ideas as transmissible, self-reproducible cultural templates; the question whether such ideas are most effective in the recipient when fully conscious or when largely subconscious, when fully rational or with the pill of rationality covered with an emotional or esthetic coating; and how and under what conditions they may be distorted in the process of translation into action by the recipients. There is the problem whether certain primitive cultures, such as that of the Congo pygmies, admirably adapted to their original conditions but obviously destined to disappear if brought into free and full contact with modern civilization, should be preserved intact as living cultural specimens for their own good and for the interest of the rest of mankind; and there is of course the greatest purely cultural problem of our time, of how to cope with the politico-ideological conflict between organized Communism and the Western world—whether by war, hot or cold, by competitive coexistence, or by some attempt at cooperative synthesis. But the limits of my competence and of my and your energy and time make such discussion impossible here.

I will close by summing up my main argument from a rather different angle. In the past half century there has been much talk, chiefly originating from cultural anthropologists, of the relativity of morals, which has often been construed to mean that no type of morality is or can be better than another; much talk too, chiefly originating from psychoanalysts and psychiatrists, but reinforced from the camp of dogmatic religion and obscurantist philosophy, of the nonrational bases of human behavior, which has often been construed to mean the supremacy of the irrational, the bankruptcy of reason, and the inadequacy of science, and has indeed led to a widespread revolt against reason and a glorification of unreason.

Even among professional biologists, who ought to know better, the thesis has been proclaimed that no organism can properly be called higher or lower than another, because all, by the fact of their existence and survival, are "equally adapted." And historians have asserted that there is not, or even cannot be, any such thing as progress in human affairs.

These unfortunate assertions turn out to be quite erroneous when considered *sub specie evolutionis*. Adaptation is not merely the capacity to survive, nor is it merely to the immediate present. It also covers adaptation to change; and when change is so rapid and drastic as it can be in the psychosocial sector, adaptation to change and to the direction of change may become of overriding importance.

As regards *higher* and *lower* in the biological sector, for one thing it is obvious to inspection that some organic types have a higher (more complex, more efficient, and more integrated) organization than others; and for another, paleontology and comparative anatomy have demonstrated that the proof of the pudding has been in the eating—the acquisition of higher organization in this sense has in fact conferred evolutionary success, the more highly organized types having become more abundant and dominant at the expense of less highly organized types. Similarly progress, when adequately defined, is seen as a fact of evolution, both in the biological and the human sector. And finally, when for *relativity* we substitute *adaptation*, in the proper sense of appropriate relatedness on all levels, we at once realize that one moral system can be "better" than another. And a morality which is adapted to a tribal community emerging from ignorance in a sparsely populated world will not be adaptive in a large industrialized community based on vastly increased knowledge in a densely populated world.

Since in the long run the decisive element in a culture appears to be the predominant "vision of destiny," better cultural adaptation connotes a more adequate relation between the formulation of that vision and the facts of the situation, including both the static and directional elements in it, both the short-term events and the long-term trends, both the actualities and the possibilities of the external environment and of human nature. This being so, cultural adaptation, like biological adaptation, will always involve a compromise between many conflicting or competing advantages. Again like long-term biological adaptation, it will tend in the long run to produce organized pattern systems of greater integration and better equilibration. Further, we must never forget the many fundamental differences between organisms and cultures, between evolution on the biological and on the psychosocial level. Besides the totally new methods of transmission available in the psychosocial sector, including culture contact and idea diffusion, and the totally new types of result involving convergence toward unity instead of only divergence toward variety, there is the fact that the average, and especially the maximum, speed of cultural evolution show a marked acceleration during their course, as against their general uniformity in biological evolution; and that in recent times cultural evolution has proceeded at speeds many hundreds of times greater than anything seen in the biological phase. This means that the emphasis in modern cultures must shift from maintenance and stability to progress and change, and that backward-looking visions of destiny must be replaced by forward-looking ones. Here again, education is needed, to ensure that these ideas enter the general awareness of the human species.

There is also the fact (often overlooked or played down owing to the overintellectualization of most philosophers and educators and learned men in general) that in all man's creative activities, including the construction of "visions of destiny," imagination and intuition are as essential as logic and reason. And there is the further fact that if knowledge is lacking on which to build a coherent and satisfying vision, imagination will almost universally be called on to provide mythical [3] explanations and interpretative extrapolations of actuality; and that these imaginative formulations may then canalize and condition the whole culture.

It follows that one of the most important steps to be taken to ensure better cultural adaptation is the application of scientific method to the study of the central explanatory and interpretative elements in man's vision of destiny, with a view to the progressive replacement of mythical elements by scientifically based concepts tested against fact. Note, however, that I do not say *scientific* but *scientifically based* concepts. The analytic and rational concepts that are effective in the natural sciences are inadequate by themselves for constructing a useful "vision of destiny," whose supporting framework must always include values. For this, the scientific and rational basis must be compounded with imagination, emo-

3. I am of course using "mythical" in the same sort of broad sense as Cassirer does.

tion, and aspiration. This is another way of saying that cultural adaptation involves adaptation both to the external facts of physical and biological nature and to the internal facts of human nature —including value judgments and their results. Furthermore, facts in this context must be taken to include our knowledge of future possibility (and limitation) as well as present actuality.

In a few final words, I must try to relate my topic to the more general field of behavior and evolution proposed for this symposium. There are two points I would like to make. The first is that in man behavior has been largely internalized and subjectivized, in the form of concepts and intellectual ideas, memories and imaginative creations. From an evolutionary point of view, human thought and indeed all higher mental processes can be regarded as latent or potential action—internal behavior. My second point is that culture, in the anthropological sense, is an organ of human behavior. A culture consists partly of overt acts of behavior such as rituals, partly of the concrete results of overt behavior in the shape of material artefacts, partly of potential behavior in the shape of assumptions, ideas, values, and other mentifacts, or of various combination of these. Thus in the perspective of evolution culture is seen as an organ of behavior of human groups, and potentially as the organ of behavior of the entire human species. Through human culture, behavior has reached a supraorganismal level.

21

Evolution and Human Behavior

Lawrence Zelic Freedman, M.D.

and Anne Roe, Ph.D.

NEW YORK UNIVERSITY

1

UNTIL RECENTLY it had seemed self-evident that the biological survival of the evolutionary experiment called man was assured. Standing erect, possessing a brain which ranked him the genius of the primate family, with manual facility, visual acuity, and eye-hand coordination of unparalleled development, he had mastered most other animals and much of nature. His prehensile agility, perceptive and cognitive superiority were integrated into a versatility which enormously expanded the range of his adaptability. His creative inventiveness had explosively enlarged his native mechanical, sensory, and intellectual capacities through technological development of machines, calibrating tools, and instruments for the manipulation of great bodies of data. Then this superior creature made—and used—the weapons of nuclear fission. With this, his greatest triumph, man's success as a surviving species could no longer be assumed as a truism, for he now seemed capable of ending his own social-evolutionary progress and of threatening his own survival.

What contributions can an evolutionary approach to his psychology make to this bizarre problem? We propose as a working hypothesis: Man's evolutionary endowment, successful though it has made him, contains within it hindrances to his social evolution as well as self-destructive potential. Unconvincing though this

455

might have been for the social Darwinian of an earlier period, a generation huddling under the hovering H-bomb and which has philologically evolved a new word, genocide, does not need demonstration that the techniques for the elimination of mankind exist or that its psychological credibility demands our acknowledgment and study. We are emboldened to emulate Cassandra with our untestable hypothesis because it provides a useful device for discussion—and you will remember that no one believed her fatal prophecies.

Greater emphasis is now placed on cultural than on biological variation in man. That is (pending further understanding and development of experimentation with atomic radiation), alterations due to learning seem to be producing more change than are genetic alterations. It is probably true of man that his biological survival and social evolution can be understood only within the context of his relationships with other humans. His greatest promise and his most fearful potentialities spring from the nature of these human dependencies. But the evolutionary endowment of species as well as the accidents of life's experience are summated in the psyche of the individual.

Modern evolutionary theory, psychology, and psychiatry are each concerned with the techniques by which the organism and the species adapt and survive. Adaptation and survival are the themes which relate man's psychology and his evolution. In psychic processes also biology interacts with environment. Following evolutionary theory, biological organisms have no longer been viewed as isolated fragments of biochemical processes within a set structure but rather as elements in an evolving process connecting all life. Psychological theory too is now committed to the fundamental significance of the development of the personality.

Darwin contributed as profoundly to our understanding of the evolution of psychological as of biological man. He conceived of man as an animal endowed with superior intelligence and social instincts. He saw in him a self-aware, concept-forming, rational, verbal creature, for whom family ties were coupled with capacity for love and sympathy for his peers and sensitivity to their approval or disapproval. Man's retention of awareness of past experiences and his anticipation of future events provided him with the elements for his self-regulating system. If we substitute for Darwin's emphasis on the social instincts the development of learned social techniques, and if we complement his 19th-century preoccupation with rational man with our knowledge of unconscious forces, we have the elements of a contemporary psychology of man.

Indeed, the appearance of Darwin's work very soon stimulated the development of evolutionary psychological systems. Spencer incorporated it in his magnificent synthesis; Galton's essay on inheritance of abilities and Lombroso's clinical studies on the atavistic nature of criminals were representative of these earlier efforts. In America, James described the behavior of animals and man in evolutionary terms and Hall lectured on the phylogenetic course of human psychology and was pleased to be called the "Darwin of the mind" (Hall, 1923). Freud saw man as a biological being with basic drives derived from his physiology, with behavioral propensities and limitations arising from his anatomy, all modified by his social experience during his life. Ferenczi, like Freud, utilizing a Lamarckian theory of evolution, postulated an ingenious relationship between the psychosexual and personality development of man and his geological-evolutionary history. Others, including Jung, Rank, Adler, Burrow, Fromm, and Kardiner, have emphasized one or another evolutionary principle in their efforts toward a unified concept of human psychology.

2

We may ask to what degree the instinctual endowment of man predisposes him to behavior which is either self-sustaining or self-destructive. One difficulty with this question is that the term "instinct" has become a controversial one.[1] Nevertheless, it seems useful to indicate the relative importance of the constitutional endowment and the vicissitudes of life's experiences. Comparative psychology, ethology, and evolutionary research have revealed wide differences among species in the relative importance of genetic predisposition and postpartum experience in the development of characteristic response patterns.

Introduced into scientific writing by Darwin and developed by the evolutionary psychologist, the term instinct remains an unclear, albeit necessary, part of theory and practice. Freud (1915) once called instinct "the measure of the demand for work im-

1. See, for example, the persuasive discussions of Beach (1955).

posed upon the mind in consequence of its connection with the body." Kubie (1948) developed this into a model which seems to have theoretical and heuristic worth. Instincts, he says, "consist of a) the direct and indirect expression of biochemical body processes, through b) inherited yet modifiable networks of neuronal synaptic patterns which c) are molded in turn by superimposed, compulsive and phobic mechanisms." We feel that such a conceptual dissection of instinctual activity may implement a comparative or evolutionary psychology since it contributes toward a research approach to the relative roles of these interacting levels in different instincts and among different species.

Kubie also points out that deprivation often precipitates the transformation of the biochemical source of energy into behavior by synchronizing the otherwise continuous asynchronous flux which goes on in body tissues during states of rest. These biochemical processes are linked to warning mechanisms which become operative before the organism actually suffers tissue deprivation. In animals that are phylogenetically higher, therefore, instinctual responses are stimulated by warning mechanisms which anticipate tissue deficiencies. The instinctual aims and objects become integrated into the warning mechanisms.

We accordingly hypothesize that psychological warning and warding-off mechanisms, if properly studied, might provide a kind of psychological-evolutionary systematics. Exposure to pain, anxiety, or danger is likely to be followed by efforts to avoid a repetition of the noxious stimulus situation with which the experience is associated. Obviously an animal with a more highly developed system for anticipating and avoiding the threatening circumstance is more efficiently equipped for adaptation and survival. Such unpleasant situations may arise either from within, in its simplest form as tissue deprivation, or from without, by the infliction of pain or injury. Man's psychological superstructure may be viewed, in part, as a system of highly developed warning mechanisms.

Man's instincts, drives, needs, or primary action tendencies do not, in general, interact directly with his external environment. His perceptions, motility, and emotions are mediated by a complex reacting and buffering system, his personality, which in turn is the resultant of his constitutional inheritance and his life's experience. It follows, therefore, that the biochemical, neuronal, and morphological elements with which his phylogenetic history has endowed him serve as a basis for human "psychic evolution." For example, the rate of man's physical development and the nature of his neuronal and hormonal systems seem to predispose him toward certain advantages as well as problems.

Bolk (1926) described, under the term "retardation," the deceleration of the rate of growth and maturation among higher mammals, especially the apes and man. Gestation is significantly prolonged, and the duration of infancy and helpless dependency on adults is greater for humans than for any other animal. This protracted immaturity creates a quantitatively unique basis for socialization, individualization, and intellectual development.

Much emphasis has been placed on the survival value of the increased brain mass of man. Comparative studies among mammals and especially the higher primates have shown progressive enlargement of the cortical mass, increased complexity and refinement of neuronal structure, and greater specificity of function as one ascends the phylogenetic scale. Capacity for learning seems to be proportionate to this forebrain enlargement (Halstead, 1947; Rensch, 1956). In man there has been a great proliferative expansion of this neocortex, covering all the other centers. His neopallial together with his archipallial structures are, in general, the most efficient nervous mechanism in the animal series. They have heightened his flexibility of adaptation to the external environment, increased the versatility of his possible responses, enabled him to abstract, to create symbols including language, to achieve new levels of consciousness, to become aware of himself.

MacLean (1949) and others have hypothesized that while the neocortex is the mediator of specialized discriminating and abstracting intellectual activity man's emotional behavior continues to be under the dominance of a system which lacks abilities for specific discrimination, for verbal or symbolic capacity, or for self-awareness. These centers, previously dominant in more primitive animal forms, have come to serve as the feeling apparatus of the newer evolutionary model. Derived mainly from the old rhinencephalon, it has now become what MacLean calls the "visceral brain." Although the phylogenetic sequence of ascent to higher forms results in increasingly greater control over the animal by the cortex, the persistently strong connections with the lower autonomic centers suggest that the rhinencephalon continues to

dominate the realm of visceral activity. The "visceral brain" provides the correlation center for ordering the affective behavior of
the animal in such basic drives as reproducing, obtaining and assimilating food, fleeing from or disposing of an enemy. "This
situation," MacLean states, "provides a clue to understanding the
difference between what we feel and what we know."

The evidence for this dichotomized system of anatomy and of
function is far from conclusive. (Pribram, 1954 and this volume).
It may prove to be less clear-cut than the theory would seem to
promise. Yet the evidence for some such discontinuity is impressive. The work done thus far is highly suggestive and coincides
so closely with clinical observations that it deserves our theoretical consideration and further experimental observation.

The principle of homeostasis (Cannon, 1932) emphasizes the
role of the autonomic nervous system and endocrine apparatus
for the maintenance of a constant state (Bernard, 1927) through
internal and external vicissitudes and the physiological responses
to stress. Fight and flee responses seem to be mediated predominantly through the lower, archipallial, "visceral centers" rather
than the neocortical "cognitive" brain. This phylogenetically old
apparatus functions in man, who because of prolonged development and delayed maturity is unable to channel responses to
threats and stresses into expressive motility during the earlier
part of his existence, and, because of the neocortical emergence
of social-evolutionary values, is usually prevented from attaining
kinesthetic expression of defense or attack arousals in maturity.
In short, barring war or some extraordinary event he can neither
fight nor flee, first because he can't, and later because he daren't.

These human biological characteristics taken together—(a) retardation or fetalization of man during a large proportion of his
life, (b) the development of a neocortex, and (c) the possible
persistence of an archaic neurological and endocrinological system
partially but not completely under cortical control—may be the
nexus of certain psychological determinants of human behavior
of some significance to our inquiry. For retardation inexorably
creates a social man, dependent on his social skills and dependent
too on a complicated system of symbolic communication based
on his superior brain, for survival. Built into this subtle, symbolic,
social organism is the affective mechanism of the archipallium,

and the endocrine and autonomic systems geared to more primitive stimulus patterns and to kinesthetic and visceral responses.

Perhaps, as we shall see, the "age of anxiety" may properly be said to have started with the emergence of *Homo sapiens*. Man's biopsychology is that of the development of adaptive and survival techniques through the learning of complex social mechanisms. One stimulus for such learning is frustration, that is, the interposition of delay between the perception of a need and its satisfaction. The goal is the resolution of the conflict which results from the dislocation between biological needs and social demands. The prolonged dependency, and the great complexity of his inner neuronal and outer social structure, are among the factors predisposing to wide choice, to delay, and to conflict. The external percept system responds to fine distinctions and social cues, while the internal neurohumoral apparatus reacts with less discrimination and is geared to motor and physiological structures relatively inefficient in limiting its response in focus and in time. All this makes of man an animal with a potent predisposition to the genesis of internal conflict and anxiety.

Only in man is there simultaneously such a rigidity of social channeling and such a degree of potential plasticity and flexibility for the individual. Incompatible aims and choices which are desirable but mutually exclusive are inevitable conditions of human development. This discrepancy between possibility and restriction, stimulation and interdiction, range and constriction, underlies that quantitatively unique characteristic of the human being: conflict.

Man is not the only conflictual or anxious animal. He may not even be alone in his propensity to become neurotic or psychotic. It seems highly likely, however, that his present state of biological evolution makes him the most vulnerable of all animals to psychopathology, and the values of his social evolution make him the animal most likely to survive in spite of severe maladaptive behavior. His capacity for symbolic communication excels that of all other mammals, and the range of his adaptive alternatives transcends theirs, but he is also the most likely to develop pathological symbolic interpretations and to make repetitive maladaptive choices. While all evidence indicates that severely impaired individuals do not have a high reproductive rate, the neurotic and the temperamentally anxious individuals seem to suffer no such reproductive interference. The evolutionary significance of a species which is prone to conflict and anxiety, susceptible to psychic pathology, and capable of surviving in spite of it is apparent.

If conflict and anxiety are implicit in his biological and social evolution, their media are the means of communication. Many mammals, especially primates, have complicated modes of communication, incorporating bodily and vocal signals; but only man speaks. He shares emotional language with lower forms, but propositional language is so far as we know uniquely human. Conditioning research has shown that the capacity to respond to substitutive stimuli (Pavlov, 1928) is not a recent phylogenetic achievement. Anthropid apes appear to be capable of behavior involving prototypic symbolic processes (Wolfe, 1936). Darwin and subsequent conscientious observers of mammals have distinguished an impressive array of communicated emotional states. But the symbolic channeling of affects and action into words is characteristic of man alone; only among humans is verbal communication able to stimulate the ideas, arouse the emotions, and affect the behavior of other individuals and groups.

The adaptive role of a highly developed system of communication for a being who is totally dependent upon interorganism sustenance is obvious. The very plasticity and variability of the human organism demand a complementary range, fluidity, and resilience for the modes of communication. Man's consciousness and awareness of himself, which may differentiate him from other animal forms, are in large part a function of the projective, abstracting, conceptualizing capacity he manifests through the verbal symbol. But the verbal symbol through which are communicated not only the ideational but also the emotional vibrations of the human animal becomes a true projection of the inconsistent, ambivalent, confused creature who created it. The human verbal symbol communicates more and less than it intends; effective as a means for binding individual to individual and providing a biosocial milieu for the group to operate in, it also guarantees that any inconsistencies that exist in man will become part of his social environment.

The human infant, preverbal and helplessly dependent, may be comparable in certain ways to prehuman primates. The stimulus, dimly experienced or acutely perceived, is closely followed by a motor response. Frustration may well be one essential prerequisite for the sharpening of consciousness, the awareness of self, and the development of thinking. Absence or delay of fulfillment of a need may result in tensions which stimulate heightened consciousness and the beginning of a self-image. If the available repertoire of motor actions fails, then certain inner processes may successively or simultaneously occur. The central intervening process may be a visual or mnemonic reconstruction of the desired but absent object, the hallucinatory precursor of thinking. This capacity to imagine desired but unattainable goals, pictorially or verbally, remains characteristic of human adults.

Harlow (1954) has contributed an important addition to frustration and the motivational theories of learning through drive or tension reduction, with his ingenious testing of exploratory and curiosity drives in the macaque. Demonstration of comparable drives in humans is entirely plausible and may prove to be an important complement to other adaptive evolutionary techniques.

Darwin considered natural selection the most important factor in organic evolution, and he also designated sexual selection among the mechanisms through which the best-adapted animal species survived. Among men, he judged from his observations on the natives of Tierra del Fuego that an indispensable requisite of social evolution, of civilization, is the "possession of property, a fixed abode, and the union of many families under a chief." Thus, sexuality, struggle, social organization, and the acquisition of property sum up his essential theoretical requirements for organic and social evolution.

Following this lead, we will discuss some implications of human aggression, sexuality, and acquisition of the means of sustenance. Since it is impossible to conceive of a human who reaches maturity outside of the framework of dependence on adults who care for him (in both senses), it follows that it is essential to our understanding of social evolution to concern ourselves with the becoming of a human being within the framework of his nuclear family.

Our suggested classification is neither comprehensive nor unique; other categories might serve equally well.[2] These do

2. This categorization derived from the senior author's work and had proved very effective for analysis of the forms of behavior against which all societies erect some sanctions. These are also forms of behavior which appear in other species than

represent important facets of the psychology of contemporary man, and taken together they delineate the dimensions of the biological needs of man which must be socialized by him if he is to adapt and to survive. By the same token, if inadequately managed they precipitate social dislocation and psychopathological conditions. War, which among mammals is solely man's prerogative, would seem to demand some understanding of man's collective aggressive, acquisitive, and possibly sexual propensities. Crime as well as mental illness in their outward manifestations, and as inner experiences, reflect malfunctioning in one or more of these three crucial areas. Stated more positively, adaptation in man, and the promise of progress in social evolution, depend on the successful adjustment of the sexual, aggressive, and economic or acquisitive relationships at intra- and interpersonal levels.

The essential condition for the survival of the human infant, and hence for the human species, is the existence of the nuclear social unit, generally the family. The human neonate adapts to a human environment and must continue to do so in order to survive. The necessity to adjust shifts from a biological to a psychological imperative in adulthood; that is, when physical independence is attained. This prolonged, intimate interdependent relationship in the family or nuclear group results in circumstances of provocation and inhibition, stimulation and control of behavior within all these vital areas. It results in a transfer from the individual to the social unit (the family and by extension to conglomerates of families, clans, tribes, governments) of the controlling function. This control need not be continuously imposed from the outside throughout the life of the individual, but during the period of greatest dependency the adaptive mechanisms are normally internalized and become part of his personality. For example, the erotic stimulation resulting from heterosexual animals living in such close association is rigidly controlled by an interdiction against sexual interaction between any members

---

man, and which have direct implications for evolutionary problems. Members of the conference would have liked to have a category of exploratory behavior included as well. It was suggested that a species which exercised its sensory and other capacities most fully in exploration of the environment would have a selective advantage over a similarly endowed one which did not. This is very persuasive, but unfortunately studies of exploratory behavior as such, in animals or humans, are infrequent. Exploratory behavior may be closely linked to behavior in any of the selected categories, but certainly occurs outside of them.

of the family group except the original procreating couple, the father and mother. Relationships between siblings or between offspring and parents are forbidden by a taboo against incest. Some such internalized structuring of sexual behavior is common to all known human communities and is unknown in any pre-human species. Similarly, while the frustrations of family existence may provoke aggressive responses, these are rigorously inhibited in the interest of continuity of these essential relationships. Since the family is a group of individuals which shares food, territory, and property, it follows that the acquisition of such materials both within and without this nuclear organization must come under rather rigid social regulation.

If we are correct in our assumptions thus far, it follows that the members of this species must have developed a number of techniques for the resolution of these potentially maladaptive predicaments. Basic to them is repression by means of which man is able to keep out of his own awareness the incompatible elements in his array of conflicting alternatives. He has also learned to sublimate his socially harmful or unacceptable impulses into more tolerable avenues, to reverse certain instinctual impulses into their opposite and to divert the object of biological drives from outside foci back toward himself. We postulate that some such psychic mechanisms were associated with historical transitional processes in the evolution of the species man as well as in the maturation of the contemporary individual man.

Unfortunately, these and other maneuvers are never completely successful, both because of the inadequacy of such psychological mechanisms to effect an internal resolution and because the external environment is neither static nor consistent. The family is relatively but not absolutely representative of the outer larger community, and neither is internally consistent in its rewards and punishments. These factors may result in another trait characteristic of the human: ambivalence, the coexistence of antithetic ideas, emotions, and attitudes. Access to sexual objects, acquisition of property, and achievement of power and dominance are rewarded by pleasure and social approbation. But denial of sexual interest, renunciation of exclusiveness of property, and abstention from power striving are requisites of family existence and become social ideals. The beloved person is the frustrating agent, and the pleasure-giving object inflicts pain. Activity strives with passivity, maleness with femaleness, even life with death. Man is a conflictful, ambivalent, bipolar animal who achieves a measure of adaptive stability by repressing some part of his incompatible strivings, delaying, inverting, or transmuting others, and fulfilling some.

Our knowledge of these psychological characteristics of man comes mainly from verbal communication of private experience, buttressed by our observations of human behavior. Among preverbal animals incompatible behavioral tendencies have been studied in the laboratory and in the field. Experimentally induced approach-avoidance, reward and punishment, and perceptual conflicts leading to "anxiety" and neurotic and psychotic-like behavior have been reported in the rat (Miller, 1951) and other animals. Analogies to the conflictful ambivalence of humans exist in the reports of the incompatible behavioral tendencies seen in birds and fishes investigated by the ethologists (Lorenz, 1935; Hinde and Tinbergen). Courting behavior in some fishes has been described as containing within it clearly discernible attacking and fleeing tendencies toward the rival which appear simultaneously and successively. Among certain birds the three incompatible tendencies are a) to copulate with the object, b) to attack, and c) to flee. These alternatives may all be discarded in favor of a related but different form of activity which is described as "displaced."

The differences between these postural inconsistencies and human ambivalences of internalized emotional attitudes are apparent. Nevertheless it is impressive to note the biological antiquity of the conflicts found in human psychology between mutually incompatible but strongly felt aggressive, sexual, or fearful responses to the same person or other object. Similarly the "displacement" behavior may be considered the early phylogenetic analogy if not precursor to the interchangeability of human objects and aims. Thus sexual behavior may provide aggressive outlets, and the acquisition of goods may serve to satisfy aggressive or sexual aims either directly or symbolically.

3

Sexuality

By any definition, heterosexual interaction and its deviate forms are basic to organic and social evolution among mammals.

Certain evolutionary changes have resulted in sexuality's becoming a basic factor in the total psychic development of man, transcending its reproductive significance. Man is pre-eminently a sexual animal. Perhaps most imporant is the permanence of the sexual drive among both male and female humans. Alone among all mammals the human is freed of the limitation of cyclical sexual drives, or to state it another way, is never truly freed from sexual aims and object seeking. Beach (1947) has described the progressive phylogenetic decrease in the importance of ovarian secretions to sexual drive in female mammals and has suggested that this change is directly related to the increasing contributions made by the higher nervous mechanisms. It seems not unlikely that this persistence of the sexual drive is an essential factor in the permanence of the human male-female relationship which, with the prolonged dependence of the human infant, results in the nuclear family unit as we know it. From the existence of this familial group springs that other unique sexual characteristic of humans, the taboo on intrafamilial sexual relationships.

Heightened encephalization has, as one concomitant effect, made higher mammals less likely to respond adequately in a sexual situation without learning, than the lower mammals. Nissen (1931) has described awkward and often ineffectual attempts of male chimpanzees to mate without previous experience. Generally rather prolonged practice is necessary before they become capable copulators. While there is little reason to think that the necessity of learning the mechanics of copulation delays genital coitus among humans, there is considerable evidence that what we might call associative learning has so enormously complicated the significance of human coital activity as to interfere with the ready response available to animals less hindered by brain power and by a protracted developmental span. Man's sexual developmental period is longer in proportion to his total life span than that of any other animal in the phylogenetic series.

As in some other mammals, man's sexual arousal is not confined to his genitalia but is intensified and dispersed over his body to orifices, breasts, and the skin surface. Sight, smell, hearing, tactile feeling, and taste may serve as transmitters of stimuli for sexual excitement. This spread and augmentation of erotic excitants is important in man's survival as a species and, as psychoanalysis has shown, in the development of his personality.

Sexual play, including foreplay and grooming behavior in the premature period, seems to increase up the phylogenetic scale among mammals. Erotic stimulation, short of genital coitus, is an important form of sexual activity in humans. Similarly, while self-stimulation is basically a mammalian pattern, it appears probable that masturbation is quantitatively a more important sexual outlet for men, particularly in the pre-adult age, than in non-human primates and other mammals in the free state (Beach, 1947; Ford and Beach, 1951). Homosexual behavior seems to occur in all observed mammalian, primate, and human groups. Only among humans, however, is there evidence for exclusive sexual interaction between members of like sex even when there is no external limiting factor such as the absence of available members of the opposite sex.

Let us consider as one complex the following factors: a) man's prolonged period of sexual immaturity, b) the evidence that sexual activity appears in humans long before genital maturity, c) the prolongation of man's life long after sexual potency has ceased, d) the persistent noncyclical urgency of the sexual drive in the human throughout most of his life, e) the prolonged intimate dependence of the developing child in the family on an adult female, probably also on an adult male, and possibly on siblings of either sex, f) the interdiction on sexual interaction between members of the same family except between the parents, and g) the rigid channeling of modes of sexual expression in the larger social group. All of these factors affect the psychosexual and psychosocial development of man.

This combination of factors leads to certain predictable results. The presence of sexual needs in a developing human who is prevented from gaining sexual access to the males and females in the familial environment, and who may in any case be biologically incapable of orgastic discharge, leads to privation, frustration, and conflict. This conflict situation is insoluble without recourse to repression, which successfully resolves the dilemma by subordination of one aspect of the conflict by the other. The repressed impulse remains, however, as a psychological entity in man capable of affecting his feelings and behavior. Under certain circumstances it may even be crippling to the attainment of full sexual development. Shifting of objects, sometimes to the self, reversal of the impulse to asceticism, or sublimation into social or creative goals may occur.

The prolonged learning period of man, his encephalization, his relative plasticity, his infinitely greater range of choices, and his aptitude for symbolization result in rich potential variability of his sexual patterns. In fact, however, the interdependence of the human social group and the strict and effective taboos during the developmental period serve as highly effective structuring mechanisms tending toward an impressive conformity as to the techniques and objects employed for sexual outlets, in spite of polymorphous mammalian endowment and relative freedom from inherited patterns.

The most common inhibitions placed on human sexual behavior seem to have adaptive value for biological and social evolution even though these are almost never given as the explanation for invoking them. The incest taboo is apparently related to the survival of the nuclear family unit, which in turn seems to be a prerequisite for the biological survival of the human offspring. Speculatively, near-human species resembling *Homo sapiens* in other characteristics may not have been able to compete with the efficiency of the mutually reinforcing family unit or group system. Homosexuality, sexual behavior between individuals with marked age disparity, and nongenital contacts have in common the fact that they do not result in reproduction. Reproduction is obviously the one completely essential requirement for survival of any species.

Even the family-engendered pattern of sexual arousal associated with sexual frustration may have a species survival significance beyond that of biological procreation. Frustrated in his sexual access to a desired object, the human being is capable of subordinating, repressing the sexual component, and through sublimation redirecting the affectionate interpersonal component to the larger group—to a love of family and to his community, state, and the world.

4

Aggressivity

The human species has survived through its sexual activity, but the method of obtaining a partner is often competitive and frequently combative. Darwin called attention to the sexual advantage adhering to the aggressive male both in subduing other males and in maintaining his sexual dominance over the female.

It is not an uncommon clinical discovery that the sexuality of male and female humans contains elements of aggressiveness. Man is also a predatory animal who pursues or breeds other animals in order to kill them for his food. Man is vulnerable and must defend himself against his physical, animal, and human environment. Indeed his arboreal, herbivorous ancestors may have survived by their skill in retreats and by dietary predilections which freed them from excessive conflict. To become terrestrial and carnivorous may have involved a behavioral transition from a retreating to an attacking pattern. Clinically we know that inner alarm and outer aggression are not uncharacteristic of man; possibly he is reflecting his mixed evolutionary heritage. Certainly a level of aggressivity is adaptive and essential for survival.

Although fight or flee responses to stress, the studies on "sham rage," and aggressive responses when certain areas on the brain are stimulated are well described (Cannon, 1932; Selye, 1950; Bard, 1941), we have no knowledge of a mechanism of physiological discharge of aggressive tension comparable to the culmination in orgasm or ejaculation of sexual arousal. Nor do we have information concerning the existence of any particular specialized organs which are adapted to aggressive stimulation and response, comparable to the erotic areas. There is some information concerning anatomical loci and biochemical excitants of aggressive behavior but it is as yet incomplete (Fulton, 1951).

Some observers (Freedman and Rosvold, in preparation) have noted markedly increased aggressive as well as sexual behavior in the female macaque after implantation of large amounts of estrogen. But whether this aggresiveness is the consequence of sheer heightened activity or cerebral irritation or is a psychic concomitant of greater sexual excitement is not known.

Freud (1920) considered aggression to be self-destructive instincts which are turned outward to other persons and the world. We need not accept this far-reaching hypothesis to confirm his clinical observation that aggressiveness, or even destructiveness, is a characteristic of human beings. Adler stressed aggressiveness as universal human overcompensation for feelings of inferiority and insecurity.

The degree to which aggressivity is determined by constitutional predispositions or is learned, the resultant of reactions to frustrations during the life history of the person, has not been determined. But thus far no environment has provided, at least to any mammalian group, a frustration-free life experience, nor has an aggression-free species appeared. The distinction between physical aggressiveness and psychic aggressiveness is the difference between behavior and fantasy, the act and the idea. But physical aggressiveness is the antecedent; the "drive" is a necessary precondition of the thought.

In the laboratory, experiments have demonstrated a relationship between genetic make-up and propensity toward aggressive behavior among rats and mice. Certain aggressive strains of mice consistently defeat individuals from less aggressive strains (Hall and Klein, 1942; Ginsburg and Allee, 1942). The possible adaptive and survival value of this trait is apparent. The important role of aggressivity in the courting and mating behavior of some birds and fishes has been beautifully described by a number of ethologists and biologists (Tinbergen, 1956; Hinde, 1956; Beach, 1947). In addition to behavioral significance, display, threat, and combat appear to have a ripening effect on the reproductive organs of male and female birds (Lack, 1943). The social efficiency of these maneuvers is shown by the observation that among mammals where there is little courtship or display by the males there tends to be more fighting (Huxley, 1948). Sexual response may appear in the presence of a number of different kinds of apparently nonsexual excitements, probably including aggression (Ford and Beach, 1951). Among most mammals the male characteristically initiates the relationship and maintains the dominant and even aggressive role. With humans, aggression as a sexual excitement is most dramatically evident in sadism and masochism, but some elements of it probably play a role in all human sexuality—not to mention provocative display and ambivalent fleeing tendencies.

We have some medical evidence that a propensity to aggressivity in humans exists as part of their genetic endowment. In very young children, in whom we always find some such tendencies, an increase in general motility is often accompanied by greater destructive and aggressive activity. A constitutional basis in children is clearly shown following neurological diseases, when aggressive behavior is not infrequently part of the postencephalitic syndrome. Youngsters who are constitutionally hyperkinetic are likely to be more aggressive and destructive than their normal peers. Even moderate attempts by adults at checking this excessive activity create a frustration which is likely to superimpose a reactive aggressivity on an organic one (Schilder, 1936). Aggressiveness in a child may be provoked by a wide range of conditions and stimuli, by pain or punishment, by the restriction of motility, deprivation of nutrition or warmth, and the withholding of love.

The family social organization characteristic of humans tends to promote conformity and passivity and to limit spontaneous nonconformist behavior and aggressivity. A child who is totally dependent on others must tailor his behavior to the dominant figures. Aggressive feelings can be translated into action only to the degree that such behavior is tolerated. Successful complete revolt against the parents is impossible, and the impulse must be repressed or other, less dangerous, outlets sought. Aggressive ideas must be relegated to the unconscious, whence they will crop out again from time to time in fantasies or by indirection. The child finds outlets in play or he may react against any aggressive forms of behavior, becoming entirely passive. The fate of the aggressive impulse may be compared to that of the sexual impulse. Inhibition of the outlets results in denial, in displacements and reversals of goals and of objects, and in conscious and unconscious fantasy.

If sexuality is the attracting force, aggressivity is the deterrent force to incest. It is fear of the counteraggression of the powerful parental figure which inhibits overt maneuvers toward gaining access to the desired sexual object whithin the family. Here we are on familiar phylogenetic ground. In most animals with social or group-forming habits the dominant male aggressively drives away other covetous but less powerful males, including sons, from his mates (Darwin).

Among most mammals, and especially primates, physical size, prowess, and aggressive activity favor the males. Although anthropologists have reported cultures where this distinction does not hold, it remains essentially true of most humans. In our culture the socially assumed masculine role is active or aggressive, the feminine role is passive. However, while aggressive behavior, as manifested for example by crime statistics and the role of the male in wars, is apparently a masculine trait, psychic aggressivity shows no such disposition to sex difference.

Yet tendencies toward mastery over inanimate and animate objects needs not be socially destructive; they can serve constructive goals and have considerable social utility. Certainly there are deep forces in man leading toward cooperation. These include not only sexuality but also aggressivity itself. The plasticity of the human organism makes for a richness of individual methods available for the discharge of fundamental drives through socially constructive channels.

5

Acquisivity

Acquisivity is an unusual category to appear in a psychological and psychiatric discussion, even one which has wandered so far from its clinical base. By this term we mean propensities and behavior directed toward acquiring substances which may be nutritive, such as food, or protective, such as clothing and shelter. Territory, and supportive relations with other animals may also be acquired. The heterogeneity of those objects will be obvious; we trust it is equally apparent that acquisition of these objects is essential for human survival. There is also the historical precedent of Darwin who made his final analogic leap to the integrating evolutionary hypothesis after reading Malthus' theory that competition for the means of subsistence would result in the impoverishment of a significant proportion of mankind due to predictable, progressive overpopulation.

Acquisivity, then, is a ubiquitous psychosocial phenomenon that is possibly of considerable evolutionary significance. It is a category of behavior which implicitly contains within its definition not only the actor, human or subhuman, but the object, which is most frequently not human. This delineation demands consideration of the specific reciprocal relationship between the environment, social or geographical, and the psychological organism. Both psychological and evolutionary adaptation have meaning and significance only when we are aware of the immediate congruency of the adapting organism and its environment.

Indeed, Simpson (1949) has indicated how evolution may be followed through a series of different adaptive zones which are occupied by the organism. Bates (1955, 1956) has observed that these adaptive zones frequently are characterized by such food-acquiring features as organs for grazing or for capturing prey. He points out also that the distinguishing characteristics of major groups of animals are frequently related to anatomical or behavioral factors which turn around food habits. For example, "Mammalia" and "Carnivora" are ordinal names descriptive of food-acquiring techniques. Methods of acquiring food are intimately related to the psychological and social habits of all animals and to their physical and nervous processes. Evans' (1940) findings of variation in neuroanatomical development among fish with differing hunting and feeding habits exemplify this.

Highly developed territorial behavior and food-gathering techniques among birds for the protection and sustenance of the nestlings have been described (e.g., Lack, 1943). The territorial system of the Atlantic seal, which is male-dominated, is designed for mating; it is contrasted with the matriarchal territorial organization of the red hind deer, with a prolonged parental tradition. The great economic efficiency of such territorial behavior in promoting reproduction, stability of population density, the mantenance of adequate feeding terrain, and the implementation of social cohesion has been stressed by Darling (1955, 1956). He compares the "beautiful biological economy" of this territorial behavior with human political territoriality based on group competition. With the possible exception of the social insects, man seems to have achieved the most complex patterns of territorial, food-getting and group existence, revolving around the family unit. Generally, among lower primates, mother-child nutritive and sustenance units are the rule. However, gibbons show a true family organization, with the procreating couple raising their offspring (Carpenter, 1940).

Man's prolonged developmental period is one of dependence for food and protection. The child must acquire such support from other humans if he is to survive. The social evolution of *Homo sapiens* might be traced systematically through the development of techniques for acquiring his means of subsistence and for safeguarding them. His remarkable transition from Paleolithic hunter and gatherer to Neolithic stock-piling agriculturalist and manufacturer has obvious survival value for the species and has fundamental importance in the personality structure of the individual. For example, the shift from spending most waking hours searching or working for food to a condition in which this effort occupies only a portion of the energy output must be as basic to the determination of the psychological structure of its participants as to their physical survival. Prolonged deprivation of parental care has quite different significance for the child in a hunting or primitive agricultural culture than it has for the child whose parents are relatively free from constant preoccupation with food production.

For the human neonate, the primary social bond is with his mother, and it is a basically nutritional and affinitive one. Other essential survival requirements involved in this relationship include protection and physical contiguity and affectionate care from another human being. Spitz (1945) has demonstrated that the absence of physical touching and exchange of affecting results, even though all other wants are satisfied, in markedly increased morbidity, marasmas (wasting), and mortality in human infants.

Excessive deprivation of needed subsistence would, of course, result in death; but relative deprivation, due either to quantities insufficient to satisfy the physiological demands or to too great a separation in time from the rhythmical arousal of the "nutritive tension" and the proffered satisfaction, is an almost unavoidable accompaniment of human development. This has important developmental consequences for the child. Indeed, if food deprivation is a consistent characteristic, as it was among the Marquesans, it might result in making hunger a significant psychological need which becomes part of the institutional structure of that adult culture (Linton, 1939).

In the earliest life experience acquisition is restricted to symbiotic relations to the mother. The father and siblings may later assume a role, and finally peers and the larger community become the source of acquisition of the nutritive and sustaining objects. Thus acquisition of the goods of life, once limited to a single nutritive process, is generalized to clothes, shelter, and other properties. The human capacity for attaching symbolic significance to other kinds of human experience applies to these acquisitive functions. The suckling of mother's milk becomes the nexus of a host of component feelings, drives, and symbols; and the later exchange of comparable subsistence materials becomes the carrier of a wide variety of psychological needs and satisfactions, far transcending the overt interchange.

Among men, then, the acquisition of property in the form of food, clothes, land, money, and even persons may transcend in psychological significance their utility as physical survival mechanisms. Fortunes are accumulated which provide for a number of human needs serving quite different ends—whether gregarious, dominant, aggressive, or sexual. Indeed, "conspicuous display" (Veblen, 1934) has been postulated as the basic utilization of excess goods. This generalization, accurate within itself, falls short of being inclusive of the full psychological meaning of acquisitive behavior; similarly inadequate is the attempt to generalize social evolution in such terms as "economic determinism," that is, the acquisition of means of sustenance by human social subgroups.

Not only may the intrinsic nature and quality of the food, clothing, or territory itself vary in its psychological significance but the methods for acquiring them may be widely dissimilar and merit diverse psychological interpretations. For example, a comparative analysis of aggressive, sexual, and acquisitive criminals indicates that acquisitive behavior may serve as a kind of substitutive action for a wide variety of psychological needs, often unrelated to the apparent value of the acquired object. Sexual, aggressive, and other motives abound (Freedman et al., in preparation).

An investigation into the psychopathogenic influences of our economic life indicated the importance of acquisitive competition as a force in the histories of some neurotic persons. Economic competition operated as a pathogenic agency in several ways. The struggle for acquisitive achievement liberated, in some patients, feelings of aggressivity which were poorly withstood. In other cases the culturally prescribed standards of success presented goals impossible of achievement, which augmented already existing conflicts. In others, economic life offered a new arena for the enactment of competitive struggles which had been going on in one guise or another since childhood. The psychological correspondence existing between economic insecurity, loss of love, and loss of self-esteem were illustrated in many cases (Leavy and Freedman, 1956; Freedman and Hollingshead, 1957).

We do not know that the ecological structure of human society "causes" neurosis or psychosis. We do have evidence however, that there are stresses inherent in man's biological drive toward subsistence and survival and the social framework in which he acts them out. We have some justification to infer that social evolution may involve adaptive stress and that resultant malfunctioning may take a heavy psychiatric toll.

We have stressed certain possible psychopathological concomitants of acquisitive interpersonal relationships. Obviously the same might have been done for aggressivity or sexuality with far richer clinical evidence. Having referred to the possibly malignant aspects of acquisitive interactions, we might make note of the survival value of this stage of ecological evolution. Increase in efficiency in the production and distribution of food and other substances, and decrease in expenditure of time in procuring means of survival, are evolutionary changes not less important than the modifications in sexuality and aggressivity we have discussed. These social-evolutionary changes synergistically affect the transition from forms whose lives are spent in dealing with their physical environment to the man whose freedom from preoccupation with the procurement of goods for survival enables him to utilize his neural overgrowth for the conceptual leaps which make him human—in spite of himself.

6

We have discussed the relationship between the evolution of animals and the psychology of man quite deliberately ignoring the myriad theoretical, substantive, and methodological obstacles, and have eschewed attempts at historical reconstruction. Our evidence and our conjectures have touched on the anatomical and social predispositions to conflict, anxiety, and discontinuity between cognitive and emotional responses. *Inter alia* we have asked whether such speculation could shed some light on the harrowing question of whether, having achieved the apotheosis of destructive potential, man will use it. Lacking prophetic powers, we cannot adequately test our hypothesis.

There is nothing in the history of evolution, with its countless mute reminders of vanished species, or in our understanding of the human psyche, with its ubiquitous and deeply buried aggressive impulses, which warrants denial of such a possibility. Yet, since his neolithic days, in spite of his murders and wars, his robberies and rapes, man has become a man-binding and a time-binding creature. He has maintained the biological continuity of his family and the social continuity of aggregates of families. He has related his own life experiences with the social traditions of those who have preceded him, and has anticipated those of his progeny. He has accumulated and transmitted his acquired goods and values through his family and through his organizations. He has become bound to other men by feelings of identity and by shared emotions, by what clinicians call empathy. His sexual nature may yet lead him to widening ambits of human affection, his acquisitive propensities to an optimum balance of work and leisure, and his aggressive drives to heightened social efficiency through attacks on perils common to all men.

REFERENCES

ABRAHAM, KARL. 1927. The first pregenital state in the libido. In Selected papers of Karl Abraham, M.D. London, Hogarth Press.

ADLER, ALFRED. 1956. The individual psychology of Alfred Adler. New York, Basic Books.

BARD, PHILIP, ed. 1941. MacLeod's physiology in modern medicine. St. Louis, C. V. Mosby.

BATES, MARSTON. 1955 and 1956. Evolution of foodgetting behavior. Ch. 10 of this volume.

BEACH, F. A. 1947. Evolutionary changes in the physiological control of mating behavior in mammals. Psychol. Rev., *44*, 297–315.

BEACH, F. A. 1955. The de-scent of instinct. Presidential address. Eastern Psychological Association.

BERNARD, CLAUDE. 1927. An introduction to the study of experimental medicine. New York, Henry Schuman.

BOLK, L. 1926. Das Problem der Menschwerdung. Jena, Gustav Fischer.

BUTLER, R. A., and HARLOW, H. F. 1957. Discrimination learning and learning sets to visual exploration incentives. J. Gen. Psychol., *57* (2), 257–64.

CANNON, W. B. 1932. The wisdom of the body. New York, W. W. Norton.

CARPENTER, C. R. 1940. A field study in Siam of the behavior and social relations of the gibbon. Comp. Psychol, Monogr., *16*, 38–206. Baltimore, Johns Hopkins Press.

EVANS, H. M. 1940. Brain and body of fish: a study of brain pattern in relation to hunting and feeding in fish. Philadelphia, Blakiston.

FERENCZI, SANDOR. 1938. Thalassa, a theory of genitality. New York: Psychoanal. Quart.

FORD, C. S., and BEACH, F. A. 1951. Patterns of sexual behavior. New York, Harper.

FREEDMAN, L. Z., ET AL. In preparation. A comparative study of aggressive, sexual and acquisitive anti-social personalities.

FREEDMAN, L. Z., and HOLLINGSHEAD, A. B. 1957. Neurosis and social class. Amer. J. Psychiat., Vol. *113*, March, 769–75.

FREEDMAN, L. Z., and ROSVOLD, H. E. In preparation. Aggressive and sexual interaction in the infra-human primate.

FREUD, SIGMUND. 1915. Instincts and their vicissitudes. Vol. *4*. Collected papers. London, Hogarth Press. Publication of this edition, 1948.

FREUD, SIGMUND. 1953. Three essays on the theory of sexuality. Vol. *7*. Complete psychological works of Sigmund Freud. London, Hogarth Press and the Institute of Psychoanalysis.

FREUD, SIGMUND. 1955. Beyond the pleasure principle. Vol. *18* in ibid. Orig. German ed. 1920.

FULTON, J. F. 1951. Frontal lobotomy and affective behavior. New York, W. W. Norton.

GINSBURG, B., and ALLEE, W. C. 1942. Some effects of conditioning on social dominance and subordination in inbreeding strains of mice. Physiol. Zool., Vol. *15*.

HALL, C. S., and KLEIN, S. J. 1942. Individual differences in aggressiveness in rats. J. Comp. Psychol., Vol. *33*, 371–83.

HALL, G. S. 1923. Life and confessions of a psychologist. New York, Appleton.

HALSTEAD, W. C. 1947. Brain and intelligence. Chicago, Univ. of Chicago Press.

HARLOW, H. F., and McCLEARN, G. E. 1954. Object discrimination learned by monkeys on the basis of manipulation motives. J. Comp. Physiol. Psychol., *47*, 71–4.

HINDE, R., and TINBERGEN, N. The comparative study of species-specific behavior. Ch. 12 in this volume.

HUXLEY, JULIAN. 1948. Man in the modern world. New York, Mentor Books.

JAMES, WILLIAM. 1890. Principles of psychology. Vols. *1* and *2*. New York, Holt.

KLEIN, MELANIE. 1932. The psychoanalysis of children. London, Hogarth Press and the Institute of Psychoanalysis.

KLEIN, MELANIE, and RIVIERE, JOAN. 1938. Love, hate and reparation. London, Hogarth Press.

KORZYBSKI, ALFRED. 1933. Science and sanity. Lakeville, Conn., International Non-Aristotelian Library Publishing Co.

KUBIE, L. S. 1948. Instincts and homeostasis. Psychosom. Med., *10* (1), 15–30.

LACK, DAVID. 1953. The life of the robin. London, Hart, Barnard.

LEAVY, STANLEY, and FREEDMAN, L. Z., 1956. Psychoneurosis and economic life. Social Problems, Vol. *4*. Waltham, Mass. Brandeis Univ.

LINTON, RALPH. 1939. In Abram Kardiner, ed., The individual and his society. New York, Columbia Univ. Press.

LOMBROSO, CESARE. 1896. L'uomo delinquenta. Turin, Fratelli Bocca.

LORENZ, KONRAD. 1935. The companion in the environment of the bird. J. f. Ornithol., *83* (2), 137–213.

MacLEAN, PAUL. 1949. Psychosomatic disease and the visceral brain. Psychosom. Med., *11*, 338–53.

MEAD, MARGARET. 1935. Sex and temperament in three primitive societies. New York, Morrow.

MEAD, MARGARET. 1949. Male and female: a study of the sexes in a changing world. New York, Morrow.

MILLER, N. E. 1951. Comments on theoretical models illustrated by the developments of a theory of conflict behavior. J. Pers., *20* (1), 82–100.

NISSEN, HENRY. 1931. A field study of the chimpanzee. Comp. Psychol. Monogr., *8* (1), 2–122.

NISSEN, HENRY. 1951. Phylogenetic comparison. In S. S. Stevens, ed., Handbook of experimental psychology. New York, Wiley.

NISSEN, HENRY. 1956. Axes of behavioral comparison. Ch. 9 in this volume.

PAVLOV, I. P. 1928. Lectures on conditioned reflexes. Vol. *1*. New York, International Publishers.

PIAGET, JEAN. 1948. The moral development of the child. Glencoe, Ill., The Free Press.

PRIBRAM, K. H., and KRUGER, LAWRENCE. 1954. Functions of the "olfactory brain." Ann. N.Y. Acad. Sci., *58* (2), 109–38.

RENSCH, BERNHARD. 1956. Increase of learning capability with increase of brain size. Amer. Nat., *90* (851), 81–95.

SCHILDER, PAUL, and BENDER, LAURETTA. 1936. Studies in aggressiveness. Genet. Psychol. Monogr., *18*, 357–564.

SELYE, HANS. 1950. The physiology and pathology of exposure to stress: Montreal, Acta, Ind.

SILLMAN, LEONARD. 1953. The genesis of man. Int. J. Psychoanal., *34*, 146–52.

SIMPSON, G. G. 1949. The meaning of evolution. New Haven, Yale Univ. Press.

SPITZ, RENE. 1945. Psycho-analytic study of the child. Vol. *1*. New York, International Univ. Press.

VEBLEN, THORSTEIN. 1934. The theory of the leisure class. New York, Modern Library.

WOLFE, J. B. 1936. Effectiveness of token-rewards for chimpanzees. Comp. Psychol. Monogr., *12* (60), 1–72.

22

Cultural Determinants of Behavior

Margaret Mead

THE AMERICAN MUSEUM OF NATURAL HISTORY

THE INTEREST of anthropologists in evolutionary theory—defined broadly as an interest in placing man within the whole evolutionary framework, or more narrowly as an interest in tracing such distinctly human products as languages, political systems, methods of utilizing energy, and so on—has taken an uneven course, in part following the oscillations in the main body of biological theory, in part reactive to the impact of certain overworked analogies between 19th-century conceptions of biological evolution and 19th-century theories of European superiority or of the inevitability of progress (Bidney, 1953, chs. 7, 8, 9). After the first quarter of the 20th-century, when anthropology included the subdisciplines of ethnology, archeology, linguistics, and physical anthropology, and a consideration of questions of cultural evolution was an intrinsic part of anthropological theory, there followed a period of divergence among these subdisciplines, which was reflected significantly in a lowered interest in problems of evolution. This artificial division within anthropology—which separated students of human genetics and human growth from students of man's past, and separated students of man's culture from students of the principal feature of the communication system on which culture is dependent, language—reduced the capacity of the discipline to deal with such an over-all problem as evolution.

During the period of low interest in evolution, there were two approaches—that of V. Gordon Childe (1951) in England and that of Leslie White (1949) in the United States—which stemmed from a Marxian determinism and stressed a theory of unilinear, universal evolution with predetermined direction. The identification of evolutionary problems with these approaches also slowed down the interest of many anthropologists in the subject.

The end of this era of indifference may be attributed, *inter alia,* to a revived interest in tracing limited multilinear evolution, to the abandonment of the search for a single universal pattern of evolution in favor of the study of parallelism in the sequence of evolutionary development in cultures in different parts of the world (see especially the work of Julian Steward, 1955), and to a growing cooperation between biologists and those anthropologists who have been preoccupied with problems of cultural transmission and transformation and who have, therefore, given increasing attention to detailed studies of child rearing and learning.[1] The Wenner-Gren Foundation International Symposium on Anthropology, in 1952, marked the end of the era of divergence (Kroeber, 1953). With the reintegration of the branches of anthropology, there has been a growing interest in evolutionary theory; so, for instance, Julian Huxley was invited to write the guest editorial for *Current Anthropology* (1952). It seems appropriate, therefore, to summarize briefly the traditional contribution of cultural anthropology in this field and then to go on to the new problems which are being explored today.

The research of the last hundred years, especially studies of the diffusion of cultural traits and detailed studies of the behavior of living primitive peoples, has established the independence of patterned cultural behavior from the racial constitution of the particular carriers and has documented in detail the transmissibility of culture from one generation to another and between adults from different cultures. Extensive efforts to demonstrate the genetic superiority of one racial group of man over another have so far failed, so that the present working assumption is that, as far as their capacity to learn, maintain, transmit, and transform culture is concerned, different groups of *Homo sapiens* must be regarded as equally competent. The differential cultural status of Eskimos and Frenchmen, Ifugao and Englishmen, is attributed to differences in opportunity, as groups, to participate in the cumulative tradition of human culture. This does not preclude the possibility of there being, in any group at any given time, a different distribution of individual genetic capacity; but there is no evidence that such a

1. For a beginning *rapprochement* between anthropology and ethology see, for example, Huxley (1947) and Tanner and Inhelder (1956).

superiority or inferiority can be maintained over many generations. People of one stock will be found in one century to be living a life of barbarism and in the next exhibiting all the behavior
associated with civilization, while the descendents of possessors of
a high civilization may sink to the level of illiterate peasants. So
far no one has identified any behavior, associated with any culture,
which will reappear in children reared completely in a culture
different from that of their forebears. As the range of human
abilities appears to be comparable within all human groups of the
same size, each cultural system which survives has to meet the same
set of minimum requirements for maintenance and for survival.
Each human language—highly diversified though languages appear to be—must be one which every normal member of the group
can learn to speak; each culturally patterned dietary must provide
for human growth; each family and community system must provide for the care of human children during their long dependency
and for their education, must regulate the patterns of mating and
of competition, and must pattern the behavior of members of the
social group. As each variant of culture must meet the same basic
requirements, cultural systems have a regularity which makes it
possible for human beings, of whatever level of culture, to recognize and borrow from the cultural behavior of members of other
cultural systems. Discussions of the capabilities of members of one
culture to learn from others which are more highly organized now
take the form of inquiring not if, but how and under what conditions, individuals or groups are able to learn. It has been demonstrated repeatedly—by the records of chieftains' sons in Western
universities and by the adaptations of immigrant groups—that it
is possible for individuals born into one culture to learn the patterns of another. The question of how much a group, which remains in the same habitat and whose behaviors perpetuate the
existing culture, is able to change in response to foreign models is
at present the subject of keen research interest, particularly because of the current emphasis upon the importance of cultural
change in economically underdeveloped countries (Mead, 1953).

The occurrence of parallelism and convergence in the development of local cultural systems has also been exhaustively demonstrated. The high cultures of the pre-Columbian New World are
conspicuous examples and, although the question of whether the
development of these high cultures took place independently or

was triggered by stimulus ideas—by small amounts of experience of more advanced Old World cultures—is still unresolved, the relative independence with which highly organized systems have developed among people who had previously much simpler systems is well established (Steward, 1955).

In the history of human culture, some of these repetitive and recurrent innovations can be viewed as cumulative—especially, for instance, in technology; others seem to be alternative solutions to the problems of organizing large groups of people. If we look at the history of human culture from the standpoint of evolutionary theory, it is possible to emphasize either the *permanent acquisition by the species* of certain culturally determined forms of adaptation or, alternatively, the *spatially and temporally limited acquisition by a particular human group* of some high form of cultural organization which may or may not become part of the heritage of the human race. An emphasis upon permanent acquisition focuses attention upon the extreme flexibility and survival strength of mankind, in that once a form of cultural behavior has been developed its continuance depends not upon the specific genetic capacities of the group who have developed it but upon the general capacities of men as a species to communicate with one another and to learn from experience. Culture, the system of behavior characteristic of a human group which is transmitted through experience, can thus be viewed as a new mode of evolutionary process, as discussed by Julian Huxley (1947). If, however, emphasis is laid upon the fragility of particular systems of higher culture which appear and disappear within periods of a few centuries, then attention is focused upon the question of whether—since the descendants of kings may become shepherds and elaborate symbolic scripts may remain closed to the efforts of later men to decipher them—mankind can take any irreversible evolutionary steps.

One resolution of this divergence of emphasis is to treat those inventions which survive—regardless of which human group may at a given moment in history be the carriers—as the mainstream of a cultural evolution in which the various items are arranged in an ascending sequence of levels of organization. In this way it is possible to arrange likely evolutionary sequences: in technology, from the stone hammer to the machine tool; in the use of energy, from the use of the human body only, through the use of draft animals and wind and water, through the use of the combustion engine, atomic energy, and solar energy. Comparably, it is possible to discuss man's ability to organize men in groups capable of living together within one system of sacredness of life and property, from the simplest known groups of a few families to modern aggregations of hundreds of millions, or to discuss the evolution of religion from systems limited to a local supernatural on family land, tied to a small consanguineous group and unexportable to or unshareable with other groups, to the great missionary religions with patterns that can be shared by millions of people who, in other respects, are culturally very diverse. In these terms, directional evolutionary change in culture may be viewed as inevitable and the only variable is the time at which a next stage will occur. In this approach, theories of orthogenesis become relevant, as each stage of development is seen to be subject only to the existing state of knowledge in a previous stage—which may limit the alternative innovations but cannot determine which of many possible innovations will appear.

The ethnocentric overevaluation of our own cultural achievment—which, in the 19th century, led students of social evolution to establish sequences whose order was determined by a belief in the superiority of 19th-century man—also bedevils thinking today insofar as it leads to a false dichotomization of permanent and transient evolutionary gains. Instead, we may consider the state of human culture—as manifested in the hundreds of living cultural systems and in the ways in which these living systems are able to conserve and utilize the *records* of former systems—in terms of reversibility and irreversibility. Then, because culture must be experienced to be acquired, it may be said that only those cultural behaviors which are shared by every group of human beings are irreversible gains. These are the patterns which, if only a small group of adult human beings survived some natural or artificial holocaust, would be maintained and would again be reinstated, modified, and elaborated by later generations having the same range of capacities as the ancestral groups who had utilized these patterns in the past. The study of existing human societies at all levels of organization indicates that, stated in conventional terms, these irreversible patterns would include language; the family (including a sexual and an age-graded division of labor); tool using; selective exploitation of the environment to provide food, shelter, and protection; the idea of a group organization which unites a group of families and determines their relationship to other like groups; some idea of the elaboration of ornamentation (including some form of patterned movement and sound, and patterned decoration of the surfaces of the human body and of artifacts); and some system of relating man to the perceived universe (Wissler, 1923). Further research by paleontologists and students of early man is needed to establish the conditions under which these now universally shared cultural acquisitions were first achieved by prehistoric and pre-*sapiens* human groups.

Besides those cultural behaviors which may be said to be permanent, there are those which show some intrinsic and humanly recognizable superiority among existing forms and which can be communicated without intensive apprenticeship learning (Kroeber, 1948). The idea of the wheel, the arch, pottery, the domestication of animals, and so on, may be grasped in its essentials by peoples of such very different levels of sophistication that at any time in history the diffusion of these ideas can be much wider than their actual use; knowledge of such possibilities can be carried for generations and the ideas put into practice only when the necessary resources are discovered or an adequate level of organization is reached. The use of a script may be expected, within the next twenty-five years, to reach this position. By then the possibility of a script will be known to all living peoples even though many of them will not yet be able to read and write; and so, if all literate peoples and their records were destroyed, the possibility of the invention of new scripts would be greatly increased.[2] Cultural behavior which is known about but is not practiced is, of course, more subject to loss than is behavior which is universally shared.

Finally, there are those elaborate patterns of behavior in which specialized knowledge is combined with elaborate forms of organizing large groups, in what we call the high cultures of the world. These remain on an experimental and reversible basis; they are cultural achievements which may not become part of the shared possession of the whole of mankind.

These are macroscopic generalizations about human cultures observed over millennia, or at least throughout centuries. The gross forms of such sequences and the extent to which parallel or

2. For a discussion of one such invention, see Kroeber (1952, pp. 344-57).

convergent development is involved can be worked out, in archeology, by placing events in time, and in other disciplines—for instance, by comparisons of languages or of blood groups—by establishing the probability that like developments have resulted
from contact of various kinds or are independent responses to
similar environmental conditions (Steward's [1955] multilinear
lines of evolution). Such findings are useful in presenting the broad
outlines of human evolution, but theory about human evolution
remains at a stage comparable to that in biology before the development of genetics. Given analysis of this order, problems of
cultural evolution are dismissed either with the statement that
culture determines the behavior most of the time and that there
is an occasional "burst" during which an unexpected number of
geniuses manifest themselves, or with the statement that evolution
can best be understood in terms of environmental challenge
(Kroeber, 1952). Both are formulations unfavorable to necessary
next steps in the study of human evolution.

During the past quarter-century, most anthropological research
has neglected the wider evolutionary framework and has narrowed
down to studies of the details of cultural sequences or of the dynamics of living cultural systems; implicitly or explicitly, these
studies have insisted upon the independence of cultural phenomena from biological phenomena and often also from ecological
phenomena. Now, however, this detailed work—in which maintenance and transmission functions have been studied in small,
carefully specified groups—has given us the tools with which to
begin a new investigation of human evolution. The fieldwork
of this quarter-century has established the main outlines of character formation (Mead, 1956a), the methods by which members
of different generation groups are involved in a series of transac-
tions of transmission, maintenance, and variation of the particular
culture of a particular group (Mead and Wolfenstein, 1955).
Earlier theoretical positions, which attached great significance to
parental influence but failed to give any weight to the effect of
individual genetic and experiential differences among those
newly born into a society, are now giving place to others which
include a recognition of such systems as both circular (in that the
infant as well as the mother supplies cues for old or new forms of
cultural activity) and open to the wider ecological system (Tanner
and Inhelder, 4). Thus it becomes clear that the conditions trig-

gering a change which may become evolutionary may occur at any point in this system—through birth, conquest, differential deaths, an alteration of habitat, natural disaster, and so on.

The artificial distinction between culture—as a purely human process—and all forms of learning through experience—in the rest of the biological sector—may have been a necessary device to dispose of theories of racial difference which assumed a racial factor in "Gallic wit" or in "Negro musical ability." Similarly, insistence upon man's mammalian ancestory has been a useful method of focusing attention upon those aspects of man's instinctual behavior which contemporary academic psychologies of the period tended to ignore. But both the isolation of man in the biological world and the narrow focus upon man's specific ancestral connections have limited our understanding of human evolution—the first by obscuring the similarities in the functions of transmitted but unsymbolized experience among human and nonhuman groups, the second by obscuring the significant analogies between some aspects of human behavior and of nonmammalian behavior (particularly that of birds [3]), seen in terms of grades of advancement. Recognition of the evolutionary importance of transmitted experience as well as genetically patterned behavior as a biological process, within which those parts of human culture which are symbolized are a special case, bridges these gaps.

We may then approach the question of the cultural determinants of behavior through a recognition of finer gradations within the obvious gross distinctions between cultureless creatures and human beings with culture. There is one kind of transmitted experience in which—if we ignore for a moment the presence of language —there is no break between the kind of learning described for red deer (Darling, 1937) or prairie dogs (King, 1955) and that which occurs in human society, that is, learning which can occur only when the behaving, individual model is present, because the learning is unverbalized, inarticulate, recorded in no artifact, and represented in no symbolic form. Posture and gesture systems and

3. Eisley's (1955) recent speculations about the role of visual perceptions of space in the evolution of man during the arboreal stage could be extended from a comparison of man with other mammals to include comparison with birds. Because of the great importance of visual stimuli and the role of ritual in courtship and mating behavior of birds, recent detailed work on birds has proved very stimulating to an understanding of courtship, mating, and parental behavior among human beings (Tanner and Inhelder, 3; Mead, 1954c).

the unsymbolized parts of a language—stress, cadence, and accent
—all belong to this category. As the senior female red deer or the
old ewes lead the herd or flock, so older members of human
groups guide the behavior of younger members through the experience of a mass of patterned behaviors, specific to a given
ecological setting and characteristic of a given society, with much
of this never becoming conscious teaching or conscious learning.[4]
Such human behaviors are potentially conscious, for just as a
"grammar," once articulated, can be taught, so too those parts of
the posture-gesture system which are recognized as correct or
elegant may be recognized and taught by conscious modeling or

4. In using the word "conscious" here, I am referring not to the distinction made
by Freudian psychology between conscious and unconscious behavior but merely
to the difference between the inarticulate and unrecognized aspects of behavior and
those aspects which are dealt with as recognizably suitable for teaching and learning.
The contribution to human evolution of those aspects of human thought which
have been variously described as prelogical (Lévy-Bruhl, 1928), the primary process
(Freud, 1949), syncretic (Piaget, 1926), paleologic (Arieti, 1956), the proto system
(Lowenfeld), and so on, and which have been studied as they are manifested in
different ways among primitive peoples (Lévy-Bruhl, 1926; Field, 1955), among
children (Erikson, 1950; Piaget, 1952; Schachtel, 1947), among neurotics (Freud, 1938)
and psychotics (Goldstein, 1943), is a different matter. These aspects of thought
have sometimes been considered antithetical to the type of rational thought which
gives man control over his environment, including control over his behavior within
it. But as these aspects of human behavior are observed and labeled and subjected
to rational analysis, they become part of the cumulative culture on which man can
draw. The kind of human thought which is the language of dreams (Sharpe, 1937,
1950) and of poetry (Armstrong, 1946; Sewell, 1952), which can sometimes be seen
more clearly in children and among primitive peoples or among peoples whose
cultures have been rationalized along different lines from ours, might come to be
identified as of less evolutionary service because evolution—to the degree that it is
dependent upon the cumulation of culture—is dependent upon those particular
kinds of thoughts which recent work by Piaget and Inhelder (Tanner and Inhelder,
1; 4) suggests come to effective fruition in late adolescence in situations in which
the adolescent is given a chance to develop them in an effective way.

But the labeling of part of human thought as of lesser evolutionary relevance or
the assignment to it of a lower status, as is done by Arieti (1956) when he treats it
as a survival of some earlier form of life, may well be as detrimental to the evolutionary process as it was to label this type of thought prelogical and peculiar to
savages, an idea which has been disproved (Boas, 1911 and 1938), or as lower in
the scale of individual development, peculiar to children as distinct from adults,
which also has been disproved (Abel, 1932; Mead, 1932). There is good reason to
believe that man's evolutionary progress depends also upon his ability to dream
and to maintain within himself and through his culture a balance between internally
oriented proprioception and externally oriented exteroception. The disturbance of
this balance may be one of the factors which account for the onset of boredom and
apathy (Mead, 1952), the loss of evolutionary vigor, and the decline of particular
civilizations for whose fall no adequate external explanation has been found.

verbalization or, today, by the use of didactic films or sound recordings. Nevertheless, much behavior of the most modern man is still completely below the level of awareness which makes teaching-learning or conscious recording or transmission possible. The recent interest in empathetic learning in both men and animals (Thorpe, 1956) is an example of the fruitfulness of focusing attention on this sector of transmission by inarticulate experience.

On the basis of comparative materials, we may assume that at the earliest stages of human evolution all transmission of experience was of this nature and that there were no ways in which human beings could instruct except by means of modeling behavior that was directly accessible to the senses of the individuals to whom the behavior was being transmitted. For instance, in the earliest tool-using situations, the unshaped tool would as yet carry no message of use to anyone who did not see it in use. Yet it has been customary to focus upon that stage in the evolutionary sequence in which the tool had assumed a form which could give information independently of its human user and to ignore the ways in which tool using, as a universal part of all existing human culture, is still taught by direct apprenticeship before a human child can understand language. Western man has been so preoccupied with the articulated and consciously transmissible part of human culture that both scientists and laymen have been tempted to identify with the whole of human culture those parts of a cultural system which are consciously transmissible and therefore cumulative and to equate progression in this sector with human evolution as a whole.

The significance for the maintenance of a society of human beings of early mother-child relationships for the creation of a series of conditions which we cannot as yet render articulate is one illustration of this point, for it has been found that children in institutions, even where the pediatric care is of a very high order, slow down, cease to develop, regress, and in many cases die (Bowlby, 1951). And we are just beginning to appreciate that there is a relationship between certain types of childhood experience and the use of those high-level abilities which are needed for the development of modern science, but this relationship has not yet been so identified as to make it part of our cumulative cultural tradition (Cobb).

Thus it seems necessary to discard the distinction once made between the cumulative character of technology and the non-cumulative character of other aspects of human culture, and to make a distinction instead among *gradations of recognition* on the one hand and *techniques of transmission* on the other. Then those aspects of culture may be regarded as noncumulative in which, either because of failure to recognize them or because of a lack of technique for transmission, apprenticeship experience is the only form of transmission from adult to child, teacher to pupil, native to immigrant, believer to convert. In any cultural system, at any point of time, these two aspects—the cumulative and the noncumulative—may be out of balance. Because systems of human relationships were regarded as noncumulative, this lack of balance was once seen as a *lag* in the nontechnical parts of modern culture. With our increased understanding of these inarticulate aspects of human culture, we can recognize that instead of a one-directional lag there is a discrepancy. This may be one of two sorts: it may be an inappropriate insistence upon formulations which omit apprenticeship and so leave out a great segment of the component experience,[5] or it may be an insistence upon an apprenticeship of so many generations that large parts of a cultural heritage, for which techniques of transmission are available, have come to be regarded as carried by "blood" and so as inaccessible to members of other races, other nations, even other classes or the other sex.

A first step in transmission beyond the completely unanalyzed type of experience, such as that of the child in the family, is the type which includes recognition within an apprenticeship situation. Transmission in this situation involves verbal prescriptions for behavior, so the articulate recognition of the behavior and the technique of transmission are present but the transmission itself is limited to apprenticeship within an immediate situation. A further step occurs when, for instance, the elders of the tribe

5. Examples of areas of inarticulate learning today are the intimate details of human relationships, which are learned within the family of orientation and later are practiced within the family of procreation; programming for a computing machine; reading an electroencephalogram; judging a somatotype; matching sets of serial data or patterned data for which no over-all formula is available; matching sets of patterned data for which no satisfactory mathematical methods have as yet been devised (as in the use of the Rorschach test); surgery; psychoanalysis; and so forth.

become the custodians of the appropriate behaviors in all recognized emergencies. However, in the absence of any kind of script or representational method of recording, this knowledge is dependent upon the lives and continuing mental competency of those few who have mastered it.

So the first insurance of the preservation of any new invention or any cultural practice which has become essential to the maintenance of a society or subgroup is diffusion among a large number of persons. But as long as there are no supplementary aids to memory, no demonstrable products or models, each member of the group has to master all the skills and knowledge that the group possesses; the strain that this puts on the members of any given group reduces the likelihood of the development of other conditions conducive to progressive change. Barnett (1953) has pointed out that there was a high level of continuous slight inventiveness among the Eskimo, yet Eskimo culture is one of the most stable and unchanging that we know. Skills were distributed with great evenness within the group, being primarily differentiated by sex and age. The spread of an invention so that many people share it simply increases the possibility that any item, widely diffused, will survive. Diffusion, therefore, is only a first step toward cultural cumulation, that essential feature of human evolution.

A second method of increasing the safe transmissibility of a cultural practice is tightness of pattern—a set of practices so closely related that each implies the other, so that the loss of any one item will at most be temporary. So, for example, the Ontong-Javanese, whose language and familial structure implied hierarchical relations with a single peak, "invented" a king after they have lived for generations as the descendants of commoners without rank and without even the remembered institution of kingship (Hogbin, 1934).

Conversely, an unintegrated practice is subject to loss. So, among a people who have no systematic need for artificial light beyond providing some visibility for events which occur at night, an introduced method of lighting by kerosene lamps may be much more easily lost than among a people who are in the habit of doing fine work like reading or copying texts at night.

This type of integration may be expressed in a variety of ways —as emotional congruence or as a tendency to forget unintegrated practices because the memory of highly traditional behavior does not reinforce them.[6]

A third way of ensuring transmissibility and potential cumulation is the creation of durable models, in the form either of artifacts (a tool or utensil made of durable material, in contrast to a basket woven from a green leaf, to hold an octopus that has been caught) or of organized, repeatable verbal blocks, including implicit or explicit instructions which may be transmitted through human agents who do not themselves carry out the instructions. Such may be the myths told by old women to boys, which include accounts of the performance of male activities—like war ritual, warfare, visions—or prescriptions of materials and procedures for cutting down a tree, hollowing out a canoe, and so on. This type of preservation of invention exists in some rudimentary form in most primitive societies. Here, the specific omission of any item of practice involves possibilities of alteration. So, for instance, the Omaha Indians publicly adopted the widespread Plains Indian belief that visions should validate membership in the religious societies, but by hiding the vision plots (which were not described, as was customary in other tribes, in the folklore) they were able to see that only certain individuals' visions would be correct (Fortune, 1932). Such omissions may result in the development of secret or incompatible behavior within a society (as, for instance, practices of classifying scientific information at present), and this in turn may lead to new types of divergence which may also contribute to evolution by encouraging diverse solutions to problems.

There are many gradations in the recognition process which make any part of culture potentially cumulative. The attitude of New Guinea natives toward language and items of culture represents one intermediate stage. We use "Romance languages" or "Germanic languages" as classifications to explain recognized similarities between languages which cannot be understood without separate learning, and we regard those languages as more easily learnable which are within one of these classifications. The New

6. In my recent restudy of the Manus of the Admiralty Islands (Mead, 1954a, 1954b, 1956b) I found magnificent, detailed memory for the events of 25 years ago (whose accuracy could be checked by my written records) but exceedingly poor memory of the period between 1929 and 1946, when the culture was in transition and the society unstable, and a return of accurate memory in dealing with events after the social system had been consciously transformed by the Paliau Movement (Schwartz).

Guinea native instead introduces the border village where "the talk is turned" and where living individuals know two languages. This provides a different continuum within which languages can be learned, characterized by a large number of individuals who can "hear" (understand when they hear spoken) several languages of which they speak only one or two. Equivalent to this is our recognition that an individual with a sufficient historical knowledge of Latin, for example, can "read" another historically related Romance language—that is, he can find meaning in a written text on the basis of recognizable common roots—which he can neither "hear" nor "speak."

We may assume that there may once have been a period when human beings had not yet sufficiently identified language as a shared learned system of communication to be able to learn by an act of choice, rather than through circumstances of birth or adoption or capture in warfare, the "language" of another group.

The New Guinea area is characterized by groups whose boundaries are exceedingly poorly defined—where intermarriage, trade, and warfare crisscross linguistic and geographical boundaries, where objects are traded far beyond the possibility of observing how they are made and so are copied by different methods of manufacture, where cultural integration is along lines of emotional congruence, and where there is a curiously indiscriminate willingness to identify and borrow the practices of another group. So not only are shells for the manufacture of ornaments and seed yams widely diffused among peoples who have never come into personal contact, but so are forms of marriage, ceremonials, and rituals. These are consciously assembled by entrepreneurial groups into "packages" of musical themes, dance steps, instruments, costumes, magic, etc.—temporary complexes of practices and items of material culture which can be bought, re-sorted and combined within a trading group, modified, and exported (Mead, 1938, 1940, 1947, 1949). Having recognized that items of culture are separable from any matrix and are recombinable into any other matrix—with emotional congruity, temporary alliance, and dialectic similarity among a few hundred people the only integrating factors—the people of New Guinea have developed a culture that is highly transmissible, superficially very varied, and yet extraordinarily noncumulative.[7]

7. The same dissociated sort of transmission occurs in contemporary forms of

Linguists are very much excited by evidence gained from glotto-chronology (Lees, 1953; Swadesh, 1955)—a method of assessing the age of a language in terms of the rate of change in a core vocabulary of deeply familiar words such as those for body parts, sun, and moon—that, in a group of languages for which we have documentary evidence, there is a relatively constant rate of change. Such constancy can be explained by the fact that the first language learning of the child has always been person-to-person learning. But on the analogy of birds, which during a maturational phase much preceding the appearance of song can be taught the song pattern of another species with no member of which they have ever come into contact except through a phonograph record (Tanner and Inhelder, 2), it is easy to see how the rate of change in the most constant elements in language or methods of singing (A. Lomax, unpublished research) can be altered by cumulative invention in some other area of culture, e.g. the ability to make sound recordings. Interdependence of this kind is illustrated also by the fact that only the very recently developed human ability to identify, isolate, and synthesize biochemicals has made it possible to demonstrate experimentally (Richter, 1943) the ability of rats to discriminate nutritionally desirable combinations of minerals and vitamins.

In sum, it is important, in order to understand the processes of cultural evolution at any period, to take into consideration both the interweaving which occurs between different areas of culture as they become cumulative and the proportions of different types of learning—by apprenticeship, by models, by prescription, and by inclusion within an integrated pattern. The recently revived interest in ecological considerations may enlarge our understanding of the part played by the environment in the gross forms of cultural institutions as peoples with comparable basic levels of culture are exposed to new resources, to climatic change, or to an invention like irrigation—whether such an invention has been made independently or has been diffused (Steward, 1955).

However, in order to take the next step in understanding how

---

diffusion, in that we are able to specify elements in our culture—an assembly line, nutritional science, phonetic writing, dial telephones, voting by ballot, trial by jury, the "conference table"—so that we can export them through transmission media in which no apprenticeship is necessary and others can import them without reference to the over-all state of the culture or the social organization of the importing society.

human evolution occurs, in either its maintenance or its innovational aspects, we need detailed studies of the loci of transmission on the one hand and of change on the other. Such studies have not advanced because students of human behavior—cultural anthropologists, social or clinical psychologists, sociologists, and so on—have failed to recognize the need for multidimensional specifications within the same human situation. Students of human growth have studied changes in height under different nutritional conditions; students of child development have studied the growth and development of specified children but have left vague the parents, the culture, and the social milieu; students of maternal behavior have made minute analyses of the rejecting behavior of the mothers without examining the relevant behavior of the infants (on such variables as food acceptance, motility, etc.), while other investigators have studied infants in detail but have neglected to study the parents and siblings; and so on. Most cultural anthropologists, even those admittedly interested in the field of culture and personality, have studied the culture but have failed to localize the behavior of which they are giving an abstract or selected illustrative account in individuals who are biologically and sociologically specified by their positions, relative to each other, in an identified network. Yet only by simultaneous specification in these different dimensions can we establish a research milieu within which the process of change can be identified.

In genetic terms, human societies need a balance between homozygosity, which may provide specialized forms of gift, and heterozygosity, which will provide a storehouse for a wide range of human capacities. Human evolution is dependent not only upon biological reproduction but also upon the cultural contributions of individuals, made irrespective of whether the individuals reproduce themselves. In cultural terms this means that cultural forms which are no longer selective for the reproductively fit may yet be favorable to the survival of those who—through very high, very low, or very deviant capacities—may be culturally creative. Thus the available range of possible human potentiality is broadened. Emphasis on population genetics alone tends to obscure this factor of the contribution of the sterile individual.

The locus of human evolution is a transactional group of individuals (Ittelson and Cantril, 1954) who share mankind's universal culture and who share also, in individual and varying degrees, the particular system of their society.[8] As unique genetic combinations, the innate capacities, relative to each other, of all individuals in the group are necessary factors in the evolutionary process. The total ecological situation of such a group is also relevant— at least negatively—to the process. Such a group may be one hamlet of a tribe in the center of New Guinea, or the College of Cardinals, or the cabinet of an Indonesian premier, or the European Advisory Council of World War II, or all scientists who are using some cybernetic model. The group may be highly articulated, as an endogamous village is, or it may be related only through an exchange of periodicals in different languages. For research purposes, the essential point is the realization that to look for the role of a "genius" without including consideration of his companions, collaborators, rivals, and associates, or to look for the "inherent rigidity or capacity for change of an artistic style," or to look for an "unstable balance of power groups" is to state the problem of cultural change—and so of cultural evolution— in a way that leads to a stalemate. We can get some picture of how change occurs only when each individual is fully specified in his genetic and experiential peculiarity, when the culture which these individuals share, the set of social relations within which they participate, the wider situation of which they are a part— a world system of trade or politics, a chain of volcanoes which periodically erupt, the cycle of hurricanes or droughts within which they must survive, the other systems with which they are in competition—are simultaneously included within the definition of the unit to be investigated.

I shall now give briefly the account of one instance of recent cultural change, in which a primitive people—the Manus of the Admiralty Islands whose shared culture was still that of savages, although they had seen and recognized the culture of the Western world—were able to take Euro-American behavior as a model and to adopt it within a quarter of a century, omitting the series of steps by which Euro-American culture has evolved to its present pattern. In presenting this case I am choosing as an illustration the simpler type of cultural change—that of cultural borrowing

8. On the basis of our present techniques, human evolution can now be studied in identified human groups with the fine-grained tools now available to us—cine film, tape recorders, the interaction chronograph, experimental settings containing some rigid mechanical and some flexible living parts such as Ramsay's and Hess's (1954) imprinting device or Bavelas' (1951) telephone networks.

—because we do not yet have any studies of cultural creativity within an original innovating group.

The conditions for the culture change among the Manus—the massive cultural contact between opposing armies and the native peoples during World War II coming after slower exposure to missionary, government, and trader—existing in many parts of the Pacific. There were scores of attempts of various sorts by various native groups to take advantage of the new models, and these failed in varying degrees. The peculiar conditions within which this special case of successful change took place can be traced in detail because this one village of the Manus tribe of the South Coast of the Admiralty Islands already had been studied as a group of individuals, with specification of the properties and relationships of each and of the functioning of each within a particular cultural system with a particular form of organization. The village could therefore be restudied by the same methods with a further specification of leaders of different villages and of different linguistic units who were involved in the change (Mead, 1956b).

In the course of twenty-five years, 1928–53, the Manus emerged from savagery and, after a period of culture contact during which the individual members of the tribe got more out of step with each other, developed a new level of integration based on a Western model, under the leadership of a native named Paliau, who was a member of another linguistic group on the nearby small island of Baluan. The Manus had been exposed to Western culture as mediated by German and Australian and American missionaries, by German and Australian government officials, by German and Australian planters, traders, miners, and recruiters, and by contact with over a million members of the United States armed forces during World War II. Seen from a distance and described macroscopically in terms of diffusion which permitted one group to take advantage of the grade of achievement of another, this would be just one more example of diffusion through culture contact between peoples of different levels of culture. Furthermore, we could place it as only one more among many such responses to contact between representatives of Western culture and the primitive peoples of the Pacific. Such contact situations have already been described many times without the descriptions throwing light on the mechanisms of culture change.

To make the study of these people contribute further to our knowledge of change and so to our knowledge of evolution, it was necessary to specify in detail the membership of the groups. In Manus, in 1953–54, we studied in detail the whole population, including the children, of one village which had been similarly studied twenty-five years before, as well as the population of a second, new, culturally hybrid village, and also the *group* of leaders from all the Manus villages and from the segments of neighboring tribes who had joined in the new political movement. The latter group included one leader of "exceptional gift," several other leaders of "gift," and several individuals of varying degrees of emotional instability who initiated and participated in the mystical aspects of the new movement. The changes which occurred, which will constitute an evolutionary step for the people of the Admiralties—whether or not they are followed by other progressive steps or harden into a new maintenance level—cannot be referred then to the situation of culture contact alone; nor to the peculiar characteristics of Manus culture alone; nor to the period within which contact occurred alone (post-World War II with its climate of opinion favorable to the development of underdeveloped peoples [Mead, 1946, 1953]); nor to the greater cultural homogeneity of the Manus, all of whom entered the movement initiated by a non-Manus leader, as compared with the land peoples who were fragmented by the conflict; nor to the age structure of the Manus population, with only a small number of living men above middle age; nor to the artificial prolongation of the stage of uncommitment in the young men because wartime conditions had prevented their settling down in marriage and trade; nor to the system of indentured labor which had exposed the group who became leaders of the new movement to diversified experiences in European types of social organization and had provided new levels of training for leadership as *boss boys*, police sergeants, schooner captains, etc.; nor to the historical accidents which placed the gifted leader back of the Japanese lines and so placed him in an initially antithetical position vis-à-vis the returning Australian administration; nor to the presence on Manus of an American occupation force, careless of the preservation of the social distance which had been characteristic of white Australian—New Guinea native relationships; nor to the presence in the American Army of Negro American troops, whom the Manus

natives perceived as members of their race who were full representatives of the Western culture to which they themselves had
never before aspired to belong; nor to the location of the different
missions—with the Manus themselves Roman Catholic and
Paliau, the leader, having never been baptized, with the Seventh-
Day Adventist group on Baluan barricading themselves against
the mystical excesses of their formerly Catholic, and so differentiated, neighbors; nor to the type of hostility which had
prevailed between the land-dwelling Usiai, the island dwellers,
and the sea-dwelling Manus. And, if we turn to specified individuals, the changes cannot be referred to the superior gifts of Paliau
alone; they are attributable also to the special constellation of
leaders who were associated with him, to the personalities of the
particular missionaries, patrol officers, district officers, local
traders involved.

Detailed analysis shows that the changes occurred *among* this
specified group of people, *within* this context of cultural, social,
and geographical conditions. At each stage in the development of
the Paliau Movement, the composition of the group of people
present on a given occasion, the way in which one person understood or misunderstood another, can be shown to have been
crucial choice-points (Schwartz). But this can only be shown when
the group is studied in detail and when the relative intelligence,
experience, and life history of one individual as compared to
another is analyzed. Paliau, born a hundred years before, *might*
have accomplished a temporary alliance between his own small
tribe and that of a neighboring island. Paliau, born fifty years
later, *might* have been a representative to the United Nations
of a unified New Guinea; but, coming from a recently developed
area, he might well have been seen not as a highly gifted leader
of lonely distinction—as he appears in the Paliau Movement—
but as an inferiority-ridden least competent member of a group
of rivals perhaps no more gifted than he but coming from more
deeply civilized areas. But when we analyze this movement, which
succeeded in reaching such an extraordinary level of rapid cultural
transformation; then Paliau, the gifted leader; Wapi of Rambutjon, the mystical seer of visions who triggered the Cargo cult
in which the paraphernalia of the past were jettisoned into the
sea; Samol, who had been a catechist; Lukas, who had been a
boss boy for the Catholic mission; Napo of Mbuke, who had

been in charge of a police station up the Sepik; the presence of a group of leaders of comparable high level, with none outstanding in the village of Pere—all these were components of the change. Within this unit of study we can begin to consider the contributions made by the intrinsic peculiarities of single individuals, as members of groups of individuals whose intrinsic peculiarities are also known.

To consider the Manus evolutionary step only under the heading of *cultural* evoluton, illustrative of diffusion or convergence, or even under the heading of the "role of genius," obscures the mechanisms involved and the wider temporal-spatial situation within which those changes were initiated. Only when such changes succeed do they become the background for evolutionary changes of such depth and breadth that outstanding inventions are made more than once, even though in these very cases very particular individuals, peculiarly placed, will make them.

The procedures for the microstudy of evolutionary change at the point of initiation must meet the same requirement: the study *in situ* of a group of fully identified living individuals, of known culture, in a known network, within a known ecological system, specified in inorganic, biological, and social terms. Preliminary work suggests that cultural variation can then be further located within the overlapping idiosyncratic versions of the culture, the *idioverses* [9] of the constituent individuals.

When evolution is studied in such specified groups, we may begin to examine the implication of the properties of the relevant groups in respect to homogeneity and heterogeneity, and this on many levels—ranging from such simple matters as height and weight and physical strength through tempo, reaction time, memory, imagery, and so on. When the choice-points of change are so located—not only in a culture, in a society, in a period, in an area, but among sociologically identified individuals in an interacting group in which the character of the network is specified —then the degree of biological implication in change, through individual differences within the significant group and differences between cultures which have been elaborated by such groups, may

9. I am indebted to my colleague in the Admiralty Island research, Theodore Schwartz, for this phrasing. This microstudy of culture change clearly must follow two lines: that found through continuous alertness to natural historical experiments, and that of detailed laboratory experiments of the sort being conducted by Alex Bavelas (1951).

be found to be one of the most important mechanisms of evolution. The purposeful assembly of groups of individuals diversified biologically, culturally, and in terms of individual life experience —as teams constructed to complement and supplement each other —may well represent a next step in man's increasingly conscious implication in the evolutionary process (Capes, 1957).

REFERENCES

ABEL, T. M. 1932. Unsynthetic modes of thinking among adults, a discussion of Piaget's concepts. Amer. J. Psychol., *44* (1), 123–32.

ARIETI, S. 1956. Some basic problems common to anthropology and modern psychiatry. Amer. Anthrop., *58* (1), 26–39.

ARMSTRONG, E. A. 1946. Shakespeare's imagination, a study of the psychology of association and inspiration. London, Lindsay Drummond.

BARNETT, H. G. 1953. Innovation. New York, McGraw-Hill.

BAVELAS, A. 1951. Communication patterns in task oriented groups. In D. Lerner and H. Lasswell, eds., The policy sciences. Stanford, Stanford Univ. Press, pp. 193–202.

BIDNEY, D. 1953. Theoretical anthropology. New York, Columbia Univ. Press.

BOAS, F. 1911; rev. ed. 1938. The mind of primitive man. New York, Macmillan.

BOWLBY, J. 1951. Maternal care and mental health. Geneva, World Health Org., Monogr. Series, No. 2.

CAPES, M., ed. In press. Proceedings of the international conference on small groups and group discussions, held at Eastbourne, England, January–February, 1956, under the auspices of the WFMH and the Josiah Macy, Jr., Foundation.

CHILDE, V. G. 1951. Social evolution. London and New York, Henry Schuman.

COBB, E. In preparation. The ecology of imagination in childhood.

DARLING, F. F. 1937. A herd of red deer, a study in animal behaviour. London, Oxford Univ. Press.

EISLEY, L. 1955. Fossil man and human evolution. In Yearbook of anthropology—1955. New York, Wenner-Gren Foundation for Anthropological Research, pp. 61–78.

ERIKSON, E. 1950. Childhood and society. New York, W. W. Norton.

FIELD, M. 1955. Activity response to Gold Coast witchcraft today. J. Ment. Sci., *101* (Oct.), 826–33.

FORTUNE, R. F. 1932. Omaha secret societies. Columbia Univ. Contr. Anthrop., *14*.

FREUD, S. 1938. Totem and tabu. In A. A. Brill, tr. and ed., The basic writings of Sigmund Freud. New York, Modern Library.

FREUD, S. 1949. Introductory lectures in psychoanalysis, a course of twenty-eight lectures delivered at the University of Vienna. 2d rev. ed. London, Allen, & Unwin.

GOLDSTEIN, K. 1943. The significance of psychological research in schizophrenia. J. Nerv. Ment. Dis., *97*, 261–79.

HOGBIN, I. 1934. Law and order in Polynesia. New York, Harcourt, Brace.

HUXLEY, J. S. 1947. Touchstone for ethics. New York, Harper.

HUXLEY, J. S. 1956. Evolution, cultural and biological. In William L. Thomas, Jr., ed., Current anthropology. Chicago, Univ. of Chicago Press, pp. 3–25.

ITTELSON, W. H., and CANTRIL, H. 1954. Perception: a transactional approach. Garden City, Doubleday.

KING, J. A. 1955. Social behavior, social organization, and population dynamics in a black-tailed prairiedog town in the Black Hills of South Dakota. Contr. Lab. Vert. Biol. Univ. Mich.

KROEBER, A. L. 1948. Anthropology. New York, Harcourt, Brace.

KROEBER, A. L. 1952. The nature of culture. Chicago, Univ. of Chicago Press.

KROEBER, A. L. ed. 1953. Anthropology today. Chicago, Univ. of Chicago Press.

LEES, R. B. 1953. The basis of glotto chronology. Language, *29*, 113–37.

LÉVY-BRUHL, L. 1926. How natives think. London, Allen & Unwin.

LÉVY-BRUHL, L. 1928. The "soul" of the primitive. Lilian A. Clare, tr. New York, Macmillan.

LOWENFELD, M. In preparation. The world book.

MEAD, M. 1932. A preliminary investigation into the thought of children, with special reference to animism. J. Roy. Anthrop. Inst., *62* (Jan.–June), 173–90.

MEAD, M. 1938. The mountain Arapesh. I. An importing culture. Amer. Mus. Nat. Hist., Anthrop. Papers, *36* (Pt. 3), 145–349.

MEAD, M. 1940. The mountain Arapesh. II. Supernaturalism. Ibid., *37* (Pt. 3), 317–451.

MEAD, M. 1946. Professional problems of education in dependent countries. J. Negro Educ., *15* (3), 346–57.

MEAD, M. 1947. The mountain Arapesh. III. Socio-economic life. IV. Diary of events in Alitoa. Amer. Mus. Nat. Hist., Anthrop. Papers, *40* (Pt. 3), 159–420.

MEAD, M. 1949. The mountain Arapesh. V. The record of Unabelin, with Rorschach analyses. Ibid., *41* (Pt. 3), 289–390.

MEAD, M. 1952. Some relationships between social anthropology and psychiatry. In F. Alexander and H. Ross, eds., Dynamic psychiatry. Chicago, Univ. of Chicago Press, pp. 401–48.

MEAD, M., ed. 1953. Cultural patterns and technical change. Paris, Unesco. Mentor Book ed. (MD 134), New York, New American Library, 1955.

MEAD, M. 1954a. Cultural discontinuities and personality transformation. J. Soc. Issues (Kurt Lewin Memorial Award Issue, Suppl. Series, No. 8).

MEAD, M. 1954b. Manus restudied: an interim report. Trans. N. Y. Acad. Sci., Series 2, *16*, 426–32. (This gives a technical summary of the Admiralty Islands Expedition.)

MEAD, M. 1954c. Some theoretical considerations on the problem of mother-child separation. Amer. J. Orthopsychiat., *84* (3), 471–83.

MEAD, M. 1956a. The cross-cultural approach to the study of personality. In J. L. McCory, ed., Psychology of personality. New York, Logos Press, pp. 201–52.

MEAD, M. 1956b. New lives for old, cultural transformation: Manus 1928–1953. New York, Morrow.

MEAD, M., and WOLFENSTEIN, M., eds. 1955. Childhood in contemporary cultures. Chicago, Univ. of Chicago Press.

PIAGET, J. 1926. The language and thought of the child. New York, Harcourt, Brace.

PIAGET, J. 1952. Dreams and imitation in childhood. New York, W. W. Norton.

RAMSAY, O. A., and HESS, E. H. 1954. A laboratory approach to the study of imprinting. Wilson Bull., *66* (3), 196–206.

RICHARDSON, S. A., and DOHRENWEND, B. The Non-scheduled Interview (tentative title; to be published by Basic Books, New York).

RICHTER, C. P. 1943. The self-selection of diets. In Essays in biology in honor of Herbert M. Evans. Written by his friends. Berkeley, Univ. of Calif. Press, pp. 409–506.

SCHACHTEL, E. 1947. On memory and childhood amnesia. Psychiatry, *10* (1), 1–26.

SCHWARTZ, T. 1958. The Paliau Movement in the Admiralties, 1946–1954. Ph.D. dissertation, Univ. of Penn.

SEWELL, E. 1952. The structure of poetry. New York, Scribner's.

SHARPE, E. F. 1937. Dream analysis. London, Hogarth Press and the Institute of Psycho-Analysis.

SHARPE, E. F. 1950. Collected papers on psycho-analysis. Marjorie Brierley, ed. London, Hogarth Press and the Institute of Psycho-Analysis.

STEWARD, J. H. 1955. Theory of culture change, the methodology of multilinear evolution. Urbana, Univ. of Illinois Press.

SWADESH, M. 1955. Towards greater accuracy in lexostatic dating. Int. J. Amer. Linguistics, *21*, 121–37.

TANNER, J., and INHELDER, B., eds. 1956. Discussions on child development. Vol. *1:* First meeting of the World Health Organization Study Group on psycho-biological development of the child, Geneva, 1953 (1956). Vol. *2:* Second meeting, London, 1954 (1957). Vols. *3* and *4* in preparation. London, Tavistock Press; New York, International Universities Press.

THORPE, W. H. 1956. Learning and instinct in animals. London, Methuen.

WHITE, L. A. 1949. The science of culture. New York, Farrar, Straus.

WISSLER, C. L. 1923. Man and culture. New York, Crowell.

Epilogue

23

Behavior and Evolution

George Gaylord Simpson

THE AMERICAN MUSEUM OF NATURAL HISTORY AND
COLUMBIA UNIVERSITY, NEW YORK

INTRODUCTION

ONE AUTHOR may write a book with one idea. Twenty-odd
authors introduce not merely twenty-odd ideas but a great many
more. Each distills, as they have here, long experience and many
thoughts, and in the resulting torrent each chapter becomes a book
in miniature, and a book of many more ideas than one. The
purpose assigned to this chapter was to summarize all that has
gone before, but what has gone before is a series of summaries.
It would be difficult, it might not be particularly interesting, and
it could be of dubious utility to summarize those summaries, just
so, and I do not intend to try. What I shall try is even more difficult but, to the extent that it may be successful, should be more
interesting and more useful. The intention is to go over more or
less the same ground (obviously in very much less detail), using
the information supplied by the other authors but with a different
sequence and approach. The lines followed will thus cut across
those previously laid down, as woof cuts across warp, and the
hope is that a coherent fabric will result.

Citations by authors' names are to preceding chapters in this
book, and are representative rather than exhaustive. Where no
authority is given, I am of course responsible but I am rarely
original. The chances are that an uncredited statement was also
derived from some other passage in this book or from statements
by the other authors and their discussants in conference.

Behavioral mechanisms and their history

Behavior involves receptors, which bring in some sort of information about the situation in which an animal finds itself, effectors, which do something about it, and mediating mechanisms, which, among other things, relate the action to the information.

The end results of long, progressive, and divergent evolution of receptors, especially the localized sense organs, are stunningly demonstrated in the modern world. The (compound) eyes of insects and the eyes of vertebrates, for instance, are in their separate ways the most complex of all sense organs, and their ways *are* separate, for beyond the requirements set by the physical properties of light they operate on entirely different principles. That divergence is congruent with the known wide phylogenetic separation of the two groups: positive, unequivocal evidence sets 500×10^6 years as an absolute lower limit for separation of their ancestries; inference and dubious evidence suggest a time on the order of twice that figure. The phylogenetic sensory divergence, which is even more striking in other modalities, warns us to expect practically no homological behavior in the two groups. As to the historical origins of the two kinds of eyes, and of the extremely numerous other photoreceptors, the details are forever lost: we know that the fossil record will not supply them. The general course of the history is nevertheless inferable from comparative anatomy. The two main problems of any such inference, to determine whether a given stage belongs in a particular phylogeny and to determine the direction of change, are here comparatively easy. It is, for instance, clear that an aggregation of simple directional light detectors (proto-ommatidia) belongs in the insect and not in the vertebrate phylogeny, and equally clear that in the vertebrate ancestry evolution of a lens necessarily preceded that of an image-resolving retina.

In the case of the vertebrate ear, next most complicated among special sense organs, the evolutionary changes of gross anatomy in later stages of the history are well documented by fossils. Part of the apparatus is (usually) bony, and the form of the rest, excluding only the comparatively unimportant mammalian pinna, is closely followed by surrounding hard parts, which readily fossilize.

With all the divergences and retrogressions (in parasites, for example), it is evident enough that there has been an *average* increase in the numbers of different kinds of sensory information received and likewise in perceptual discrimination and patterning within each kind. The tendencies culminate, separately, in the dominant groups of terrestrial animals: insects and tetrapods (especially birds and mammals).

Effectors are for the most part, although by no means exclusively, separately movable parts of the body. Where they are most elaborated, which is again in the insects (or arthropods generally) and the vertebrates, specialized muscles, often significantly called the "behavioral muscles," move skeletal segments. Divergence and lack of homological behavior between insects and vertebrates are again illustrated, for the external skeleton-internal muscle apparatus of an insect obviously had a different origin from the internal skeleton-external muscle apparatus of a vertebrate. Here the historical evidence, especially for the vertebrates, is excellent. The behavioral muscles, themselves, are rarely preserved in fossils, but the attachments of the more important of them generally leave definite marks on the skeleton from which the muscles can be restored without undue guesswork. Moreover, the skeleton itself usually determines the direction of motions. Thus, for instance, the evolution of locomotion among vertebrates can be followed in great detail (Colbert, Romer). Probably the most interesting single example of the crucial involvement of effector systems in behavioral evolution is in the origin of man, and here, too, the details are becoming clear (Washburn and Avis).

What were, for brevity, called "mediating mechanisms" above do a great deal more than merely mediate, and they seem both literally and figuratively to be more deeply implicated in the evolution of behavior than the receptors and effectors, important and fascinating as those are. They do mediate, providing the hyphen in the classical S-R (stimulus-response) reaction of psychology. They also organize, combine, and formalize stimuli, convert them into perceptions, store information received as past stimuli, pattern responses in (as a rule) adaptive directions, program successive items of behavior, and in general coordinate all the activities of the organism. Among the mediators in this extended sense the most completely general,[1] but the least struc-

1. They occur and are almost the only mediators in plants, but plant behavior (fascinating as it was to Darwin and still is to many) was deliberately excluded from this symposium.

tured above the molecular level, are chemical. In their most specialized forms (which, once again, culminate separately in arthropods and vertebrates) they are specific hormones some of which are compounded locally in endocrine glands. The elaboration reached at this level is exemplified in mammals in the sequence of nerve impulses from the hypothalamus, leading to secretion of gonadotrophic hormones in the pituitary, which stimulate secretion of androgens in the testis, which somehow release or trigger development of male sex characters and associated behavior (Beach).

Hormones, and numerous other biochemical factors, put the organism in states appropriate for certain types of behavior and may initiate or trigger the behavior, but they do not pattern or more immediately control the specific forms of response, which are so enormously diverse among different animals (Beach). In virtually all animals except protozoans [2] and sponges the most important mediator-coordinator-etc. is of course the nervous system, whether diffuse (retiform, e.g. in coelenterates), partly centralized in cords with more or less formation of small ganglia (e.g. many worms), or strongly centralized and differentiated, with a brain or large brainlike ganglia (e.g. vertebrates, insects). That sequence is not *demonstrably* historical, but it unquestionably has occurred often, independently, in numerous phylogenies (Bullock).

The nervous system, the central nervous system, and the brain, at the levels where these severally occur, are by far the most intricate parts of the behavioral mechanism. It has, especially for the vertebrate brain, been generally assumed that this is the limiting factor in the evolution of behavior, that evolutionary progression in behavior must be accompanied by and cannot proceed either slower or faster than correlated changes in the brain. There is good authority for that view (Sperry), but the point is disputable and this symposium includes conflicting opinions in different sections. Harlow maintains, in effect, that the neural apparatus is commonly capable of mediating more complex or advanced behavior than actually occurs. As evidence he cites experimental learning, from worms to apes, that does not occur in nature and that could not, in his opinion, be of the slightest utility to the animal if it did occur. In discussion at the

2. And even some protozoans have conductive tracts that are functional equivalents and just possibly the primitive homologues of nerves.

conferences it was agreed that worms rarely encounter T-mazes in their native heaths, but it was argued that learning—even such very slow learning—to choose the more rewarding of two directions is a part, and a useful part, of earthworm existence. Similarly for the primate examples, the things learned in captivity have no close counterparts in nature but the demonstrated capacities for learned discrimination would seem to be highly useful there. On the opposite side, Washburn and Avis suggest in a specific instance that change in behavior led genetic change in the brain: their hypothesis is that adoption of tools by creatures with ape-sized brains (cf. the australopithecines) eventuated, through the implicit action of strong natural selection, in brains of human size. The evidence is admittedly inconclusive. Finally, Mayr discusses the related question as to whether structural change precedes correlated behavioral change (with its concomitants in the nervous system) or vice versa. He concludes that "there is no general answer to the question . . . Each case must be analyzed separately . . ."

The brains of recent vertebrates, highly varied and divergent rather than sequential in many respects, do in a more general way show different degrees of advance from which a phylogenetic progression can be inferred (Romer, Pribram). This is confirmed in major outline, although not in detail, by the historical evidence of fossils, in which some of the external features of the vanished brain can be determined from the size and shape of the cavity in which it was lodged (Patterson).[3] The supposed "phylogenetic" arrangement of the brains of recent ungulate mammals, for instance, turns out to be grossly misleading: the brain of eohippus was radically unlike a "generalized" or "primitive" ungulate brain as inferred from recent animals and was quite like that of an opossum. Nevertheless the available fossils do not seriously invalidate the usual picture from recent brains in a generalized sequence

$$\text{fish} \longrightarrow \text{reptile} \begin{cases} \longrightarrow \text{bird} \\ \longrightarrow \text{primitive mammal} \longrightarrow \text{advanced mammal.} \end{cases}$$

3. Although a written version was not received in time for inclusion in this volume, this subject was discussed by Bryan Patterson at the second conference. The following publications supply background and many details. Edinger also has in preparation a new, extensive compilation and synthesis. Edinger, T. 1929. Die fossilen Gehirne. Ergeb. Anat. u. Entw. gesch., III Abt., Z. Gesell. Anat., Vol. 28. Edinger, T. 1948. Evolution of the horse brain. Geol. Soc. Amer., Mem. No. 25.

The most striking single change in gross anatomy is the expansion of the upper and medial parts of the cerebrum, the so-called neopallium, beginning among reptiles but most accentuated between primitive and advanced mammals. Changes in over-all behavior certainly accompanied this change (and others!) in the brain. The usual conclusion is that the neopallium is particularly involved with newer and "higher" intellectual functions, flexibility and elaboration of reactions, complex learning, reasoning, and so on, while the rest of the brain, phylogenetically older, is concerned with more instinctual, simpler, more rigid, or generally more primitive parts of behavior. In this symposium Freedman and Roe, among others, have understandably accepted the consensus on this point.

Pribram has here entered an emphatic dissent. The brain has not evolved by simple accretion but by general remodeling, a conclusion that is, even a priori, practically inescapable. It is simply incredible that so complexly coordinated an organ could continue to function as smoothly as it does by, so to speak, simply plugging in new parts on the old chassis.[4] Pribram denies that there is a relationship between neopallium and learning, paleo- and archipallium and instinct. He finds a more significant functional separation between the inner core of the brain, concerned with behavior sequences, and an outer part, related to discrimination. Both inner and outer divisions have both old and new stuctural elements. Behavioral progression in the vertebrate series, reflected in the remodeling of the brain, is believed to involve increase not in extent of repertory or in the ratio of learned to innate behavior but rather in multiple sensory and motivational determination of responses. Establishment of the relationship between brain architecture and behavior demands new taxonomies of behavior, with categories that would be testable anatomically in place of earlier categories (such as "learned" and "innate") which seem, in this connection, to have failed. The approach cannot be quite as simple as all that, and Pribram plainly knows that it is not, but here is an exciting program for new approaches to old problems! (On

4. Of course the new-brain, old-brain dichotomists are not really so naïve. Changing behavior (in which the *direction* of change may have been mistaken) is reasonably supposed to be correlated with the most obviously changing part of the brain, without at all excluding the idea that the other parts of the brain also, and necessarily, have changed in accommodation to the "accreted" structure and behavior.

the taxonomy of behavior and on instinct versus learning see especially Nissen; both subjects are mentioned again below.)

There is a fairly clear distinction between the functional properties of elements in a system (physiology) and the number and arrangement or architecture of those elements (anatomy). Bullock shows that all neurophysiological properties known in the vertebrates (including man) also occur widely among invertebrates, including many with behavior radically different from and remarkably simpler than any vertebrate's behavior. The differences in behavior must, therefore, either be purely architectural or use now quite unknown neurophysiological mechanisms—or else involve something called "mind" that is not amenable to any such naturalistic explanations. As a matter of sheer faith Bullock rejects the dualistic or mystical third alternative, but he is highly dubious about the first and apparently pessimistic about progress toward discovering the postulated new parameters of the second alternative. Perhaps this, too, is a profession of faith, but many of us will agree with McCulloch (cited by Bullock) and with Sperry [5] (herein) that the known neurological parameters are more than adequate to account for any conceivable complication of behavior merely by architectural modification of finite numbers of neurons. A perhaps oversimple but probably valid analogy is that, given contractile units and jointed skeletal elements, no conceivable motion would require new physiological properties but only multiplication and arrangement of those given. A further pertinent (and fascinating) observation by Bullock would seem to go far in countering his own skepticism: "the typical synapse in integrative systems [is no longer considered to be] a digital device exclusively . . . but rather a complex analog device which finally converts into digital output" and even the output of many neurons may be a graded event. The potentialities of a device that is both digital and analog, that has millions of units, and that can be interconnected in more millions of ways stagger the imagination —mine, at least!

Consonant with Bullock's conclusion as to the great antiquity and generality of (known!) neurophysiological properties is Har-

5. Sperry has a passing doubt as to linguistic behavior, but given even one single abstraction to a verbal symbol—and even in invertebrates the basis for such abstraction occurs—the appearance of the whole linguistic panoply is a simple matter of multiplication.

low's argument that properties involved in learning, or that the *kinds* of learning, are as old as learning itself and have never changed. Yet Harlow sees in this no contradiction with the observation that the amount of learning and its repertory have certainly changed tremendously in the course of many phylogenies. It seems again, and now in full agreement with the author cited, that the *principles* of the mechanism need not become different as the mechanism becomes structurally more complex and able to cope with a wider range of activities. That the range of activities, in learning and other behavior, has indeed tended to widen in the total course of the history of organisms, and in many individual phylogenies, seems to be not only the consensus but also beyond reasonable doubt. As regards particular segments of phylogeny, the generalization may not apply. Pribram believes that there is no complication in behavioral repertory from fish to mammals (as exemplified by *recent* organisms). Probably there is a semantic question here as to what one wishes to call an "increase in complexity of total behavior repertoire." Harlow suggests (for learning, again) that from the Devonian, when they had a common ancestry, into the late Cretaceous, when fishes reached approximately their present status, the more progressive fishes and tetrapods (amphibians-reptiles-mammals) may both have independently increased their behavioral capacities in their respective spheres. Then in the late Cretaceous it would be true to say there was no increase as between (contemporaneous) fishes and tetrapods, but the statement would not be true of either group historically or phylogenetically. There is in this discussion a grasp of the distinction between comparative studies of contemporaneous forms and historical studies of phylogenetic series that has hitherto been lacking in comparative psychology and that may serve as a model. Returning to the previous point, I may add that because fishes have changed very little structurally (including brain structure) since the late Cretaceous and because mammals have changed a great deal (especially in brain structure), it stretches credulity to believe that it is still true of contemporaneous recent forms that they are level as to complication of behavioral repertory.[6]

It is tempting here to go into the subject of progress (not only

6. Of course Pribram does not maintain that there is no difference now or no progression historically in the range of behavior in fishes and mammals. He only argues for a different categorization of the evident differences and changes.

progression) in evolution, but the temptation will be resisted except for this short paragraph. Huxley has discussed the subject in this symposium, and at greater length in well-known earlier publications. Here the context is cultural evolution, but the concept is given as equally applicable to biological evolution in general. All the authors in this symposium seem to accept—at least none explicitly denies—that progress has occurred in the evolution of behavior, as seen over the total history, perhaps now in one phylum and now in another, checked in some lineages, reversed in others, and yet with an upward trend through a series of apexes. The concept of evolutionary progress may apply most meaningfully to the evolution of certain of the behavioral mechanisms. Whether a leg is better than a fin depends on where they are, but there is no doubt that an eye is in some valid and more universal sense better than a pigment spot and a central nervous system better than a nerve net.

Kinds of Behavior

Early in the conferences it was suggested that we state explicitly what we were talking about, that we define "behavior." Animated discussion produced neither unanimity nor consensus but gave the impression that it might be well to leave the subject undefined. Then nothing pertinent would be excluded by definition, and if anything not plainly pertinent crept in, it might help to catalyze the synthesis.[7]

It was and is nevertheless clear that even if "behavior" itself is left undefined there is imperative need for a taxonomy of behaviors, including, necessarily, definitions of distinguishable categories of behavior. The general problem is discussed by Nissen, who remarks that neither the unit movements of behavior, such as the extension of a limb, nor its broad concepts, such as intelligence, are useful taxonomic categories. There is a metataxonomy (analogous to metamathematics) dealing not directly with the operations and categories of systematics but with the principles by which those are selected and judged. In biological metataxonomy various bases for categorization are considered: anatomi-

---

7. It similarly appears in biology that a clear-cut definition of "life" is likely to be more hindrance than help in exploring the frontiers of the subject. Attempted definitions are commonly given to beginning students, but the working biologist pays little attention to them.

cal resemblance, ecological association, phylogeny, behavior, and others. Apart from certain special applications, one criterion is generally adopted: phylogeny. In principle (and if we perform the prodigious feat of overlooking the fact that ignorance here still exceeds knowledge) phylogeny permits the biological classification of any and all organisms by a single *kind* of categorization, in a system that is, so to speak, unidimensional or has a single axis of comparison, that of phylogenetic affinity.[8] When Pribram calls for a taxonomy of behavior with categories testably related to the properties and architecture of the nervous system, he is in effect suggesting a unidimensional system. The suggestion is, however, more general than explicit, and even if a complete system of that sort proves to be possible, it evidently is not practicable at present.

Nissen suggests as basis for a metataxonomy (not the direct categorization of behaviors but the categorization of possible categorizations) this framework:

A. Functional or finalistic [i.e. adaptive, according to the ends served by, or the biological utility of kinds of behavior].

B. Descriptive [i.e. by comparisons and by identification of common formal elements].

C. Explanatory
　　1. Phylogenetic [or more broadly, historical].
　　2. By physical substrates.
　　3. By operational principles, models, etc.

Pribram's proposal corresponds with C 2. There is also a degree of correspondence with the kinds of scientific explanation discussed by Pittendrigh:

1. Functonal—by the end served. Nissen's A, which although he contrasts it with explanatory categories seems clearly to *be* an explanatory category.

2. Historical—by how observed properties were acquired. Nissen's C 1.

3. Causal or, preferably, physiological—by the working of the system studied. Nissen's C 2.

Nissen's B involves a behavioral taxonomy analogous to the old typological taxonomy of comparative anatomy. That was an essential but primitive stage in the development of biological sys-

---

8. Of course phylogeny itself is in another sense multidimensional, but the term is there in a different universe of discourse.

tematics, and it was outgrown and abandoned precisely because it has no directly explanatory element (Mayr). Perhaps a typological and purely descriptive stage in the taxonomy of behavior is unavoidable, but one can predict that only some form of explanatory taxonomy will eventually be satisfactory. Nissen's C 3, absent among Pittendrigh's explanatory categories, does indeed seem to be miscalled "explanatory." The erection of a model, principle, or "law" of behavior without regard for function, origin, or physical substrate is a generalized description with minimal or no real explanatory value. I would place this under Nissen's B and would again remark that pure description, no matter how deeply abstracted or broadly generalized and in spite of being both valuable and necessary in itself, is not likely to be a satisfactory basis for a classificatory system.

Regardless of whether a descriptive axis is now necessary or desirable and even if only the diverse explanatory axes be admitted, the point is made that for the present, at least, the classification of behavior seems inevitably to involve more than one axis (more than one category of categorizations) and hence to be multidimensional. The problem is correspondingly complex, and no general or complete classification of behavior is, in fact, attempted. Examples of classifications of limited aspects of behavior are presented: mating behavior (Spieth), social behavior (Thompson), and territoriality (Carpenter; not a formal classification but implicit in his list of functions of territoriality). The metacategory of mating behavior is functional (Nissen's A), and Spieth's classification is descriptive. The metacategory of social behavior is descriptive, and Thompson's classification is multidimensional. The metacategory of territoriality is also descriptive (or in Nissen's system abstracted to the level of C 3), and Carpenter's listing is functional (A).

Still another approach to the categorization of behavior, too formal or descriptive and too little explanatory to be advanced as a likely basis for definitive classification and yet useful in its own way, is by levels. As suggested in the first chapter,[9] a distinction may be made between first-order or molecular behavior (example: locomotion, Colbert) and second-order or compound behavior (example: courtship, Hinde and Tinbergen). To these

9. Where it is not original. The idea was advanced and discussed in the conferences by Mayr and others.

may be added a third level of compounding or of complexity beyond the simple unitary movements: from social to cultural behavior (examples especially in Huxley, Freedman and Roe, Mead).
These levels are further related to increasing aggregation of the
behaving organisms and to behavioral organization of their populations. First-order behavior includes the units that are constructed into behavior at all levels, but those units are the actions
of individuals. Second order behavior is commonly a mutual patterning between or among interacting individuals: predator and
prey (Colbert, Bates), mating couple (Hinde and Tinbergen),
mates and rivals (Carpenter), and others. In third-order behavior
a whole group behaves characteristically as such and over more
sustained periods of time. Of course the levels are not clear-cut.
Territoriality (Carpenter), for instance, involves for the most part
second-order behavior, but it also frequently tends to structure a
broader group and to merge into third-order behavior. Indeed,
third-order behavior is characteristically compounded from more
temporary, interindividual reactions (Thompson).

When most strongly developed, behavior here called third-order
has an "emergent" aspect. That is, the behavior of the group has
characteristics that are not evidently predictable from individual
behaviors; the group as a whole becomes a behaving (and evolving) unit.[10] Emerson has elaborately and fascinatingly exemplified
this aspect of behavior in the social insects, especially the termites.
Among the most remarkable things about this example is the fact
that termites make artifacts, their nests, which are manifestations
of unitary group behavior. The evolution of that behavior can be
studied morphologically, and many of the principles of evolution
of anatomical morphology are here analogically applicable.

Aspects of behavioral evolution in the supreme artifact producer can also be followed historically, in the archeological record of human artifacts (Washburn and Avis), and comparatively
among existing cultures (Mead). Culture, so characteristic of

10. We may go so far without admitting that group behavior is other or more than
the summation of the behavior of the included individuals which it seems (to me)
quite obviously to be. Individuals in a group do not act as they would if isolated—
hence the "emergent" characteristics—but in any case there is no such thing as an
isolated individual. A close-knit and highly organized group does, through summation, act as a unit of higher than individual order. To call such a group a "suprain-
dividual," as Emerson does, is a matter of personal definition and nomenclature, but
it does bring up problems of semantics, concepts, and implications that have been
hotly debated. There is no need to debate them again here.

man but confined to man only by definition or in degree of complexity, seems to be both a culmination of third-order behavior and an emergence of still another order. In the former aspect, culture is a biological adaptation, and cultural evolution is a continuation of biological evolution by other means—an example of the quite common evolutionary maneuvers of substitution and opportunism (Huxley, largely by implication here, more explicit in other works). In its latter, "emergent" aspect, human cultural evolution is a new (in the sense of "emergent") kind of behavioral evolution with different means of heredity and progression—by transmission and cumulation of objects and symbols (Mead).

The achievement of exceptionally high-order behavior in man, which is, so to speak, piled up on and compounded with the still present lower orders, gives human behavior an absolutely unique nature and complexity. That is so obviously true as to be a truism, even if we agree with Harlow that the status has been only gradually achieved and steadily through all our prehuman ancestors and that nothing new as to basic process and principle was suddenly added. Whether this involves mental abilities rudimentary or absent in other contemporaneous animals (Dobzhansky, cited by Harlow) is a matter of definition of "abilities" and perhaps not worth debating in those terms. Certainly *something* about our abilities and behaviors is different and was once, even if not suddenly, new! Freedman and Roe show that there is a projection of biological inheritance and changing trends into newly elaborated and changing cultural milieus and that the rich result is not without its penalties. Conflict of old and new, of deep-seated biological characteristics and strong cultural controls, makes man not only *sapiens* but also ambivalent and anxious.

The Biological Significance of Behavior

Organisms are so called because they are literally *organized*. Variable as they may be, the anatomy, physiology, and behavior of any species are structured in characteristic and complex ways. Organization implies a further relationship: things are organized only if this is *with respect to* something else. The manifest and comparatively very simple organization of faces on a crystal is with respect to the physical properties of its constituent atoms.

The almost incomparably more complex organization of a living thing is, for the most part, utilitarian: it is with respect to the usefulness to the individual or to a population of which the individual is a member. It serves an end, and in that sense is finalistic (Nissen); it has a purpose, and in that sense is teleological (Pittendrigh). The words "finalistic" and "teleological" have, however, had an unfortunate history in philosophy which makes them totally unsuitable for use in modern biology. They have too often been used to mean that evolution as a whole has a predetermined goal, or that the utility of organization in general is with respect to man or to some supernal scheme of things. Thus these terms may implicitly negate rather than express the biological conclusion that organization in organisms is with respect to utility to each separate species at the time when it occurs, and not with respect to any other species or any future time. In emphasis of this point of view, Pittendrigh here suggests that the new coinage "teleonomy" be substituted for the debased currency of teleology.

What is useful to an organism is adaptation, an almost tautological statement in spite of the fact that "adaptation" is an ambiguous word, as Pittendrigh has carefully explained. Biological organization is therefore relative to adaptation. Pittendrigh goes on to point out that adaptation is not reciprocal between organism and environment; the organism is adapted to the environment and not vice versa. So far, and beyond possible quibbles as to the wording, I agree, but not so entirely when he goes on to say that "The word 'adaptation' should be restricted to discussion and description of the organism," and especially not when he equates organization with adaptation. No more satisfactory is the frequent opposite attitude (e.g. in Nissen here) that because what is adapted *to* is the environment (broadly speaking) adaptation is basically controlled by or uniquely relative to the environment. Adaptation is a relationship between organisms and environments (Pittendrigh's definition 1) or the processes mediating that relationship (Pittendrigh's 3 and 4) or the result of those processes in the organism (Pittendrigh's 2). A *relationship* between two things (organism, environment) is not to be confused with either one of those things nor usefully discussed in terms of only one of them. Only in the last (in Pittendrigh's list the second) and most limited of the meanings of "adaptation" can it be said that organization *is* adaptation, or adaptation organization, and then only with strong reservations. A few extremists dissent, but most evolutionists agree that organisms may or frequently do have nonadaptive characteristics that nevertheless enter into their organization.

Such important niceties aside, there is no reasonable denying of Pittendrigh's conclusion that organization is basically adaptive and "teleonomic." That is fundamentally the biological meaning of organization, whether of behavior or of other aspects of the organism. (And the origin of adaptation, reviewed in the last section of this chapter, is the prime problem of evolutionary biology.)

Considered as an element in evolutionary adaptation, behavior is of course dependent on and not clearly separable from other aspects of adaptive organization (anatomical, physiological). It has, nevertheless, certain greater or lesser distinctions that give it peculiar interest in this connection. It is commonly the actual means of interaction between physical organization and the environment, hence the direct and visible expression of the relationship that is adaptation. Size, bill, tongue, digestion, musculature, wings of hummingbirds are all adaptations (in Pittendrigh's sense 2) to nectar feeding. That this is true and that adaptation (sense 1) exists is manifest in, and only in, the behavior of the bird. So, too, of the adaptive organization of the human hand, of a cat's teeth, of a whale's respiration, of an earthworm's digestion, and of innumerable other examples that will crowd into the reader's mind.

Behavior is also commonly (although not invariably) unusual in the complexity of its genetic determination and in the length and intricacy of the causal chain between that determination and the actual behavior (Caspari, Sperry, and next section of this chapter). These and other ontogenetic factors, such as individual experience (e.g. Freedman and Roe), add tremendously to the ramifications of behavior in the course of adaptation. Behavior is usually more obviously and more specifically goal-directed than the mechanisms on which it depends. Some biologists might quibble as to inference from hummingbird structure to adaptation or as to whether the structure should be called "goal-directed," but no one can deny the applicability of that term to the bird's behavior with a flower or question that the behavior is adaptive. Nevertheless, the ramifications of behavior commonly include items not obviously goal-directed or adaptive; note Hinde and Tinbergen's exposition of the manifold and puzzling peculiarities of kittiwake behavior that are finally found all to reduce to one adaptive basis, the nesting site.

Behavior may be just as stereotyped as structure—perhaps in some instances even more so—both in the individual and among individuals of one population. Nevertheless the possibilities of behavioral variation are enormous and have important corollaries for adaptation. Learning is a means of individual adaptation (Pittendrigh's 3) markedly more flexible than somatic modification.[11] Genetical variation of behavior in populations also unquestionably occurs and is a basis for adaptation (Pittendrigh's 4) in the same way as somatic genetical variation. Whether behavior is on a special footing in this respect is not at all clear, but note Caspari's suggestion that behavioral genetic variability may *itself* be an adaptation favored by selection, for instance in mammals.

There is a distinction, highly pertinent to the study of behavior, between immediate and long-range adaptation (Huxley). Immediate adaptation tends to be narrower (more specific in its correlation with environmental factors) and less variable. Long-range adaptation must be maintained in the face of extremes of environmental fluctuation and of inevitable evolution of the environment itself. ("Environment" of course includes all biotic associations and not only physical factors.) It therefore tends to be broader (less specific) and more variable. An enduring species must of course be successful not only at each immediate point but also over its whole range in time, and so the opposing tendencies must somehow balance. The balance sometimes inclines one way and sometimes the other, but it always involves some measure of what may be called adaptive compromise. The balance is never at the extreme of complete adaptation of a whole population to a single state of the environment: there are *no* genetically or behaviorally homogeneous species in nature. Here again behavior, especially learned behavior, has peculiar adaptive significance. It may be, and indeed generally is, highly specific in adaptation to an immediate

11. The objection may be made that learning and individual somatic modification have no evolutionary significance unless one accepts (as I and almost all other modern evolutionists most decidedly do not) neo-Lamarckian inheritance of acquired characters. The apparatuses for learning and for somatic modification, determining the ranges and kinds of possible learning and modification, are genetically controlled, hence heritable and subject to adaptive evolution under the influence of natural selection. Moreover some learning is heritable, passed on by example or symbol from generation to generation, and unquestionably can come to influence evolution, even genetical change, although its original variations were nongenetic.

situation, and yet it may be quickly and quite precisely adjustable in maintenance of adaptation through long-range fluctuations and trends. Behavior is commonly more adaptively labile than the genetic system in a population, even though its lability is itself dependent on the genetic system. Moreover, the evolution of learned behavior is to some extent reversible (as Mead has shown for cultural evolution), not without restrictions but certainly far more so than genetical evolution.

Nissen has brought out an interesting relationship between factors of behavior, variabilty of environment, and maintenance of adaptation. There is a triple ratio in the organizing functions of behavior, perception: learning: reasoning, according to the extent of their development in particular species. Adaptation may be maintained with low environmental variation or strong dependence on environment when the ratio is heavier to the left. In more variable environments or over longer periods shift of weight to the right is, if not absolutely necessary, at least likely to have adaptive value, and when such shift has occurred the species is more independent of environmental controls.

To this point adaptation has been considered as a complex of processes (and results of processes) bringing about and maintaining an organism-environment relationship useful to individual organisms and populations. That is the fundamental aspect, but when any multispecific community is considered another aspect becomes striking. In such a community each species has a characteristic over-all adaptation, and under usual conditions that adaptation is distinctly different for each. In ecological terms, each species has its niche, and each niche is occupied by only one species. The fact is usually quite apparent from its morphological concomitants, for instance in museum collections of preserved specimens. Its really adaptive nature—its explanation in functional terms—is almost entirely behavioral. The basis of what might be called the niche specificity of animals is usually in such behavioral traits as food preferences and food getting (Bates), home or nesting sites and territoriality (Carpenter), access to appropriate breeding places, timing or diurnal rhythm of activities, or movement into favorable microclimates (Pittendrigh). On such bases the total activity of the community is parceled out among a great many different (genetic) populations which can coexist, packed into the same area, because behavioral specialization gives each a separate role.

That is the functional explanation of niche specificity and of its result, the multiplicity and diversity of kinds of organisms.[12] The historical explanation is adaptive radiation: the tendency for animals as a whole and any successful group of animals in particular to expand in the course of their evolution and to diverge in separate lineages, each developing characteristic over-all adaptation and all collectively occupying whatever niches are available to the group. The radiation, like the resultant niche specificity, is of course fundamentally behavioral although usually studied by means of the structural substrates of behavior (Colbert).

For radiation to occur and for niche specificity to result, a population must be broken up, for no matter how variable it may be and how many niches it may spread through these cannot otherwise be parceled out and become literally niche-*specific*. The nexus that prevents significant divergence (in the usual biparental species) is interbreeding, with its constant canceling of incipient genetic divergence, feeding it back into the general stock of the population. The isolating mechanisms that lessen and finally stop interbreeding between segments of what was once a single population do not seem to be predominantly behavioral, but behavior commonly becomes involved in them sooner or later and it may take over the main role when other mechanisms are weak (Spieth). Specific differences in behavior here have quite different biological significance from those involved in niche specificity. They are not developing or consolidating new divergent adaptations. They are making such adaptations genetically possible by creating an isolate in which they can arise and persist. Hinde and Tinbergen point out that as a rule behaviors tend to be more alike in more closely related animals; that is, species that have diverged least phylogenetically also have diverged least in their behavior, as one would probably expect. But courtship behavior is exceptional: it may be strongly divergent in related and otherwise similarly behaving species. In such cases courtship behavior is an isolating mechanism and a prerequisite for ecological adaptive divergence.

The observation that similarity of behaviors tends, like structural similarity, to be proportional to phylogenetic affinity gives

12. Another factor in the total diversity of organisms is geographic, for groups geographically separated may essentially duplicate each other ecologically. That, however, is only indirectly related to the evolution of behavior.

behavior further biological significance and another role in systematics. It may be used (with certain precautions briefly noted later in this chapter) as evidence on existing degrees of phylogenetic relationship. It thus adds importantly to the total evidence, anatomical, physiological, and other, and it may well be decisive when other evidence is equivocal or conflicting. Mayr has given striking examples, and I cannot forbear giving one more from personal experience. Rheas and tinamous, groups of birds both long isolated in South America, differ radically in that tinamous fly and have a keeled sternum and other adaptations to flight, quite absent in rheas. Therefore authorities have commonly considered the two groups as unrelated and have placed the rheas with the ostriches. On the other hand rheas and tinamous do share some anatomical peculiarities, in the palate and elsewhere, that have caused other students to maintain that they are related and that rheas are not so closely related to ostriches. As observed in the field, rheas and tinamous are so similar in behavior,[13] apart from the phylogenetically unimportant difference in size and the fact that tinamous do fly (reluctantly and poorly), that the conclusion that they are related is inescapable.

Systematics, dealing with the nature and origins of organic diversity and hence also with phylogeny and classification, among other things, is one of the fields of biology in which comparative behavior is most deeply involved, as shown by Mayr and others in this symposium. Not only in phylogeny and classification, as just noted, but also in niche-specific behavior, behavioral isolating mechanisms, and other topics, systematists and comparative psychologists have innumerable common problems that neither specialty can solve alone.

THE ONTOGENY OF BEHAVIOR

The medium in which evolution, as a historical series of events, occurs is phylogeny: the whole complex of populations genetically continuous through time. Phylogeny is compounded from ontogenies, the life histories of the individuals composing popula-

13. Both are polygynous, several hens lay in one nest which is a hollow on the ground, the male covers the eggs and rears the chicks, they run similarly, and their escape behavior is similar until the tinamou is compelled (as last resort) to fly, food habits overlap as much as would be expected in the light of other factors, and so on.

tions. Thus historical explanation in biology has ontogeny as its
material unit. Functional ("teleonomic") and physiological explanation must also take account of ontogeny, because adaptation
of the individual must apply to the whole life cycle and not a
single phase or instant, and physiological mechanisms likewise
must function continuously in varying ways throughout the cycle.

The study of ontogeny logically begins with genetics, the informational aspect of the material derived from a parent or (usually) the two parents and becoming a new individual. Some organization, and therefore some information in the genetic sense, is
always present in the parental—mostly the maternal when that
distinction exists—cytoplasm. It is, however, well known that the
most specific organization of the new individual and much the
greatest part of the information required for its subsequent development are in the nucleus, and there almost entirely within
the chromosomes. It is equally familiar that the informational
content of a chromosome is in its longitudinally differentiated
organization and that the experimentally unreduced units of the
linear sequence are operationally defined as genes. Genes are specific in their effects; the primary action of a gene is believed to be
control (probably even so through intermediate steps) of production and activity of a particular enzyme in the cell. The enzymes
in turn affect differentiation in development and metabolism
throughout life, and those activities determine or modify tissue
and organ development, hence anatomical structure and physiological function, and so ultimately behavior. (Caspari, Sperry.)

The classical, "Mendelizing" gene includes among its (often
quite remote) effects one readily observable phenotypic characteristic. However, the (probably) single, specific primary chemical
activity of a gene becomes involved in intricate, long, chain, circular, and branching reactions and the ultimate phenotypic effects
are usually multiple, i.e. pleiotropic—perhaps invariably so in
multicellular organisms and above the level of enzyme production. On the same basis and at the same levels, it is virtually impossible that a phenotypic character should be wholly determined
by a single gene: there is always gene interaction, and the somatic
organization as a whole is not a mosaic of separate gene correlates
but a reflection of the genic-chromosomal organization as a whole.
Some genes modify or buffer the effects of others; whole series
of genes (polygenes) act additively and without evident single-

gene dominance on some characters; different forms, alleles, of genes are commonly present on the two chromosomes of a homologous pair and their joint action may be different from, or in some respect superior (heterotic) to, the effects of paired identical alleles (Caspari).

It is fairly obvious that genetic control of behavioral mechanisms—receptors, integrators, effectors—must also affect behavior. Experimental mutants with nonfunctioning eyes, reduced brains, or loss of wings necessarily behave differently from their "wild-type" relatives. These artificial examples are crude in comparison with the genetic situation in natural populations, but those and similar behavior-correlated structural peculiarities do in fact occur in various species. Caspari further shows that genes recognized by some structural character frequently have pleiotropic effects on behavior, often with no obvious relationship to the gene-labeling structural characters. Thus single mutant genes have repeatedly been seen to influence such specific behavior as mating or such diffuse behavioral traits as wildness or tameness. Selective breeding for such traits as learning ability or emotionality has been successful, and inbred lines may become as distinctive in behavior as in morphology. Those and related facts not only show that behavior is indeed under genetic influence but also suggest that pleiotropy and polygenic systems are generally involved. Genetic heterogeneity and variability in relationship to behavior are common and may be highly adaptive, and heterosis may occur for behavior as for other characteristics. From all these relationships, the genetic determination of behavior would appear to be comparatively loose or labile in many of its potentialities, at least, and perhaps even unstable (Caspari). Undue instability is nevertheless under the control of integrative, homeostatic features of the genetic systems of populations (Lerner, cited by Caspari).

Development is the process through which genetic mechanisms operate to produce the behaving, developed individual. "To produce" is, to be sure, neither a precise nor an exclusive statement of genetic function in this connection. Since all the differentiated cells of a complex, multicellular animal have (usually) the same genetic constitution, genes obviously do not produce cellular differentiation independent of other factors; their actions must depend on their cytoplasmic and somatic environments. Nevertheless the initial nucleus, in spore, zygote, or the like, must contain essentially the whole set of plans for development, evoked stage by stage, or all the necessary information implicit in organization (Pittendrigh). Sperry points out that, of all the characteristics of an organism, its behavior is likely to be furthest removed from the direct action of the genes, and he concludes that "the possible patterns of causal sequence by which a gene mutation may affect a change in behavior are, for practical purposes, almost infinitely varied."

Development of the peripheral organs of behavior (receptors and effectors) is concomitant with that of their nerves and of the central nervous system (where one exists). The complexity of the central nervous system is so great, and its role in mediation and coordination so literally central, that it is the limiting factor as regards both development and evolution of behavior. That means in individual development that a central nervous system of sufficient complexity for coordination of any given level of behavior must already be developed and functional when the behavior begins. In evolutionary terms, one of the implications is that learning cannot be wholly substituted for prior organization of the central nervous system or, if you like, for the instinctual elements of behavior, because learning is possible only if a sufficiently complex central nervous system *already* exists. In embryology it appears, indeed, that the development of the central nervous system is highly specific from the start. Its architecture is determined altogether by heredity, plus whatever nonspecific modifications may result from extrinsic environmental variations. The structure is not visibly modified by the training effect of its own operations (Sperry).

Nevertheless animals *do* learn and the operation of the central nervous system *is* affected by its own past operations, training, or experience. The answer would necessarily seem to lie not in development or architecture but in physiological processes, especially at the synapses and presumably at molecular and lower levels (Bullock). Development sets up a machine with number and arrangement of parts rigidly determined and unchangeable, and nevertheless the subsequent working of the machine is always somewhat flexible and often astonishingly so. (The question whether the architectural patterns and the known physiological properties are sufficient to account for complexities of behavior, and the differing viewpoints of Sperry and Bullock on this question, have been mentioned before.)

At this point arises the always vexatious problem of instinctive, or innate, or unlearned versus learned behavior. Most of the authors in this book have mentioned it, some in passing and several in considerable detail. All (unless I have overlooked a dissent) seem to accept the necessity for some distinction more or less along the traditional lines, whatever misgivings they may have as to the exact formulation (e.g. Pribram). Elsewhere outspoken opposition has been common enough: there is no real distinction; a distinction exists but is incorrectly identified; a theoretically existing distinction cannot be made operationally; the terminological implications are wrong; and so on. That the genetic constitution directly and solely determines any behavior is certainly wrong— the determination is indirect (Sperry, paraphrased above), and is influenced by organism-environment interaction as well as by genetics (Caspari). That any behavior is wholly independent of genetic limitations (hence with no degree of genetic determination) is also wrong, for the whole behavioral system develops with such limitations (also Sperry, as well as Caspari, above).

In somatic development, the genetic system does not always rigidly control. It delimits reaction ranges, and the position of the individual within a genetically determined range depends on the surrounding conditions of its development and, to less extent, later life. A reaction range may be narrow, virtually to a single point (e.g. blood types), or broad (e.g. weight). Even in setting up the somatic mechanisms of behavior there is thus a factor of "experience" or, in some sense, "learning." In the central nervous system this factor is minimal (Sperry, above), but it is clear that the developed mechanisms there also have reaction ranges, the extents of which vary from one species to another and also from one process to another within individuals. The range for variation under external influence may be practically nil, so that the behavior is virtually unmodifiable by experience (e.g. "innate" bird songs), and it is fair enough to say that there is then no learning. In other cases the reaction range determines the kinds of things that can be learned and, probably less rigidly, their total number but not the objective or specific items. For example man's linguistic ability or a bird's imprinting mechanism are clearly set up under almost complete genetic control, but the language learned or the individual imprinted depends entirely on experience. The proposition that behavior is *either* innate *or* learned may be as meaningless as "either-or" statements are likely to be, but there certainly are two different factors involved. Neither excludes the other, but they vary in the nature and extent of their influence on given items of behavior. (This paragraph is an individual synthesis based on several authors in the symposium, notably Pribram, Caspari, Nissen, Harlow, although perhaps not fully acceptable to any one of them.)

In this discussion the phenomena of maturation (mentioned by Sperry) are not separately considered because they are in principle hardly separable from those of development in general. The onset of sexual behavior in mammals (Beach), for instance, is no less and no more developmental and genetically correlated for occurring well after and not before birth, although due allowance is required for its occurring under less uniform circumstances and at a time when experience has greater influence. In this connection, at least passing reference should be made to the many organisms in which a young but independent (not merely embryological) stage—a larva—has a distinctive morphology, behavior pattern, and adaptive niche, all completely transformed in a later, generally reproductive, stage (Romer). (Note, also, the so-called "alternation of generations" in, e.g., coelenterates and the quite different phenomenon of haplophase-diplophase alternation sometimes given the same name in many plants.) In complete metamorphosis, as from caterpillar to butterfly, the later structures and behavior do not simply develop from the earlier; the earlier breaks down and the later is essentially constructed anew. It seems that one and the same genetic system must comprise two complete sets of plans and a timer to determine when each shall be used! This peculiar situation, which may well have been involved in the origin of the vertebrates and hence in our own ancestry (Romer), offers to the play of evolutionary forces *two* complete behavioral systems within a *single* genetic lineage. The two may evolve together, or differently, or one at the expense of the other.

Finally, on the topic of ontogeny, the tremendous and (in comparison with other animals) disproportionate role of experience in the ontogeny of human behavior need be no more than mentioned at this point (Freedman and Roe).

EVOLUTIONARY PRINCIPLES AND BEHAVIOR

The widely accepted theories, principles, and generalizations about evolution have had three main bases: the historical (paleontological) record; comparative anatomy and systematics of recent organisms; and experiments (mainly genetical) on living organisms.[14] As already exemplified in this chapter and others throughout the symposium, each of these fields involves behavior, directly or indirectly, but their data are more commonly morphological. That evolutionary principles so based nevertheless also apply to or underlie the evolution of behavior is fundamental to the thesis of this book, accepted by all its authors and the conference discussants, and demonstrated in some detail by several of them (e.g. Mayr, Emerson).

The unit of phylogeny is ontogeny, as noted in the last section, but it is essential to the modern viewpoint that evolution occurs in *populations* in which ontogenies succeed one another, spread, and usually interconnect. Only in populations can genetic changes throughout the generations be followed, and such secular genetic changes are the principal or primary mechanism of evolution. A population consists of organisms of common ancestry, more or less contiguous in space, similar or coordinated in ecological role, somatic characteristics, and behavior, and reproductively continuous over several or many generations. The concept of evolving populations applies to *all* organisms, even the comparatively few that are completely asexual, but most attention has quite properly been paid to populations also characterized by interbreeding—they are most abundant and also most subtly complex in their evolution.[15]

Among the essential genetical processes within sexual populations are gene and chromosome mutations, chromosome assortment and gene recombination in meiosis, and chromosome recombination in fertilization. In themselves these processes have no orientation with respect to adaptation; in that sense they are

14. Biogeography, ecology, comparative physiology, and other biological sciences have, of course, also contributed.

15. Mead makes the interesting suggestion that recent preoccupation with population genetics may have led to overlooking the evolutionary significance of nonbreeders in a population. The persistent presence of a large percentage of post-juvenile nonbreeders in a completely sexual species is indeed a—not altogether unique—recent human peculiarity with an important bearing on our evolutionary status and prospects. The evolutionary importance of functionally asexual nonbreeders in insect societies has by no means been overlooked, as Emerson shows. It remains true in all cases, whatever the basis of nonbreeding, that the characteristics of nonbreeders depend for the most part on the genetics of the population and that even for them population genetics is the evolutionary substrate. Their influence on evolution, surely present in many cases, is also ultimately genetical even though their own genes are not passed on.

random. In the absence of any other factors they will produce
either no persistent genetic change at all or fluctuating, unoriented, nonadaptive changes. But, as previously stressed, the organization that makes living things organisms is with respect to
adaptation. Even long before there was any knowledge of the
actual mechanisms of genetics, naturalists recognized that accounting for adaptation is the one central, inescapable problem of biology (Pittendrigh). Attempted solutions have ranged from ascribing
adaptation to divine fiat (which may be claimed in either evolutionary or nonevolutionary contexts) to denying that adaptation
does exist in fact. Neither of those extremes is admissible in
science, even as a hypothesis, the first because it is nontestable
and therefore outside the realm of science, and the second because
in effect it eliminates its own subject matter. (There is no life
without organization and no organization without adaptation.)
Most biologists now agree that the orienting, nonrandom, antichance process in evolution, the necessary and sufficient requirement for adaptation, is natural selection (e.g. Pittendrigh). In
this acceptance, natural selection is differential reproduction:
greater or less *average* success in reproduction (no matter how
slight) is correlated with genetic factors. This correlation automatically and inevitably assures that genetic evolution will be in
the direction of greater reproductive success. There are, indeed,
immense complexities behind that simple statement. Pertinent
reproductive success is that of the population, not necessarily of
any individuals, and this end may involve reduction of the reproduction of a certain continuing proportion of individuals. Natural
selection can work only with existing external circumstances and
with genetic factors actually present and really correlated with
reproductive success. It may be opposed by (although only in exceptional cases is it weaker than) random genetic processes. Natural selection produces adaptation, but for the most part this is
not immediate cause and effect. The sole functional end of selection is reproductive success; adaptation in a broader sense is
favored by selection only to the extent that such adaptation does
contribute to reproductive success.

Relationships between behavior and adaptation in adaptive
radiation, evolutionary divergence, specific diversity, niche specificity, and isolating mechanisms have already been mentioned,
briefly but sufficiently for present purposes. So has the fact that

behavioral resemblances tend, by and large, to be positively correlated with phylogenetic affinities; but here a word must be added. Adaptations to similar ways of life or to the same particular elements of the environment may occur in distinct, even phylogenetically very distant, lineages, and some degree of functional resemblance then arises by *convergence*. This is no less true, and would indeed appear to be rather more usual, in behavior than in morphology. (E.g. kangaroos are not really similar in appearance to ungulates, toward which they have nevertheless converged in many features of ecology and behavior.) As Mayr points out in general discussion of this and related topics, early classifications of animals based on their behavior were nonphylogenetic and have been discarded because the traits used in definition were largely convergent; and nevertheless when convergent resemblances are recognized and eliminated as evidence, behavior can be used in erecting phylogenetic classifications.

Here the problems of evolutionary interpretation of behavior hinge, as they long have for morphology, on the terms and concepts of homology, homoplasy, and analogy. By widely accepted definitions homology is resemblance due to inheritance from a common ancestry, homoplasy is purely convergent resemblance (without inheritance in common), and analogy is functional equivalence that is not homologous and not necessarily homoplastic. Behavioral examples are: homologous eye-hand manipulation in man and other primates, homoplastic nectar feeding in hummingbirds and sphinx moths, analogous locomotion in earthworms and moles. (Mayr and Emerson, especially, give other examples.) Phylogenetic inferences regarding behavior depend essentially on distinguishing homologies, homoplasies, and analogies.[16]

16. A few years ago there was a flare-up of highly polemic discussion on the definitions of these terms, especially "homology." As usual in polemics there was much heat and little light. A group that insisted that "homology" should *not* imply community of inheritance was definitely in the minority, and the usual implication given above is obviously in the minds of all the authors who have used the term in this symposium. On the other hand, there did seem to be a consensus among morphologists and systematists that "homology" applies to similarity of structure only, *not* of function or behavior. Nevertheless several authors in this symposium, including systematists (e.g. Mayr, Emerson), have applied the term "homology" to behavior with tacit assumption that the usage is acceptable and will be understood, and no conference member objected. As a personal opinion, I maintain that the concept of homology applies to behavior as well as to structure.

It must by now be evident that morphology, physiology, and behavior are so inextricably united in functioning and in evolution that it is only to be expected that most of the concepts and principles of evolution in general apply to all three aspects. When suitable discrimination is used, the transfer from, say, morphology to behavior need not be merely metaphorical or analogical but may be an exemplification of the *same* principle in a different aspect of the same objective materials, the organisms. That could be illustrated for many other principles, and indeed it is in earlier chapters. Here only two or three more can be barely mentioned. Evolution is opportunistic; it has to make do with what is at hand, accumulated through history and under earlier conditions perhaps quite irrelevant later. Transformation of what already exists is simpler and more usual than addition of the wholly new. Note among other examples: Beach on changing targets of hormones; Hinde and Tinbergen on displacement and emancipation; Pribram on evolution of brain structure; Harlow on evolution of learning. Evolution is irrevocable; it never wholly returns to an earlier state, but neither does it eliminate all traces of earlier states. Perhaps the evolution of man (Washburn and Avis), with its plain evidence of successive earlier stages but with no conceivable reversion to them, is as good an example as any. Sustained evolutionary trends are always adaptive; they do not continue either steadily or indefinitely but stop, change direction, or are reversed with the conditions to which they are adaptive. Here I find some difficulty in adducing detailed examples from previous pages, because few really long-range behavioral trends are as yet documented in detail, but the workings of the principle are reasonably clear in the over-all history of vertebrate behavior (Romer) or, again, in our immediate ancestry (Washburn and Avis).

When we turn, finally, to the evolution of culture a certain extra discrimination must be used in transferring to this field the biologically based principles of evolution. Culture is a biological adaptation (Huxley) and its origins, the setting up of the mechanisms, must have followed biological evolutionary principles. But its variations in historic time and at present are mostly if not entirely *within* the reaction range of an established mechanism. There is no definite evidence that these variations are genetically controlled (Mead). Therefore the transfer to the study of cultural evolution within the species *Homo sapiens* of principles dependent on genetic evolution is likely to be metaphorical or analogical, and consequently tricky. Thus natural selection—a genetical process—between cultures or cultural elements as such is impossible.[17] Culture affects natural selection (rather than vice versa) if it produces a differential in reproduction between groups that are also genetically distinct. That does plainly occur, but the natural selection is between the culture-bearing groups, not between their cultures, which is quite a different matter. The laws of cultural inheritance are very different from those of biological inheritance. Cultural evolution is (within limits) revocable, and genetical evolution is not. On the other hand, culture does show elements of opportunism, of adaptive trends and radiation, of convergence, and other features that are descriptively similar and even functionally *analogous* to phenomena in biological evolution (Huxley, Mead).

Human evolution shows the old dualities of stability-change, unity-diversity, instinct-learning, and here they permeate the newer duality of biology-culture (Freedman and Roe, Huxley). With all this behind us, and with us, we are—who can doubt it?—sexual, aggressive, and acquisitive; in closing, my only regret is that Freedman and Roe intentionally omitted from this list the characteristic best exemplified in and by this book—exploratory curiosity.

17. That is one of several reasons for the invalidity of "social Darwinism."

Index

Abel, T. M., 488 n.
Abilities, inheritance of, 457
Acorn worms, 53, 55-7
Acquisivity, 473-7
Acrididinae, 351
Adapt, definitions of term, 391-2
Adaptation(s), 18, 20, 25, 27, 29, 32, 35, 260, 339, 390-416, 438, 442, 456, 458, 464, 520, 522-4, 526, 531-3; random, 16; of populations, 16, 422; occurrence of random evolution, unoriented with respect to, 18; a result of natural selection, 20; importance of slow shifts in environment and consequent, 25-6; quality of, 26; environmental, 27, 368; of dinosaurs, 28 ff.; of mammal-like reptiles, 33 ff.; structural, 72, 212, 330; linear series, 100; alternatives, 188; orienting factor, 200; substitutiveness, 201; sensory, not separable from learning, 286; ecological, 325; definitions of term, 391-2; somatic, 392; as organization, 394-7; behavioral, 403 f., 413; biological, 418, 452, 519; applied to cultures, 438; and behavior and natural selection, *see* Behavior, adaptation and natural selection; cultural adaptedness, 439, 442, 449; directional, 445; diversificational adaptedness, 445; long-range adaptedness, 445; cultural, 452 ff.; flexibility, 459; psychological, 473; evolutionary, 473, 521; maintenance of, 523

   Adaptive: evolution, 18, 24, 317, 330 f., 400, 522; orientation of evolution, 18 ff.; adjustment, 25; zones, 25 f., 199, 209, 216, 416, 473; values, 94, 110; behavior, 186, 204, 399, 411-12, 522; changes vs. behavior-determining changes, 187; mechanisms, 187 ff., 200, 244, 464; characters, 188; internal vs. external, 189; radiation, 220, 315, and convergence of behavior, 315-22; evolutionary changes, 270; divergence, 401; differentiation, 402; differences, 402 f., 407 f., 410; responses, 406, 410; alternatives, 461; role, 462; directions, 509; compromise, 522
Adler, Alfred, 457, 470
Admiralty Islands, 492 n., 496

Adriaanse, A., 348
Adrian, E. D., 175
Africa, tribal cultures, 445-6
Aggression, aggressiveness, 305, 342, 386, 469-73, 476 f.; in children, 471-2
Allee, W. C., 212, 227 f., 302 f., 305 f., 320, 322, 329, 471
Alleles, 18, 104, 107 f., 110 f., 527; mutations, 103, 528; substitutions, 107; pool, 109 f., 244, 397; population, 274; patterns, 317; interaction, 526; recombination, 531
Allen, A. A., 233
Altruism, 308; in animals, 295-6
Altum, J. B. T., 225
Ambivalence, 465-6
American culture, modern, 438
American Museum of Natural History, 431 n.
American Philosophical Society, 390 n.
American Psychological Association, v
Amitermes, 320; *excellens*, 320; *meridionalis*, 326
Ammophila, 357; *campestris*, 348; *urnaria*, 352
Amoeba, 270
Amphibians, 270; mating practices, 382-3
Amphioxus, 53, 56, 61-3, 143
Anatidae, 342, 356
Anatomy vs. physiology, 513
Andrew, R. J., 252 n., 259, 263
Andrews, 346
Androgen, 86, 91, 95; therapy, 83; treatment, 87; hormone, 88; testicular, 89; effects, 97
Annelids, 52, 270
Anopheles, 404-6, 412-16
Anoplius, 357
Anoplotermes, 314
Anteaters, 213
Antelope, nyala, 300
Ants, 313 ff., 320, 322, 329; communication, 293; fungus-growing, 314, 325; ponerine, of South America, 314, queen, 316; queens, 318, 321, 328; army, 324; sanguinary, 329; thief, 329
Anxiety, age of, 461
Apartheid, racial, 447
Apes, 281; anthropoid, 276; aphasia in, 278; learning capacity of, compared with man's, 278; brain and special

Daanje, A., 257 f., 354

Darling, F. F., vi, 227, 237 ff., 302 ff., 474, 487; *Herd of Red Deer*, 238; "Social Life in Ungulates," 239

Darlington, C. D., 438; *Evolution of Genetic Systems*, 438 n.

Darwin, Charles (Darwinian, neo-Darwinian, Darwinism), 7 ff., 13 n., 18 ff., 315, 355, 393, 397, 456 f., 463, 469, 472 f., 509; finches, 220; pre-Darwinian taxonomists, 344; social, 456, 535 n.; "Darwin of the mind," 457; *Origin of Species*, 315, 393

Das, B. C., 91

David, K., 85

David, P. R., 116

Davis, D. E., 87, 236 f., 253, 301, 304

Dawson, W. M., 116, 118

De Vries, H., 18

Deer, 41–6, 238–40; correlation of morphology and behavior in, 41–5; red, 238–9, 303 f., 487, hind, 474, territorial behavior of, 228; roe, 303; white-tailed, 300

D. lacour, J., 346

Demerec, M., 104

Democracy, 447

Dendrites, 173–4

Dentition. *See* Teeth

Dependency, long, of human infant, 423–4, 459, 474 f., 482

Desneux, J., 312 f., 320, 322, 357

Dethier, V. G., 209, 213, 217 f.

Deuterogenesis, 317 f.

Dicaeidae, 347

Dicrocerus, 44

Dicruridae, 262

Diet, 39, 51, 73, 189, 421, 425, 432 f., 435, 482; of australopithecines, 432 ff.; in humans, 470

Dinosaurs, morphology and the possible behavior in, 28–32

Diptera, 364; mating practices, 368

Display movements: evolutionary origin, 256–7; three primary sources, 257; principles on which intention movements and displacement activities merge into display, 258–9; function, 260–1, in fighting, 260, in courtship, 260

Divine Right, concept of, 442

Dobzhansky, T., 105 ff., 116, 120, 278, 363, 373 f., 401, 404, 519

Dodd, J. M., 85 ff.

Dogfish, 272

Dogs, 37–41, 307; African wild, 434; and cats, correlation of morphology

and behavior in, 37–41; communication, 293

Domm, L. V., 87

Douglas, M. D., 305, 307

Douglas Lake, Michigan, 230

Doves, 254; ring, 234, 254

Dreams, 488 n.

Drongos, 262

Droogleever Fortuyn, J., 151

Dropkin, V. H., 329

Drosophila, 106, 113, 115, 117, 123, 252 n., 342, 356, 364, 371; *funebris*, 107; *pseudoobscura*, 107; *melanogaster*, 112; differences between closely related species, 357; evolutionary trends in courtship behavior, 358; mating practices, 370 f., in certain North American species, 372–9 *(tables)*, 376 ff.; distribution of, in North American, 372–9, 401–2; comparative study of light response in, 399 f., 401–12; response to light and moisture *(tables)*, 402 f., 405 ff., 410

Ducks, 252 n., 342, 356, 359; canvasback, 235; reclassification of, 346

Duyvené de Wit, J. J., 86

Ears, development of, 508

Earthworms, learning capacity of, 273–4, 284–5

East Greenland, amphibians from Devonian of, 67

Eccles, J. C., 166

Echinoderms, 51, 54, 270 f.

Eciton, 318, 324; *burchelli*, 325; *hamatum*, 325

Ecology, concerns of, 206 f.

Edinger, T., 71, 511 n.

Effectors, 508–15, 528

Egyptian culture, ancient, 439, 441; resistant to change, 440–1

Eidos, 351

Eisley, L., 487 n.

Elk, 238, 239–40

Elton, C., 212

Emerson, A. E., vi, 311–35, 518 and n., 531 and n., 533 and n.

Emlin, J. T., 301

Empathy, 295

Enders, R. K., 94

Engelhardt, M. von, 107

Enteropneusta, 55

Environment, 522; organisms, 8; one of four classes composing objective data for historical study, 10; influences, 15; adaptations, 27, 368; conditions,

136
R69

Date Due

54730

	NO 15 '67			
NO 26 '68				
A 12 '64	Reserve			
JY 31 '64	1-10-68			
	Prof. G. Morrell			
SE 3 '64	DE 16 '68			
MR 20 '65	AP 17 '65			
MY 6 '65	OC 22 '69			
MY 20 '65	DE 1 '69			
AP 25 '66	OCT 29 1971			
MY 18 '66				
May 24				
OC 22 '66				